THE FOUNDATIONS OF EUCLIDEAN GEOMETRY

BY

HENRY GEORGE FORDER, B.A.

DOVER PUBLICATIONS, INC.

NEW YORK

This new Dover edition first published in 1958 is an unabridged and unaltered republication of the first edition. It is published through special arrangement with Cambridge University Press.

Manufactured in United States of America

Dover Publications, Inc.
920 Broadway
New York 10, New York

THE FOUNDATIONS OF EUCLIDEAN GEOMETRY

Denn die Wahrheit ist ewig, ist göttlich ; und keine Entwickelungsphase der Wahrheit, wie geringe auch das Gebiet sei, was sie umfasst, kann spurlos vorübergehen ; sie bleibt bestehen, wenn auch das Gewand, in welches schwache Menschen sie kleiden, in Staub zerfällt. GRASSMANN.

PREFACE

IN the beginning of last century, it was still possible to regard the Greek Geometry as the most rigorously logical body of doctrine ever erected, for the mathematics of that day which was of modern origin was clearly based on insecure foundations. The critical mathematicians of the last century and of this have succeeded in placing Analysis on what seems to most an unassailable basis, and the results of their labours are readily accessible in a number of excellent text-books. But although the Euclidean Geometry is the oldest of the sciences and has been studied critically for over two thousand years, it seems that there is no text-book which gives a connected and rigorous account of that doctrine in the light of modern investigations; for Hilbert's *Grundlagen* is a work of research, while the books of Vahlen, Schur, Veblen and Baker are preoccupied with Projective Geometry. It is hoped that this book will fill that gap.

Part of the book deals with the elementary Geometry taught in schools, and it might be thought that when the foundations had been laid, we could refer to the school-texts for this portion of the work; and this I should have done, but for the fact that scarcely one proof in any school-text will survive a critical examination, even from the point of view of the writers, still less from ours. This seems to shew that it would be unwise to leave to the reader the task of erecting the school Geometry on the basis supplied in this book; and for this reason I have included proofs of the theorems usually taught in schools. In cases where they are merely a correction of the traditional proofs, I have put them in small type. Other matter which is not of first-rate importance has also been put in small type, and so have certain elucidatory paragraphs, headed '*Note*,' which are not part of the logical argument, and in which a freer phraseology is allowed than in the main part of the text.

This book is clearly not intended for beginners; but the teachers of elementary Geometry and the writers of elementary text-books can learn from it how far short of logical perfection are the proofs usually received; and this should result in an improvement of Geometrical teaching, unless indeed it be contended that an unsound proof has an educational value not possessed by a sound one. Geometry, in its first stages, is rightly taught empirically, and all propositions, regarded by the unsophisticated mind as obvious, are rightly assumed; and while the content of mathematical knowledge is being increased, demonstration can only be divorced from experience and intuition at great sacrifice. But when some well-defined field has been covered, minds of a critical and logical bent will wish to derive logically the propositions in that field from as small a number of assumptions as possible. At this stage the utmost rigour and abstractness are desirable; and this stage can be reached, by some, in the latter years of school-life. As Professor G. H. Hardy has recently said, "Anyone who has the faintest hope of a scholarship at Oxford or Cambridge could learn the nature of an axiom, and how a system of axioms may be shewn to be consistent with, or independent of, one another."

Logical investigations, besides being of interest in themselves, often point the way to extensions of knowledge previously unthought of. It was from such investigations that the classical non-Euclidean Geometries arose, and they freed the mind from its age-long bondage to the obvious, and made possible the bolder conceptions of space reached in our day. For the virtue of a logical proof is not that it compels belief, but that it suggests doubts.

I have tried not to overcrowd the text with references to propositions previously proved. It is hoped that the references which are given will be sufficient for the reader. The first chapter contains a résumé of non-geometrical work which is needed subsequently. In a first reading, after the first few pages of that chapter have been read, Chapter II and the following chapters should be taken, the first chapter being consulted when necessary.

No attempt has been made to trace propositions or proofs to their original authors. I have referred in the body of the book only to those papers and books that I have made use of.

In matters of pure logic, I have tried not to be controversial. Where alternative views of some logical process are widely held, I have sometimes given alternative methods. The attentive reader will be led to consider many logical questions, some of which are not yet answered and some of which are possibly unanswerable.

Professor H. F. Baker, F.R.S. read most of the work before and after it reached its final form, and suggested many improvements in exposition and arrangement, and finally read many of the proofs as they passed through the Press. For this help I tender my best thanks.

Readers who are familiar with the Literature will know how full it is of errors, how numerous are the pitfalls. In avoiding some, I have doubtless fallen into others. For these I must accept full responsibility, and I pray the reader to be charitable.

Acknowledgment is due to Mr R. Cooper, B.A., Scholar of Trinity College, Cambridge, who read some of the work in manuscript, and discussed some difficulties with me.

My best thanks are due to the Staff of the University Press for the careful way in which the printing has been done, and to the Readers of the Press for pointing out slips that had escaped me.

H. G. F.

March 1927

CONTENTS

THE FOUNDATIONS OF EUCLIDEAN GEOMETRY

CHAPTER I

GENERAL INTRODUCTION

The object of this work is to shew that all the propositions of Euclidean Geometry follow logically from a small number of Axioms explicitly laid down, and to discuss to some extent the relations between these Axioms. The most famous work whose aim was a logical deduction of the propositions of Geometry is of course that of Euclid, but many flaws have been noticed in his treatment during the two thousand years that have elapsed since his work was written. In particular, Euclid almost completely ignored the relations of order, suggested by such words as 'between,' 'inside,' though such relations are, in fact, of great importance in a deductive treatment. They are fundamental in much of the present work.

A point in which Euclid was criticised in earlier days, his introduction of a Parallel Axiom, is now recognised as a mark of his insight. He proved the propositions for congruent triangles without the use of that Axiom; that Axiom—roughly equivalent to 'Not more than one straight line can be drawn through a given point parallel to a given straight line'—was first used in shewing the fundamental properties of parallels. The fruitless efforts to prove it from the other assumptions of Euclid resulted at length in the creation of the non-Euclidean Geometry of Bolya and Lobatschefsky—a landmark in the history of human thought. While we shall be mainly concerned with Euclidean Geometry, some reference now and again to non-Euclidean Geometries is inevitable. In the Hyperbolic Geometry, as that of Bolya and Lobatschefsky is called, all Euclid's Axioms hold, except that an infinity of straight lines can be drawn through a given point so as not to meet a given straight line, though coplanar with it*. Propositions in

* An introductory account of that Geometry will be found in Carslaw, "The elements of plane Non-Euclidean Geometry" (1914), and a more complete account in Coolidge, "The elements of Non-Euclidean Geometry" (1909).

the Euclidean Geometry, whose proof does not depend on the Euclidean parallel Axiom, will still be true in the Hyperbolic Geometry, but those whose proofs do depend on that Axiom will now be false. Thus the results of the Hyperbolic Geometry are different from those in the Euclidean; nevertheless, as we shall subsequently shew, that Geometry is self-consistent, it does not contradict itself. The Hyperbolic Geometry was the forerunner of numerous non-Euclidean Geometries, differing more or less from the Euclidean. In fact, almost any body of doctrine, based on Axioms, which resembles in some way the Euclidean Geometry, is now styled by courtesy a Geometry.

We assume, without discussion, the principles of modern logic and the fundamental properties of the natural numbers. Most of these are known by common sense and need not be consciously before the reader. We will only explain one or two terms whose meaning may not be immediately clear.

1. We use the word '*class*' in its everyday sense, and mean thereby a set of objects connected together in the mind because they possess some common properties*; examples of classes are 'even numbers,' 'points,' 'men.' We leave aside all logical difficulties connected with the use of the term class.

A '*unit class*' is one containing only one member, e.g. the class of the present kings of England. An '*empty class*'† is one containing no members, e.g. the class of round squares. If all members of a class A are also members of a class B, then A is a '*sub-class*' of B. If, also, there are members of B which are not members of A, then A is a '*proper*' sub-class of B. Thus the class 'men' is a proper sub-class of the class 'mammals.' The members of a class are also called its elements.

2. We use the word '*relation*' in its everyday sense. Thus 'A is north of B' asserts a relation between A and B. Similarly 'A is the son of B,' 'A is greater than B' assert relations. Verbs often indicate relations, as in 'A loves B,' 'A precedes

* These statements and some of the following are not to be taken as definitions (see 6 below), but merely as explanations.

† An empty class is sometimes called a 'null-class,' but as the adjective 'null' has been appropriated by writers on Analysis, another word is necessary.

B.' We generalise these examples by writing *aRb* to mean '*a* is in the relation *R* to *b*.'

A relation may relate three terms, e.g. the relation 'preferred' in the fact '*A* preferred *B* to *C*.' Such three-termed relations will be of the utmost importance to us. They often appear under the guise of '*operations*.' Thus in Arithmetic $a+b=c$ is essentially a relation between *a*, *b* and *c*, though we shall usually regard this equation as asserting that the operation of adding *b* to *a* produces *c*. Two classes may be related by the fact that there is a '*correspondence*' between the elements of one class and those of the other. Thus the class of men and the class of their names are so related.

3. An '*ordered couple*' is a pair of entities* (a, b) distinct or not (for example, a pair of points or of numbers) such that (a, b) is identical with (c, d) if and only if *a* is identical with *c*, and *b* is identical with *d*. Thus (a, b) and (b, a) are identical if and only if *a* and *b* are identical. Similarly we can introduce ordered triads, etc.

4. *Use of the sign* '='.' If the sign = be put between any two entities those so connected are thereby asserted to be the same entity. *No other use of this sign is permitted in this book.* Thus, in Geometry $\triangle ABC = \triangle DEF$ means that the triangles are identical, and not merely congruent or of equal area. $a \neq b$ always means *a* is distinct from *b*.

5. If we have two classes (which need not have a finite number of members) such that a correspondence can be set up between the members of one class and those of the other, so that one and only one member of the first class corresponds to one and only one member of the second, then the classes are said to be put '*in* (1, 1) *correspondence*.' For example, natural numbers and even numbers can be put in (1, 1) correspondence, by making each number correspond to its double. In this instance, if *a*, *b* are in the first class, and a', b' correspond to them in the second, then a' will be greater than b', if and only if *a* is greater than *b*. We express this by saying that the classes are '*similar*' for the relation 'greater than.'

* We use the word 'entity,' in default of a better, to mean element or class or relation.

We can generalise this thus: if we have a class C and relations R, S, ... between certain of its members, and a class C' and relations R', S', ... between certain of its members, and if a (1, 1) correspondence can be set up between C and C' such that two members of C are in relation R, if and only if the corresponding members of C' are in relation R', and similarly for S, S', ... then we shall say, C with the relations R, S, ... is '*similar to*' C' with the relations R', S', ...

6. Our Geometry will consist of a series of propositions each of which is deduced from some earlier ones. There must then be some propositions which are assumed as the basis of our deductions. These are what we call '*Axioms*.' They need not be self-evident or simple; they are *merely* foundation-propositions from which others are deduced. Our Axioms will always be propositions about a certain class or classes and certain relations between the elements of those classes. All other entities spoken of in deductions from these Axioms must be defined in terms of those occurring in the Axioms. And by definition we mean *nominal* definition, i.e. an agreement to replace a long phrase by a shorter. Thus instead of saying 'a quadrilateral whose opposite sides are parallel' we say 'parallelogram.' In the formal treatment, a Definition will be preceded by the sign *Def.*, an Axiom by the sign *Ax.* and a deduced Theorem occasionally by the sign *The.* Of the classes and relations in the Axioms themselves it may be possible to define some in terms of those which occur earlier, but it is clear we must ultimately reach entities which are not defined.

Thus our Axioms are finally unproved propositions about undefined entities. (When a new Axiom is introduced it may of course be then possible to prove an earlier Axiom. This may then be dropped.)

Any entities which do satisfy the Axioms, also satisfy all the propositions deduced from them, and give an interpretation of the Geometry. A Geometry may have and usually does have more than one interpretation. Instances of this will be given subsequently.

We shall introduce our Axioms gradually. At any stage our propositions will hold not only in the Euclidean Geometry but in any in which the Axioms in force are true. Each time we introduce a new Axiom we narrow the range of Geometries for which the succeeding propositions are true.

In our deductions it is not necessary, though it may be helpful, to have in mind *any* interpretation. We may pretend we are just playing a game, deducing in accordance with logical laws propositions containing terms which do not have assigned definite meanings, from Axioms of the same sort. This is the formalist view. The game will be worth our playing if it has an interpretation which is interesting in itself.

7. Our Axioms and Definitions must be *consistent*, i.e. it must not be possible to deduce from them two contradictory propositions. To shew that the Axioms are consistent we exhibit a set of entities which are known to satisfy them. These entities are generally sets of numbers of some sort, real, complex, and so on, and relations between them. Hence it is presupposed that the properties of these numbers are consistent. For this reason we sketch in this chapter the deduction of the properties of the numbers subsequently used from the properties of the natural numbers. We shall assume that the properties of the natural numbers themselves are consistent.

We must also shew that the entities defined in our definitions exist. This we shall do, when necessary, by constructing them by means of earlier theorems and definitions.

We shall also strive to make our Axioms as simple as possible, that is, to *weaken* them as much as we can. It is an advantage if they be also *independent*, i.e. if none follows from the others; this is the case if the systems got by replacing one Axiom by its contradictory and leaving the rest unchanged are consistent. For example D cannot be deduced from A, B, C, if A, B, C and not-D are consistent. To shew the independence of the Axioms we must thus exhibit entities satisfying the modified sets. It is found, however, that whether Axioms are independent or not depends very much on their verbal or symbolic formulation and the question is not so interesting or so important as it appears. We shall accordingly only trouble about shewing independence when the system which shews it, is interesting on its own account.

The following important characteristic of certain sets of Axioms, though given now for completeness, will be better understood later. A set of Axioms about an undefined class K and undefined relations R, S, ... between its members, will be called a '*complete*' set, if all the interpretations of the Axioms (such as a definite class K_1 with definite relations $R_1, S_1, \ldots$ and a definite class K_2 with definite relations $R_2, S_2, \ldots$) are similar* (5). Then if P be any proposition involving only $K, R, S, \ldots$, either P or its contradictory proposition, not-P, is inconsistent with the set of Axioms; for we could not have two sets of entities satisfying the Axioms in one of which P is false and in the other true. Whether any proposition, consistent with the Axioms, is necessarily deducible from them when they form a complete set is an interesting logical question which does not seem to have been discussed.

For example; we shall shortly give a complete set of Axioms for integral numbers. A theorem such as Goldbach's Theorem, "Every even integer is the sum of two primes" (whose truth or falsehood is unknown), either is inconsistent with these Axioms or its contradictory is inconsistent with them. The question is whether its proof, if true, or its disproof, if false, can be set up from these Axioms in a finite number of steps.

If a set of Axioms be not complete a proposition and its contradictory may both be consistent with them. For example, the Axioms common to Euclidean and Hyperbolic Geometry form an incomplete set, and both the Euclidean and the Hyperbolic parallel Axioms given above are consistent with them.

If a set of Axioms be given, entities satisfying them are sometimes said to be *defined by the Axioms*. This is a different kind of definition from that in 6. 'Definition' used alone always means 'nominal definition.'

* A set of Axioms and Definitions is '*complete*' when it has the same property.

Linear Order

8. *Def.* If there be a relation $\prec$ (read 'precedes') between certain members of a class and the relation satisfies ·1·2·3 below, then the class is said to be '*in linear order for the relation* $\prec$.'

·1. *If x, y be any distinct members of the class, then either $x \prec y$ or $y \prec x$.*

·2. *If x, y be members of the class and $x \prec y$, then $x \neq y$.*

·3. *If x, y, z be members of the class and $x \prec y$ and $y \prec z$, then $x \prec z$.*

Thus the natural numbers are in linear order for the relation 'less than.' The above statements are thus consistent and they can easily be shewn to be independent. From them we can deduce ·4·5.

·4. If x, y be members of the class, then $x \prec y$ and $y \prec x$ cannot both be true (·3·2).

·5. In a finite sub-class of the class there are two elements a, b such that if x be any other element of the sub-class, then $a \prec x \prec b$.

·6. *Defs.* x is the '*maximum*' or '*last*' member of a class in linear order if all other members of the class precede it; x is the '*minimum*' or '*first*' member if it precedes all other members of the class.

·7. *Def.* A non-empty sub-class C of a class D in linear order is '*bounded above*'* (in D) if there is a member of D such that every other member of C precedes it. (The member of D in question may or may not be a member of C.)

Types of Relations

9. *Defs.* A relation R between two terms is '*symmetrical*' if aRb implies bRa. Thus the relation 'parallel' between straight lines is symmetrical. A relation R is '*asymmetrical*' if aRb implies that bRa is false. Thus 'father of' is asymmetrical. A relation may be neither symmetrical nor asymmetrical; thus 'A loves B' does not imply either that B does or does not love A. A relation R is '*aliorelative*' if xRx is always false, '*reflexive*' if xRx is always true. 'Perpendicular' between lines is aliorelative; 'congruent' between triangles is

* We shall omit the word 'above.'

reflexive. A relation R is '*transitive*' if aRb and bRc always imply aRc. The relation 'is earlier than' between moments of time is transitive. The relation $\prec$ of 8 is transitive, aliorelative and asymmetrical (8·3·2·4). The sign = has the properties of a symmetrical, reflexive, transitive relation. Such a relation is called '*equable*.' In the proposition 'the segment AB equals or, as we prefer to say, is congruent to the segment CD' the relation 'congruent to' is equable. If an equable relation holds between each pair of a class of entities, the entities are often spoken of as having a common property, which is said to be *defined by abstraction*. Thus from the relation 'congruent to' between segments, the 'length' of segments is defined by abstraction and congruent segments are said to have the same length. There is a difficulty here in that the supposed common property (even if it exists) is not isolated, we are left to guess which one is meant. In Russell's logic the difficulty is turned thus: the length of a segment would be defined as the class of all segments congruent to the given segment. The common property is then that of belonging to this class. We shall avoid discussion of these logical points and shall simply call attention to them when they arise.

10. The three-termed relation most important for us is 'between,' to which we now turn. A class is said to be '*ordered by the relation between*' when there is a relation called 'between' relating certain triads of members of the class, which has the following properties: If we use the symbol ABC to mean the proposition 'B is between A and C,' then

If A, B, C, X are in the class,

·1. *ABC implies that A, B, C are distinct.*

·2. *ABC implies that ACB is false* (i.e. if B is between A and C then C is not between A and B).

·3. *ABC implies that CBA is true* (i.e. if B is between A and C, it is between C and A).

·4. *If A, B, C are distinct, then BAC or CAB or ABC or CBA or ACB or BCA.*

·5. *If A, B, C, X are distinct, then ABC implies ABX or XBC.*

It must be distinctly understood that nothing is to be assumed about the relation 'between' save these statements and what can be deduced from them. Any three-termed relation satisfying these statements has a right to be called 'between.' Points on a straight line can be ordered by the relation between; points on a circle cannot, for whatever three-termed relation be taken among the points of a circle, some of the above statements will not hold for that relation. We can compare the above statements with those which would hold for the three-termed relation $a+b=c$ for numbers. If we write *abc* for this relation, then *abc* would imply *bac* (since if $a+b=c$ then $b+a=c$). The above statements are independent*.

11. We shall build up the whole of Euclidean Geometry using as undefined entities a class of elements called '*points*' and a relation relating three points which turns out to have the properties of the between relation. This development starts in the next chapter. The rest of this chapter contains a summary treatment of certain number-systems, etc. which are subsequently used. Its reading can be postponed until reference is made to it.

The Natural Numbers

12. We shall not attempt to define the natural numbers, but we shall outline how their properties can be deduced from the four following and how other types of numbers can be constructed from them. By 'successor' we mean immediate successor, thus 4 is the successor of 3, and for the present, 'number' means natural number.

·1. The natural or finite numbers 0, 1, 2, ... have the following properties†:

·11. *There is at least one number* (i.e. the class of numbers is not empty).

·12. *The successor of a number exists and is a number.*

* Huntingdon, "A new set of postulates for betweenness," *Trans. Amer. Math. Soc.* 1924, XXVI, p. 257.

† Pieri, "Sopra gli assiomi aritmetici," *Bollettino dell' Acc. Gioenia in Catania*, Serie 2ª, 1908, p. 26.

12·13. *In any class of numbers, which is not empty, there is a number which is not the successor of any number of the class* [i.e. a first number].

·14. *There is not more than one number which is not the successor of any other.*

·2. From these statements the following can be shewn:

·21. There is only one number which is not the successor of any other. We denote the number by 0, and the successor of a by a^+.

·22. Each number save 0 is the successor of one and only one number.

·23. *The principle of induction.* If the truth of a theorem for a number n implies its truth when n is replaced by n^+, and if it be true when $n=0$, then it is true for all natural numbers.

·24. In a certain sense all ordinary mathematical analysis, e.g. the Differential and Integral Calculus, can be deduced from the above four statements. (19·5 below.)

·3. By means of induction we can define addition of numbers thus*:

Def. $a+0=a$, $a+(b^+)=(a+b)^+$.

Our definition defines what is meant by adding b^+ when we know what is meant by adding b. It is a *definition by induction.*

·31. Hence $a^+=a+1$ where $1=0^+$; $(a+1)^+=a+2$ where $2=1^+$, and so on.

·32. Hence the second part of the Def. can be written

$$a+(b+1)=(a+b)+1.$$

·4. Again by induction we can prove the following:

·41. If a, b be fixed natural numbers, so is $a+b$.

·42. $(a+b)+c=a+(b+c)$. The *Associative law*, denoted by *Assoc* +.

·43. $a+b=b+a$. The *Commutative law*, denoted by *Comm* +.

·44. $a+c=b+c$ implies $a=b$. *The Binary law*, denoted by *Bin* +.

As an example we will shew ·42. The theorem is true for $c=0$, for by ·3, $(a+b)+0=a+b$ and $a+(b+0)=a+b$.

* For the following, cf. Peano, *Formulario Mathematico.* Bocca, Turin (1895–1910).

Assuming it true when $c=n$ we can shew it for $c=n+1$ thus: Since $(a+b)+n=a+(b+n)$ we have by ·12

$$[(a+b)+n]+1=[a+(b+n)]+1.$$

But by repeated use of ·32

$$[(a+b)+n]+1=(a+b)+(n+1)$$

and $\quad [a+(b+n)]+1=a+[(b+n)+1]=a+[b+(n+1)].$

Whence $(a+b)+(n+1)=a+[b+(n+1)]$. So that if the theorem holds when $c=n$, it holds when $c=n+1$, and since it holds when $c=0$, it holds generally by induction.

12·45. *Def.* The operation which produces $a+b$ from a is called '*adding b.*'

·5. Similarly we can define the product of two numbers by induction thus:

Def. by induction. $a0=0$, $a(b+1)=ab+a$, and shew

·51. If a, b be fixed natural numbers, so is ab.

·52. $(ab)c=a(bc)$. *Assoc* ×.

·53. $ab=ba$. *Comm* ×.

·54. If $c\neq 0$ then $ac=bc$ implies $a=b$. *Bin* ×.

·55. $(a+b)c=ac+bc$. The right-hand distributive law. *R Distrib* + ×.

·56. $c(a+b)=ca+cb$. The left-hand distributive law. *L Distrib* + ×.

If both distributive laws hold (as here) we denote them by *Distrib* + ×.

·57. *Def.* The operation which produces ab from a is called '*right-hand multiplication by b.*'

·6. We do not regard the statements in ·1 as the definitions by Axioms of the natural numbers, because not only do the natural numbers 0, 1, 2, ... satisfy them, but also the odd numbers, the prime numbers in their natural order, and in fact so does any class of elements for which a relation 'successor of' can be found satisfying the statements. Any class of elements satisfying these statements where 'number' and 'successor of' can now be treated as undefined, and where the above definitions of sum and product are set up, will be called a class of '*integers*' or '*integral numbers.*' Natural numbers are thus a special kind of integers. We cannot adopt the formalist view (6) of our statements, if they are intended to refer to natural numbers, but we can adopt that view if they be regarded as giving a definition by Axioms of integers. The whole of the arithmetic of integers can be deduced from ·1 if we assume a knowledge of the natural numbers. As illustrating the difference between integers and natural numbers, we note that though we may say '$a+b$ is an integer if a and b are' we may not say 'the sum of 2 integers is an integer,' if by '2' we mean the integer 2, but we may say so, if by '2' we mean the natural number 2. Again the sum of a natural number of integers is an integer, but 'the sum of an integral number of integers' is, in our use of the words, a meaningless phrase.

12·61. The statements ·11—·14 regarded as a set of Axioms for integers can easily be shewn to be complete.

·62. If n be a natural number and a an integer,

$$na = a + a + \dots \text{ to } n \text{ terms.}$$

·7. *Def. by induction.* If a, n be integers, $a^0 = 1$, $a^{n+1} = a^n . a$.

·71. Hence, if n be a natural number and a an integer, then $a^n = aaa \dots$ to n factors.

·8. *Def. and The.* If the integer a be the sum of an integer b and another c, then c is uniquely fixed by a, b and is denoted by $a-b$. The operation which produces $a-b$ from a is called '*subtracting b*.'

·9. *Def. and The.* If the integer a be the product of an integer $b \neq 0$ and another c, then c is uniquely fixed by a, b and is denoted by a/b. The operation which produces a/b from a is called '*division by b*.' We can now define 'factor,' 'prime,' 'multiple,' 'co-prime.'

13. Any class of elements satisfying 12·11—·14 can be put in (1, 1) correspondence with the natural numbers. (12·61.)

·1. *Def.* An '*enumerable*' class is one which can be put in (1, 1) correspondence with the natural numbers. (See 15·7 below.)

Positive and Negative Integers

14. *Defs.* If a be an integer the '*positive integer*' $+a$ is the *operation* of adding a; the '*negative integer*' $-a$ is the operation of subtracting a. A '*signed integer*' is a positive or negative integer.

·1. If a, b are integers and $a=b$, then $+a=+b$, $-a=-b$. Also $+0=-0$.

·2. *Defs.* If $+x$ is a positive integer, $+(+x)$ is the operation of adding x. If $-x$ is a negative integer, $+(-x)$ is the operation of subtracting x. That is, $+(+x)=+x$, $+(-x)=-x$. [The operations may here be supposed to be on integers.]

·3. *Def.* If x, y be signed integers, then $x+y$ is the signed integer z such that, if u be an integer such that we can apply to it the operation $+x$ and then the operation $+y$ on the result, then always $u+x+y=u+z$. It can be shewn that z is unique.

·4. *Def.* If x be a signed integer, then $-x$ is that signed integer y for which $x+y=+0$. (It can be shewn to be unique.) *Def.* If x, z be signed integers, then $x-z=x+(-z)$. Hence $-(+z)=-z$ and $-(-z)=+z$.

It is now easy to define the multiplication of signed integers (by the 'rule of signs') and to shew that 12·41—·44 and 12·51—·56 hold, and also

·5. If $x+y=z$ and two of x, y, z be any fixed signed integers, the third exists and is fixed.

·6. *Defs.* If a, b are signed integers (or integers) $a<b$ means there is a positive integer $x\neq+0$ (or an integer $x\neq 0$) such that $a+x=b$. $a>b$ means $b<a$.

Ratios

15. *Defs.* If a, b be integers and $b\neq 0$ the '*ratio*' a/b is the operation 'multiply by a and divide by b.' $a/1$ is often written a.

·1. $a/b=c/d$ if and only if $ad=bc$ where a, b, c, d are integers*.

·2. *Defs. and Thes.* If $r=a/b$ be a ratio and u an integer divisible by b, then ur means the integer ua/b. If x, y be ratios, then $x+y$ means the operation z such that $ux+uy=uz$

* Two operations are identical, if they operate on the same elements and produce the same effects on them.

whenever u, ux, uy are integers. It can be shewn to be unique. The def. of xy is similar. From these defs. follow the laws of 12·41—·44 and 12·51—·56, also the theory of division of ratios, and

15·3. If $xy = z$ and two of x, y, z be any fixed ratios ($x, y \neq 0$) the third exists and is fixed.

·4. *Note.* It is illogical to define a/b as an ordered couple (as is often done), for then $a/b = c/d$ if and only if $a = c$, $b = d$ (3).

·5. We can now define '*subtraction*' of ratios as in 12·8, '*signed ratios*' as in 14, the relation $<$ between ratios or signed ratios as in 14·6, the addition and multiplication of signed ratios as in 14·3·4. All the laws of 12·41—·44 and 12·51—·56 hold for signed ratios and also 14·5 and 15·3.

·6. As in 12·7 we can define the nth powers of all our numbers, n being an integer.

·7. *The class of ratios is enumerable* (13·1).

*Dem.** We can arrange the ratios p/q in sets, in order of increasing $p + q$. The ratios in each set which have not occurred in previous sets shall be arranged in order of increasing magnitudes (·5), the others shall be rejected. Since the number of ratios in each set is finite, a given ratio will have a place allotted to it somewhere. The ordered set starts thus:

$$0/1,\ 1/1,\ 1/2,\ 2/1,\ 1/3,\ 3/1,\ 1/4,\ 2/3,\ 3/2,\ 4/1,\ 1/5,\ \ldots$$

and if we make the ratio in the nth place correspond to the natural number n, we have a (1, 1) correspondence between the ratios and the natural numbers.

·8. *The class of signed ratios and the class of ratios between* 0 *and* 1 *are enumerable.*

16. *The integers, signed integers, ratios, signed ratios are in linear order for the relation* $<$. (8, 14·6, 15·5.)

·1. *Defs.* A class is '*condensed*' if it is in linear order (for $\prec$) and if when x and y are in the class and $x \prec y$, there is an element z in the class with $x \prec z \prec y$. If M is a class in linear order for $\prec$, a sub-class N is '*relatively dense*' in M, if when x, y are any elements of M and $x \prec y$, there is an element z of N with $x \prec z \prec y$.

* The sign *Dem.* precedes a formal proof.

16·2. *All enumerable condensed classes with no first or last element are similar with their relations* < *. (See 5.)

·3. *The ratios and signed ratios are condensed classes.* Thus the definitions of condensed classes are consistent.

·4. If n is a natural number and m is an integer† which is not the product of n equal integers†, then there is no ratio x with $x^n = m$.

Dem. If $x = p/q$, where p, q are co-prime integers, then $(p/q)^n = m$ implies $p^n = mq^n$. But in p^n each prime factor occurs a multiple of n times while in mq^n not all prime factors so occur, since m is not the product of n equal integers. Nevertheless we need numbers x which satisfy $x^n = m$. We construct them next.

Real Numbers

17. *Defs.* If a is a class of ratios, containing at least one ratio but not all ratios, then the class of ratios which are less than at least one member of a is called a '*real number*.' If r is a ratio the class of ratios less than r is the '*rational* (*real*) *number*' corresponding to r.

·1. *Note.* By this def. we avoid *postulating* the existence of new numbers called real numbers, just as we avoided postulating the existence of signed integers, etc. Thus the class of ratios whose squares are less than 2/1 is a real number, which will shortly be written $\sqrt{2}$. We shall later give a definition of real numbers (or rather of signed real numbers, see ·7 below) by a complete set of Axioms and then any class satisfying these Axioms can be called a class of (signed) real numbers. If Analysis is founded on such a set of Axioms—and this method has many advantages—the difficulty is to shew the set consistent. We generate from the natural numbers one class satisfying the Axioms in question with the sole object of shewing the consistency of these (and other) Axioms.

·2. *If all ratios be divided into two classes A and B, neither empty, such that each ratio of A is less than each of B, and that*

* Cantor (*Math. Ann.* XLVI, 1895). "Contributions to the Founding of the Theory of Transfinite Numbers." Translation by Jourdain, p. 124.

† More exactly, integer-ratios, but see 17·9.

A has no maximum element, then the 'lower class' A is a real number. Conversely any real number is such a lower class.

17·3. *Def. and Thes.* If a, b be real numbers and $a \neq b$, one must contain the other. If a contain b, we say $b < a$. *The real numbers are in linear order for* $<$.

·4. *Def. and Thes.* If a, b be real numbers, $a+b$ is the class of ratios got by adding each ratio of a to each of b. Similarly we can define ab. Whence, if a is the class of ratios whose squares are less than 2/1, then a is a real number and a^2 is the class of ratios less than 2/1 and so is a real number. We write $a = \sqrt{2}$ where now '2' is the real number 2 (i.e. the class of ratios less than 2/1). The laws of 12·41—·44 and 12·51—·56 and 15·3 hold for real numbers. If a, b be real numbers and $a < b$ there is a real number $x > 0$ with $a + x = b$.

·5. A real number less than 1 can be represented by a decimal (terminating or not).

·6. *The class of real numbers less than* 1 *is not enumerable.*

Dem. For suppose a (1, 1) correspondence could be set up between the natural numbers and the real numbers less than 1, expressed by decimals as in the margin, where if a decimal ends in an infinity of 9's it is to be replaced by the equal terminating decimal. We can define a real number less than 1 thus: let the first figure of the decimal representing it be 0 if $a_1 = 9$ or 8 and be $a_1 + 1$ otherwise; let the second figure be 0 or $b_2 + 1$ and the third be 0 or $c_3 + 1$ under like conditions, and so on. Clearly this number cannot equal any of the numbers in the table and our assumed (1, 1) correspondence breaks down.

1	$\cdot a_1 a_2 a_3 \ldots$
2	$\cdot b_1 b_2 b_3 \ldots$
3	$\cdot c_1 c_2 c_3 \ldots$
...	....

·7. We can define '*signed real numbers*' (and the real number $0 = +a - a$) and the relation $<$ between them and their addition and multiplication as in 14·2·3·4·6. They satisfy the laws of 12·41—·44 and 12·51—·56 and 14·5 and 15·3. As in ·4 we can define the real number $\sqrt[p]{a}$, where p is an integer and a any (positive) real. We can then define a^r, where a is any (positive) real and r any signed rational or signed real.

·8. *The classes of real numbers and of signed real numbers are not enumerable.*

then $a + b < a + b'$. (By ·31·3.)

n be *natural numbers* $\neq 0$ we define the *m*th

magnitude *a* by induction thus: $1a = a$,

$(m - 1)\, a + a$. Hence

$= (m + n)\, a = na + ma$. (By induction.)

$(mn)\, a = (nm)\, a$. (By induction and ·36.)

if and only if $m = n$.

n then $m = n + p$ or $n = m + q$ where *p*, *q* are

; then $ma = na + pa$ or $na = ma + qa$ contrary

if and only if $m < n$.

b are distinct magnitudes then either $a < b$ *or*

$= a + b'$ then $b = b'$. (By ·34·4.)

$= b + a$ *if the elements indicated are in M.*

*y Axs. and The.** A set of elements satisfying

'*magnitudes*.' They are in linear order for the

fined in ·31. (·4·2·32.) The Axioms are consistent

e true for the natural numbers $\neq 0$. '*Subtraction*'

in 12·8.

A set of magnitudes is '*Archimedean*' if it satisfy

' Axiom as follows:

a, b be any magnitudes and $a < b$ *then there is a*

nber m such that $ma > b$.

et of elements satisfying ·1·2·3·4·6 *also satisfies* ·5 *and*

Archimedean set of magnitudes.

Ve need five lemmas which we shew first.

ltiples of the same magnitude satisfy ·5 by ·36.

$a + b$. For if $a > b$, there is a magnitude *y* with

Hence $a + b = (b + y) + b = b + (y + b)$; whence

by ·31. If $a = b$ then $b < b + b$ by ·31. If $a < b$ then

ere is a natural number *n* with $na < b \leqq (n + 1)\, a$.

y ·34, $a + na < a + b$ and by ·36, $b \leq na + a = a + na$.

$< a + b$. (·32.)

defined' entities may be 'defined by a set of Axioms.' See 7.

17·9. *Note.* It is usual to identify the integer 2, the signed integer $+2$, the ratio $2/1$, the signed ratio $+2/1$, the real number 2 and the signed real number $+2$. This does not lead to trouble, because a true formula among real numbers is true in one of the other sets, provided the elements indicated in the formula exist in that set. If the signed real numbers are defined by Axioms, the distinctions between the above entities need never be made, and $+2$, $2/3$, -2 and $\sqrt{2}$ are then elements of the same kind. The natural number 2 is of course an entirely different entity.

Continuity

18. *Defs. and Thes.* If *C* be a class linearly ordered for $\prec$ and *D* be a sub-class, the '*upper bound*' of *D* (in *C*) is an element *l* of *C* such that *either* *l* is an element of *D* and all other elements of *D* precede *l*, *or all* elements of *D* precede *l* and if *y* is in *C* and precedes *l* then it precedes some element of *D*. Neither the maximum element (8·6) nor the upper bound of *D need* exist, but if either does, it is unique. If the maximum exists, it is the upper bound.

·1. *Note.* As an illustration of 18, take for *C* the real numbers between 0 and 2 ordered for $<$, and for *D* the numbers $\frac{1}{2}$, $\frac{3}{4}$, $\frac{7}{8}$, $\frac{15}{16}$, ... Their upper bound is 1, but they have no maximum.

·2. *Def.* A class *C* in linear order has '*Dedekind continuity*' if it is condensed (16·1) and if every bounded (8·7) sub-class of *C* has an upper bound in *C**.

·3. *If C is in linear order and has Dedekind continuity and it be divided into two proper sub-classes X, Y so that each element of C is in one only of X, Y and so that each element of X precedes each element of Y, then either X has no maximum but Y has a minimum, or X has a maximum but Y no minimum and*

·4. *The upper bound of X is an element A of C and each element* $\neq A$ *of X precedes A, and A precedes each element* $\neq A$ *of Y.*

* Those who compare with Russell's definition in the Mathematical Philosophy should note that he does not require the class to be condensed.

18·5. *The real numbers and the signed real numbers are in linear order with Dedekind continuity.* Thus Def. 18·2 is consistent. For the proof see 19·1.

19. *Def.* A class in linear order has '*Cantorian continuity*' if it has Dedekind continuity and also has an enumerable relatively dense sub-class. (16·1.)

·1. *The class of real numbers has Cantorian continuity and the rationals are an enumerable relatively dense sub-class* (15·7). Hence Def. 19 is consistent.

Dem. If a, b be any real numbers and $a < b$, there are ratios in b which are not in a. (17·3.) If x be one of them, the class of ratios $< x$ is a real rational number c and $a < c < b$.

To shew that the class of real numbers has Dedekind continuity, consider a bounded set S of real numbers, that is, by 17·2, a set S of lower classes C of ratios all contained in some lower class*. All the ratios considered constitute a lower class D, since, if any ratio occurs, so do all those less than it, and there is no maximum among the ratios considered. Then D is the upper bound of the set S of real numbers, for all classes C are sub-classes of D and if C_1 be any class of S, then either $C_1 = D$ or there is a class C_2 of S containing C_1.

·2. *A linearly ordered class can have Dedekind continuity without having Cantorian continuity.*

Dem. Let K be the class of ordered couples (a, b) where a, b are reals and $0 \leqq a \leqq 1$, $0 \leqq b \leqq 1$, and let $(a_1, b_1) \prec (a_2, b_2)$ when $a_1 < a_2$, or when $a_1 = a_2$ and $b_1 < b_2$. K is then linearly ordered and has Dedekind continuity but a relatively dense sub-class would contain couples (a, b) corresponding to each real number between 0 and 1 and thus would not be enumerable. (17·6.)

·3. *Def.* A linearly ordered class with Cantorian continuity and with no first or last element is a '*(one dimensional) continuum.*'

·4. It can be shewn that *all one dimensional continua with their relation < are similar*†. Our definitions for the same, if

* We avoid all difficulties connected with the Doctrine of Types. See Whitehead and Russell, *Principia Mathematica*, I (1925).

† Cantor, *loc. cit.*, p. 134.

regarded as
defining cont
tinuum.

19·5. *Note.*
bers, entities w
numbers of A
ordinary Mathe

We shall now
ments have som
considered. The
when they hold fo
above.

20. *Undefined.*
magnitudes and an
(a, b) of magnitudes
$a + b$.

Ax. ·1. *If a, b are m*
when a, b are.

Ax. ·2. $a + b \neq a$, *if th*

Ax. ·3. $(a + b) + c = a +$
in M.

·31. *Def.* If a, b are in
nitude x with $a + x = b$. a

·32. If $a < b$ and $b < c$ th

·33. Not more than one

Dem. If $a < b$ and $a > b$ th
with $a + x = b$ and $b + y = a$.

$$a + (x + y) = (a +$$

contrary to ·2. Similarly for t

* Entirely different views have bee
of the continuum. See his *Das Ko*
Mathematische Zeitschrift, X (1921), p

† Huntingdon, "A complete set of
Magnitude," *Trans. Amer. Math. Soc.*

20·34. If $b < b'$

·35. *Def.* If m,
'*multiple*' of the
$2a = 1a + a$, $ma =$

·36. $ma + na =$

·37. $m(na) =$

·38. $ma = na$

Dem. If $m \neq$
natural number
to ·2.

·39. $ma < na$

Ax. ·4. *If a,*
$b < a$.

·41. If $a +$

Ax. ·5. $a +$

·51. *Def.* b
·1·2·3·4·5 are
relation < de
since they a
is defined as

·52. *Def.*
Archimedes

Ax. ·6. *I*
natural nu

·61. *A*
hence is an

Dem. V

(i) Mu

(ii) $b <$
$a = b + y$
$b < a + b$
by ·6 th
Hence
Hence

* 'Un

(iii) If $a < a'$ then $a+b < a'+b$. For there is x with $a+x=a'$ (·31). Also $b < x+b$ by (ii). Hence $a+b < (a+x)+b$. (·34·3.) Hence $a+b < a'+b$.

(iv) If $a < a'$, $b < b'$ then $a+b < a'+b < a'+b'$ by (iii) and ·34.

(v) If $a+b=a+b'$ then $b=b'$. (·34·4.) If $b+a=b'+a$ then $b=b'$. ((iii) and ·4.)

Now either there is a least element E in the class or there is not. If there is, then we shew that all other elements are multiples of E. For suppose the element b is not; then since $E < b$ there is by ·6 a natural number n such that

$$nE < b < (n+1)E.$$

Hence there are elements y, z with $nE+y=b$, $b+z=(n+1)E$ and so $nE+(y+z)=nE+E$. (·3·36.) Thus $y+z=E$ (v), and $y < E$ (·31) cont. hyp. The theorem follows now in this case from ·36.

Secondly, suppose there is no least element in the class, and suppose $a+b < b+a$. Then there are elements x, y, z with $(a+b)+x=b+a$ and $y+z=x$. (·31.) Let w be less than y, z, a, b (8·5), then $2w=w+w < y+z=x$ (iv), and there are natural numbers m, n with $mw < a \leqq (m+1)w$, $nw < b \leqq (n+1)w$. Hence by (iv), (iii) $mw+nw < a+b$,

$$(mw+nw)+x < (a+b)+x = b+a \leqq (n+1)w+(m+1)w$$
$$= (n+m+2)w = (mw+nw)+2w < (mw+nw)+x.$$

(We have used ·36 and (i).) But

$$(mw+nw)+x < (mw+nw)+x$$

is contrary to ·33. Hence our theorem follows.

20·62. *Def.* A class of magnitudes is '*condensed*' if it satisfy the following:

Ax. ·7. *If a be a magnitude of the class, there is another less than a.*

·71. *The ratios >0 are a condensed Archimedean class of magnitudes.* Hence Axs. ·1—·7 are consistent.

·72. *A condensed class of magnitudes is a condensed class in linear order for $<$.* (16·1.)

Dem. If $a < b$ there are magnitudes x, y, z with $a + x = b$, $y < x, y + z = x$. (·31·7.) Hence $a + (y + z) = b$, $a < a + y < b$. (·31·3.)

20·8. *Def. by induction.* If $n > 2$, then

$$a_1 + a_2 + \ldots + a_n = (a_1 + a_2 + \ldots + a_{n-1}) + a_n,$$

n being a natural number.

·81. *If a set of elements obey Assoc+ and Comm+, the sum of a finite number of elements is independent of the order and grouping of the terms.*

Dem. If the elements indicated are in the set, then

$$a + (x_1 + \ldots + x_n) = a + x_1 + \ldots + x_n \text{ .... (i).}$$

For, assume the theorem true when there are n elements in the bracket, then by ·8 and *Assoc*+,

$$\begin{aligned} a + (x_1 + \ldots + x_{n+1}) &= a + [(x_1 + \ldots + x_n) + x_{n+1}] \\ &= [a + (x_1 + \ldots + x_n)] + x_{n+1} \\ &= (a + x_1 + \ldots + x_n) + x_{n+1} \text{ (hyp.)} \\ &= a + x_1 + \ldots + x_{n+1} \text{ (def.).} \end{aligned}$$

Hence (i) is true in general. Hence also

$$a + (x_1 + \ldots + x_n) + b = a + (x_1 + \ldots + x_n + b) = a + x_1 + \ldots + x_n + b.$$

Thus if *Assoc*+ holds, any bracket pair may be removed. And if *Comm*+ holds, any two adjacent terms may be interchanged, and from the properties of natural numbers, it follows that by such interchanges any order can be produced from any other.

·82. *With the same assumptions, if n be a natural number, we have* $n(a_1 + a_2 + \ldots + a_s) = na_1 + na_2 + \ldots + na_s$.

·83. If $a < b$, then $na < nb$ and conversely. If $a = b$, then $na = nb$ and conversely. If $a > b$, then $n(a - b) = na - nb$.

21. *A class of magnitudes with Dedekind continuity* (for $<$) *is Archimedean.*

Dem. Suppose the theorem false, then there are elements a, b with $na \leqq b$ and hence $na < 2b$ for *all* natural numbers n. The sub-class $a, 2a, 3a, \ldots$ being bounded, has an upper bound l such that (i) $na \leqq l$ for all n, and (ii) if $l' < l$ there is a natural number m with $ma > l'$ (18, 18·2). Since by (i) $a < l$ we can take l' such that $a+l'=l$ (20·31). Hence $l'+a=l$, $l'<l$ (20·5·31), and $a+ma>a+l'$ (20·34), whence $(m+1)a>l$ contrary to (i).

21·1. In this proof we have assumed 20·5 but not 20·7, though the latter is implied by Dedekind continuity. (See ·2.)

·2. *Def. and The.* A class of elements satisfying 20·1·2·3·4·5 with Dedekind continuity for $<$ is a class of '*continuous magnitudes.*' Such a class satisfies 20·6 by 21, and also satisfies 20·7. For, if a be any element, there are x, y with $a<x<2a$ (18·2, 16·1), $a+y=x$. Hence $a+y<2a$, $y<a$ (20·4·34).

·3. *The real numbers (greater than* 0) *are a class of continuous magnitudes.* Thus the definition is consistent.

·4. If x be an element of a condensed class of magnitudes and n a natural number, $\neq 0$, there is an element y of the class with $ny<x$.

Dem. There are elements a, b, a_1 with $a+b=x$, $a_1<a, b$, and hence $2a_1<x$. Similarly there is an element a_2 with $2a_2<a_1$, ... and an element a_v with $2^v a_v<x$. But there is a natural number v such that $n<2^v$, for which therefore $na_v<x$.

·5. *If x be a given element of a class M of continuous magnitudes and n a natural number* $\neq 0$, *there is a unique magnitude y of the class with $ny=x$.*

Dem. Consider the class Z of magnitudes z with $nz<x$ for the *given n*. It exists by ·4 and is a bounded sub-class of M, since $z \leqq nz<x$. Hence Z has an upper bound y. Then $ny=x$. For if not, there will be *either* y' with $ny+y'=x$, *or* y' with $ny=x+y'$. In both cases there is an element y'' with $ny''<y'$ (·4). Hence in the first case, $n(y+y'')<x$, and $y+y''$ is in Z contrary to the definition of y, and in the second case

$$ny>x+ny''>ny''.$$

Hence $y>y''$ and $n(y-y'')>x$, again contrary to that definition. Hence $ny=x$. That y is unique follows by 20·83.

·51. *Def.* $\dfrac{1}{n}.x$ is that element y satisfying $ny=x$.

·6. We can now define (in a class M of continuous magnitudes) $\dfrac{p}{q}x$ where x is an element of M and p/q is a ratio, i.e. where p, q are natural numbers.

21·7. *In any class of magnitudes, if the elements indicated exist and are unique*

$$\frac{1}{n}(a_1+\ldots+a_s)=\frac{1}{n}a_1+\ldots+\frac{1}{n}a_s,\quad \frac{1}{n}(a-b)=\frac{1}{n}a-\frac{1}{n}b,$$

where n is a natural number.

Dem. $n.\frac{1}{n}(a_1+\ldots+a_s)=a_1+\ldots+a_s$ (·51), and by 20·82

$$n\left[\frac{1}{n}a_1+\ldots+\frac{1}{n}a_s\right]=n.\frac{1}{n}a_1+\ldots+n.\frac{1}{n}a_s=a_1+\ldots+a_s.$$

The first part now follows by 20·83. Next if $a-b$ exists, there is x with $a=b+x$. Hence $\frac{1}{n}(a-b)=\frac{1}{n}x$, and

$$\frac{1}{n}a-\frac{1}{n}b=\frac{1}{n}(b+x)-\frac{1}{n}b=\frac{1}{n}b+\frac{1}{n}x-\frac{1}{n}b=\frac{1}{n}x.$$

·8. We could now define '*signed magnitudes*' as in 14 and magnitude $0=+a-a$.

*Axioms for Groups**

22. *Undefined.* A class G called a '*group*,' consisting of at least two elements, and an operation which from an ordered couple (a, b) of G produces a third element denoted by ab.

Ax. ·1. *If a, b are in the group so is ab and this is fixed when a and b are in the group and taken in a definite order.*

Ax. ·2. $(ab)c=a(bc)$ *if all the elements indicated are in the group.*

Ax. ·3. *There is an element* ι *of G such that for each a in G we have* $a\iota=a$.

Ax. ·4. *If* ι *be such an element and a be any element of G, there is an element* a' *of G with* $aa'=\iota$.

·41. *Def. by induction.* $x_1x_2\ldots x_n=(x_1\ldots x_{n-1})x_n$, n being any natural number >2.

·42. *Def.* If $ab=ba$ for all elements a, b in G, then G is an '*abelian*' group.

* L. E. Dickson, "Definitions of a Group and a Field," *Trans. Amer. Math. Soc.* 1905, VI, p. 199.

22·43. *The class of signed integers form an abelian group for the operation* $+$. *The class of ratios* >0 *form an abelian group for the operation* $\times$. Hence the Axioms and ·42 are consistent.

Other illustrations of the group idea are: (i) the class of displacements in Euclidean space when they are compounded; (ii) the class of vectors in statics for the operation of vector addition; (iii) the transformations $x' = \frac{ax+b}{cx+d}$ in algebra, a, b, c, d being any (signed) real numbers, with $ad - bc \neq 0$; if S and T be two such transformations, ST will mean the transformation which results from applying first S and then T; the transformation $x' = x$ of the set is the one that corresponds to ι in ·3. *The number of elements in a group may be finite* (see 29) *or enumerable* (e.g. ratios >0 for $\times$) *or not enumerable* (e.g. real numbers >0 for $\times$).

·44. The 'product' of a finite number of elements is independent of their grouping, and if G be abelian, of their order also (20·81).

·5. *If* $aa' = \iota$ *then* $a'a = \iota$, *where* ι *satisfies* ·3·4.

Dem. a'' exists with $aa' = \iota = a'a''$ (·4). Hence

$$a = a\iota = a(a'a'') = (aa')a'' = \iota a'' \quad (·3·2).$$

Hence $$a'a = a'(\iota a'') = (a'\iota)a'' = a'a'' = \iota.$$

·6. *For every* a *in* G, $\iota a = a$, *where* ι *satisfies* ·3·4.

Dem. With notation of ·5 we have $aa' = a'a = \iota$.

Similarly $$a'a'' = a''a' = \iota.$$

Hence $$\iota a = (\iota\iota)a = [\iota(a''a')]a = (\iota a'')(a'a) = a\iota = a,$$

since $\iota a'' = a$ by ·5 *Dem.*

·7. *The element* ι *of* ·3·4 *is unique.*

Dem. If $a\iota = a\iota_1 = a$ for all a, then $\iota\iota_1 = \iota_1\iota = \iota$ by ·5. But $\iota_1\iota = \iota_1$ by hyp.

·71. *Def.* This unique element is called the '*identity*' or '*modulus*' of the group.

·8. *The element* a' *of* ·4 *is fixed when* a *is fixed.*

Dem. If $aa' = aa_1' = \iota$ then by ·5·6,

$$a_1' = a_1'\iota = a_1'(aa') = (a_1'a)a' = \iota a' = a'.$$

22·81. *Def.* This element fixed by a is called the '*inverse*' of a and is denoted by a^{-1}. Thus $aa^{-1}=a^{-1}a=\iota$; $(a^{-1})^{-1}=a$.

·82*. If $ax=b$ then $x=a^{-1}b$; if $ya=b$ then $y=ba^{-1}$.

·83. If $ab=ac$ then $b=c$; if $ba=ca$ then $b=c$ (*Bin* ×); if $aa=a$ then $a=\iota$ (since $aa=a\iota$).

·84. $(ab)^{-1}=b^{-1}a^{-1}$.

·9. We might have denoted by $a+b$ the element got by the operation of the group on (a, b). We should then denote the '*inverse*' of a by $-a$. Then ·81 to ·84 become

·91. $$a+(-a)=(-a)+a=o;\ -(-a)=a$$

where the modulus is now o.

·92. If $$a+x=b \text{ then } x=-a+b;$$

if $$y+a=b \text{ then } y=b+(-a).$$

·93. If $a+b=a+c$ then $b=c$; if $b+a=c+a$ then $b=c$ (*Bin* +); if $a+a=a$ then $a=o$.

·94. $$-(a+b)=(-b)+(-a).$$

We shall seldom use + as the sign for the group operation for non-abelian groups. When we do use it, $a-b$ will mean $a+(-b)$.

Axioms for Quasi-Fields and Fields†

23. *Undefined.* A class K called a 'quasi-field' containing at least two members, and supporting two kinds of operation denoted by + and × (or juxtaposition), K being an abelian group for + with modulus denoted by o, and satisfying 22·1·2·3 for × and 22·4 when $a\neq o$, the modulus for this operation being denoted by u, and further satisfying $a(b+c)=ab+ac$, $(b+c)a=ba+ca$. If also $ab=ba$ for all a, b in K then K is a '*field*.' (Of course only one *Distrib* + × need then be assumed.)

·1. *In a field K we can shew* $a+b=b+a$ *from the other Axioms* (i.e. if Comm × holds we can omit Comm + from the list of Axioms).

* Note that b/a might mean either $a^{-1}b$ or ba^{-1}, which need not be equal save for abelian groups.

† L. E. Dickson, *loc. cit.*

Dem. By *Distrib* $+\times$ and *Comm* $\times$ we have

$$(\beta+\gamma)(b+c)=(\beta+\gamma)b+(\beta+\gamma)c=b(\beta+\gamma)+c(\beta+\gamma)$$
$$=b\beta+b\gamma+c\beta+c\gamma.$$

Interchange b with β and c with γ, then $(\beta+\gamma)(b+c)$ is unchanged, and hence by *Comm* $\times$ and *Assoc* $+$

$$b\beta+b\gamma+c\beta+c\gamma=b\beta+c\beta+b\gamma+c\gamma.$$

Hence by *Bin* $+$ (22·93) we have $b\gamma+c\beta=c\beta+b\gamma$. Put $\beta=\gamma=u$, then $b+c=c+b$.

23·2. *In a quasi-field* $ao=oa=o$ *for all* a.

Dem. Since $a(b+c)=ab+ac$,

we have $ao=a(o+o)=ao+ao$,

that is $e=e+e$ where $e=ao$. Thus $ao=o$ for all a (22·93). Similarly from the right distributive law, $oa=o$ for all a. We can however deduce this from the left distributive law and the first part. For $oa=(oo)a=o(oa)$ for all a since $oo=o$. Now if $oa\neq o$ there is an element x with $(oa)x=u$, then

$$u=oax=(oo)ax=o(oax).$$

Hence $u=ou=o$ (22·3). Hence $b=bu=bo=o$ for all b, contrary to hyp. that there are at least two elements in the class. Hence $oa=o$.

·3. *If* $ab=o$, $b\neq o$, *then* $a=o$.

Dem. $o=ox=(ab)x=a(bx)$ for all x. Take $x=b^{-1}$ then $o=au=a$.

·4. *The number of elements in a field may be finite* (see 29) *or enumerable* (e.g. the signed ratios for $+\times$) *or not enumerable* (e.g. the signed real numbers for $+\times$). The last two examples shew that our Axioms for a field are consistent but not complete. It can be shewn that 22·1·2·3·4 for $+$ and $\times$ and Comm $\times$ and L Distrib $+\times$ are independent*.

·5. Since o and u have the 'formal' properties of 0 and 1 for $+$ and $\times$ we often write 0 and 1 for them.

·6. $-a$ is the '*inverse*' of a for $+$ (22·9), that is, it is the element x with $a+x=o$. (Cf. 14·4.)

Since $o=ob=(a+(-a))b=ab+(-a)b,$

* Dickson, *loc. cit.* Also *Göttinger Nachrichten*, 1905, p. 358. In 22·4 for $\times$ we must of course have $a\neq o$.

we have $(-a)b=-ab$. Similarly $a(-b)=-ab$.

Hence $(-a)(-b)=-[(-a)b]=-[-ab]=ab$.

23·7. *Assoc* + and *L Distrib* + × imply

$$a(b_1+b_2+\ldots+b_n)=ab_1+ab_2+\ldots+ab_n.$$

·8. *Note.* The above treatment may well illustrate the formalist view (6). We have left our elements quite undefined, but given them laws of combination from which much of algebra may be deduced. To shew the laws consistent we are however compelled to use ultimately the *natural* numbers. And even in the above deductions it seems (for this view is not universally held) that what may be called the logical properties of the natural numbers, or of things, are implicitly used. Thus $a+b=b+a$ is not merely a series of marks on paper, but a set of recognisable individuals, which can be regarded as things and not merely as symbols signifying other things. Even to play the game, as a game, we must note that the a and b are in different positions on the two sides of the equation, and that there is not a third way of arranging a, b, + provided for in the rules. It would thus not be possible to construct logic itself, or to deduce the properties of the natural numbers in this purely formal way.

We shall soon see that there are fields and quasi-fields other than the field of ordinary algebra.

Ordered Groups and Fields

24. *Def.* A group for + is '*fully ordered*' when its elements are in linear order for a relation < (say) and when $a<b$ implies $h+a<h+b$ for every h in the group.

·1. $a<b$ if and only if there is an element x with $x>0$, $a+x=b$.

Dem. There is an x with $a+x=b$ (22·92). If $0<x$, then $a<a+x=b$. And if $a<b=a+x$, then $0<-a+a+x=x$ by 24. It is not however possible to use this as a definition to put an arbitrary group in linear order. (Cf. 29.)

·2. The signed integers in their natural order are a fully ordered group for their +<, and the ratios >0 in their natural order are so for their ×<.

24·3. If $a<0$ then $0<-a$. If $a<b$ then $-b+a<0$. If $a<b$ then $a+a<a+b$. If $a<0$, $b\leqq 0$ then $a+b<0$. There is no first or last element, since $x<a$ implies

$$(x-a)+x<(x-a)+a=x.$$

All these follow by 24.

·4. A fully ordered group for + whose elements greater than 0 satisfy Archimedes' Axiom (20·6) is abelian when multiples are defined as in 20·35.

Dem. The elements greater than 0 are a class of elements satisfying 20·1·2·3·4·6 whence their addition satisfies *Comm* + (20·61). It is then easy to shew that

$$a+(-b)=-b+a, \quad -a+(-b)=-b+(-a).$$

25. *Def.* A quasi-field is '*fully ordered*' when it is a fully ordered (abelian) group for + and when $a>0$, $b>0$ imply $ab>0$.

·1. If $h>0$, $a<b$ then $ha<hb$, since $h>0$, $b-a>0$ give $h(b-a)>0$. Similarly $ah<bh$.

·11. $0<1$. *Dem.* If $1<0$ then $0<-1$ (24·3). Hence $0<(-1)(-1)=1$ cont. hyp.

·12. If $a>0$, $b<0$ then $-b>0$, hence $-ab=a(-b)>0$, $ab<0$ (23·6).

·13. If $a<0$, $b<0$ then $-a>0$, $-b>0$,

hence $$ab=(-a)(-b)>0 \text{ (23·6)}.$$

·14. If $a>1$ then $0<a^{-1}<1$. For since $1>0$ and $a>1$, we have $a>0$, and thence, since $a.a^{-1}=1$ we have $a^{-1}>0$ (·12·13). Hence $1<a$ gives $a^{-1}<a^{-1}a=1$ by ·1.

·15. If $0<a<1$ then $a^{-1}>1$. Proof as for ·14.

·16. If a is any element of the quasi-field save 0, then $a^2>0$. (25 and ·13.)

·2. If $a>0$, $b>c$ then $ba^{-1}>ca^{-1}$, $a^{-1}b>a^{-1}c$.

·21. The signed rationals in their natural order are a fully ordered field for their $+ \times <$.

·3. *If K be a fully ordered field with Dedekind continuity and $x>0$ be an element of K, and n a natural number then there is an element y of K with $y^n=x$.*

Dem. The elements >1 of K satisfy 20·1·2·3·4·5 when + is replaced by $\times$. Also 20·31 is satisfied, for if $1 < a < b$, and $ax = b$ then $0 < ax - a = a(x - 1)$. Hence $x > 1$ (25, ·11·12·13). Hence 21·5 gives our theorem at once when $x > 1$ since here $ny = x$ is replaced by $y^n = x$. And if $0 < x < 1$ then $x^{-1} > 1$ (·15) and there is z with $z^n = x^{-1}$, whence $(z^{-1})^n = x$.

25·4. Any quasi-field K has elements u, $u + u$, $u + u + u$, ... where u is the modulus for $\times$. Let $u_r = u + u + \ldots$ to r terms, r being any natural number. If $u_r = u_s$ then $u_{r-s} = 0$.

·41. *Def.* The least natural number n (if there is one) such that $u_n = 0$, is the '*grade*' of u. If $u_n = 0$ then $a + a + \ldots$ to n terms is 0 for any a in K, since $au = a$. n must be prime, for if $n = pp'$ then $u_p u_{p'} = u_n = 0$. Hence $u_p = 0$ or $u_{p'} = 0$ (23·3) and $n = p$ or p'. (See 29.)

·5. *Any fully ordered quasi-field K has 'integral' elements u, $u + u$, ... corresponding to the integers or natural numbers with the same relations of order*, since $u > 0$, $u_n > 0$, and $u_n > u_m$ if and only if $n > m$ (24). *Hence K must be infinite.* We may denote the integral elements by 1, 2, 3, ... *K also has 'rational' elements corresponding to the signed ratios with the same relations of order*, and often denoted by the same symbols as the corresponding ratios. These constitute the '*rational sub-field.*'

·51. If u_n be the integral element corresponding to the natural number n then $a + a + \ldots$ to n terms $= u_n a = a u_n$.

·6. *The elements of the rational sub-field are commutative for multiplication with any element a of the quasi-field.*

Dem. $u_n a = a u_n$. Hence $a(-u_n) = -a u_n = -u_n a = (-u_n) a$; and $u_n a u_n^{-1} = a u_n u_n^{-1} = a$. Hence $a u_n^{-1} = u_n^{-1} a$ and

$$(u_m u_n^{-1}) a = u_m (u_n^{-1} a) = u_m (a u_n^{-1}) = (u_m a) u_n^{-1}$$
$$= (a u_m) u_n^{-1} = a (u_m u_n^{-1}).$$

·61. The set of Axioms and Definitions for the fully ordered field is not complete, since both the signed reals and the signed rationals satisfy them and between these sets a (1, 1) correspondence cannot be set up. (15·8, 17·8.)

·7. *Def.* A quasi-field (or field) K fully ordered for $+$ is '*Archimedean*' if, when a, b are any given elements >0 of K there is an integral element n with $na > b$.

·8. *A fully ordered field F with Dedekind continuity is*

Archimedean. For the elements greater than 0 are a continuous class of magnitudes for $+<$ and hence by 21 they satisfy 20·6. Hence by ·51·7, F is Archimedean.

There is a rational element of F between 0 and any positive element a, for there is an integral element n with $u/n < a$, otherwise we should have $na \leqq u < 2u$ for all integral elements n, and F would not be Archimedean. Hence there is a rational element between any two positive elements $a, b, (b > a)$, namely $a + r$, where r is a rational element between 0 and $b - a$. Whence there is a rational element between any two members of F, and *hence the field has Cantorian continuity* (19).

Hence every element l of the field is the upper bound of all rational elements less than itself; for if r be a rational element less than l, there is a rational element between r and l.

26. *A fully ordered field F with Dedekind continuity is similar to the field Q of signed reals for* $+ \times <$. (See also ·5 below.) That is, F and Q can be put in (1, 1) correspondence so that if a, b of F correspond to a', b' of Q, then $a < b$ if $a' < b'$, and $a + b$ corresponds to $a' + b'$ and ab to $a'b'$.

Sketch of Dem. F has a rational sub-field which can be made to correspond to the rational real numbers. If a be an irrational element of F the set of rational elements of F that are less than a will correspond to a set of rational real numbers of Q having an upper bound a'. This we make correspond to a. The proof can now be completed using 25·8.

·1. The set of Axioms and Definitions for a fully ordered field with Dedekind continuity is complete by 26. We can regard them as a set of Axioms which give for the signed real numbers a definition by Axioms. Then $+2$, $1/2$, -2, $\sqrt{2}$ are elements of precisely the same kind.

We shall henceforth adopt the ordinary nomenclature *and say 'real' instead of signed real*, distinguishing when necessary positive and negative real numbers.

Of course other classes of entities than the real numbers constructed from the natural numbers will satisfy the Axioms of real numbers. But all such classes are similar for $+ \times <$. As Examples of classes satisfying the Axioms we may give:

(i) The class of all reals >0 with 'less than' taken in the ordinary sense, but with $a+b$ replaced by ab, and ab replaced by exp. (log a . log b).

(ii) The class of all reals with 'less than' and ab taken in the ordinary sense, but with $a+b$ replaced by $(a^{\frac{1}{3}}+b^{\frac{1}{3}})^3$.

26·2. *A fully ordered quasi-field K which contains a relatively dense sub-field F is a field.*

Dem. If a, b be members of K and greater than 0 then $ab>0$. If $ab>ba$ there is k in F with $ab>k>ba$ whence $b^{-1}k>a$, $a>kb^{-1}$, $b^{-1}k>kb^{-1}$ (25·1). Hence there is h in F with $b^{-1}k>h>kb^{-1}$, whence $b^{-1}>hk^{-1}$, $k^{-1}h>b^{-1}$. But since $hk^{-1}=k^{-1}h$ this gives a contradiction. Hence $ab=ba$ when $a, b>0$ and so always (23·6).

·21. Conversely a fully ordered field contains a relatively dense sub-field, viz., itself; since by 24·3, if $a<b$ then

$$a<\tfrac{1}{2}(a+b)<b.$$

·3. *A quasi-field K whose elements are fully ordered for + and whose rational sub-field is relatively dense is Archimedean and conversely.*

Dem. If the rational sub-field is relatively dense and $x>a>0$ are in K, there are rational elements pq^{-1}, hk^{-1} with $0<pq^{-1}<a$ and $x<hk^{-1}<x+1$.

Hence $$x<hk^{-1}\leqq h\leqq hp<hqa.$$

Conversely, if K is Archimedean there is an integral element m with $m(x-a)>2$ and since $ma>0$ and K is linearly ordered and Archimedean there is an integral element n with

$$n>ma>n-2\geqq 0.$$

Hence $\quad mx>ma+2>n>ma$ and $x>nm^{-1}>a$.

Hence the rational sub-field is relatively dense.

·4. *A fully ordered Archimedean quasi-field K is a field.*

Dem. The rational elements are relatively dense (·3) and they form a field (25·5). The theorem now follows by ·2.

·5. *A fully ordered quasi-field K with Dedekind continuity is similar to the field of real numbers.*

Dem. As in 25·8, K is Archimedean and so is a field (·4). Hence by 26.

27. We saw that a fully ordered quasi-field K which contains a relatively dense sub-field F is a field, and that if F be

the rational sub-field then K is Archimedean (26·3). We will now shew that *if the relatively dense sub-field F is not the rational sub-field then K need not be Archimedean.*

Dem. Consider the expressions

$$A = a_0 x^m + a_1 x^{m+1} + a_2 x^{m+2} + \dots \quad (a_0 \neq 0),$$

where the a are real and the m any signed integers. Add and multiply them as if they were infinite polynomials, and define their inverses by means of $(x^m)^{-1} = x^{-m}$ and

$$[1 + a_1 x + a_2 x^2 + \dots]^{-1} = 1 - [a_1 x + a_2 x^2 + \dots] + [a_1 x + a_2 x^2 + \dots]^2 - \dots.$$

These expressions then form a field. It is important to notice that no questions of convergency arise. We might have taken as elements of the field the sets of coefficients $(\dots a_0, a_1, a_2, \dots)$; the 'parameter' x merely serves as an aid in our presentation.

To order this field let $A > 0$ when the first (non-zero) coefficient of the expression for A is greater than 0; let $A > B$ when $A - B > 0$. Thus we have $1 - kx > 0$ for all integers k; that is, no multiple of the element x exceeds 1. Hence the field is not Archimedean, but it is easily seen to be fully ordered and hence it contains a relatively dense sub-field (26·21), but the rational sub-field $\{a_0 x^0\}$ is not relatively dense. Cf. 19·2.

27·1. We can derive a class having the order relations of the above field by replacing each element of the one-dimensional continuum C by such a continuum, thus getting C_1, then replacing each element of C_1 by such a continuum and so on, and regarding C as a point of a continuum C' of elements like C, and C' as a point of a continuum C'' of elements like C', and so on. This '*hyper-continuum*' corresponds more closely to the intuitive idea of a continuous class than does the classical continuum of Analysis.

·2. We get a hyper-continuum of even higher type*, if in 27 we take expressions of the form

$$A = a_{m_1} x^{m_1} + a_{m_2} x^{m_2} + \dots \quad (a_{m_1} \neq 0)(m_1 < m_2 < \dots),$$

* For the whole question of hyper-continua see Hausdorff, *Grundzüge der Mengenlehre* (1914), pp. 194—209, and Veronese, *Fondamenti di Geometria* (Padua, 1891).

where the m instead of being integers are now rationals with a finite greatest common denominator λ (which will vary from element to element). The rest of 27 is unchanged.

Each positive element of the present field has a square root.

Dem. If $a_{m_1} > 0$

then $$z = a_{m_1} x^{m_1} \left[1 + \frac{a_{m_2}}{a_{m_1}} x^{m_2 - m_1} + \dots \right] = a_{m_1} x^{m_1} z' \text{ (say).}$$

Let $$z' = 1 + b_1 x^{\mu_1} + b_2 x^{\mu_2} + \dots.$$

This can be written $1 + c_1 y + c_2 y^2 + \dots$

where $y^\lambda = x$, and of course some of the c may be zero. This element is the same as $(1 + h_1 y + h_2 y^2 + \dots)^2$, provided that

$$2h_1 = c_1,\ 2h_2 + h_1^2 = c_2,\ 2h_3 + 2h_1 h_2 = c_3,\ 2h_4 + 2h_1 h_3 + h_2^2 = c_4, \dots$$

and these give successively $h_1, h_2, h_3, \dots$. Hence z' has a square root in the field, and since $\sqrt{a_m} x^{m/2}$ is the square root of $a_m x^m$ our theorem follows.

27·3. *The Axiom of Archimedes is independent of the Axioms and Definitions of the fully ordered field.* This is shewn by the examples in 27 and ·2.

·4. We will now exhibit *a fully ordered quasi-field which is not a field and so has not a relatively dense sub-field and which is accordingly not Archimedean* (26·3). *Thus Comm × cannot be deduced from the Axioms of the fully ordered quasi-field** (cf. 26·4).

Dem. Consider the expressions

$$X = a_0 x^n + a_1 x^{n+1} + \dots$$

where n is any signed integer and the a are real. ($a_0 \neq 0$.)

Let $$Y = y^m X_0 + y^{m+1} X_1 + \dots \quad \dots\dots\dots\dots\dots(1),$$

where $X_0 (\neq 0)$, X_1, X_2, ... are any expressions of the form X and m is any signed integer. We add the expressions Y like ordinary polynomials and multiply them thus:

$$(y^m X_0 + y^{m+1} X_1 + \dots)(y^l X_0' + y^{l+1} X_1' + \dots)$$
$$= y^m X_0 y^l X_0' + (y^m X_0 y^{l+1} X_1' + y^{m+1} X_1 y^l X_0') + \dots \quad \dots(2).$$

If then, as we may, we put

$$xy = 2yx \dots\dots\dots\dots\dots\dots\dots\dots(3),$$

* Hilbert, *Grundlagen der Geometrie* (1909), § 33.

we can reduce (2) to the form (1). [It must be remembered that x, y are *not* numbers; they are merely introduced for convenience and theoretically could be dispensed with.]

For (3) gives

$$x^n y = 2x^{n-1}yx = 4x^{n-2}yx^2 = \dots = 2^n yx^n,$$

and $$xy^{-1} = \tfrac{1}{2}y^{-1}x, \quad x^{-1}y = \tfrac{1}{2}yx^{-1}.$$

With these definitions the Y form a quasi-field provided we can shew that the inverse of any non-zero element exists and is unique. Now an inverse of

$$y^m X_0 + y^{m+1}X_1 + \dots = y^m(X_0 + yX_1 + y^2X_2 + \dots)$$

will be $$(Z_0 + yZ_1 + y^2Z_2 + \dots)y^{-m},$$

where the Z depend on x only, provided that

$$(Z_0 + yZ_1 + y^2Z_2 + \dots)(X_0 + yX_1 + y^2X_2 + \dots) = 1,$$

that is, if

$$Z_0X_0 = 1, \; Z_1X_0 + Z_0'X_1 = 0, \; Z_2X_0 + Z_1'X_1 + Z_0''X_2 = 0, \; \dots \qquad \dots\dots(4),$$

where Z_0', Z_0'', Z_1', ... satisfy

$$Z_0y = yZ_0', \; Z_0y^2 = y^2Z_0'', \; Z_1y = yZ_1', \; \dots.$$

Hence Z_0', Z_0'', Z_1', ... can be found. Then $Z_0X_0 = 1$ gives the coefficients of Z_0, and $Z_1X_0 + Z_0'X_1 = 0$ gives those of Z_1 and so on. Hence an inverse exists and its uniqueness follows as in 22·8.

Thus the expressions Y form a quasi-field which we can order thus: $Y > 0$ if the first (non-zero) coefficient of X_0 is greater than zero. $Y_1 > Y_2$ if $Y_1 - Y_2 > 0$. Then Archimedes' Theorem fails, since $x - ky > 0$ for all integers k.

Complex Numbers

28. *Def.* An '*ordinary complex number*' is an ordered couple of real numbers (a, b) with addition and multiplication defined as follows.

·1. *Def.* +. $(a, b) + (c, d) = (a + c, b + d)$.

·2. *Def.* ×. $(a, b) . (c, d) = (ac - bd, bc + ad)$.

28·3. From these definitions it is easy to shew that *the complex numbers form a field with* (0, 0) *as the modulus for* + *and* (1, 0) *as the modulus for* ×.

·31. In the same way *from any field F we can construct another, provided that if x, y be in F then $x^2+y^2 \neq 0$ unless $x=y=0$.*

·4. For ordinary complex numbers, it is usual to identify $(a, 0)$ with the real number a and to write i for $(0, 1)$. Then (a, b) can be written $a+ib$ (cf. 17·9), and we have $i^2=-1$. This field cannot be fully ordered (25·16).

·5. $a_n x^n + a_{n-1}x^{n-1} + \ldots + a_0 = 0$ $(a_n \neq 0)$, where the a are real or (ordinary) complex numbers, cannot be satisfied by more than n real or complex values of x. The proof of this will be found in any text-book on algebra.

·6. *Def.* An '*algebraic number*' is one which satisfies an equation like that in ·5 with the a all *integers* (positive or negative). A '*transcendental number*' is a real or complex number which is not algebraic.

·7. Since the number of equations (·5) with

$$n + b_n + b_{n-1} + \ldots + b_0$$

fixed (where b_ι is the absolute value of the integer a_ι) is finite, the number of algebraic numbers that are the roots of such equations is finite by ·5. Hence it easily follows that the set of algebraic numbers is enumerable. Hence since the set of real numbers is not enumerable, we have

·8. *Transcendental numbers exist.* It is well known, for example, that e and π are transcendental*.

Modular Fields

29. We shall now give an example of a finite field which we shall need later.

·1. *Def.* Two natural numbers a, b are '*congruent to one another, modulo p*' if $a-b$ is divisible by p. We write this relation $a-b \equiv 0$ (mod. p) or $a \equiv b$ (mod. p).

·11. Let us put all the natural numbers congruent mod. p to a given natural number in one class. We then have p classes, viz. those corresponding to 0, 1, 2, ..., $(p-1)$. If all the natural

* Hobson's *Trigonometry*, p. 306. We do not need this example.

numbers in one class C are added to those of another class C' we get a third class, which we denote by $C+C'$. Similarly if all natural numbers of C are multiplied by all of C' we get a class denoted by CC'. All the laws for a field hold obviously for these classes, except 22·4 for multiplication. We shew this law below, for classes of natural numbers when p is prime. The classes corresponding to 0 and 1 are the moduli for addition and multiplication respectively.

29·12. (Fermat.) If a is a natural number prime to p and p is a prime natural number, then $a^{p-1} \equiv 1 \pmod{p}$.

Dem. If $r, s < p$ and $r \not\equiv s$, then $ra \not\equiv sa \pmod{p}$. For if $ra \equiv sa \pmod{p}$ then would $(r-s)a$ be divisible by p, while neither $r-s$ nor a can be so divisible. Hence $a, 2a, \ldots, (p-1)a$ must be congruent to $(p-1)$ different natural numbers greater than 0 and less than p, and hence to $1, 2, \ldots, (p-1)$ in some order. Whence multiplying the sets together, we have

$$a^{p-1} \underline{|p-1} \equiv \underline{|p-1} \pmod{p} \text{ and } a^{p-1} \equiv 1 \pmod{p}.$$

·13. Now 22·4 follows for multiplication of classes of natural numbers when p is prime, for $ax \equiv 1 \pmod{p}$ has the unique solution (less than p), $x \equiv a^{p-2} \pmod{p}$ when $a \not\equiv 0 \pmod{p}$.

·14. If a, m be co-prime natural numbers, then $ax \equiv b$ (mod. m) has only one solution $x < m$; for as in ·12 the natural numbers $0, a, 2a, \ldots, (m-1)a$ are incongruent (mod. m), and hence one and only one is congruent to b.

·15. Hence if a, m be co-prime natural numbers, there are natural numbers x, y such that $ax - my = 1$; for take $b = 1$ in ·14.

·16. Hence if a, m have d for greatest common divisor, there are natural numbers x, y such that $ax - my = d$, as is seen by dividing through by d.

·2. *Let now p be prime.* We shall represent the classes (mod. p) by the same signs as the natural numbers, thus 1 is the class of numbers congruent to 1 (mod. p), and so on*. *Or* we may regard all natural numbers as having been divided by p and their remainders alone retained.

* Thus $a \equiv b$ (mod. p) will now be written $a = b$. Indices are still natural numbers.

29·21. *Def.* We have seen that if $a \neq 0$ then $a^n = 1$ for some natural number n (·12). The least n for which this is true is the '*period*' of a; a '*belongs to*' that n; if the period of a is $p-1$ then a is a '*primitive* root' of p. Then will $a, a^2, \ldots, a^{p-1}$ be the numbers $1, 2, \ldots, p-1$ in some order and $a^{(p-1)/2} = -1$.

·22. If $a^n = 1$, $a^m = 1$, then $a^d = 1$ where d is the greatest common divisor of m, n.

Dem. There are natural numbers x, y such that $mx - ny = d$ (·16). Hence $a^d = (a^m)^x / (a^n)^y = 1$.

·23. If $a \,(\neq 1)$ belongs to n, then $a^m = 1$, if and only if m is a multiple of n.

Dem. Let d be the greatest common divisor of m, n, then $a^d = 1$; and if m were not a multiple of n we should have $d < n$ contrary to ·21.

·24. If a, b belong resp. to n, m, and n, m are co-prime then ab belongs to nm and $a^x . b^y$ $(x = 0 \ldots n-1,\ y = 0 \ldots m-1)$ are all distinct.

Dem. If ab belongs to r then $1 = (ab)^{rn} = a^{rn} b^{rn} = b^{rn}$. Hence m divides rn (·23) and so m divides r. Similarly n divides r. Hence so does mn, for m, n are co-prime. But $(ab)^{mn} = 1$. Hence $mn = r$ and ab belongs to mn.

If $a^x b^y = a^{x'} b^{y'}$ where x, x' are between 0 and $(n-1)$ inclusive and y, y' between 0 and $(m-1)$ inclusive, there would be natural numbers s, t in the same ranges with $a^s b^t = 1$, since for example if $x > x'$, $y > y'$ we have $a^{x-x'} b^{y-y'} = 1$. Hence

$$1 = (a^s b^t)^n = a^{sn} b^{tn} = b^{tn}.$$

Hence tn is a multiple of m (·23), which is impossible since $t \leqq m-1$ and m, n are co-prime.

·25. Just as in elementary algebra it can be shewn that an equation $a_n x^n + a_{n-1} x^{n-1} + \ldots + a_0 = 0$ where the a are elements of our field cannot have *more than* n roots. (It may have fewer.)

·26. $x^{p-1} - 1 = 0$ has just $(p-1)$ roots $1, 2, \ldots, p-1$. (·12.)

·3. *Primitive roots of any prime p exist.*

Dem. If d divides $p - 1 = df$ we have

$$(x^{p-1} - 1) = (x^d - 1)(x^{d(f-1)} + \ldots).$$

The L.H.S. vanishes for $(p-1)$ values of x (·26) while the second factor on the R.H.S. cannot vanish for more than $d(f-1)$ values (·25). Hence $x^d-1=0$ for just d values of x. Hence if $p-1=p_1^{n_1}p_2^{n_2}\dots$ in prime factors and $p_1'=p_1^{n_1-1}$ etc., then $x^{p_1p_1'}-1=0$ has just $p_1^{n_1}$ roots. Those roots $\neq 1$ which satisfy an equation $x^r-1=0$ where $r<p_1^{n_1}$ must also satisfy $x_1^{p_1'}-1=0$ (·22·23) and there are just p_1' roots of this equation. Hence there are by ·24,

$$p_1'p_2'\dots(p_1-1)(p_2-1)\dots=(p-1)\left(1-\frac{1}{p_1}\right)\left(1-\frac{1}{p_2}\right)\dots$$

primitive roots of p.

29·31. For example every prime of the form 2^n+1 $(n>1)$ has the primitive root 3. (Reid, *Algebraic Numbers*, 1910, p. 151). If $n>3$ then 5 and 7 are also primitive roots*.

·4. The grade of any element $a\neq 0$ in our field in the sense of 25·41 is p, since p is the least natural number n such that $a+a+\dots$ to n terms is 0. That section makes clear why we take p to be a prime here.

·5. The elements of our field form a finite group for + with modulus 0; the elements excluding 0, form a finite group for × with modulus 1. As a geometrical example of a finite group consider the set of rotations of a circle round its centre through angles 0, $2\pi/p$, $4\pi/p$, ..., $2n\pi/p$, (p being prime). If a be any element of this group (not the modulus u) the group is the set of elements $u, a, a^2, \dots, a^{p-1}$ where $a^p=u$. Multiplication of elements means combination of the rotations.

·6. If we tried to order the last group using 24·1 as definition, we should have: $a<b$ if there is an element $x>u$ with $ax=b$. Suppose $a>u$ then $a.a=a^2$ gives $a<a^2$. Similarly

$$a^2<a^3, \dots a^{p-1}<a^p=u.$$

Hence $a<u$ and we have a contradiction.

Linear Equations in Quasi-Fields

30. In quasi-fields the theory of linear equations is slightly more complicated than in fields.

·1. If $x_1\neq 0$, we can find L so that

$$Lx_1+y_1=0, \text{ viz. } L=-y_1x_1^{-1}.$$

* Cf. Wertheim, "Primitive Wurzeln," *Acta Mathematica*, Bd. XX, 1896, p. 143.

30·2. If $x_1, y_1, z_1, x_2, y_2, z_2$ are given non-zero elements we can in general find L, M so that

$$\begin{cases} Lx_1 + My_1 + z_1 = 0 \\ Lx_2 + My_2 + z_2 = 0. \end{cases}$$

For multiply on the right by y_1^{-1}, y_2^{-1} resp. and subtract then

$$L(x_1y_1^{-1} - x_2y_2^{-1}) + z_1y_1^{-1} - z_2y_2^{-1} = 0.$$

Hence L can be found (·1) unless $x_1y_1^{-1} - x_2y_2^{-1} = 0$. Similarly M can be found unless $y_1x_1^{-1} - y_2x_2^{-1} = 0$. If $x_1y_1^{-1} = x_2y_2^{-1}$ then

$$\begin{cases} Lx_1y_1^{-1} + M + z_1y_1^{-1} = 0 \\ Lx_1y_1^{-1} + M + z_2y_2^{-1} = 0. \end{cases}$$

Hence, *either* $z_1y_1^{-1} = z_2y_2^{-1}$ also, and the equations are the same, and L can be found for any given value of M, *or* $z_1y_1^{-1} \neq z_2y_2^{-1}$ and then the equations are inconsistent.

·3. Under all conditions we can find at least one set of L, M, N, not all zero, so that

$$Lx_1 + My_1 + Nz_1 = 0,\ Lx_2 + My_2 + Nz_2 = 0.$$

·4. If A, B, C do not vanish, and

$$\begin{cases} x_1A + x_2B + x_3C = 0 \\ y_1A + y_2B + y_3C = 0 \\ z_1A + z_2B + z_3C = 0 \end{cases} \qquad \text{(i)},$$

we can always find at least one set of L, M, N, not all zero, so that

$$\begin{cases} Lx_1 + My_1 + Nz_1 = 0 \\ Lx_2 + My_2 + Nz_2 = 0 \\ Lx_3 + My_3 + Nz_3 = 0. \end{cases}$$

Dem. We can find L, M, N to satisfy the first two equations (·3). Multiply the equations of (i) on the left by L, M, N resp. and add and we get $(Lx_3 + My_3 + Nz_3)C = 0$, which, since $C \neq 0$, gives the third equation.

·5. We can under certain conditions extend these theorems to any number of equations, the conditions being that certain expressions do not vanish. The full investigation of these conditions by elementary means is easy but very tedious*. We shall need

* Vahlen, *Abstrakte Geometrie*, 1905, pp. 70—88.

30·6. If

$$x_1 A + x_2 B + x_3 C = x_4,\quad y_1 A + y_2 B + y_3 C = y_4,$$
$$z_1 A + z_2 B + z_3 C = z_4,\quad A + B + C = 1,$$

then we can always find a, b, c, d, not all zero, so that $ax + by + cz + d = 0$ is satisfied by $(x_1 y_1 z_1)$ $(x_2 y_2 z_2)$ $(x_3 y_3 z_3)$ $(x_4 y_4 z_4)$. For the equations can be written

$$(x_1 - x_3) A + (x_2 - x_3) B + x_3 - x_4 = 0;$$
$$(y_1 - y_3) A + (y_2 - y_3) B + y_3 - y_4 = 0;$$
$$(z_1 - z_3) A + (z_2 - z_3) B + z_3 - z_4 = 0.$$

Apply ·4 and the theorem follows.

CHAPTER II

ORDER

Introductory Remarks

The main properties of Euclidean space are those connected with (1) the intersections of lines and planes and the number of points needed to fix a line or a plane, (2) the order of points on a line or plane or in space, (3) the congruence of figures and (4) continuity.

We shall first deal with order and take as our basic undefined entities, a class of things called 'points' and a certain three-termed relation which holds between certain points. If this relation holds between A, B and C we express that fact by saying 'A, B, C are in the order ABC.' This statement we shall often abbreviate by writing $[ABC]$. If A, B, C be any three points, then $[ABC]$ is a proposition either true or false.

If the points A, B, C be in the order ABC, we can *picture* the relation by taking 'point' to mean an ordinary point of space and $[ABC]$ to mean, B is on the straight line AC and between A and C; but nothing must be assumed from this picture, everything stated must be deduced from the Axioms laid down. Other representations may also be suitable; for instance as far as the Axioms **O** I—VI below are concerned we may take 'point' to mean any point of an ordinary sphere except one fixed point N, for instance the North Pole, and we may take $[ABC]$ to mean that A, B, C, N are on a circle of the sphere and B, N separate A, C. Or we can take 'point' to mean an ordered couple of real numbers (x, y) and, if

$$A=(x_1, y_1),\quad B=(x_2, y_2),\quad C=(x_3, y_3),$$

we can take $[ABC]$ to mean that there are real positive numbers m, n such that

$$mx_1+nx_3=(m+n)x_2,\quad my_1+ny_3=(m+n)y_2.$$

Any set of entities satisfying the Axioms will give a representation of the Geometry.

If we illustrate our argument by figures, nothing save what is explicitly stated and deduced may be used from these figures. Theoretically, figures are unnecessary; actually they are needed as a prop to human infirmity. Their sole function is to help the reader to follow the reasoning; in the reasoning itself they must play no part.

From our Axioms of Order we shall deduce, using suitable definitions, many of the properties (1), p. 42, with the important exception of those relating to parallels. From the Axioms of this chapter we cannot deduce the whole of Euclidean Geometry since they hold in other Geometries, e.g. in the Hyperbolic Geometry, but in addition to these Axioms we shall only need two more for this purpose, one of which is introduced in Chapter VI and the other in Chapter XIII. It will then be seen on what an extremely narrow basis the whole of Euclidean Geometry can be erected.

Most of our Axioms if regarded as treating of the Physical Space in which we live, would be considered trivial, but the fact that all Euclidean Geometry follows from them is most surprising and anything but trivial and it is the main purpose of this book to shew just this fact. Our Axioms and Definitions could also be regarded as a final analysis of the properties of Euclidean Space.

Whenever possible, it is best to take the formalist view of our deductions and to regard the investigation as a game played in accordance with our rules, the Axioms, and starting from the fixed positions of the pieces given in the hypotheses of the theorems. And in order that no unstated assumption may creep in, we must move slowly and warily. The proof of the first theorems will be written out fairly fully and formally. Later, when the 'intuitive' theorems have been established, more will be left to the reader, but he is advised to make sure that the full formal proof can be given.

Our Geometry is an abstract Geometry. The reasoning could be followed by a disembodied spirit who had no idea of a physical point; just as a man blind from birth could understand the Electromagnetic Theory of Light.

The system of Axioms we use in this chapter is due to

Veblen*, and we shall lean rather heavily on his work. The formal treatment now begins.

§ 1. *Undefined Entities*

As undefined entities we take

(1) A class of elements called '*points*,' denoted by Latin Capitals.

(2) A three-termed relation between points indicated either by the phrase 'the points A, B, C are in order ABC' or by the symbol $[ABC]$.

Thus $[ABC]$ is a proposition. It is to be considered as distinct from the propositions $[BAC]$, $[CBA]$ and so on. If A, B, C are any points then $[ABC]$ is either true or false; it is never meaningless.

Ax. O I. If A, B, C be points in order ABC then A, B, C are distinct.

Notation. $A \neq B$ means A, B are distinct; $A, B \neq C$ or $C \neq A, B$ means $A \neq C$ and $B \neq C$. (I 4.)

Ax. O II. If A, B, C be points in order ABC they are not in order BCA.

Introduction of Lines

Our first object is to introduce some entities called lines; a line is to be a class of points and is to contain an infinity of points and is to be fully determined by any two points it contains. But in order to use as few Axioms as possible we shall proceed by a route which may at first seem artificial.

1. *Temporary Definition.* If A, B be any two distinct points, taken in a fixed order, the set of points consisting of A, B and of all points P for which either $[PAB]$ or $[APB]$ or $[ABP]$ will for the present be called the '*sequence* AB.' This must be distinguished at present from the sequence BA which consists of B, A, and of all points P for which either $[PBA]$ or $[BPA]$ or $[BAP]$.

* Veblen, "A system of Axioms for Geometry," *Trans. Amer. Math. Soc.* 1904, v, p. 343, and an article by the same writer in *Monographs on Topics of Modern Mathematics* (Longmans), 1915.

1·1. When we speak of the sequence AB in the hypothesis of a theorem it will be understood that $A \neq B$. Similar understandings will be assumed for all entities subsequently defined, that is, if any entity is mentioned in the hypothesis of a theorem the conditions, if any, for its existence will be assumed to be fulfilled.

Ax. O III. If *C*, *D* be distinct points of the sequence *AB* then *A* is a point of the sequence *CD*.

Thus by the Axiom itself, A belongs to the sequence DC also, since the hypothesis says that D, C are distinct points of the sequence AB; but it is not stated that B belongs either to the sequence CD or to the sequence DC.

The conclusion of **O** III depends on the arrangement of the two premisses 'C is a point of the sequence AB and D is a point of that sequence.' If this type of proposition is objected to, the conclusion of the Axiom should be amended to read 'A is a point both of the sequence CD and of the sequence DC.' Modern logicians do, however, often allow propositions wherein the conclusion depends on the arrangement of the premisses: e.g. 'p or q implies q or p.'

§ 2. Axioms **O** I—III imply the following:

2. $[ABC]$ *implies* $[CBA]$, *and implies that* $[BCA]$, $[CAB]$, $[BAC]$, $[ACB]$ *are all false.*

Dem. $[ABC]$ implies $A \neq C$ (**O** I) and C, A are in the sequence BC (1). Hence B is in the sequence CA (**O** III). Also $B \neq C, A$ (**O** I). Hence either $[BCA]$ or $[CAB]$ or $[CBA]$ (1). But $[ABC]$ implies that $[BCA]$ is false (**O** II). And if $[CAB]$ were true then $[ABC]$ would be false (**O** II), whereas it is true. Hence $[CAB]$ is also false, and the only remaining possibility, $[CBA]$, is therefore true.

Thus we have shewn that $[ABC]$ implies $[CBA]$ and implies that $[BCA]$ and $[CAB]$ are both false. Similarly if $[BAC]$ were true, then $[CAB]$ would be true, whereas it is false. And if $[ACB]$ were true, then $[BCA]$ would be true, whereas it is false. Hence $[BAC]$, $[ACB]$ are also both false.

·1. *Every point of the sequence* AB *is a point of the sequence* BA *and conversely, that is, these sequences are identical.*

Dem. If P is in the sequence AB then either $P=A$ or $P=B$ or $[PAB]$ or $[APB]$ or $[ABP]$, and the last three imply resp. $[BAP]$, $[BPA]$, $[PBA]$. Whence the theorem.

2·12. *Note.* In view of 2 we can now, if we wish, translate $[ABC]$ by the phrase 'B is between A and C' which means of course that the *object* denoted by B is 'between' the *objects* denoted by A and C. When the proposition is written $[ABC]$ the *letter* B is between the *letters* A and C in the sense in which 'between' is used by the unsophisticated man. This makes the notation suggestive, but it must not mislead the reader into assuming that our 'between' has any properties save those actually mentioned. Any three-termed relation with these properties might be called 'between.' Let the reader work through the above argument using BAC to mean 'B is between A and C.' It will be equally valid.

·2. *Notation.* If all points of a set of points X are in a set Y and vice versâ we write $X=Y$. When this is not so, we write $X \neq Y$. (See I 4.)

3. *Defs.* If A, B be distinct points the '*line AB*' is the set of points in the sequence AB; we can hence by 2·1 speak of the line AB instead of the sequence AB or the sequence BA.

The '*open interval*' AB is the set of all points X in order AXB.

The '*closed interval*' AB is the set of all points of the open interval AB together with A and B; A, B are the '*ends*' both of the open and the closed intervals AB. The line AB and the open and closed intervals AB are said to '*join*' A and B.

When we use the word 'interval' alone we shall always mean 'closed interval.'

Any two sets of points are said to '*meet*' in their common points.

·1. *Notation.* The line AB may be denoted by AB simply and in future AB will always mean the line AB: we shall never again require the sequence. The open interval AB may be denoted by $A^{-}B$, the closed interval AB by $A^{\vdash\dashv}B$, the open interval AB together with A by $A^{\vdash}B$, and the open interval AB together with B by $A^{\dashv}B$*.

* These symbols seem to be due to Peano. See *Formulario Mathematico* (1895—1910).

3·2. If $A \neq B$ then $AB = BA$, $A^{-}B = B^{-}A$. $A^{\vdash\!\dashv}B = B^{\vdash\!\dashv}A$.

·3. If C, D be distinct points of AB, then A, B are distinct points of CD.

·4. If C be on AB and $C \neq A$, then B is on AC.

Dem. A, C are on BA (·2). Hence by **O** III.

·5. If C be on AB and $C \neq A$ then $AB = AC$ (2·2).

Dem. Let X be on AB. If $X = C$ then X is on AC (1, 3). If $X \neq C$, then since X, C are distinct points of AB, A will be on XC (·3). Hence A, C are distinct points of XC, and so X is on AC (·3).

Thus if C be on AB and $C \neq A$, then all points of AB are on AC.

But the same hypothesis implies B is on AC (·4) and $B \neq A$ (1·1) and hence, by the first part of this proof, all points of AC are on AB. Hence the theorem by 2·2.

·6. If C be on AB and $C \neq A, B$ then $AB = AC = BC$ (·5 and ·2).

·7. *Note.* Ax. **O** III has enabled us to shew that $AB = BA$ and this has been done by means of 2 which is deduced from **O** III. Another plan is to introduce an *additional* Axiom, as follows:

Ax. **O**′. If A, B, C be points in order ABC, they are in order CBA.

If then we define the line AB as the set of points A and B together with all points X such that either [XAB] or [AXB] or [ABX] we have 3·2 at once. As a minute consideration it may be noted that from **O** II and **O**′ part of **O** I follows, namely, that if we have [ABC] then $B \neq A$ and $B \neq C$.

4. *If $A \neq B$ there is one and only one line on which both A and B lie.*

Dem. To shew this we prove that if A, B be on CD then $AB = CD$. Now since $C \neq D$, therefore $A \neq C$ or $A \neq D$. Suppose $A \neq C$, then $CD = CA = AC$ (3·5·2). But B is on CD and so is on AC (2·2) and $B \neq A$. Hence $AC = AB$ (3·5). Hence $CD = AB$. Similarly if $A = C$, since then $A \neq D$.

·1. If $AB = AC$ and $B \neq C$ then $AB = BC$ (4).

·2. If A be not on BC, then B is not on AC, and C is not on AB. Thus AB, BC, CA are distinct lines (4).

·3. *Two distinct lines cannot meet in more than one point.*

4·4. *Def.* A set of points on the same line are said to '*colline*' or '*be collinear.*'

·5. *Def.* A set of lines with a common point are said to '*concur*' or '*be concurrent*' at that point.

·6. If A, B, C colline and are distinct, then $[ABC]$ or $[BCA]$ or $[CAB]$ (4, 3).

·7. *Note.* So far as we know at present, the only points on AB might be A and B. In fact we have not yet said that *any* points exist. We therefore formally introduce the following Axioms.

§ 3. *Existence Axioms and the Transversal Axiom*

Ax. O IV. If A, B be distinct points there is at least one point C in order ABC.

Ax. O V. There exist three points not on the same line.

These two Axioms are existence Axioms and will give us many of the points we need.

O V could be replaced by the slightly weaker form: There exist three distinct points A, B, C not in any of the orders ABC, BCA, CAB.

In the presence of the earlier Axioms and Definitions the two forms of **O** V are equivalent and either form gives:

If any line be given there is a point not on it.

Ax. O VI. (The transversal Axiom.) **If A, B, C are distinct points and A is not on BC and if D, E be points such that $[BCD]$ and $[CEA]$ then there is a point F on DE with $[AFB]$*.**

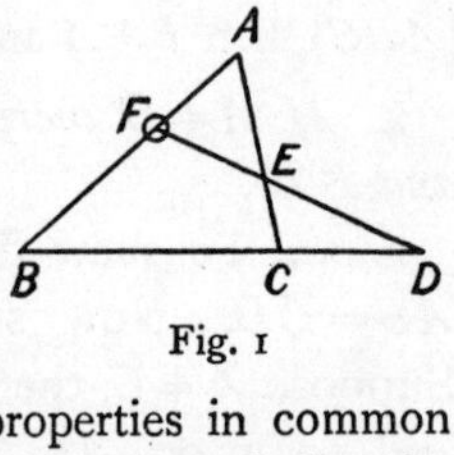

Fig. 1

Note. This Axiom is of central importance. A set of elements for which the other Axioms are true, but this false, would have very few properties in common with those of our Geometry†. It must be carefully noted what the Axiom asserts. If we have $[BCD]$ and then $[AFB]$ instead of $[CEA]$ we do not assert the existence or any properties of E. This question

* Peano, *Revista di Mat.* IV (1894), p. 65.

† Cf. Geiger, *Systematische Axiomatik der Euclidischen Geometrie* (Filser, 1924).

is considered in 11·6, where we shew that $[BCD]$ and $[AFB]$ imply $[CEA]$.

5. (**O** I—III, VI)*. *With the hypotheses of* **O** VI, *F satisfies* $[AFB]$ *and* $[DEF]$. The additional assertion here is that $[DEF]$.

Dem. $D \neq E$, for D is on BC and E on CA (3) and these lines are distinct (4·2) and hence have only the point C common (4·3) and by **O** I, $D, E \neq C$.

Similarly D, E, F are all distinct but F is on DE (**O** VI). Hence if we shew $[EFD]$ and $[FDE]$ are both false, we shall have $[DEF]$ (3).

Suppose $[EFD]$ were true; D is on BC and so not on CA (4·3), that is, D is not on CE (3·5) whence $[CEA]$ $[EFD]$ would give a point X on AF with $[DXC]$ (**O** VI). But since X lies on the distinct lines $CD = BC$ and $AF = AB$, we must have $X = B$ (4·3) and hence $[DBC]$. But this contradicts the hypothesis that $[BCD]$ (**O** II).

Similarly we can shew $[FDE]$ is false. Whence the theorem.

6. (**O** I—III, VI). *If A, B, C do not colline and* $[BA'C]$, $[CB'A]$, $[AC'B]$, *then A', B', C' do not colline.*

Using terms defined later this means that a line cannot meet the three sides of a triangle.

Dem. $A', B' \neq C$ (**O** I) and A' is on BC and B' on AC. Hence by 4·2·3 we have $A' \neq B'$. Similarly A', B', C' are all distinct. Hence if they colline either $[A'B'C']$ or $[B'C'A']$ or $[C'A'B']$ (4·6).

Now C' is not on BA', for C', B are distinct points of AB and B is on $BA' = BC$ (3·5) which is distinct from AB.

Also we have $[BA'C]$; hence if $[A'B'C']$ there would be a point X with $[BXC']$ such that C, B', X colline (**O** VI). Thus (as in 5) $X = A$ and we have $[BAC']$, contrary to the hypothesis that $[AC'B]$. Hence $[A'B'C']$ is impossible. Similarly the other cases are impossible.

·1. *Note.* This seems the place to point out the significance of **O** VI, and since this note is not part of our logical development, we use the ordinary language of Geometry. If a line meets the three

* The Axioms in the bracket are those used in the proof.

sides of a triangle internally we shall say the type of this transversal is III; if it meets one side internally and two externally we say the type is IEE, and so on. Thus in the Euclidean Geometry we have the types EEE and IIE but no others. Let us call two types contradictory when their symbols agree in two letters, but differ in the third. Thus EEE and IEE are contradictory. Consider now a triangle ABC and let F, E be points such that $[AFB]$ $[AEC]$ and let FE meet BC in D. If we do not assume a transversal Axiom any of the orders DBC, BDC, BCD, and any of DFE, FDE, FED are possible. When the matter is investigated, it is found that we have *contradictory types of transversal* in our figure (considering its different triangles) unless *either* $[BCD]$ and $[FED]$, *or* $[DBC]$ and $[DFE]$ which are the Euclidean cases, and then the types in the figure are EEE, IIE.

It is true that if we start from points on the prolongations of the sides of the triangle, instead of from F, E we can get non-Euclidean figures which do not themselves have contradictory types of transversals; in fact there are two such cases, viz.

(1) $[DBC]$ $[ECA]$ $[AFB]$ $[DEF]$, types IEE.

(2) $[DBC]$ $[CEA]$ $[ABF]$ $[DEF]$, types IEE.

But they contradict the only non-contradictory types obtained above. Hence, apart from the statement of existence in **O** VI, we could replace that Axiom by the statement, that transversals of contradictory types do not exist*.

The Orders of Points on a Line

§ 4. Axioms **O** I—VI imply:

7. *If* $A \neq B$ *there is a point* F *with* $[AFB]$, *that is between any two points lies another point.*

This does not yet mean that between any two points there is an infinity of others, for we have yet to shew that if X is between A and B, and Y between A and X, then Y is between A and B.

Dem. There is a point E not on AB (**O** V) and a point C with $[AEC]$ (**O** IV). Hence $AC = AE \neq AB$ (3·5, 4·2). But $A \neq B$, hence B is not on AC (4·3) and hence A is not on BC (4·2). But there is a point D with $[BCD]$ (**O** IV) and since $[CEA]$ there is by **O** VI a point F with $[AFB]$.

·1. *Note.* We now know by **O** IV, 2, 7 that a line AB contains at least five points, viz., A, B and X, Y, Z in orders XAB, AYB,

* An analogous argument to that sketched here is given in Geiger, *loc. cit.*

ABZ, for X, Y, Z are distinct by 2. Our next step is to shew that a line has an infinity of points in it and to investigate the order-relations of n points on a line.

8. *If O be any point of a line, the other points of the line can be divided into two sets $[X]$, $[Y]$ such that each set contains an infinity of points and no point is in both sets, and such that if X_1, X_2 be any points of $[X]$ and Y_1, Y_2 any points of $[Y]$ then $[X_1OY_1]$ but neither $[X_1OX_2]$ nor $[Y_1OY_2]$.*

We first shew 8·1 to 8·93.

·1. $[ABC]$ $[BCD]$ imply $[ABD]$.

Dem. A, B, C, D colline and $A \neq D$ (**O** II). As in 7 there are points Y, W not on AB with $[BYW]$. Now W is not on AB and $[ABC]$ $[BYW]$, hence there is a point Z with $[AZW][CYZ]$ (5). Since Z is on AW and $Z \neq A$ therefore Z is not on CD. Hence $[DCB]$ $[CYZ]$ give a point X with $[BYX][ZXD]$ (5) and $W \neq X$. Since Z is not on AD $(= CD)$, and $[AZW]$ $[ZXD]$, there is a point B' on WX with $[AB'D]$ (5). But since B' is on AD and WX, and $WX = WB$ (since $[BYW][BYX]$), and $WB \neq AD$ we have $B' = B$ and so $[ABD]$.

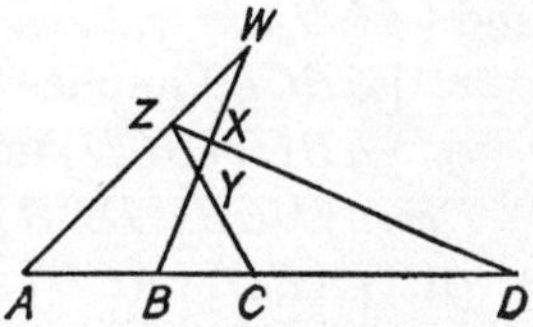

Fig. 2

·2. $[ABC]$ $[ABD]$ and $C \neq D$ imply $[BCD]$ or $[BDC]$.

Dem. A, B, C, D colline and $B \neq C, D$ (**O** I). Hence $[BCD]$ or $[BDC]$ or $[CBD]$.

We shew that $[CBD]$ is false. If possible let it be true. There are points P, S not on AC with $[SCP]$ (**O** IV, V). Then since S is not on AC, $[SCP]$ $[CBA]$ give a point R with $[PBR]$ $[ARS]$. And since S is not on CD, $[SCP]$ $[CBD]$ give a point Q with $[PBQ]$ $[DQS]$. But since $[PBR]$ $[PBQ]$ therefore R, B, Q colline and since D, S, A do not colline, $[SRA]$ $[ABD]$ $[DQS]$ are impossible together (6). Hence $[CBD]$ is false.

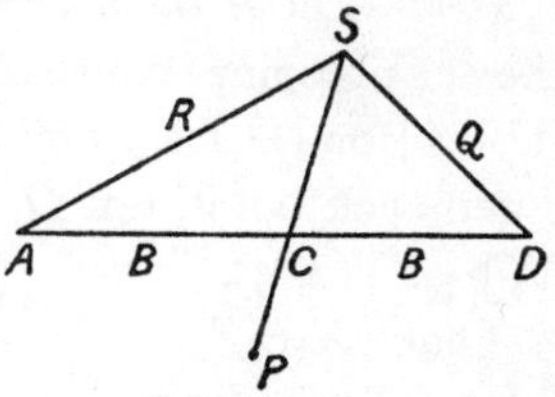

Fig. 3

·3. $[ABD]$ $[ACD]$ and $B \neq C$ imply $[ABC]$ or $[ACB]$.

Dem. Since A, B, C colline (3) and are distinct (**O** I) we have $[ABC]$ or $[ACB]$ or $[BAC]$ (4·6). But $[BAC]$ $[ACD]$ imply $[BAD]$ (·1) contrary to $[ABD]$.

8·4. $[ABC]$ $[ABD]$ and $C \neq D$ imply $[ACD]$ or $[ADC]$.

Dem. By ·2 we have $[BCD]$ or $[BDC]$. But $[DCB]$ $[CBA]$ imply $[DCA]$, and $[CDB]$ $[DBA]$ imply $[CDA]$ (·1).

·5. $[ABC]$ $[ACD]$ imply $[BCD]$.

Dem. As usual we have $[BCD]$ or $[CBD]$ or $[CDB]$. But the second is false since with $[CBA]$, $A \neq D$ it gives $[CAD]$ or $[CDA]$ (·4) contrary to $[ACD]$. And the third is false since with $[ACD]$ it gives $[ACB]$ (·1) contrary to $[ABC]$.

·6. $[ABC]$ $[ACD]$ imply $[ABD]$ (·5·1).

·7. *Def.* If A, B, C, D are points $[ABCD]$ means $[ABC]$ and $[ACD]$.

·8. $[ABCD]$ implies $[ABC]$ $[ACD]$ $[BCD]$ $[ABD]$ (·5·6·7).

·9. $[ABD]$ $[BCD]$ imply $[ABCD]$.

Dem. $[DCB]$ $[DBA]$ imply $[CBA]$ $[DCA]$ (·5·6).

·91. $[ABD]$ $[ACD]$ and $B \neq C$ imply $[ABCD]$ or $[ACBD]$ (·3·7).

·92. $[ABCD]$ implies $[DCBA]$ and all other orders are false.

·93. If $[ABC]$ and X is on AB and $X \neq B$ then $[ABX]$ or $[XBC]$. (Cf. I 10·5.)

Dem. If $[XBC]$ is false we have $[BXC]$ or $[BCX]$ or $X = C$. Now $[ABC]$ with $[BCX]$ or $X = C$ give $[ABX]$ (·1). Further $[CXB]$ $[CBA]$ give $[XBA]$ (·5).

These Theorems lead readily to the proof of 8.

Dem. Let A be any point, not O, of the line and let $[X]$ be the set of points consisting of A and all points X such that $[OXA]$ or $[OAX]$, and $[Y]$ the set of points with $[YOA]$. Then each point, not O, of the line is in one and only one of $[X]$, $[Y]$ (2, 3).

That $[X_1OY_1]$ is always true and $[X_1OX_2]$ $[Y_1OY_2]$ both false follows from the theorems just shewn. For example $[Y_1OA]$ $[Y_2OA]$ imply $[AOY_1]$ $[AOY_2]$ and so $[OY_1Y_2]$ or $[OY_2Y_1]$ or $Y_1 = Y_2$ (·2). Hence $[Y_1OY_2]$ is false.

To shew that there is an infinity of points in $[X]$ we proceed thus: There are points X_1, X_2 with $[OAX_1]$ $[AX_1X_2]$ (**O** IV). Hence X_2 is in $[X]$ (·1) and $X_1 \neq X_2$. Similarly there is a point X_3 with $[AX_2X_3]$, and hence $[OAX_3]$ and $X_3 \neq X_1, X_2$. For if, for example, $X_3 = X_1$ then $[AX_1X_2]$ would contradict $[AX_2X_3]$. This process and reasoning can be continued indefinitely. Similarly for $[Y]$.

9. Using the notation of 8, $[X_1Y_1X_2]$ *and* $[Y_1X_1Y_2]$ *are false.* For example $[X_1Y_1X_2]$, with $[OX_1X_2]$ or $[OX_2X_1]$, give $[Y_1X_1O]$ or $[Y_1X_2O]$ (8·5) contrary to $[X_1OY_1]$ and $[X_2OY_1]$.

10. If $A \neq B$ *there is an infinity of points* Z *between* A *and* B.

Dem. There is a point Z_1 with $[AZ_1B]$ (7) and Z_2 with $[AZ_2Z_1]$ (7) and hence with $[AZ_2B]$ (8·6) and $Z_2 \neq Z_1$. Again there is a point Z_3 with $[AZ_3Z_2]$ and hence $[AZ_3B]$ (8·6) and $Z_3 \neq Z_1, Z_2$. And so on.

·1. If C is on A^-B then any point, save C, on A^-B is on one and only one of A^-C, C^-B and all points on these open intervals are on A^-B.

Dem. $[AXB]$ $[ACB]$ and $X \neq C$ imply $[AXC]$ or $[CXB]$ (8·93) and both cannot hold together, since together they give (since $A \neq B$) $[XAB]$ or $[XBA]$ (8·2). The converse follows from 8·6.

·11. *Def.* If C is on A^-B, it '*divides*' A^-B into A^-C and C^-B.

·2. If C, C_1 be on A^-B then each point of C^-C_1 is on A^-B (·1).

·3. *Defs.* If $O \neq A$, the '*ray* OA,' or $[OA$, is the set of points consisting of A and all points X in order OXA or OAX. The '*ray*' $OA]$, written $OA]$, is the set of all points Y in order YOA. O is the '*end*' of these rays, and they '*go from*' O, (which is not on them). $[OA$ and $OA]$ are '*opposite*' rays.

The reader will have no difficulty in proving the following.

·4. Any point, save O, of OA is on one and only one of $[OA$, $OA]$.

·5. If B is on $[OA$ then $[OA = [OB$ and is $O{\dashv}B$ together with $BO]$.

·51. If B is on $OA]$ then $OA] = [OB$ and is $O{\dashv}B$ together with $BO]$.

·52. If B, C are on opposite rays from O then $[BOC]$ and conversely.

·53. If $[OA = OB]$ then $OA] = [OB$.

10·54. If $[AOB]$ then $[OB$ is the set of points X with $[AOX]$.

·55. If X, Y be both on the same ray from O, then $X=Y$ or $[OXY]$ or $[OYX]$.

·56. And Y is on $[XO$ or X is on $[YO$ or $X=Y$.

·57. If $[OAB]$ then all points of $[AB$ are on $[OA$.

·58. If B is on $[OA$ and $[OBC]$ then C is on $[OA$.

·6. *Def.* If B is on $[OA$ or on $OA]$ it '*divides*' the ray into $O{-}B$ and $BO]$.

11. *The. and Def. If $n\,(>2)$ points be given on a line, we can assign letters $P_1 \dots P_n$ to them so that $[P_iP_jP_k]$ if and only if $i<j<k$ or $i>j>k$. Every other point of the line is in one and only one of $P_1P_2]$ or $P_1{-}P_2$ or $P_2{-}P_3$ or ... or $P_{n-1}{-}P_n$ or $P_nP_{n-1}]$. We say the points are 'in order $P_1P_2 \dots P_n$' or that $[P_1P_2 \dots P_n]$.*

Dem. We shew the theorem by induction. For $n=3$ the theorem follows at once from 10·1. Suppose it true for n points, so that $P_1 \dots P_n$ are names for points satisfying the conditions. Then by hyp. any other point Q on the line is in $P_1P_2]$ or $P_1{-}P_2$ or $P_2{-}P_3$ or ... or $P_{n-1}{-}P_n$ or $P_nP_{n-1}]$.

If Q is on $P_1P_2]$ it divides that ray into $P_1{-}Q$ and $QP_1]$ (10·6). Also $[QP_1P_2]\,[P_1P_2P_i]$ if $i>2$ and hence $[QP_1P_i]$ (8·1) if $i>1$. But since we know $[P_1P_iP_j]$ if $1<i<j$ we have $[QP_iP_j]$ if $i<j$ (8·1) and we have now merely to rename Q and P_i resp. as P_1 and P_{i+1} for $i=1 \dots n$. Similarly if Q is on $P_nP_{n-1}]$.

If Q is on $P_i{-}P_{i+1}$ it divides that open interval into $P_i{-}Q$ and $Q{-}P_{i+1}$ (10·1). Then since we know $[P_rP_iP_{i+1}]\,[P_iP_{i+1}P_s]$ if $r<i$, $i+1<s$ we have $[P_rP_iQ]\,[P_iQP_s]$ (8·5·6). Hence

$$[P_rQP_s] \text{ if } r \leqq i,\ i+1 \leqq s.$$

Rename Q as P_{i+1} and P_j as P_{j+1} for $j=i+1, i+2, \dots, n$ and we have the theorem for $(n+1)$ points assuming it for n points.

The present notation $[P_1P_2 \dots P_n]$ clearly agrees with the notation $[ABCD]$ of 8·8.

·1. If $[P_1P_2 \dots P_n]$ there are points P, Q with

$$[PP_1P_2 \dots P_nQ].$$

·11. If $\quad [P_1P_2P_3]\,[P_2P_3P_4] \dots [P_{n-2}P_{n-1}P_n]$

then $\quad [P_1P_2 \dots P_n]$.

11·2. Given a finite set of points on a line, if A is on the line but not in that set, then there is an interval AB of the line which contains no points of the set, and an interval AC of the line such that C is the only point of the set in it, and there is a ray of the line containing no points of the set.

·3. If a ray OA or an open interval OA meets a finite number of lines there is a point X on it such that $O^{\dashv}X$ does not meet the lines (·2).

·4. Through a given point O a line can be drawn so as not to pass through any of n given points.

Dem. Let the joins of O to the n points meet any other line in the set of points $[X]$, which may be empty. The join of O to a point of the line, not in $[X]$, satisfies the conditions.

·5. *Given a finite set of lines, there is an infinity of points not on any of the lines.*

Dem. There are points X, Y on distinct lines of the set. Then XY is not a line of the set, hence it meets the lines of the set in a *finite* number of points, but it contains an infinity of points (8).

·6. *If A, B, C do not colline and $[AFB]\,[BCD]$ then there is a point E with $[CEA]\,[DEF]$.*

Dem. There is a point H with $[FBH]$ (**O** IV)]. F, B, D do not colline, hence $[FBH]\,[BCD]$ give a point R with $[DRF][HCR]$ (5). From $[AFB]\,[FBH]$ we have $[AFH]$ (8·1), and since A, F, D do not colline, this with $[FRD]$ gives L with $[DLA][HRL]$. From $[HCR]\,[HRL]$ we have $[LRC]$ (8·5) and since A, L, C do not colline, this with $[ALD]$ gives E on $DR = DF$ with $[CEA]$. Finally since A, B, C do not colline $[BCD]$ $[CEA]$ give a point X on AB with $[DEX]$ and as in earlier theorems we shew $X = F$.

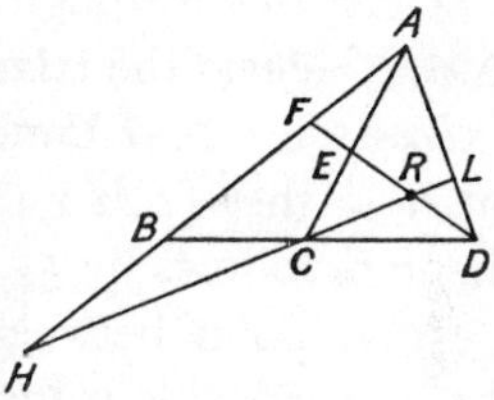

Fig. 4

The Triangle

·7. *Defs.* If A, B, C do not colline, the '*triangle*' ABC, or ΔABC, is the set of points on $A^{\vdash\dashv}B$, $B^{\vdash\dashv}C$, $C^{\vdash\dashv}A$. A, B, C are the '*vertices*,' $B^{-}C$, $C^{-}A$, $A^{-}B$ the '*sides*,' $B^{\vdash\dashv}C$, etc. the '*side intervals,*' and BC, etc. the '*side lines*' of the triangle. The side, interval, and line AB are '*opposite*' C.

Note carefully that a *side of a triangle does not include its ends.*

The following sums up 5 and 11·6 and is fundamental.

12. *A line which meets one side of a triangle and another side-line, not on its side-interval, meets the third side of the triangle.*

The reader will note that we deduced the Theorems on the orders of four points on a line by means of the very weak Axiom **O** VI and then deduced the strong Theorem 12 by means of them.

·1. *Def.* A point is '*inside*' a triangle if and only if it is between two points on *different sides* of the triangle. [A side is an *open* interval.]

·2. A point inside a triangle is between each vertex and some point of the opposite side.

Dem. If X is inside $\triangle ABC$ there are points M, N on different sides, say $A{-}B$, $A{-}C$ such that $[MXN]$. Considering first the line BX (or CX) and then AX, the theorem follows easily from 5 and 8·6.

·3. If ABC be a triangle and $[AMB]\,[ANC]\,[BXC]$ then $A{-}X$ meets $M{-}N$ (11·6, 8·1).

·4. A line through a point X inside and a point Y on $\triangle ABC$ meets the triangle again in a point Z with $[YXZ]$.

Dem. By ·2, AX meets the side BC in M say. If $Y \neq M$ is on $B{-}C$, then $[CMY]$ or $[BMY]$ (8·93) and since $[MXA]$ the theorem follows by 5.

·5. A point between a vertex of a triangle and a point of the opposite side is inside the triangle (·4 Dem. and ·1).

·6. If A, B, C do not colline and $[BCD]$ and $[AX_1X_2 \dots X_nB]$ then $[AY_1Y_2 \dots Y_nC]$ where Y_i is the point where DX_i meets $A{-}C$ (11·6).

Dem. $[AX_1B]$ $[BCD]$ give $[AY_1C]$ $[X_1Y_1D]$. Also $[X_1X_2B]\,[X_1Y_1D]\,[BCD]$ give $[Y_1Y_2C]\,[X_2Y_2D]$ (·3). And so on. Then use 11·11.

·7. If A, B, C do not colline and $[BCD]\,[X_1X_2X_3]$ where X_1, X_2, X_3 are on $A{-}B$, then $[Y_1Y_2Y_3]$ where Y_i is the point where DX_i meets $A{-}C$.

Dem. Either $[AX_1X_2]$ and then $[X_1X_2B]$, or $[BX_1X_2]$ and then $[X_1X_2A]$ (8·93·5).

Hence either $[AX_1X_2X_3B]$ or $[BX_1X_2X_3A]$ and then ·6 gives the Theorem.

The Plane

13. *Def.* If A, B, C do not colline, the '*plane*' ABC, written ABC simply, is the set of all points on all lines joining two points of $\triangle ABC$. Thus the points of $\triangle ABC$ are on ABC.

$ABC = DEF$ means all points of either plane are on the other. See 2·2 and I 4. $ABC = BCA$ etc., all permutations being allowed.

Sets of points on the same plane are said to '*coplane*' or '*be coplanar*.'

·1. *Note.* We could also take as def. the following: If A, B, C do not colline, the plane ABC is the set of all points on all lines joining the vertices of $\triangle ABC$ to the points of the opposite side-intervals. Points on a plane ABC in accordance with this def. are so with our def. also, as a mere matter of logic. Conversely, in the presence of the Axioms, this def. can be deduced from ours (III 13·1). We adopt the def. in 13, because it can be generalised to give a def. of space, whereas the alternative def. does not generalise so immediately.

Consider also the following definition. 'If A, B, C are any distinct non-collinear points, the plane ABC is the set of all points on lines joining A to points of (the line) BC.' It will be noted that in this definition the order of the points A, B, C is relevant. It is clear that if we took this definition we could not have a line from A in the plane ABC which does not meet BC. Further, if we wish the plane ABC to be the same plane as the plane XYZ where X, Y, Z are any distinct non-collinear points of the plane ABC, we should have to shew that PX meets YZ when P is any point of the plane ABC, that is, we should have to shew the following theorem, 'If P, X, Y, Z be any points on the plane ABC then PX, YZ meet.' This cannot be shewn from the Axioms so far introduced for *they* are true in the Euclidean Geometry while *this* is not, since it denies the existence of parallel lines in the plane ABC. The Theorem in question is thus independent of our Axioms though it is consistent with them*. Hence the suggested definition, which will be considered later in connection with Projective Geometry, necessitates more Axioms than those we

* See Chapter XIII.

now have, if a plane is to have the properties ordinarily associated with entities so named.

The most important Theorems to be shewn on a plane are (i) any three non-collinear points of a plane determine it, (ii) a line which has two points common with a plane lies on it. These two properties have often been taken as Axioms and it is remarkable that they can be deduced from our def. The following theorem as well as the two just mentioned is taken as an Axiom in Hilbert's *Grundlagen.*

13·2. If X be in plane ABC and Y be on a side of $\triangle ABC$ then XY meets the triangle in a point $Z \neq Y$.

Dem. There are points M, N on $\triangle ABC$ which colline with X (13). The Theorem follows at once from Theorems 12 to 12·5 when X is on a side-line, or when X is not on a side-line but M or N is a vertex, or when X is inside $\triangle ABC$. Finally if $[MNX]$ and M be on A^-B and N on A^-C say, then $[AMB]$ gives Z with $[ANZ][XZB]$. But since $[ANC]$ and $Z \neq C$ we have either $[AZC]$ or $[ACZ]$ (8·3), and the Theorem follows by applying 12 to triangles BCZ and BZA.

·3. If X be on A^-B the points of ABC are the set of all points on all lines joining X to points of $\triangle ABC$ (·2).

·4. If D be on ABC and not on BC then $ABC = DBC$.

Dem. First let D be on a side-line of $\triangle ABC$, say on AB. If $[DAB]$ take X such that $[AXB]$, and if $[ADB]$ such that $[DXB]$. Then all lines through X which meet $\triangle ABC$ again, meet $\triangle DBC$ again and conversely (12). Hence by ·3, $ABC = DBC$ (since X is on A^-B and on D^-B). That is, if C is not on AB and (i) $[DAB]$ or (ii) $[ADB]$, then $ABC = DBC$.

Hence if C is not on AB then $[DBA]$ implies $BAC = DAC$ by (i), and if C is not on AB then $[ABD]$ implies $ADC = BDC$ by (ii).

Hence as $[ABD]$ and $[DBA]$ imply each other, either gives

$$ABC = BAC = DAC = ADC = BDC = DBC.$$

Hence if D be any point, not B, on AB and C be not on AB then $ABC = DBC$ (and hence $ABC = CBD$ and so on).

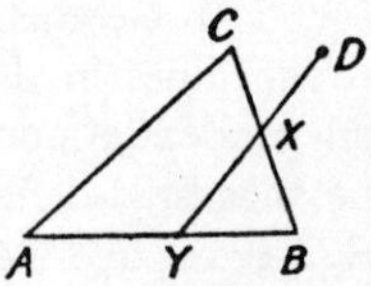

Fig. 5

Next let D be not on a side-line of $\triangle ABC$ and let X satisfy $[CXB]$. Since D is on ABC, DX meets $\triangle ABC$ again in $Y \neq X$ (·2) and

Y is on $A^{\vdash}B$ or $A^{\vdash}C$, say the first. Then by the earlier part of the proof

$$ABC = ABX = YBX = DBX = DBC.$$

14. *If D, E, F are distinct non-collinear points of ABC then $ABC = DEF$. Hence any plane is fully determined by three distinct non-collinear points lying on it.*

Dem. One of D, E, F say D is not on BC and one, say E is not on DC and F is not on ED. Hence by 13·4, $ABC = DBC$. Hence E is on BDC (and not on DC), hence $BDC = EDC$. Similarly $CED = FED = DEF$.

·1. *Def.* A line or ray is said to be '*on a plane*' if all its points are.

15. *If A, B be distinct points on DEF then AB is on DEF.*

Dem. If C is on DEF and not on AB then $ABC = DEF$ (14) and AB is on ABC (13) and hence on DEF.

·1. *A plane and a line not on it cannot meet in more than one point.*

·2. *Two distinct planes cannot meet in three non-collinear points* (14).

·3. *If two planes meet in the distinct points A, B they meet in AB* (15).

16. *If a line a be on ABC and be not a side-line of $\triangle ABC$ and one point X of a be inside $\triangle ABC$ or on a side of $\triangle ABC$ then the line meets $\triangle ABC$ in two and only two points.*

Dem. Let $P \neq X$ be on a. If X be on a side of $\triangle ABC$ the theorem is 13·2. If X be inside $\triangle ABC$ then AX meets $B^{-}C$ in N, hence $ABC = ABN$. Hence PX, lying on ABN meets $\triangle ABN$ and hence $\triangle ABC$ in a point $\neq X$. (13·2, note case when A, X, P colline.) Hence PX meets $\triangle ABC$ in two points (12·4) and in two only since a is not a side-line of the triangle (6).

·1. A line $\neq AB$ on ABC which meets $A^{-}B$, meets $A^{\dashv}C$ or $B^{-}C$.

·2. A line on ABC which does not meet $A^{\vdash\dashv}C$ or $B^{\vdash\dashv}C$ cannot meet $A^{\vdash\dashv}B$.

17. A ray from an inside point X of $\triangle ABC$ and on ABC meets the triangle in one point only (16, 12·4, 10·52).

17·1. Given a finite set of lines in a plane, and O a point not on any of them, then there is a triangle in the plane with O inside it, not meeting any of the lines.

Dem. Draw in the plane any line through O; on it are points X, Y such that $O^{\dashv}X$, $O^{\dashv}Y$ do not meet the lines and $[XOY]$ (11·3). There is a point A not on OX and points Z, W on YA such that $Y^{\dashv}Z$, $Y^{\dashv}W$ do not meet the lines and $[ZYW]$ (11·3). Then O is inside ΔXZW (12·5) and no given line meets the triangle (16·2).

18. If A, B, C do not colline and $[BDC]$, then all points inside ΔABC, and only those points, are inside ΔABD or inside ΔACD or on $A^{-}D$ (10·1, 12·2).

Space

§ 5. Ax. O VII. Not all points are on the same plane.

Axioms **O** I—VII imply the following.

19. If XYZ be any plane there is a point not on it.

·1. *Given a finite set of planes there is an infinity of points not on them.* (Cf. 11·5 *Dem.*)

·2. If AB is any line there is an infinite set of planes through AB (4, 19, 10).

·3. *If AB is any line, $[P]$ a finite set of points not on AB, then there is a plane through AB not containing any of the $[P]$* (·2).

·4. If a finite set of planes go through a point O, there is a line through O not on any of the planes (·1).

·5. Given a finite set of points $[P]$ and of lines $[l]$ there is a ray from *any* point O, and a line through any point O not on $[P]$ or any $[l]$, which does not meet $[P]$ or $[l]$ (·4).

·6. *Defs.* If A, B, C, D be distinct points which do not coplane (and hence no three of which colline) then the '*tetrahedron*' $ABCD$ or $\Delta ABCD$ is the set of all points inside and on the triangles ABC, ABD, ACD, BCD. The points A, B, C, D are the '*vertices*'; the open intervals AB, etc. the '*edges*'; the intervals AB, etc. the '*edge intervals*'; the insides of ΔABC, etc. the '*faces*'; and the planes ABC, etc. the '*face-planes*' of the tetrahedron. (Note that the faces do not contain the edges or vertices, and that the edges do not contain their ends.) Two edges are '*opposite*' if they have no common end.

20. *Def.* The set of all points on all lines joining any two points of $\triangle ABCD$ is the '*space*' $ABCD$, denoted by $ABCD$ simply*. Thus points of AB and of ABC are on $ABCD$.

$ABCD = EFGH$ means every point of each space is on the other. See 2·1, I 4.

$ABCD = BADC$ all permutations being permissible.

·1. *Note.* For all we know at present, there may be several spaces, e.g. a point in space $ABCD$ need not necessarily be in space $ABCE$. We shall later restrict ourselves to one space. With our use of the term, space is necessarily 'three dimensional.' For what are usually called four-dimensional spaces we need another word, say, hyperspaces.

The most important Theorems to be shewn about spaces are that any four non-coplanar points of a space determine it and that a line which has two points in common with a space lies in it.

Suppose we took as our definition of space the following: 'If A, B, C, D be distinct points, no three coplanar, then the space $ABCD$ is the set of all points on all lines joining points of AB to points of CD.' The order of A, B, C, D is relevant. With this definition, let X be in space $ABCD$ and not on AB or CD; through X goes a line meeting AB and CD and since this line lies on the plane XAB, that plane must meet CD. If then E, F, G, H be any non-coplanar points in space $ABCD$ and we wish spaces $EFGH$ and $ABCD$ to be identical, it follows that if X be any point of $ABCD$ then the plane XEF will have to meet GH. Hence if we wish any four non-coplanar points of a space to determine it then any line and any plane in the space must meet. On this definition we can make the same remarks as on an analogous one in 13·1.

·2. *Def.* X is '*inside*' $\triangle ABCD$ if and only if there are points M, N on *different faces* of $\triangle ABCD$ such that $[MXN]$.

In the following T means $\triangle ABCD$.

21. If X is inside T then AX meets BCD in a point P inside $\triangle BCD$ with $[AXP]$.

Dem. There are points M, N on *different* faces of T with $[MXN]$. Thus at least one of M, N is on a face with vertex

* Our def. of space is slightly different from that of Veblen. But he seems to use ours nevertheless. Compare Def. 7 and The. 22 in *Trans. Amer. Math. Soc.* V, 1904.

A, for the faces are the insides of triangles ABC, ACD, ADB, BCD. Let M be inside $\triangle ABC$ then AM meets BC in V and $[AMV]$ $[BVC]$ (12·2).

Case (i). If N is also on a face with vertex A, say inside $\triangle ACD$, then AN meets CD in U with $[ANU]$ $[DUC]$. Then applying 12·1·2 to $\triangle AVU$ we find AX meets VU in P with $[VPU]$ $[AXP]$.

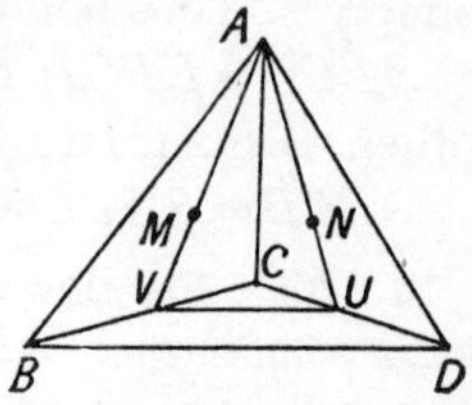

Fig. 6

Case (ii). If N is not in a face with vertex A it is inside $\triangle BCD$. Then there is a point U on a side-interval, not $B \vdash C$, of $\triangle BCD$, satisfying $[VNU]$ (12·4). Applying 12·1·2 to $\triangle AVU$ we find AX meets VU in P with $[VPU]$ $[AXP]$. Since $[BVC]$ and U is on a side-interval, not $B \vdash C$, of $\triangle BCD$, therefore $[VPU]$ implies P is inside $\triangle BCD$ (12·1·5).

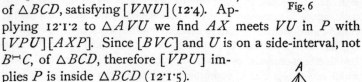

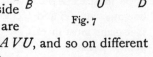

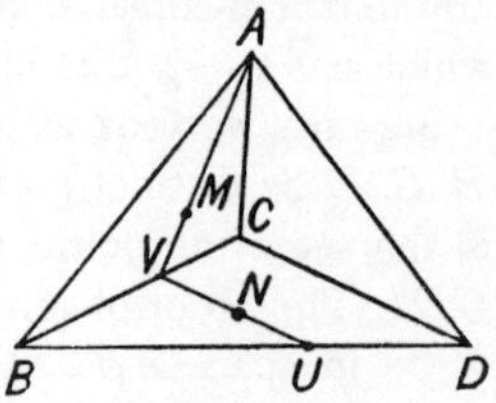

Fig. 7

21·1. If P is inside $\triangle BCD$ and $[AXP]$ then X is inside T.

Dem. There are points V, U on different sides of $\triangle BCD$ such that $[VPU]$ (12·1). But $[AXP]$, so X is inside $\triangle AVU$ (12·5), and thus there are points Y, Z on different sides of $\triangle AVU$, and so on different faces of T, such that $[YXZ]$ (12·1·5).

·2. If P, Q be on T and not on the same face planes and $[PRQ]$ then R is inside T.

Dem. By 20·2 and 21·1 we need only consider case when P is on an edge $A{-}B$, say, and Q on the edge opposite to $A{-}B$ or on a face. Let Q be on $C{-}D$ or inside $\triangle BCD$. Consider lines BQ and AR and use ·1.

22. *If X be inside T and Y on or inside T then XY meets T in two points Q, R with* $[QXR]$. (Fig. 8.)

Dem. Y is not on *all* the faces of T. Suppose it is not on or inside $\triangle BCD$. If $Y = A$ the theorem is 21. If at $Y \neq A$ then there is a point M inside $\triangle BCD$ and a point N on or inside $\triangle BCD$ with $[AXM]$ $[AYN]$ (21, 12·2). Hence MN meets $\triangle BCD$ in two points V, U with $[VMU]$ and either $N = U$ or V or $[VNU]$ (16, 12·4). Hence X is inside and Y

inside or on ΔAVU (12·5) and thus XY meets ΔAVU in two points Q, R with $[QXR]$ and Q, R are on T (16, 12·1·4).

22·1. If M, N be on different faces of T and $[MNO]$ and P is on any face of T, then OP meets T in a point $Q \neq P$.

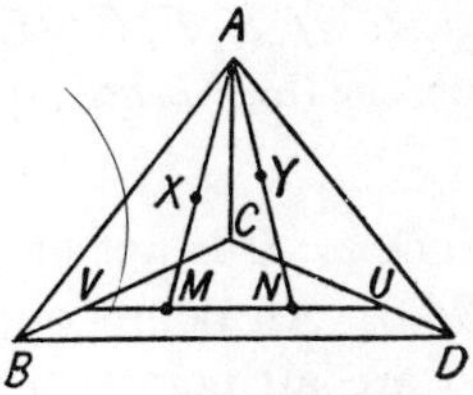

Fig. 8

Dem. Case (i). Let P be on the same face as M and let X be on the same face and $[MPX]$. Then OP meets NX in Y with $[NYX]$, hence Y is inside T (20·2) and so $PY = PO$ meets T again in Q say (22). Similarly if P is on the same face as N.

Case (ii). If P be not on the same face as M or N, let it be inside ΔBCD (say). Then AM, AN meet the sides of ΔBCD in X, Y say with $[AMX]$ $[ANY]$. Hence if $[XZY]$ then either OZ will meet ΔAXY in W with $[ZWO]$ or $[WZO]$ or O is on XY (13, 13·2), for $[WOZ]$ is impossible, since that would imply that O was inside ΔAXY and hence $[MON]$ (12·4). If $[ZWO]$ or $[WZO]$ we have case (i) again since P is on the same face as Z. If O is on XY and P on BCD the theorem is trivial.

23. *If O is in (space) $ABCD$ and P on a face of T, then OP meets T again in a point distinct from P.*

Dem. There are points M, N on T such that O is on MN (20). Hence the theorem by 22, 22·1, if M, N be on different faces of T, and by 21·2, 22 if $[MON]$ and M, N are on T and not on the same face-planes. The remaining cases, when $[MNO]$ or $[NMO]$ and M, N are on the same face-plane, or one is at a vertex, or one or both on an edge are shewn as in 21·2.

24. *If E, F be distinct points in (space) $ABCD$ then all points of EF are in $ABCD$.*

Dem. If E, F be on T then all points of EF are on $ABCD$ (20). If E, F be not both on T, let P be on a face of T and not on EF, then PE, PF meet T in points Q, $R \neq P$ resp. (23) and P, Q, R do not colline. Hence EF is in PQR (15). Hence any point X on EF is on the join of two points Y, Z of ΔPQR and since P, Q, R are on T therefore Y, Z are on or inside T and hence either YZ is on T or it meets T in two points L, M (22). But X is on LM and hence in $ABCD$.

25. *If E, F, G, H be distinct points of $ABCD$, which do not coplane (and hence no three of which colline) then*

$$EFGH = ABCD.$$

Dem. E is not on *all* the face-planes of T; let E be not on BCD. All points on edges of $\Delta EBCD$ are on $ABCD$, hence so are all points of faces of $\Delta EBCD$ and hence so are all points of space $EBCD$ (24, 20).

We next shew that all points of space $ABCD$ are in space $EBCD$. Let X be inside ΔBCD then EX meets T again (23). Suppose they meet in Y inside or on ΔACD.

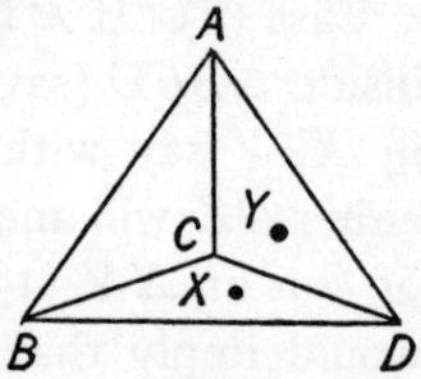

Fig. 9

If $[XEY]$ then E is inside T (21·2) and hence AE meets the inside of ΔBCD (21).

If $E = Y$ then either $E = A$ or AE meets $C^{\vdash\dashv}D$.

If $[EXY]$ then either $Y = A$, or AY meets $C^{\vdash\dashv}D$ in Z with $[AYZ]$, and then AX meets $E^{-}Z$ in a point inside or on ΔECD, so that A is on the join of a point inside ΔBCD to a point inside or on ΔECD.

If $[XYE]$ and $Y \neq A$ then AY meets $C^{\vdash\dashv}D$ in Z, and Y is inside $\Delta EBCD$ (since X is inside ΔBCD); hence ZY meets $\Delta EBCD$ again (22) and so A, being on ZY, is in $EBCD$ (20). If $[XYE]$ and $Y = A$ then $[XAE]$.

Hence in all these cases A is in $EBCD$. Thus we have shewn that if E is on $ABCD$ and not on BCD then A is on $EBCD$. Hence, as in the first part of the argument, all points on $ABCD$ are on $EBCD$, and hence $ABCD = EBCD$.

Hence F is in $EBCD$ and not on all the planes EBC, ECD, EBD. Suppose it not on ECD, then $EBCD = EFCD$. Since E, F, G do not colline, then G is not on both EFD, EFC. Suppose it not on EFD then $EFCD = EFGD$. And H is not on EFG, hence $EFGD = EFGH$. Hence $ABCD = EFGH$.

26. *If X, Y, Z do not colline and all lie in $ABCD$ then all points of the plane XYZ lie in $ABCD$.* (As in 15 *Dem.* or by 24.)

27. *If α, β, γ be planes and βγ, γα, αβ meet in lines a, b, c resp. and if a, b meet in O then a, b, c all meet in O.*

Dem. *O* is on *a*, *b* and hence on α, β and γ, and hence on *c*.

Restriction to 'Three dimensions'

§ 6. Ax. O VIII. All points are in the same space.

28. *Note.* This Axiom restricts our set of points to form a three-dimensional manifold. If we wished our set of points to form at least a four-dimensional manifold, we should replace this Axiom by: All points are *not* in the same space (cf. **O** VII).

Axiom **O** VIII could be replaced by the following proposition.

29. *Two planes which meet in a point meet in another point and so in a line* (15·3).

Dem. Let *O* be the common point and α one of the planes; take *A*, *B*, *C* on α so that *O* is inside $\triangle ABC$ (cf. 17·1). Let *X* be on the other plane β and not on α and let $Y (\neq X, O)$ be in β, then *YO* is in β (15) and *Y* is in space *XABC* (**O** VIII). Hence *YO* meets $\triangle XABC$ in another point *Z*, say, (23). If *Z* is in α, then α, β have two common points. If it is not, then *XZ* is in β and it meets $\triangle ABC$ in a point common to α and β.

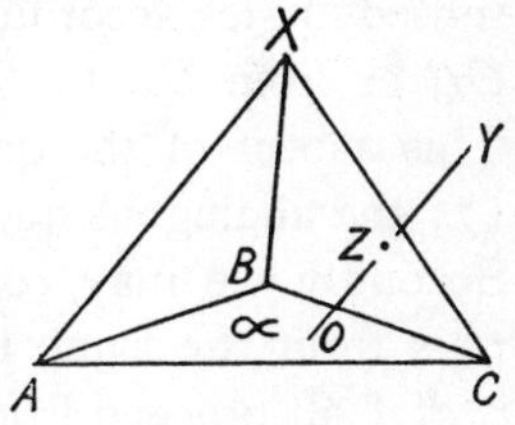

Fig. 10

30. If a plane meet a side of a triangle, but does not contain that side, it meets the triangle in just two points (29, 16·1).

We have now laid the foundations of Geometry. Our Axioms **O** I—VIII together with a continuity Axiom and a Euclidean parallel Axiom enable us to erect a complete Euclidean Geometry. If we replace the Euclidean parallel Axiom by the Hyperbolic, we can erect a complete Hyperbolic Geometry.

Furthermore our Axioms **O** I—VIII together with a continuity Axiom enable us to introduce algebraic methods. As far as the Euclidean case is concerned, this will be shewn in this work.

We shall quote Axioms **O** I—VI as $\mathbf{O}_p$ and Axioms **O** I—VIII as **O**.

CHAPTER III

FURTHER THEOREMS ON ORDER

Introductory Remarks

This chapter continues the development of Chapter II on the basis of the Axioms of order. We begin by shewing some theorems on angles*, that are needed in the succeeding chapter, where we treat of congruence.

We next discuss the order-relations between rays from the same point. There are two aspects of this question which are of importance to us. First we might adjoin to any angle a sense of rotation and then to an angle AOB would correspond two sensed angles according as we think of a rotation from OA to OB or from OB to OA *via* the rays inside the angle AOB. This aspect of the question is dealt with, and generalised, in 17; the analogous question of sense on a line is treated in 16. Secondly we may consider the 'separation' relation among rays from the same point. Two rays a, b separate the rays c, d, if all proceed from the same point and if one of a, b is inside the angle cd, and the other outside. To investigate this relation we take up in 18 ff. the question of the outside and inside of an angle.

Finally we touch on certain order-relations in space.

All the theorems of this chapter are valid in much more general spaces than the ordinary Euclidean space. For example, they all hold in Hyperbolic space. It should also be noticed that no continuity considerations are used. Between any two points of any line lie an infinity of other points but we do not assume that the line is in any sense a continuous set of points; we do not, for instance, assume that there is any correspondence between the points of a line and the real numbers.

* The definition of angle in 3 below must be carefully noted. An angle is a *pair of rays*, not in the same line, proceeding from one point, together with that point.

§ 1. **Basis O** or **O_p** according as the figures are not or are coplanar.

Definitions

1. *Defs. and Thes.* A '*way* $A_1A_2 \dots A_n$' (written simply $A_1A_2 \dots A_n$) is a finite set of points $A_1 \dots A_n$ called '*vertices*' of the way, together with all points of the open intervals $A_1A_2, A_2A_3, \dots, A_{n-1}A_n$ which are called '*sides*' of the way. The lines $A_1A_2, \dots, A_{n-1}A_n$ are the '*side-lines*,' and the (closed) intervals $A_1A_2, \dots, A_{n-1}A_n$ the '*side-intervals*' of the way. The way '*goes from*' A_1 to A_n and '*goes from*' A_n to A_1 and '*joins*' A_1 to A_n. The vertices A_i, A_{i+1} are '*adjacent*.' Unless the contrary is stated, we shall always suppose that A_{i-1}, A_i, A_{i+1} do not colline for any values of i.

If no two side-intervals meet in any point which is not a vertex and no three side-intervals meet in any point, the way is '*simple*.' (Thus a simple way does not meet itself.)

If $A_1 = A_n$ the way $A_1A_2 \dots A_n$ is a '*polygon*,' 'simple' if the way is simple, and this polygon is usually denoted by $A_1A_2 \dots A_{n-1}$. Hence if A, B are vertices of a polygon there are two ways, formed of points of the polygon, which join A to B.

A '*region*' is a set of points not all collinear, any two of which may be joined by points of a way consisting entirely of points of the set. A region is '*convex*' if, when A, B are any points of it, then all points of A^-B are points of the region.

·1. *Defs.* If X, Y be sets of points and if there is a set of points S such that every way which joins a point of X to a point of Y meets S then S '*separates*' X from Y. The '*boundary*' of a region, if it exists, is the set of points, not in the region, which separates the set of points in the region from those not in*.

·2. The points common to two regions constitute a region, convex if both regions are so.

* Simply to avoid clumsiness of language we often say 'points are *in* a region,' instead of 'the points are points *of* a region.' All the regions considered by us will be what are known as 'open' regions; so that in the cases in which we use it, our definition of boundary agrees with the usual definition, in which points of the region may also be points of the boundary.

1·3. *Note.* The plane is a convex region and, as will be shewn later, the inside of a triangle is a convex region; the outside is a region, not convex.

In 1·1 'every' way means every way *in the plane* when we are dealing only with coplanar figures. Similarly the boundary of a region in a plane is the set of points *in the plane* satisfying the conditions specified.

The Separation of a Plane by a Line in it

§ 2. **Basis O_p.** All points considered are in one plane.

2. *Any line a separates the other points of a plane ϖ in which it lies, into two convex regions bounded by a.*

Dem. Let A be on a; let X, Y be points of ϖ and not on a, with $[XAY]$, then if $P^{\vdash\dashv}X$, $Q^{\vdash\dashv}X$ do not meet a neither does $P^{\vdash\dashv}Q$ (II 16·2), and if S be on $P^{-}Q$ neither does $S^{\vdash\dashv}X$ (II 16·2). Hence the set of points $[P]$ such that $P^{\vdash\dashv}X$ does not meet a is a convex region. Similarly the set of points $[R]$ such that $R^{\vdash\dashv}Y$ does not meet a is a convex region. Further, if Z be any point on ϖ, and not on a, one and only one of $Z^{\vdash\dashv}X$, $Z^{\vdash\dashv}Y$ meets a, for if both or neither meet a, then $X^{\vdash\dashv}Y$ will not (II 16, 16·2), cont. hyp. Thus each point of ϖ, not on a, is in one and only one of these convex regions.

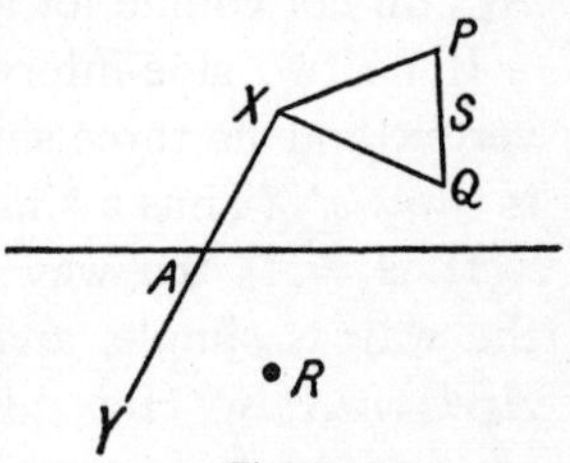

Fig. 11

To shew that a separates these regions, and hence is their boundary, let X_1 be in $[P]$ and Y_1 in $[R]$; hence $X_1{}^{\vdash\dashv}X$, $Y_1{}^{\vdash\dashv}Y$ do not meet a. If possible, let $X_1 \ldots X_n (X_n = Y_1)$ be a way from X_1 to Y_1 not meeting a. Since $X^{\vdash\dashv}X_1$, $X_1{}^{\vdash\dashv}X_2$ do not meet a, neither does $X^{\vdash\dashv}X_2$; and if $X^{\vdash\dashv}X_i$, $X_i{}^{\vdash\dashv}X_{i+1}$ do not meet a, neither does $X^{\vdash\dashv}Y_{i+1}$ (II 16·2). Hence by induction $X^{\vdash\dashv}X_n$, and so, also, $X^{\vdash\dashv}Y$ does not meet a, cont. hyp. Hence any way from X_1 to Y_1 meets a, that is, a separates $[P]$ from $[R]$.

·1. *Def.* The regions into which a line a separates a plane ϖ in which it lies are the '*half-planes from a in ϖ*' or '*the sides of a in ϖ*.' If $\varpi = ABC$, then $\{AB, C\}$ represents that side of

AB in which C lies. The other side is often called the '*opposite*' side. For convenience, we often speak of a *side of a ray*, meaning thereby a side of the line on which the ray lies. $\{AB, C\}$ together with AB, is the '*closed half-plane* or *closed side*' $\{AB, C\}$.

2·2. If $X \vdash\!\dashv Y$ does not meet a then X, Y are on the same side of a and conversely.

·3. If A^-X and B^-Y meet then X, Y are on the same side of AB.

Angles

3. *Def.* If $h=[OA$, $k=[OB$ (II 10·3) and h, k are not in the same line, then the set of points of $[OA$, $[OB$ together with O is the '*angle*' $\widehat{hk}$ or $A\hat{O}B$. Thus $\widehat{hk}$ and $\widehat{kh}$ are the same angle, $A\hat{O}B$, $B\hat{O}A$ are the same angle; O is the '*vertex*,' $[OA$, $[OB$ the '*sides*,' OA, OB the '*side-lines*' of $A\hat{O}B$. When we speak of $A\hat{O}B$ in a hypothesis, it is assumed that A, O, B do not colline. Cf. II 1·1.

4. *Def.* If $[AOD]$ $[BOC]$ and A, O, B do not colline, then $A\hat{O}B$, $A\hat{O}C$ are '*adjacent*' angles, and $A\hat{O}B$, $C\hat{O}D$ are '*opposite*' angles, then

·1. Since $[AOD]$ $[BOC]$ imply $[BOC]$ $[DOA]$ therefore $B\hat{O}A$, $B\hat{O}D$ are also adjacent. Thus each angle has two adjacent angles.

5. *Def.* $[OX$ and O^-X are '*in*' $\widehat{hk}$ (with vertex O) if and only if there are points H, K, Y on h, k, $[OX$ resp. with $[HYK]$.

·1. *Note.* We shall subsequently define the '*inside*' of an angle. We use the word '*in*' here so as not to suggest results proved later.

·2. *Every angle has an infinity of rays in it* (II 10).

6. If O is on AB and P not, then all points of $[OP$ are on the same side of AB in PAB; there are points of OP on each side of AB; points of $OP]$ are on the opposite side of AB from points on $[OP$ (2, 2·2 and II 10·4·52).

·1. If O is on AB and P not, and if O, P, Q colline and P, Q be on the same side of AB then $[OP=[OQ$ (2·2 and II 10·5).

6·2. If X is in $\{AO, B\}$, and $[AOA']$, then $[OX$ meets $A \dashv B$ or $A'-B$.

Dem. OX meets $A \dashv B$ or $A'-B$ in a point Z (say) on $\{AO, B\}$ (2, II 16·1) and $[OZ=[OX$ (·1).

·3. If $[AOB]$ and X is in $\{AO, C\}$, and $B-X$ meets OC, then it meets $[OC$.

7. If $[OX$ is in $A\hat{O}B$ and M is on $[OA$, N on $[OB$ then $[OX$ meets $M-N$.

·1. And A, B are on opposite sides of OX.

·2. And B, X are on the same side of OA.

·3. And there is no ray both in $A\hat{O}X$ and in $B\hat{O}X$.

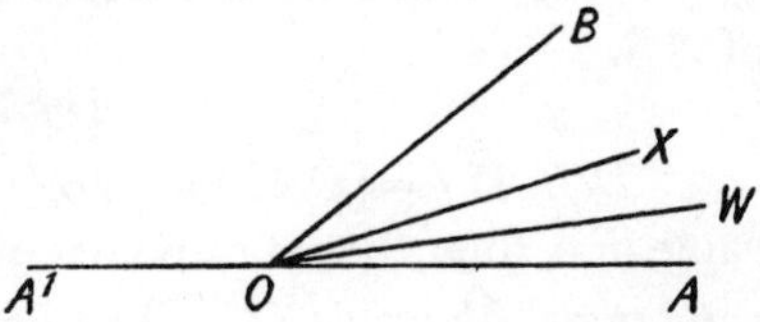

Fig. 12

Dems. There are points H, K, Y on $[OA$, $[OB$, OX resp. with $[HYK]$ (5). Hence H, K are on opposite sides of OX; but H, M are on the same side and so are K, N (6). Thus M, N are on opposite sides of OX, whence 7 follows. Since A is on $[OA$ and B on $[OB$, ·1 follows. Hence $[OX$ meets $A-B$ in Z, say. Thus $[AZB]$, hence B, Z are on the same side of OA and so are X, Z since Z is on $[OX$ (6). Hence ·2. A ray both in $A\hat{O}X$ and in $B\hat{O}X$ would meet both $H-Y$ and $K-Y$ (7) contrary to II 10·1. Hence ·3.

·4. If $[OW$ is both in $A\hat{O}B$ and in $A\hat{O}X$ then X, B are on the same side of OA (·2).

·5. If X, B are on opposite sides of OA there is no ray both in $A\hat{O}B$ and in $A\hat{O}X$ (·4).

·6. If $[OX$ is in $A\hat{O}B$, then $[OX$ is not in $A'\hat{O}B$ where $[AOA']$ (7 and II 6).

8. If $[OX$ is in $A\hat{O}B$ and $[OW$ in $A\hat{O}X$ then $[OW$ is in $A\hat{O}B$ (II 8·6).

·1. And $[OX$ is in $W\hat{O}B$ (II 8·5).

·2. And if also $[OY$ is in $A\hat{O}B$ then $[OY$ is in $A\hat{O}X$ or in $X\hat{O}B$ or $[OY=[OX$ and only one of these is true (II 10·1).

·3. If $[OX$ is in $A\hat{O}B$, there is an infinity of rays both in $A\hat{O}B$ and in $A\hat{O}X$ (5·2, 8).

·4. And $[OB$ is not in $A\hat{O}X$ (O II, 7).

·5. If $[OX_1$, $[OX_2$, $[OX_3$ be distinct rays in $A\hat{O}B$, one and only one of them is in the angle formed by the other two (5, 7, II 4·6).

8·6. If $[OX_1$, $[OX_2$ be distinct rays in $A\hat{O}B$ and $[OY$ is in $X_1\hat{O}X_2$ then $[OY$ is in $A\hat{O}B$ (·2, 8).

9. If B, X be on the same side of OA, and O, B, X do not colline and if $[AOA']$ then $[OX$ is in $A\hat{O}B$ or $[OB$ is in $A\hat{O}X$, but only one of these statements is true (8·4).

·1. And $[OX$ is in $A\hat{O}B$ or in $A'\hat{O}B$, but not in both (7·6).

·2. And there is an infinity of rays both in $A\hat{O}B$ and in $A\hat{O}X$.

Dems. First for 9·1, $[OX$ meets A^-B or A'^-B (6·2). Next for 9. If $[OX$ is not in $A\hat{O}B$ it is in $A'\hat{O}B$ by ·1 and hence meets A'^-B in F, say. Then since $[A'OA]$ $[A'FB]$, therefore OB meets A^-F in G say with $[FGA]$ $[OGB]$ (II 11·6). Whence 9. Then 8·3 gives ·2.

·3. If there is no ray both in $A\hat{O}X$ and in $A\hat{O}B$ then B, X are on opposite sides of OA (·2).

·4. If $[OX$ is in $A\hat{O}B$ then $[OB$ is in $A'\hat{O}X$ where $[A'OA]$.

Dem. B, X are on the same side of OA (7·2) and $[OB$ is not in $A\hat{O}X$ (8·4) and $[OB \neq [OX$. Hence $[OB$ is in $A'\hat{O}X$ (·1 interchanging B with X).

·5. If there is a ray both in $A\hat{O}X$ and in $A\hat{O}B$ then $[OX$ is in $A\hat{O}B$ or $[OB$ is in $A\hat{O}X$ or $[OX = [OB$ and only one of these is true (7·4, 9).

·6. If (i) A, X are on the same side of OB and (ii) B, X are on the same side of OA, then $[OX$ is in $A\hat{O}B$.

Dem. O, X, B do not colline, by the def. of side (2·1). Hence by (ii) $[OX$ is in $A\hat{O}B$ or in $A'\hat{O}B$ but not in both (·1) where $[A'OA]$. If $[OX$ is in $A'\hat{O}B$, then A', X are on the same side of OB (7·2). Hence so are A, A' by (i), contrary to $[AOA']$.

·7. If there is no ray both in $A\hat{O}X$ and in $B\hat{O}X$ and if $[AOA']$ $[BOB']$ then there is no ray both in $A'\hat{O}X$ and in $B'\hat{O}X$.

Dem. B, A are on opposite sides of OX (9·3 with X, A interchanged) and so are A, A' since $[AOA']$ and so are B, B' since $[BOB']$. Hence so are A', B'. The Theorem now follows by 7·5 with A', B', X for B, X, A.

10. If [OX is in $A\hat{O}B$ and [AOA'] [BOB'] [XOX'] then [OX is not in $A'\hat{O}B'$.

·1. And [OX' is in $A'\hat{O}B'$ and not in $A\hat{O}B$.

Dems. Since [OX is in $A\hat{O}B$, B, X are on the same side of OA (7·2). But [BOB'], hence X, B' are on opposite sides of OA, that is, of OA'; hence [OX is not in $A'\hat{O}B'$ (7·2). Hence 10 follows. And since [XOX'], therefore X', B' are on the same side of OA'. Similarly X', A' are on the same side of OB'. Hence [OX' is in $A'\hat{O}B'$ (9·6) and hence not in $A\hat{O}B$ (10).

·2. If there is no ray both in $A\hat{O}X$ and in $B\hat{O}X$ and if A, O, B do not colline, then [OX is in $A\hat{O}B$ or in $A'\hat{O}B'$ where [AOA'] [BOB'].

Dem. A, B are on opposite sides of OX (9·3). Hence OX meets $A^{-}B$. Thus either [OX or [OX' meets $A^{-}B$; in the first case, [OX is in $A\hat{O}B$, in the second case [OX' is in $A\hat{O}B$ and hence [OX is in $A'\hat{O}B'$ (·1).

Separation of a Plane by two Non-meeting Lines

11. *Two (coplanar) lines which do not meet separate the other points of the plane into three convex regions.* [*We do not say such lines exist.*]

Dem. Let AX, BY not meet. Take C, D, E so that [$CADBE$] (II 10; 11·1). Then $\{AX, C\}$ and $\{BY, E\}$ are convex regions (2) and so is the region common to $\{AX, D\}$ and $\{BY, D\}$ (1·2). The first and third are separated by AX, the second and third by BY, the first and second by AX and BY. Hence the regions contain no points common to two of them, and they are separated by the lines.

·01. *Def.* If AX, BY do not meet, the points Z such that [PZQ] where P, Q are on AX, BY resp. are said to be '*between*' AX and BY.

Quadrilaterals

11·1. *Def.* A '*quadrilateral*' is a *simple* polygon with four vertices (cf. 1).

12. If *FEAB be a quadrilateral and E, B be on opposite sides of AF, and A, F be on opposite sides of EB, then* $E^{-}B$, $A^{-}F$ *meet, and if* [EXA], [FYB] *then* $X^{-}Y$, $A^{-}F$ *meet.*

Dem. Since E, B are on opposite sides of AF therefore $E^{-}B$ and AF meet (2). Similarly $A^{-}F$ and EB meet. Hence the first part. Since $[EXA]$ $[FYB]$ and E, B are on opposite sides of AF, so must X, Y be (2·2), whence $X^{-}Y$ meets AF in Z say. And since $E^{-}B$ and $A^{-}F$ meet, E, F must be on the same side of AB (2·3), hence so are X, Y, F and hence so are Z, F. But $Z \neq F$. Hence $[AZF]$ or $[AFZ]$. Similarly Z, A are on the same side of EF. Hence $[AZF]$ is alone possible and therefore $X^{-}Y$ meets $A^{-}F$.

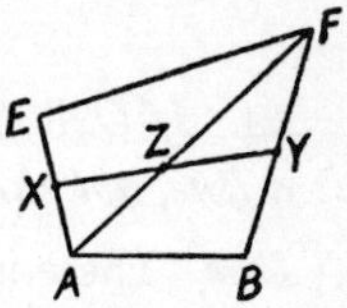

Fig. 13

12·1. If A, F be on opposite sides of EB, then $FEAB$ is a quadrilateral.

Dem. The polygon is simple, for if $F^{-}E$ met $A^{-}B$ or if $F^{-}B$ met $A^{-}E$, then A, F would be on the same side of EB (2·3).

An Alternative Definition of the Plane

13. *If A, B, C, D are distinct (coplanar) points, no three collinear, and if $A^{-}B$ does not meet CD and if $C^{-}D$ does not meet AB then either $A^{-}C$ and $B^{-}D$ meet or $A^{-}D$ and $B^{-}C$ meet.*

Dem. Since C, D are on the same side of AB (2·2), either $[BC$ is in $A\hat{B}D$ or $[BD$ is in $A\hat{B}C$ (9) and hence either (i) BC meets $A^{-}D$ in X say or (ii) BD meets $A^{-}C$. Similarly $[AC$ is in $B\hat{A}D$ or $[AD$ is in $B\hat{A}C$ and hence either (iii) AC meets $B^{-}D$ in Y say or (iv) AD meets $B^{-}C$. (i) and (ii) cannot hold together, nor can (iii) and (iv).

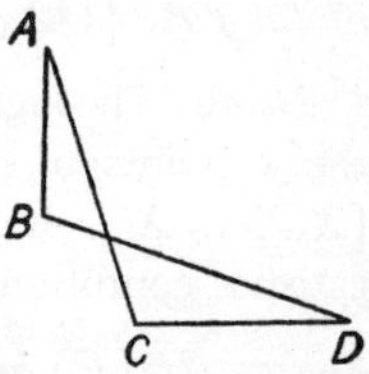

Fig. 14

If (i) and (iii) hold together, then BX, AY meet in C and $[BYD]$. This with $[AXD]$ makes CD meet $A^{-}B$ (II 11·6, 5) cont. hyp.

Hence (i) and (iii) and similarly (ii) and (iv) cannot hold together. Hence either (i) and (iv), or (ii) and (iii) hold together and these give the Theorem.

·1. If D be in plane ABC, either AD meets $B \vdash C$, or BD meets $C \vdash A$ or CD meets $A \vdash B$.

·2. *Note.* This, as mentioned in II 13·1, would serve as a definition of a plane. But though equivalent to our def. (in the presence of Axioms $\mathbf{O}$) it says *more* than ours.

Miscellaneous Propositions

14. *If OA, OB, OC be three (coplanar) lines through O, there is a line, not through O, which meets all three.*

Dem. There is a point C_1 on OC such that B, C_1 are on the same side of OA (6). Hence $[OB$ is in $A\hat{O}C_1$ or $[OC_1$ in $A\hat{O}B$ (9). Hence OB meets A^-C_1 or OC_1 meets A^-B (7).

·1. If there be n rays from O on one side of OA there is a line through any point $C \neq O$ on OA which meets them all.

Dem. Let $[COD]$. Join D to a point on one of the rays. There is a point E on the join such that $D^{\dashv}E$ meets no ray (II 11·3). Hence CE meets all the rays (6·2).

15. *If there be n rays from O on the same side of OX_0 they can be named $[OX_1$, $[OX_2$, ..., $[OX_n$ so that no ray of the set is in $X_i\hat{O}X_{i+1}$ $(i=0, \ldots, n-1)$ and $[OX_j$ is in $X_i\hat{O}X_k$ if and only if $i<j<k$ or $k<j<i$.*

·1. *And there is a ray $[OC \neq [OX_i$ $(i=0, \ldots, n)$ so that none of the rays $[OX_i$ $(i \neq 0)$ is in or on $X_0\hat{O}C$.*

Dems. Through X_0 goes a line meeting all the rays (14·1). To the n points of meeting we can assign names X_1, ..., X_n so that $[X_0X_1 \ldots X_n]$ (II 11). Hence 15. Let Y satisfy $[X_0YX_1]$ then $[OY$ satisfies conditions for $[OC$ by II 11.

·2. *If $[P]$ be a finite set of points, O not one of them, then there is a triangle with O as inside point such that no point of $[P]$ is inside or on it.*

Dem. There is a line through O not through any $[P]$ (II 11·4) and points X, Y on it, so that $[XOY]$, and points Z, W not on it with $[ZYW]$. Then O is inside ΔXZW. There is a ray XA in $Y\hat{X}Z$ and a ray XB in $Y\hat{X}W$ such that no rays from O to $[P]$ are on or in $Y\hat{X}A$ or $Y\hat{X}B$ (·1). $[XA$, $[XB$ meet WZ in P, Q say, then ΔXPQ satisfies the conditions (II 18, 12·2 and III 5).

·3. If $[P]$ be a finite set of points inside ΔABC or on B^-C, then there is a point of $[P]$ such that none of the points is inside ΔABP and none save P on that triangle.

·4. And there is a point Y such that none of the points is inside or on ΔABY.

Dems. The rays from A to the points of $[P]$ can be named $[AX_1, \ldots, [AX_n$ so that no ray $[AP$ is in $B\hat{A}X_1$ (·1). The points of $[P]$ on $[AX_1$ can be named $Q_1, \ldots, Q_r$ so that $[AQ_1Q_2 \ldots Q_r]$ (II 11). Then no point of $[P]$ is inside $\triangle ABQ_1$ (II 12·2) and none save Q_1 is on that triangle. Hence ·3. If Y satisfies $[AYQ_1]$ it satisfies conditions of ·4.

15·5. Given a finite set of points and lines and two points A, B such that $A^{-}B$ does not meet the lines, then there are rays AC, BC through none of the points such that $A^{\dashv}C$, $B^{\dashv}C$ do not meet the lines (·1, II 11·3, 16·2).

*Sense on a Line**

16·01. *Defs.* If A is on the line OU then '*A precedes B with respect to the ordered couple* (O, U),' written $A\,(\prec OU)\,B$, means that

either (i) A is on the ray $[OU$ and B on the ray $AO]$

or (ii) A is on the ray $OU]$ and B on the ray $[AO$

or (iii) $A = O$ and B is on $[OU$.

Under the same conditions '*B succeeds A with respect to* (O, U),' written $B\,(\succ OU)\,A$. We shall keep (O, U) fixed till ·5 and write $\prec$ for $(\prec OU)$.

·11. If $A \prec B$ then $A \neq B$.

·12. $O \prec B$ if and only if B is on $[OU$.

·13. $B \prec O$ if and only if B is on $OU]$.

·14. If A is on $[OU$ then $A \prec B$ if and only if $[OAB]$ (II 10·3).

·2. *$A \prec B$ if and only if one of the following holds:* $[OUAB]$ or $[OAUB]$ or $[OABU]$ or $[AOUB]$ or $[AOBU]$ or $[ABOU]$, or $A = U$ and $[OAB]$, or $A = O$ and B is on $[OU$, or $B = O$ and A is on $OU]$ (II 10·3, 8·2·7).

·3. If A, B are distinct points of OU then $A \prec B$ or $B \prec A$.

Dem. (i) If A or $B = O$ by ·12·13. (ii) If both A, B be on $[OU$ then $[OAB]$ or $[OBA]$ (II 10·55). Hence by ·14. (iii) If A be on $[OU$ and B on $OU]$ then $[AOB]$ (II 10·52), hence A is on $[BO$ and $B \prec A$. (iv) If both A, B be on $OU]$ then B is on $[AO$ or A is on $[BO$ (II 10·56). Hence the Theorem.

·4. If $A \prec B$ and $B \prec C$ then $A \prec C$ and $[ABC]$.

* For 16 and 17 cf. Pieri, "La Geometria Elementare," *Mem. di Mat. e di Fisica della Soc. Italiana delle Scienze*, 1908, XV, p. 345.

Dem. (i) If $A = O$ then B is on $[OU$, hence $[OBC]$, C is on $[OU$ (II 10·58) and $O \prec C$.

(ii) If A is on $[OU$ then $[OAB]$, hence B is on $[OU$ (II 10·58). Hence $[OBC]$ and $[ABC][OAC]$ (II 8·5·6) and hence $A \prec C$ (·14).

(iii) If A is on $OU]$ then B is on $[AO$. Hence $OU] = [OA$ and $[OU = OA]$ (II 10·51·53). If then $[AOB]$, B will be on $OA] = [OU$ and $B \prec C$ means $[OBC]$ (·14). Hence $[ABC][AOC]$ (II 8·1) and $A \prec C$ (·01 ii). But if $[ABO]$ then B will be on $[AO = OU]$. Hence C is on $[BO$ and A is on $BO]$. Hence $[ABC]$ (II 10·52). Also C is on $[AO$ (II 10·57). Hence $A \prec C$. Finally if $B = O$ then A will be on $OU]$ and C on $[OU$ (·12·13) and hence C on $[AO$ (II 10·57) since $[AOU]$. Hence $[AOC]$ (II 10·52) and $A \prec C$.

16·5. If $[ABC]$ then $A \prec B \prec C$ or $A \succ B \succ C$.

Dem. Let $A \prec B$ then shew $B \prec C$ as in ·4.

·6. *The set of points on OU are in linear order for the relation* $(\prec OU)$.

Dem. by ·3·11·4 and I 8. Thus $A \prec B$ and $B \prec A$ cannot hold together.

·7. $(\prec OU) = (\succ UO)$, *that is* (I 4), *if* $A (\prec OU) B$ *then* $A (\succ UO) B$ *and conversely.*

Dem. (i) If A, B be on $O\text{-}U$, then $A (\prec OU) B$ if $[OAB]$ (·14). Hence successively $[OABU]$, $[UBA]$ and $A (\succ UO) B$ (·14). (ii) If $[OUA]$ then $A (\prec OU) B$ gives $[OAB]$. Hence $[OUAB]$. Thus B is on $UO]$ and A on $[BU$; hence $A (\succ UO) B$. (iii) Similarly if $[AOU]$. (iv) If A or B is O or U the Theorem is clear.

Hence $A (\prec OU) B$ always implies $A (\succ UO) B$. Hence also $A (\succ UO) B$, that is $B (\prec UO) A$, implies $B (\succ OU) A$, that is $A (\prec OU) B$.

·8. If $[ABC]$ then $(\prec AB) = (\prec AC) = (\prec BC)$.

Dem. Since $[ABC]$ therefore $(\prec AB) = (\prec AC)$ by ·01 and II 10·5, 8·1. But $[CBA]$, hence likewise by ·7

$$(\prec BC) = (\succ CB) = (\succ CA) = (\prec AC).$$

·9. $A (\prec OU) B$ implies $(\prec OU) = (\prec AB)$, and conversely (·8·2·3·7·6).

·91. *Defs.** If $A (\prec OU) B$, then the ordered couples (A, B) and (O, U) '*have the same sense*' on the line OU. If $A (\succ OU) B$ then (A, B) and (O, U) '*have opposite senses*' on OU. These definitions are possible by ·97.

* We do not define the '*sense*' of (A, B), but only the property which two ordered couples may possess of '*having the same sense.*'

16·92. (O, U) and (U, O) have opposite senses on OU, since $O\,(\prec OU)\,U$ by ·01.

·93. If (C, D) be any ordered couple on OU, it has the same sense as either (O, U) or as (U, O), but not as both.

The Sense of Angles

17·01. *Def.* Two rays '*lie on the same side*' of a line if all their points do.

·011. If r be a ray we shall for the present denote the opposite ray by r'.

·02. *Def.* If x, y, a, b be rays from a point O and $a \neq b, b'$ then '*x precedes y with respect to Oab*' (where a, b is an ordered couple) means $x' \neq y$ and
either (i) $x = a$ and b, y are on the same side of a or $x = a'$ and b, y are on opposite sides of a
or (ii) x, b are on the same side of a, but y, a on opposite sides of x
or (iii) x, b are on opposite sides of a, but y, a on the same side of x.

Under the same conditions '*y succeeds x with respect to Oab.*'

We write these relations thus $x\,(\prec Oab)\,y$, $y\,(\succ Oab)\,x$.

Note that in (iii) y may coincide with a. The reader should write down the conditions that $y\,(\prec Oab)\,x$.

·1. $(\prec Oab) = (\prec Oa'b')$; that is, $x\,(\prec Oab)\,y$ and $x\,(\prec Oa'b')\,y$ imply each other for any x, y. See I 4. $a\,(\prec Oab)\,b$.

We shall keep O, a, b fixed till ·4 and write $\prec$ for $(\prec Oab)$.

·2. *$x \prec y$ and $y \prec x$ cannot hold together.*

Dem. (i) If $x = a$ then $x \prec y$ implies that b, y are on the same side of a. But x, a are on the *same* side of y since $x = a$. Hence $y \prec x$ is false by ·02 (ii).

(ii) If x, b are on the same side of a, then $x \prec y$ means y, a' are on the same side of x, hence either $y = a'$ or y is in $\widehat{xa'}$ or in $\widehat{x'a'}$ (9·1). In the first case, since b, x are on the *same* side of a, $y \prec x$ is false by ·02 (i). In the second case y, x and hence y, b are on the same side of a (7·2), but x, a are on the *same* side of y. In the third case y, x and hence y, b are on opposite sides of a (7·2) but x, a on *opposite* sides of y (7·1). Hence $y \prec x$ is false in both cases by ·02 (ii and iii).

(iii) If $x = a'$ or if x, b' lie on the same side of a', interchange a with a' and b with b' and we have the previous cases.

17·3. *If x, y be rays from O and $x \neq y, y'$ then either $x \prec y$ or $y \prec x$.*

Dem. (i) If $x = a$ this follows by ·02 (i and iii).

(ii) If x, y, b be on the same side of a, then y is in $\widehat{xa'}$ or in $\widehat{ax}$ (9·1) and in the first case y, a' are on the same side of x (7·1) and hence $x \prec y$, and in the second case a, x are on opposite sides of y (7·2) and hence $y \prec x$ (·02 ii).

(iii) If x, b are on the same side of a, and y on the opposite side then y is in $\widehat{a'x'}$ or in $\widehat{ax'}$ (6, 9·1). In the first case y, a' are on the same side of x and hence $x \prec y$ (·02 ii), and in the second case a, x' are on opposite sides of y and hence $y \prec x$ (·02 iii).

(iv) If $x = a'$ or x, y, b' be on the same side of a or if x, b' be on the same side of a but y on the opposite side, then we interchange a with a', b with b' in the above.

·4. $x \prec y$ implies $x \succ y'$ and $x' \succ y$. Hence it suffices to consider rays on one side of a fixed line through O.

·5. *$y(\prec Oab)x$ implies $y(\succ Oba)x$ and conversely.*

Dem. (Note the use of ·2·3 in this *Dem.*) Let $y(\prec Oab)x$.

(i) If $x = a$ then y, b are on opposite sides of a (·02 iii) and hence $y(\succ Oba)x$ (·02 ii with a, b interchanged).

(ii) If x is in $\widehat{ab}$, then x, b are on the same side of a (7·2) and hence y, a are on the *same* side of x (·02 ii, ·2·3). Hence y, b are on opposite sides of x (7·1). Hence $y(\succ Oba)x$ by ·02 ii since x, a are on the same side of b.

(iii) If x is in $\widehat{ba'}$ then x, b are on the same side of a and hence y, a on the *same* side of x (·02 ii, ·2·3). Hence so are y, b since b is in $\widehat{ax}$ (9·4). But x, a are on opposite sides of b; hence $y(\succ Oba)x$ by ·02 iii.

(iv) If $x = b$ then y, a are on the *same* side of b (·02 ii, ·2·3). Hence $y(\succ Oba)x$ by ·02 i.

(v) If $x = a'$, or x, b' be on the same side of a' interchange a with a', b with b'.

·6. $(\prec Oab) = (\succ Oab') = (\succ Oa'b)$ (·02·3).

·7. If $c(\prec Oab)d$ then $(\prec Oab) = (\prec Ocd)$.

Dem. Let $x(\prec Oab)y$. If the rays b, c, d, x, y all lie on one side of a there is a line meeting the rays a, b, c, d, x, y in A, B, C, D, X, Y say (14·1). It is easily shewn that $x(\prec Oab)y$ gives $X(\prec AB)Y$ and conversely. The Theorem follows in this case from 16·9 since $(\prec AB) = (\prec CD)$ and $X(\prec AB)Y$ and hence

$$X(\prec CD)Y, \; x(\prec Ocd)y.$$

If the rays are not all on the same side of a we use ·4·5·6 to reduce the Theorem to this case.

17·71. If $\qquad c(\prec Oab)\,d$ then $a(\prec Ocd)\,b$.

·8. If a, b, c, d be distinct rays from O and $a \neq b'$ and $c \neq d'$ then $\qquad (\prec Oab) = (\prec Ocd)$ or $(\prec Odc)$ (·3·7).

·81. *Note.* We have no theorem corresponding to 16·4. *Hence we cannot say that the rays from O are in linear order.*

·82. *Defs.* An *ordered* couple of rays (a, b) distinct and not opposite, from a point is called a '*sensed angle*' and is denoted by $a\hat{,}b$. If $a = [OA$, $b = [OB$ then $a\hat{,}b$ may be written $OA\hat{,}OB$.

If x, y, a, b be rays from O and $x\,(\prec Oab)\,y$ then $x\hat{,}y$ '*has the same sense with respect to O*' as $a\hat{,}b$. If $x\,(\succ Oab)\,y$ then $x\hat{,}y$ '*has the opposite sense to* $a\hat{,}b$ *with respect to O*.' These defs. are possible by ·7·5. We do not define the '*sense*' of $a\hat{,}b$.

Down to ·88 below, all senses are with respect to O.

·83. $a\hat{,}b$ and $b\hat{,}a$ have opposite senses (·5·1).

·84. If x, y, a, b be rays from O and $x \neq y, y'$ and $a \neq b, b'$ then $x\hat{,}y$ has the same sense as either $a\hat{,}b$ or as $b\hat{,}a$ (·3) but not as both (·2).

·85. If P, P' be on the same side of OQ then $OP\hat{,}OQ$ and $OP'\hat{,}OQ$ have the same sense.

·86. If $OA\hat{,}OX$ and $OX\hat{,}OB$ have the same sense there is no ray in both (·02 ii, 7·5).

·87. If $OA\hat{,}OX$ and $OX\hat{,}OB$ and $OA\hat{,}OB$ have the same sense then $[OX$ is in $A\hat{O}B$.

Dem. Since $OA\hat{,}OX$ and $OA\hat{,}OB$ have the same sense, therefore B, X are on the same side of OA (·02 i). Hence $[OX$ is in $A\hat{O}B$ or $[OB$ in $A\hat{O}X$ (9). Also since $OA\hat{,}OX$ and $OX\hat{,}OB$ have the same sense, therefore A, B are on opposite sides of OX (·02 ii). But if $[OB$ were in $A\hat{O}X$, they would be on the same side of OX (7·2).

·88. If $OA\hat{,}OX$ and $OX\hat{,}OB$ have the same sense and $[OX$ is in $A\hat{O}B$ then $OA\hat{,}OB$ has that same sense.

Dem. If not, then $OA\hat{,}OB$ has the same sense as $OA\hat{,}OX'$ and as $OX'\hat{,}OB$ where $[XOX']$ (·4). But then $[OX'$ would be in $A\hat{O}B$ (·87) contrary to 10·1.

Note. So far we have compared the senses of angles with the same vertex, we now wish to compare the senses of any angles in the plane.

17·9. *Defs.* (i) Take a fixed point O in the plane. $\widehat{OP, OQ}$ and $\widehat{PR, PO}$ '*have the same*' or '*opposite senses with respect to O*' according as R, Q are on the same or opposite sides of OP.

(ii) Any other sensed angle with vertex P '*has the same*' or '*opposite sense with respect to O*' as $\widehat{OP, OQ}$ according as it has the same or opposite sense to $\widehat{PR, PO}$ with respect to P.

We can now compare the sense of any angle in the plane (with respect to O) with any angle with vertex O.

(iii) Two sensed angles '*have the same sense with respect to O*' if they both have the same sense or both have opposite senses to an angle with vertex O with respect to O; in the contrary case they '*have opposite senses with respect to O.*'

These definitions are easily seen to be consistent with ·82 in view of the earlier Theorems.

·91. If $\widehat{O'P, O'R}$ and $\widehat{PQ, PO'}$ have the same sense with respect to O then R, Q are on the same side of $O'P$.

Dem. $\widehat{OO', OP}$ and $\widehat{O'P, O'O}$ have the same sense with respect to O (·9 i) and so have $\widehat{OP, OO'}$ and $\widehat{PO', PO}$ (·9 i). Hence so have $\widehat{OO', OP}$ and $\widehat{PO, PO'}$ (·9 ii). Hence so have $\widehat{O'P, O'O}$ and $\widehat{PO, PO'}$ (·9 iii). Now if R, Q were on opposite sides of $O'P$, then one, say R, is on the same side of $O'P$ as O, and Q is on the opposite side; then will $\widehat{O'P, O'O}$ and $\widehat{O'P, O'R}$ have the same sense with respect to O' and so with respect to O (·9 ii), while $\widehat{PO, PO'}$ and $\widehat{PQ, PO'}$ will similarly have opposite senses with respect to O. Hence $\widehat{O'P, O'R}$ and $\widehat{PQ, PO'}$ will have opposite senses with respect to O, cont. hyp. The Theorem now follows.

·92. *If two sensed angles have the same sense with respect to one point O, they have the same sense with respect to any point.* (By ·91·9.) This makes possible the following definition.

·93. *Def.* Two sensed angles '*have the same sense*' when they have the same sense with respect to a fixed point O.

·94. *Any two given angles in the plane have either the same or opposite senses.*

·95. If $\widehat{OX, OA}$ be any sensed angle and $O'X'$, $O'Y'$ be any lines through O' there is a point A' on $O'Y'$ such that $\widehat{OX, OA}$ and $\widehat{O'X', O'A'}$ have the same sense.

The Inside and Outside of Angles

18. *The. and Defs.* If $A\hat{B}C$ be any angle, the points X such that $[BX$ is in $A\hat{B}C$ (5) are '*inside*' $A\hat{B}C$. The points of the plane not inside $A\hat{B}C$ and not on $A\hat{B}C$ are '*outside*' $A\hat{B}C$. *The points inside $A\hat{B}C$ form a convex region; the points outside form a region. $A\hat{B}C$ separates the inside and the outside points of $A\hat{B}C$ and bounds the inside and the outside regions* (1·1).

Note. It does *not* follow that any line through an inside point must meet $A\hat{B}C$. In fact this is not always the case in the Hyperbolic plane, and all our Axioms $\mathbf{O}_p$ hold for that plane.

Dem. Let X_1, X_2 be inside $A\hat{B}C$ and let Y satisfy $[X_1YX_2]$. If $[BX_1=[BX_2$ then $[BX_1=[BY$ and $[BX_1$ is in $A\hat{B}C$ and hence Y is inside $A\hat{B}C$. If $[BX_1 \neq [BX_2$ then $[BY$ is in $X_1\hat{B}X_2$ (5), hence $[BY$ is in $A\hat{B}C$ (8·6) and Y is inside $A\hat{B}C$. *Thus the points inside $A\hat{B}C$ form a convex region.*

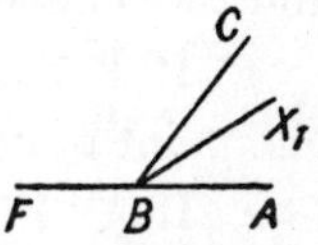

Fig. 15

Let F satisfy $[ABF]$. Since $[BX_1$ is in $A\hat{B}C$, $[BC$ is in $F\hat{B}X_1$ (9·4). Hence F^-X_1 meets $[BC$ (7). Conversely, if Z is on $[BC$ and T satisfy $[FZT]$, then T is inside $A\hat{B}C$, for $[BZ$ is in $F\hat{B}T$ and hence $[BT$ in $A\hat{B}C$ (9·4). Hence the set of points inside $A\hat{B}C$ is the set $[X]$ such that F^-X meets $[BC$, while the set outside $A\hat{B}C$ is the set $[Y]$ such that $F^{\dashv}Y$ does not meet $[BC$. And hence any two points Y_1, Y_2 of $[Y]$ can be joined by a way Y_1FY_2 whose points are all outside $A\hat{B}C$. *Hence the set $[Y]$ is a region.*

But by def. 18 and 6 we have

·1. *If X_1 is inside $A\hat{B}C$ it is in $\{AB, C\}$ and in $\{BC, A\}$.*

Continuing the proof of 18; if X_1 is inside $A\hat{B}C$ and $X_1{}^{\dashv}P$ does not meet $A\hat{B}C$ it cannot meet the *lines* AB or BC; for if, say it met $BA]$ in D, then D is on the opposite side of BC from A and since X_1 is in $\{BC, A\}$, D^-X_1 must meet BC (2) and hence $[BC$ (6·3); hence $X_1{}^{\dashv}P$ meets $[BC$ (since D is on $X_1{}^{\dashv}P$), cont. hyp.

Hence P, like X_1, is in $\{AB, C\}$ and similarly in $\{BC, A\}$. Now F^-X_1 meets BC and $X_1{}^{\vdash\dashv}P$ does not, hence F^-P meets

BC (II 16·1) and so meets $[BC$ (6·3). Hence P is inside $A\hat{B}C$. *Thus if* X_1 *is inside* $A\hat{B}C$ *and* $X_1 \dashv P$ *does not meet* $A\hat{B}C$ *then* P *is inside* $A\hat{B}C$.

Hence a way $XP_1 \ldots P_n Y$ from X of $[X]$ to Y of $[Y]$ must meet $A\hat{B}C$. Hence *the sets* $[X]$ *and* $[Y]$ *are separated by* $A\hat{B}C$ and 18 is proved.

18·2. Any two distinct rays from O (opposite or not) together with O, separate the plane into two regions (1, 18).

19. *If* Y_1, Y_2 *be outside* $A\hat{B}C$ *and* $Y_1 - Y_2$ *does not contain* B *then it meets* $A\hat{B}C$ *in no point or in two points.*

Dem. Suppose $Y_1 - Y_2$ meets $A\hat{B}C$ in $D \neq B$, and let D be on $[BC$ then C is inside $Y_1\hat{B}Y_2$. If A is outside this angle, $A - C$ will meet $[BY_1$ or $[BY_2$ (18) and hence Y_1 or Y_2 is inside $A\hat{B}C$, cont. hyp. Hence A is inside $Y_1\hat{B}Y_2$ and so $[BA$ meets $Y_1 - Y_2$ and the Theorem follows.

·1. If Y be outside (inside) $A\hat{B}C$ and $X - Y$ meet $A\hat{B}C$ in one point only, not B, then X is inside (outside) $A\hat{B}C$.

·2. If $X - Y$ meets $A\hat{B}C$ in just two points P, Q then X, Y are both outside $A\hat{B}C$. (Consider Z with $[PZQ]$.)

·3. If X be inside $A\hat{B}C$ and Y outside then $X - Y$ meets $A\hat{B}C$ in one point only.

20. *Two lines which meet in O separate the other points of the plane into four convex regions.* (Cf. 11.)

Dem. Let OA, OB be the lines and $[A_1OA][B_1OB]$, then the points inside each of $A\hat{O}B$, $A_1\hat{O}B$, $A\hat{O}B_1$, $A_1\hat{O}B_1$ form a convex region. No point is inside two of these angles (7·6, 10). Any point of $\{AA_1, B\}$ not on OB is inside $A\hat{O}B$ or $A_1\hat{O}B$ (9·1). Thus any point not on OA or OB is inside one and only one of these regions. Since two points in different regions lie, one inside, the other outside one of the angles, they are separated by OA, OB (18).

·1. *Def.* A set of points $[X]$ '*decomposes*' a region R into regions $R_1, \ldots, R_n$ if all points of R are in at least one of the sets $[X]$, $R_1, \ldots, R_n$, and each pair of regions R_i, R_j is separated by the set composed of $[X]$ together with all points of the plane not in R. Hence no pair R_i, R_j has any common points, save perhaps points of $[X]$.

For illustrations of this idea, see the next Theorems.

21. *If* $[OA$ *is in* $C\hat{O}D$ *it decomposes the inside of* $C\hat{O}D$ *into two convex regions, the insides of* $A\hat{O}C$ *and* $A\hat{O}D$ *respectively.*

Dem. If X is inside $C\hat{O}D$ and not on OA, it is inside one and only one of $A\hat{O}C$, $A\hat{O}D$ (8·2) and hence is outside the other. Hence by 18.

22. *If* $[OA$ *is not in* $C\hat{O}D$ *and* $[OA \neq [OC, [OD$ *then* $[OA$ *decomposes the outside of* $C\hat{O}D$ *into two regions one at least convex.*

Dem. (i) If $[OC$ is in $A\hat{O}D$, the points outside $C\hat{O}D$ are outside or on $A\hat{O}D$ or inside $A\hat{O}C$, since those inside $A\hat{O}D$ are inside $C\hat{O}D$ or inside $A\hat{O}C$ or on $[OC$ (8·2). But points outside $A\hat{O}D$ are not inside $A\hat{O}C$, since the latter points are inside $A\hat{O}D$ (8). Hence the points outside $C\hat{O}D$ are in two mutually exclusive sets, those inside $A\hat{O}C$ and those outside or on $A\hat{O}D$ and these sets are separated by $[OA$, $[OC$, $[OD$. [Note that if the sets of points $[X]$ and $[Y]$ be separated by the set $[S]$, they are separated by $[S]$ together with *any* other set of points (1·1). Hence our definition 20·1 is satisfied.]

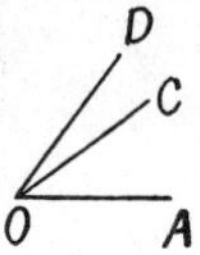

Fig. 16

(ii) Similarly if $[OD$ is in $A\hat{O}C$.

(iii) If $[OC$ is not in $A\hat{O}D$ and $[OD$ is not in $A\hat{O}C$, then A, C are on opposite sides of OD, for if they were on the same side, either $[OC$ would be in $A\hat{O}D$ or $[OD$ in $A\hat{O}C$ or $[OA = [OC$ (9) all of which are false. Hence $A^{-}C$ meets OD in E, say (our notation assumes that A is not on OC or on OD). Now $A^{-}C$ cannot meet $[OD$, since $[OD$ is not in $A\hat{O}C$. Hence $[DOE]$ and O is inside $\triangle ACD$ (II 12·5). Hence a ray from O which does not meet $C^{\vdash\dashv}D$ must meet $A^{\vdash}C$ or $A^{-}D$ and only one of these (II 17). Hence a point outside $C\hat{O}D$ and not on $[OA$ is inside one of $A\hat{O}C$, $A\hat{O}D$ and one only.

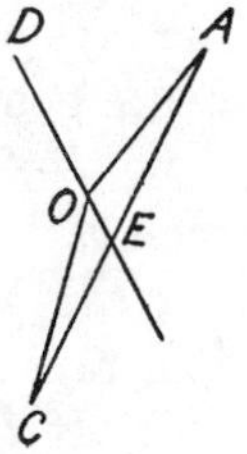

Fig. 17

(iv) If A is on OC or OD the Theorem follows by 2 and 9·1.

23. *n rays from O together with O, decompose the plane into n regions one at most of which is not convex; each ray is part of the boundary of two of the regions, each region is bounded by two rays and O. The points of any other ray from O are all inside one of the regions.*

Dem. The Theorem is true when $n = 3$ by 22 and (if two of the rays are on the same line) by 2, 9·1. Assume it true for $(n-1)$ rays. The points of an nth ray from O are inside one of the $(n-1)$ regions, and this region being bounded by two rays is the inside or outside of an angle and hence is decomposed by the new ray into two regions, one at least convex (22, 23). Hence the Theorem follows by induction.

The Order of Rays from the same Point and Separation

24. *The. and Def. If we have n rays from O we can assign them names $a_1, \ldots, a_n$ so that the n regions into which they decompose the plane are bounded by $\widehat{a_1 a_2}, \widehat{a_2 a_3}, \ldots, \widehat{a_{n-1} a_n}, \widehat{a_n a_1}$ resp. The rays are then said to be 'in order $(a_1 a_2 \ldots a_n)$.' Hence they are also then in order $(a_2 \ldots a_n a_1)$ or $(a_3 \ldots a_n a_1 a_2)$ and so on, and also in order $(a_n a_{n-1} \ldots a_2 a_1)$ or $(a_{n-1} a_{n-2} \ldots a_2 a_1 a_n)$ and so on.*

Dem. The Theorem is true when $n = 3$. Assume it true for $(n-1)$ rays. The points of an nth ray are all in a region bounded by $\widehat{a_i a_{i+1}}$ for some $i = 1, \ldots, (n-1)$ $(a_{i+1} = a_1$ if $i = (n-1))$ and the region is decomposed by a_n into regions bounded by $\widehat{a_i a_n}$ and $\widehat{a_n a_{i+1}}$ resp. Hence the n regions are bounded by $\widehat{a_1 a_2}, \ldots, \widehat{a_i a_n}, \widehat{a_n a_{i+1}}, \ldots, \widehat{a_{n-1} a_1}$. Hence by suitably renaming the rays $a_n, a_{i+1}, \ldots, a_{n-1}$ we have the Theorem for n rays and hence generally by Induction.

·1. *Def.* If the rays a, b, c, d from O are in order $(abcd)$ then b, d '*separate*' a, c.

Note. We shall not need this relation of separation between four rays so frequently as the relations discussed in 17.

·2. If b, d separate a, c then d, b separate a, c, and a, c separate b, d.

·3. If b, d separate a, c and a, c are not opposite then one of b, d is in, and the other not in $\widehat{ac}$; and conversely (for if both b and d were in $\widehat{ac}$ or both not in $\widehat{ac}$, one of the regions would be bounded by a, c).

24·4. If b, d do not separate a, c, and b is in $\widehat{ac}$, so is d.

·5. If b, d separate a, c and also a_1, c then b, d do not separate a, a_1 (·2·3).

·6. If b is in $\widehat{ac}$ and a, a' are opposite then a, b do not separate a', c (7·6).

§ 3. *Space.* **Basis O.**

25. *A plane* α *separates the other points into two convex regions bounded by* α. *Dem.* as for 2.

·1. *Def.* The regions into which a plane ABC separates the other points are the '*half spaces*' or '*sides*' of ABC. $\{ABC, D\}$ is that side of ABC which contains D. The other side is often called the '*opposite*' side. We often speak of a '*half space of a half plane*' instead of that of the plane containing the half plane.

·2. *Def.* If $\{AB, C\}$ and $\{AB, D\}$ be two half planes not in the same plane, then the set of points on $\{AB, C\}$, $\{AB, D\}$ and AB is the '*dihedral angle*' between the half planes. AB is the '*edge*' of the angle. The dihedral angle between the half planes α, β (from the same edge) is denoted by $\widehat{\alpha\beta}$.

·3. *Def.* If the rays $a=[OA$, $b=[OB$, $c=[OC$ be not coplanar and if no two be in the same line then the '*trihedral angle*' $O.A\hat{B}C$ or $O.a\hat{b}c$ is the set of points on the rays, together with the point O and the points on rays in the angles $\widehat{ab}$, $\widehat{bc}$, $\widehat{ca}$. O is the '*vertex*' of the angle, the rays OA, OB, OC are '*edges*,' the set of points on rays in the angles $\widehat{ab}$, $\widehat{bc}$, $\widehat{ca}$ constitute the '*faces*,' the dihedral angles between the faces are the '*angles*' of the trihedral angle.

·4. *Def.* If α, β, γ be half planes from AB then γ is '*in*' $\widehat{\alpha\beta}$, when there are points H on α, K on β such that γ meets H^-K.

26. If α, β *be half planes from* AB *and not opposite then all points of* β *are in the same half space of* α.

·1. *If the half plane* γ *is in* $\widehat{\alpha\beta}$ *and* H, K *be any points on* α, β *resp. then* γ *meets* H^-K. *Dem.* as for 7.

·2. *If the half plane* γ *is in* $\widehat{\alpha\beta}$ *and if a plane through one point only of the edge of* $\widehat{\alpha\beta}$ *meet* α, β, γ *in the rays* a, b, c *resp. then* c *is in* $\widehat{ab}$.

26·3. *If the half plane γ goes from the edge of $\widehat{\alpha\beta}$ and a plane through a point of the edge of $\widehat{\alpha\beta}$ meets α, β, γ in rays a, b, c and c is in $\widehat{ab}$, then γ is in $\widehat{\alpha\beta}$.*

27. As in 17 we can introduce '*sensed dihedral angles*' with the same edge.

CHAPTER IV

THE AXIOMS OF CONGRUENCE

Introductory Remarks

The idea of congruent figures is suggested to us by our experience of rigid bodies. Two bodies are called congruent when they are of the same size and shape; or when, but for the impenetrability of matter, one could be moved so as to coincide with the other, or with its image in a mirror. The latter possibility is illustrated by a right-hand glove congruent to a left-hand glove.

It is our task to characterise these ideas logically, and thus it is a matter of indifference to us whether any actually rigid bodies exist in the space in which we live. According as this is so or not, our geometry will or will not apply to that particular space.

Let us first replace solid bodies by figures made up of 'points,' then we may either regard congruent figures as having to each other some *relation* or *correspondence* to be specified in logical terms, or we may lay down Axioms governing the *transformation* of one figure into a congruent figure. This transformation may correspond in experience either to a motion or to a motion followed by a reflection in a plane mirror. The point of view of correspondence is emphasised in this chapter, the transformations are dealt with in Chapter XIV.

The most obvious definition of the correspondence between congruent figures is the following: Two figures F, F' are congruent when the points of F can be put into one-to-one correspondence with those of F' in such a way that, if A, B in F correspond to A', B' in F', then the *distance* AB *equals the distance* $A'B'$.

This would be quite a satisfactory definition if we had previously defined the distance of any pair of points in terms of our earlier entities. This we shall do later, but for the present we shall replace the phrase italicised above, by the phrase 'the point couple (A, B) is congruent to the point couple (A', B'),' and we shall treat the congruence of point couples as a *new undefined relation.* We see that in terms of this relation, the congruence of figures in general can be defined. Thus two angles $A\hat{B}C$, $X\hat{Y}Z$ will be congruent if the points on them can be put into one-to-one correspondence such that if (P, Q) on $A\hat{B}C$ corresponds to (P', Q') on $X\hat{Y}Z$ then (P, Q) is congruent to (P', Q').

We now want some Axioms on this relation between point couples which will serve as a basis for further reasoning. Our experience of rigid or of approximately rigid bodies suggests the following statements:

(α) If (A, B) is congruent to (A', B'), and (A, C) to (A', C'), and (B, C) to (B', C') and if C is on the line AB, then C' will be on the line $A'B'$.

(β) And if C is between A and B, then C' will be between A' and B'. That is, the relation of congruence should preserve 'collinearity' and 'betweenness.' Another important property which might easily be overlooked is

(γ) The ordered couple (A, B) is congruent to the ordered couple (B, A).

The next question is how far a figure, satisfying certain conditions, can be made congruent to another; that is, speaking roughly, how far congruence ties down the congruent figures.

As far as collinear points are concerned this is answered by (α) (β) and the following:

(δ) If (A, B) is any ordered couple of points, then on any ray $A'X$ there is *one and only* one point B' such that (A', B') is congruent to (A, B).

(ϵ) If $[ABC]$ and $[A'B'C']$, and (A, B), (B, C) be congruent respectively to (A', B') and (B', C'), then (A, C) is congruent to (A', C').

Next turning to the plane, in order to have congruent angles at all, with the vertices corresponding, the following must be true.

(ζ) If A, B, C do not colline and A', B', C' do not colline and $(A, B), (B, C), (C, A)$ are congruent respectively to (A', B'), (B', C'), (C', A'), and if D, E be on $[AB$, $[AC$ respectively and D', E' on $[A'B'$, $[A'C'$ respectively, and if (A, D), (A, E) be congruent respectively to (A', D'), (A', E'), then (D, E) is congruent to (D', E').

As we noted above, we can then say the angles $B\hat{A}C, B'\hat{A}'C'$ are congruent.

We can now finish imposing limitations on our congruence relation:

(η) If $B\hat{A}C$ be a given angle there is one and only one ray $[A'C'$ from a given point A' and in a given half plane $\{A'B', X'\}$, such that $B'\hat{A}'C'$ is congruent to $B\hat{A}C$.

(θ) Space is congruent to itself in such a way that to a given point A, ray AB from A, side $\{AB, C\}$ of AB and side $\{ABC, D\}$ of ABC correspond respectively a given point A', ray $A'B'$ from A', side $\{A'B', C'\}$ of $A'B'$ and side $\{A'B'C', D'\}$ of $A'B'C'$, and the congruence is thereby fully fixed, that is, the point in the second figure corresponding to an assigned one in the first is uniquely fixed. A similar statement holds for two planes.

(κ) We have also implicitly assumed (i) that each figure is congruent to itself, (ii) that if F is congruent to F', then F' is congruent to F, (iii) that if F is congruent to F', and F' to F'' then F is congruent to F''.

The above statements (α) to (κ) would serve as a basis of a treatment of congruence, but as they are clearly not all independent it is our duty to select from them a smaller number of statements, each as weak as possible, which will give us all the others.

Essentially we shall assume δ, ϵ, γ in Axioms **C** I, III, IV, and we assume a weakened form of (ζ) in **C** V. As to (η) we break it up into two parts; in **C** VI we assume in a weakened form that there is not more than one ray of the kind mentioned; in **C** VII we assume an axiom which gives the rest of (η).

We do not assume α, β or θ, but deduce them.

From (κ) we shall assume only that the congruence of point couples (and hence of congruence in general) is transitive (κ iii). In particular we do not assume that congruence is a symmetrical relation (κ ii). To indicate that congruence may not be symmetrical we first write its symbol as $\rightarrow$. When symmetry has been shewn it will be written $\simeq$.

The treatment we give in this chapter is ultimately a revision of Euclid's, only we lay bare certain assumptions that he tacitly made, such as that angles were a set of magnitudes. The Theory of Congruence from this standpoint can probably never be so elegant as one based on considerations of Projective or Differential Geometry, and the Theorems, regarded in themselves and not as cases of Theorems in some wider and freer domain, are so intertwined that it is to some extent a matter of taste which are selected as a basis of the rest. Two considerations have determined our choice; we wished to make as few assumptions as possible and we wished to develop as fully as possible the assumptions in hand, before making new ones. We have also had the later chapters in view.

Nowhere in this chapter do we assume any parallel Axiom, but from our Axioms **O**, **C** we can shew that parallels exist (59). All the Theorems in this chapter are true in Hyperbolic Geometry, and many of them are true in the Geometry known as Elliptic Geometry, wherein all coplanar lines meet, and there are thus no parallels. It is clear by 59 below that in the latter Geometry all our Axioms **O**, **C** cannot hold; we shall point out where the proofs break down for some of the Theorems false in that Geometry. This course will be useful to us when we consider the Geometry on a sphere.

It is also possible to build up the Theory of Congruence assuming as undefined, not only the congruence of point-pairs, but also the congruence of angles. Hilbert adopts this method in the *Grundlagen*, but it needs a larger number of Axioms than ours. In return it suggests an interesting non-Euclidean Geometry*—with which we cannot deal—in which the angles at the base of an isosceles triangle are *not* congruent.

The Theory we expound is suggested by

R. L. Moore, "Sets of metrical hypotheses," *Trans. Amer. Math. Soc.* IX (1908), p. 487.

* Hilbert, *Grundlagen*, Anhang II; Rosemann, "Der Aufbau der ebenen Geometrie ohne das Symmetrieaxiom," *Math. Ann.* XC (1923).

Rosenthal, "Vereinfachungen des Hilbertschen Systems," *Math. Ann.* LXXI (1911), p. 257.

Veblen's article in *Monographs on Topics of Modern Mathematics.*

Hilbert, *Grundlagen der Geometrie.*

As a method of proof, we must of course utterly rule out the method of superposition, the fallacies inherent in which have been frequently shewn*. We may briefly exhibit them by taking Euclid's proof of his I 4. The triangles ABC and XYZ have the sides AB, BC and the angle B congruent resp. to XY, YZ and the angle Y; Euclid takes up the triangle ABC and fits it on XYZ. We leave aside all questions as to what 'moves' and what are the properties of 'motion,' and merely point out this: If, in the motion, AB and BC and the angle B remained the same size but AC *shortened*, the argument would shew that AC in its original position was longer than XZ. But, says an objector, it is impossible that AC should shorten. No doubt, but that assertion assumes the Theorem to be proved.

§ 1. *The First Axioms of Congruence*

Basis. Axs. **O** I—VI for theorems on one plane.
Axs. **O** I—VIII for theorems on space.

We assume there is an undefined relation which holds between certain ordered couples of points. If the relation holds between (A, B) and (C, D) we write, $A, B \rightarrow C, D$, and read (A, B) is '*congruent to*' (C, D). We do not assume that $A, B \rightarrow C, D$ implies $C, D \rightarrow A, B$. When we say $A, B \rightarrow C, D$ it is tacitly assumed that $A \neq B$, $C \neq D$. When subsequently we introduce congruence by definition it will be necessary to define a relation between ordered couples of points for which the Axioms of this chapter hold.

Ax. C I*a*. If (A, B) is any ordered couple of points then on any ray $[A'X$ there is at least one point B' such that $A, B \rightarrow A', B'$.

* It is a scandal that in some public examinations questions are still set, which demand *formal* proofs involving this vicious method; a method of which Euclid himself was clearly ashamed, as he only used it twice, and was prepared to make any detour to avoid it.

Ax. C I*b*. If (A, B) is any ordered couple of points then on any ray $[A'X$ there is at most one point B' such that $A,B \rightarrow A',B'$.

Note. **C** I*a* makes **O** IV superfluous. **C** I*a*, **C** I*b* are together quoted as **C** I.

Ax. C II. If $A,B \rightarrow C,D$ and $C,D \rightarrow E,F$ then $A,B \rightarrow E,F$.

Ax. C III. If $[ABC]$ and $[A'B'C']$ and $A,B \rightarrow A',B'$ and $B,C \rightarrow B',C'$ then $A,C \rightarrow A',C'$.

Ax. C IV. $A,B \rightarrow B,A$.

1. (**C** I.) If B, C, A', B' be given points and if $B \neq C$, $A' \neq B'$ then there is one and only one point C' with $[A'B'C']$ and $B,C \rightarrow B',C'$.

Dem. If $[A'B'X]$ then on $[B'X$ there is a unique point C' with $B,C \rightarrow B',C'$ (**C** I) and since C' is on $[B'X$ and $[A'B'X]$ we have $[A'B'C']$ (II 10·54).

2. (**C** I, III.) If $[ABC]$ and C' is on $[A'B'$ and $A,B \rightarrow A',B'$ and $A,C \rightarrow A',C'$ then $[A'B'C']$ and $B,C \rightarrow B',C'$.

Dem. Since $B \neq C$ and $A' \neq B'$ there is a point C'' with $[A'B'C'']$ and $B,C \rightarrow B',C''$ (1). Since $[ABC][A'B'C'']$ and $A,B \rightarrow A',B'$ and $B,C \rightarrow B',C''$ we have $A,C \rightarrow A',C''$ (**C** III). But $A,C \rightarrow A',C'$ (hyp.) and C', C'' are on $[A'B'$. Hence $C' = C''$ (**C** I). Hence $[A'B'C']$ and $B,C \rightarrow B',C'$.

3. (**C** II, IV.) $A,B \rightarrow A,B$.

Dem. $A,B \rightarrow B,A$ (**C** IV), $B,A \rightarrow A,B$ (**C** IV). Hence $A,B \rightarrow A,B$ (**C** II).

4. (**C** I—III.) If $A,B \rightarrow A',B'$ then $A',B' \rightarrow A,B$.

Dem. On $[AB$ there is a point B'' with $A',B' \rightarrow A,B''$. Hence $A,B \rightarrow A,B''$ (**C** II). But $A,B \rightarrow A,B$ (3) and B, B'' are on $[AB$. Hence $B = B''$ (**C** I) and $A',B' \rightarrow A,B$.

5. Hence *the relation $\rightarrow$ between ordered point pairs is reflexive* (3) *symmetrical* (4) *and transitive* (**C** II) *and so equable* (I 9). We shall now write $\simeq$ for it. Further, $A,B \simeq B,A$ (**C** IV). The above Theorems and Axioms all hold when $\simeq$ is put for $\rightarrow$ and they will be quoted as if this were done.

5·1. Such Theorems as 5 and **C** IV and such consequences as $A, B \simeq C, D$ implies $B, A \simeq D, C$ will be often used without quotation.

6. (**C** I—IV.) If C is on $[AB$, C' on $[A'B'$ and $A, B \simeq A', B'$; $A, C \simeq A', C'$ and $B \neq C$ then $B, C \simeq B', C'$, and further $[ABC]$ implies $[A'B'C']$; $[ACB]$ implies $[A'C'B']$.

Dem. If $[ABC]$ the Theorem follows by 2. If $[ACB]$ then since B' is on $[A'C'$ and $A,C \simeq A',C'$ and $A,B \simeq A',B'$ we have $C,B \simeq C',B'$ and $[A'C'B']$. (Th. 2 with B, B' interchanged with C, C'.) And $C,B \simeq C',B'$ gives $B,C \simeq B',C'$.

·1. (**C** I—IV.) If $[ABC]$ and $A,C \simeq A',C'$ there is a point B' with $[A'B'C']$; $A,B \simeq A',B'$; $B,C \simeq B',C'$.

7. (**C** I—IV.) If $[ABC]$ and A', B', C' colline and $A,B \simeq A',B'$; $B,C \simeq B',C'$; $A,C \simeq A',C'$ then $[A'B'C']$. (Cf. 18 below.)

Dem. Since A', B', C' are distinct and colline, if $[A'B'C']$ is false then either $[C'A'B']$ or $[A'C'B']$. If $[C'A'B']$ then since $C,B \simeq C',B'$ there is a point A'' with $[CA''B]$, $C',A' \simeq C,A''$ (6·1). But $C',A' \simeq C,A$ and A, A'' are both on $[CB$. But since $[CBA]$ $[CA''B]$, A cannot coincide with A''. Hence we have a contradiction with **C** I. Hence $[C'A'B']$ and similarly $[A'C'B']$ are impossible. Hence $[A'B'C']$.

8. *Def.* If $[X]$, $[Y]$ be two sets of points then $[X] \simeq [Y]$ means we can set up a (1, 1) correspondence between $[X]$ and $[Y]$, such that if X_1, X_2 of $[X]$ correspond to Y_1, Y_2 of $[Y]$ then $X_1, X_2 \simeq Y_1, Y_2$. When such a correspondence can be set up we say $[X]$, $[Y]$ are '*congruent*.'

·1. *The relation of congruence between sets of points is equable* (5).

§ 2. *The Congruence of Lines and Intervals*

Basis O, C I—IV.

9. If $[AB$ and $[A'B'$ be any rays then $[AB \simeq [A'B'$.

Dem. We must set up a correspondence with the properties mentioned in 8. If X be any point on $[AB$, there is just one point X' on $[A'B'$ with $A,X \simeq A',X'$ (**C** I). Make X'

correspond to X. Thus the correspondence is one-to-one. If X', Y' correspond resp. to X, Y then $A,X \simeq A',X'$ and $A,Y \simeq A',Y'$ give $X,Y \simeq X',Y'$ (6).

10. *Any line is congruent to any line, in such a way that a given point A and given ray [AB from A on one line, correspond to a given point A' and given ray [A'B' from A' on the other line.*

Dem. Let $X \neq A$ be any point on the ray $[AB$. There is one and only one point X' on $[A'B'$ with $A,X \simeq A',X'$. Make A correspond to A' and X to X' and as in 9 we find $[AX \simeq [A'X'$. Similarly to Y with $[XAY]$ make correspond Y' with $[X'A'Y']$ and $A,Y \simeq A',Y'$. Then by **C** III $X,Y \simeq X',Y'$.

11. If $A,B \simeq A',B'$ then $A \vdash\!\dashv B \simeq A' \vdash\!\dashv B'$ and $A^{-}B \simeq A'^{-}B'$.

Dem. Make A correspond to A', and X on $[AB$ to X' on $[A'B'$ when $A,X \simeq A',X'$. Then the points of $[AB$ and of $[A'B'$ are in (1, 1) correspondence and B corresponds to B'. Also if X is in $A^{-}B$ then X' is in $A'^{-}B'$ and $X,B \simeq X',B'$ (6). And if X, Y are in $A^{-}B$, then the corresponding points X', Y' are in $A'^{-}B'$, and $X,Y \simeq X',Y'$ (6).

·1. If $A \vdash\!\dashv B \simeq A' \vdash\!\dashv B'$ then $A,B \simeq A',B'$ or $A,B \simeq B',A'$.

Dem. If Z is the point of $A \vdash\!\dashv B$ which corresponds to A' and $Z \neq A,B$ then there are points X, Y on $A^{-}B$ with $[XZY]$. Let X', Y' on $A' \vdash\!\dashv B'$ correspond resp. to X, Y then since $X,Z \simeq X',A'$; $Z,Y \simeq A',Y'$; $X,Y \simeq X',Y'$ and $[XZY]$ we have $[X'A'Y']$ (7) contrary to the fact that X', Y' are both on $A' \vdash\!\dashv B'$. Hence A' must correspond to A or B. Similarly so must B'. But the correspondence between $A \vdash\!\dashv B$ and $A' \vdash\!\dashv B'$ is one-to-one. Hence the Theorem.

·2. *Notation.* In view of 11, 11·1 we could write $A \vdash\!\dashv B \simeq C \vdash\!\dashv D$ for $A,B \simeq C,D$ or the equivalent proposition $A,B \simeq D,C$. To express these relations we shall write

$$AB \simeq CD$$

the interval sign being understood. We shall assume this done in all the above propositions, and shall quote them in that form.

The Measures of Intervals as Magnitudes

12. *Def.* The '*measure*' of an interval AB, written μAB, is the set of all intervals congruent to AB; or alternatively it may be regarded as a distinctive common property of these intervals (I 9).

Thus $\mu AB = \mu CD$ and $AB \simeq CD$ assert the same fact.

·1. If AB, CD be any intervals, then an interval XY exists such that there is a point Z satisfying $[XZY]$, $AB \simeq XZ$, $CD \simeq ZY$. All such intervals XY are congruent (**C** I, III). This enables us to lay down the following definition.

·2. *Def.* $\mu AB + \mu CD$ means μXY where XY is an interval such that a point Z exists satisfying $[XZY]$, $AB \simeq XZ$, $CD \simeq ZY$.

·3. If $[ABC]$ then $\mu AB + \mu BC = \mu AC$. Also by 7, if A, B, C colline and $\mu AB + \mu BC = \mu AC$ then $[ABC]$.

13. *The measures of intervals form a condensed set of magnitudes* (I 20·51·62).

Dem. (i) If AB, CD be any intervals then $\mu AB + \mu CD$ exists and is unique (12·1).

(ii) Also $\mu AB + \mu CD \neq \mu AB$.

(iii) $(\mu AB + \mu A_1B_1) + \mu A_2B_2 = \mu AB + (\mu A_1B_1 + \mu A_2B_2)$; for there are points C, D with $[ABCD]$, $A_1B_1 \simeq BC$, $A_2B_2 \simeq CD$. Hence $\mu AB + \mu A_1B_1 = \mu AC$, $\mu AC + \mu A_2B_2 = \mu AD$,

$$\mu A_1B_1 + \mu A_2B_2 = \mu BD, \quad \mu AB + \mu BD = \mu AD.$$

(iv) $\mu AB + \mu A_1B_1 = \mu A_1B_1 + \mu AB$; for there is a point C with $[ABC]$, $A_1B_1 \simeq BC$, and a point D with

$$[ADC], \ A_1B_1 \simeq AD, \ AB \simeq DC \ (6·1).$$

(v) If AB, CD be two intervals, either there is a point X on $A^{-|}B$ with $AX \simeq CD$ or there is a point Y on $C^{-}D$ with $CY \simeq AB$. For there is a point X on $[AB$ with $AX \simeq CD$. If X is not on $A^{-|}B$ then $[ABX]$ and then there is a point Y on $C^{-}D$ with $CY \simeq AB$ (6·1). Thus either $\mu AB = \mu CD + \mu XB$ or $AB \simeq CD$ or $\mu CD = \mu AB + \mu YD$.

(vi) As in I 20·31 we introduce

Def. If a, b be measures of intervals then $a < b$ and $b > a$ mean there is a measure x such that $a + x = b$.

(vii) Hence if a, b be measures of intervals either $a=b$ or $a<b$ or $b<a$ (v).

(viii) If AB be an interval there is an interval XY with $\mu XY < \mu AB$; for if $[ACB]$ then $\mu AC < \mu AB$.

The Theorem now follows from I 20·51·62.

13·1. If $[A_1A_2 \ldots A_n]$ then $\mu A_1A_n = \mu A_1A_2 + \mu A_2A_3 + \ldots + \mu A_{n-1}A_n$.

·2. If $\mu AB < \mu CD$ there is a point X on $C^{-}D$ with $AB \simeq CX$.

·3. If A, B be on $C^{\vdash\!\dashv}D$ then $\mu AB \leqq \mu CD$.

·4. All multiples of all measures of intervals exist and are unique (I 20·35).

·5. Subtraction of measures of intervals can be defined (I 20·51, 12·8).

The Mid-points of Intervals

14. *Def.* If AB is an interval and $AM \simeq MB$, M on the line AB, then M is the '*mid-point*' of $A^{\vdash\!\dashv}B$ or '*mid AB*.'

Note. If $[ABC]$ and $AB \simeq BC$ then B is mid AC. We do not yet know if *every* interval has a mid-point.

·1. If M is mid AB then $[AMB]$; for $M \neq A, B$ by 12 and $[MAB]$ and $[ABM]$ are impossible by **C** I.

·2. *An interval AB cannot have two mid-points M, N.*

Dem. If $AM \simeq MB$, $AN \simeq NB$ then $[AMB]$ $[ANB]$ (·1) and $M \neq N$ implies $[ANM]$ or $[AMN]$ (II 8·3). If $[ANM]$ there is a point N' with $[BN'M]$, $BN' \simeq AN$ (6·1). Since $[ANM]$ $[AMB]$ we have $[NMB]$; since $[NMB]$ $[MN'B]$ we have $[NN'B]$ (II 8·5·6). But $BN \simeq AN$, $AN \simeq BN'$ give $BN \simeq BN'$ and thus $[NN'B]$ is impossible. Hence so is $[ANM]$, and similarly $[AMN]$ is impossible. Thus $M=N$.

·3. If $AB \simeq CD$ and M is mid AB, and N is mid CD then $AM \simeq CN$.

Dem. $AB \simeq CD$, $[AMB]$ imply existence of N' with $AM \simeq CN'$, $MB \simeq N'D$ and $[CN'D]$ (6·1). But $AM \simeq MB$, hence $CN' \simeq N'D$. Thus N' is mid CD and so $N=N'$ (·2) and $AM \simeq CN$.

·4. If M is mid AB then $2\mu AM = \mu AB$ (12·3, 14·1, I 20·35).

·5. *Note. We cannot yet prove, nor shall we assume, the following:*

Theorem **M**. *Every interval has at least one mid-point.*

The Congruence of Angles and Triangles

§ 3. We have now brought the Theory of congruent intervals to such a stage that we can begin profitably the study of congruent angles and triangles. We know by the general definition of congruence (8) what is meant by saying that the angles ABC and DEF are congruent, but we do not yet know that when these two angles are congruent their vertices must correspond in the congruence; for all we know, it might happen that E corresponded to a point on $[BA$ or $[BC$. A similar remark holds for congruent triangles. These matters are cleared up in 19, 20 below. We first introduce the following Axiom and generalise it in 15 and 15·1.

Ax. C V. If A, B, C do not colline and A', B', C' do not colline and $[ACD]$ $[A'C'D']$ and $AB \simeq A'B'$, $BC \simeq B'C'$, $CA \simeq C'A'$, $AD \simeq A'D'$, then $BD \simeq B'D'$.

The following Theorems are based on $\mathbf{O}_p$, **C** I—V.

15. *If A, B, C do not colline and A', B', C' do not colline and D is on $[AC$ and D' on $[A'C'$ and $AB \simeq A'B'$, $BC \simeq B'C'$, $CA \simeq C'A'$, $AD \simeq A'D'$, then $BD \simeq B'D'$.*

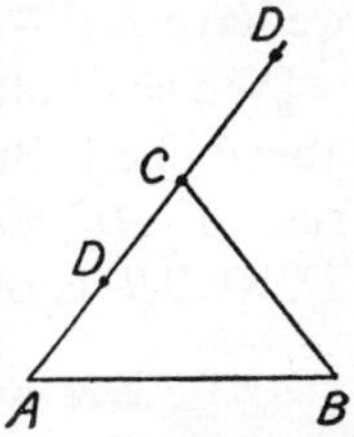

Fig. 18

Dem. Since $AD \simeq A'D'$, $AC \simeq A'C'$ and D is on $[AC$, D' on $[A'C'$, therefore $[ACD]$ implies $[A'C'D']$, and $[ADC]$ implies $[A'D'C']$ (6), and $C = D$ implies $C' = D'$ (**C** I). In the last case the Theorem is trivial. If $[ACD]$ and $[A'C'D']$ then **C** V gives the Theorem.

If $[ADC]$ and $[A'D'C']$ there is a point E with $[CAE]$ and so with $[DAE]$ and a point E' on $[C'A'$ with $CE \simeq C'E'$. Hence $[C'A'E']$ (2) and $[D'A'E']$.

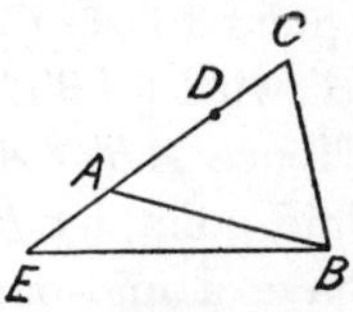

Fig. 19

Since $CB \simeq C'B'$, $BA \simeq B'A'$, $AC \simeq A'C'$, $CE \simeq C'E'$ and $[CAE]$ $[C'A'E']$ we have by **C** V, $BE \simeq B'E'$.

Since $CA \simeq C'A'$, $CE \simeq C'E'$, $[CAE]$ $[C'A'E']$ therefore $AE \simeq A'E'$ (2). Since $AE \simeq A'E'$, $AD \simeq A'D'$, $[DAE]$ $[D'A'E']$ therefore $ED \simeq E'D'$ (**C** III). And now since $EA \simeq E'A'$, $AB \simeq A'B'$, $BE \simeq B'E'$, $ED \simeq E'D'$ and $[EAD]$ $[E'A'D']$ we have by **C** V $BD \simeq B'D'$. This argument gives the Theorem and an analogous argument gives:

15·1. *If A, B, C do not colline and A', B', C' do not colline, and D is on $[AC$ or $AC]$ according as D' is on $[A'C'$ or $A'C']$, and $AB \simeq A'B', BC \simeq B'C', CA \simeq C'A', AD \simeq A'D'$, then $BD \simeq B'D'$.*

·2. *Note.* It is most important to notice that we do not yet know whether it is possible to have two triangles ABC, $AB'C$ with B, B' on the same side of AC and yet with $AB \simeq AB'$, $CB \simeq CB'$. The following Theorem throws some light on the question.

16. If A, B, B', C coplane and are distinct, and B, B' are on the same side of AC, and $AB \simeq AB'$, $CB \simeq CB'$, then BB' does not meet AC.

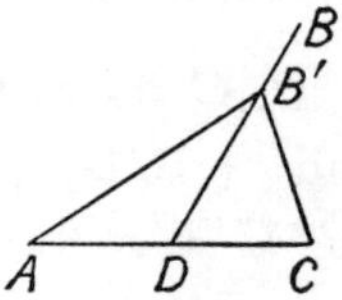

Fig. 20

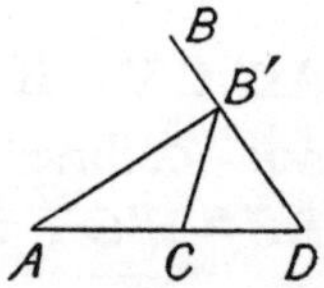

Fig. 21

Dem. Since $AB \simeq AB'$ and $B \neq B'$ therefore B' is not on $[AB$ (**C** I). Similarly B' is not on $[CB$. If possible, let BB' meet AC in D. Hence $D \neq A, C$. Then since $AB, BC, CA, AD \simeq AB', B'C, CA, AD$ we have $DB \simeq DB'$ (15·1).

[We shall often write a set of congruent relations as in the above line.] But D, B, B' colline and B, B' are on the same side of AC, hence $[DB = [DB'$ (III 6) and $B \neq B'$, whence $DB \simeq DB'$ is contrary to **C** I.

17. *Three collinear points cannot be congruent to three non-collinear points A, B, C.*

Dem. Suppose this congruence possible and let X, Y, Z with $[XYZ]$ correspond resp. to A, B, C. Since X, Z correspond to A, C we have $XZ \simeq AC$ (11). There is a point B' with $[AB'C]$, $XY \simeq AB'$, $YZ \simeq B'C$ (6·1). Hence $AB' \simeq AB$, $B'C \simeq BC$. If BB' have no mid-point, let L be any point on $B{-}B'$. If BB' have a mid-point M, there is a point L on $B{-}B'$ with $L \neq M$, and a point N with $BN \simeq B'L$, $[BNB']$ (6·1). Hence $BA, AB', B'B, BN \simeq B'A, AB, BB', B'L$, and N is on $[BB'$ and L on $[B'B$, hence $AN \simeq AL$ (15). Similarly $CN \simeq CL$. But L, N are on $B{-}B'$ and so on the same side of AC, and further $L \neq N$ since

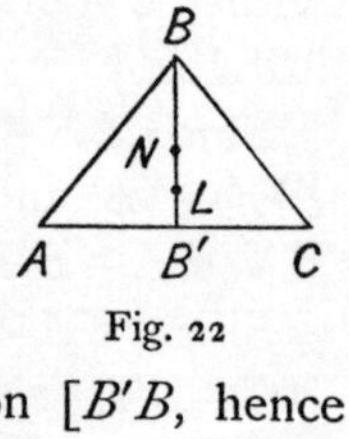

Fig. 22

$BN = B'L$ and L is *not* the mid-point of BB' (14·2). Hence since LN meets AC we have a contradiction with 16 and thus the Theorem follows*.

18. *If* $(A, B, C) \simeq (A', B', C')$ *and* A, B, C *correspond resp. to* A', B', C', *and if* $[ABC]$ *then* $[A'B'C']$. (17, 7.)

19. *If* $B\hat{A}C \simeq Y_1\hat{X}_1Z_1$ *then* A *corresponds to* X_1 *in that congruence, and points on the same side of* $B\hat{A}C$ *correspond to points on the same side of* $Y_1\hat{X}_1Z_1$.

Dem. By the general definition of congruence in 8,

$$B\hat{A}C \simeq Y_1\hat{X}_1Z_1$$

means *there is a* (1, 1) *correspondence between the points of the two angles such that a point-couple on one is congruent to the corresponding point-couple on the other.* If A and X_1 do not correspond in this correspondence, then X_1 corresponds to a point X on $[AB$ or on $[AC$, say on $[AB$, and A corresponds to a point A_1 on $[X_1Y_1$ or $[X_1Z_1$. Suppose first A_1 is on $[X_1Y_1$, then there is a point E with $[AXE]$ and to it corresponds a point E_1 with $[A_1X_1E_1]$ (18). Hence E_1 is not on $[X_1A_1$ i.e. not on $[X_1Y_1$, nor on $[X_1Z_1$, although E is on $[AB$. But this is contrary to $B\hat{A}C \simeq Y_1\hat{X}_1Z_1$. We get a similar contradiction if A_1 is on $[X_1Z_1$. Hence A and X_1 correspond.

If Y_1 corresponds to a point Y on $[AB$, then all points on $[X_1Y_1$ correspond to points on $[AB$, since none can correspond to points on $[AC$ by 17. And all points on $[AB$ correspond to points on $[X_1Y_1$. Similarly all points on $[X_1Z_1$ will correspond to points on $[AC$ and vice versâ. Analogous conclusions follow if Y_1 corresponds to a point Y on $[AC$.

·1. *Notation.* We shall now use $B\hat{A}C \simeq B'\hat{A}'C'$ to mean there is a relation of congruence between the points on the angles, *wherein* A *corresponds to* A' (as it must by 19), *and points on* $[AB$ *to points on* $[A'B'$, *and points on* $[AC$ *to points on* $[A'C'$. Thus if X, Y on $[AB$, $[AC$ correspond resp. to X', Y' on $[A'B'$, $[A'C'$ then

$$AX \simeq A'X', \; AY \simeq A'Y', \; XY \simeq X'Y' \text{ (8).}$$

* Veblen, in his article in *Monographs on Topics of Modern Mathematics* (1915), does not get this Theorem till a much later stage.

19·2. If $B\hat{A}C \simeq B'\hat{A}'C'$ and $AB \simeq A'B'$, $AC \simeq A'C'$ then $BC \simeq B'C'$.

Dem. Points on $[AB$ correspond to points on $[A'B'$ (·1) and since $AB \simeq A'B'$ therefore B corresponds to B'. Similarly C corresponds to C'. Hence $BC \simeq B'C'$ (8).

20. *If* $\triangle ABC \simeq \triangle XYZ$ *then* A, B, C *correspond to the vertices of* $\triangle XYZ$.

Dem. Let A_1, B_1, C_1 correspond on $\triangle XYZ$ to A, B, C. Then A_1, B_1, C_1 cannot all be on the same side-interval of $\triangle XYZ$ (17). Hence two of them, say A_1, B_1 must be on different side-intervals of $\triangle XYZ$. To a point E with $[AEB]$ corresponds a point E_1 with $[A_1E_1B_1]$ (18). Unless both A_1 and B_1 are vertices of $\triangle XYZ$, E_1 will not be on the triangle, contrary to the congruence. Hence A_1 and B_1 are vertices of $\triangle XYZ$; say $A_1 = X$, $B_1 = Y$. Then the same argument shews that $C_1 = Z$. Hence the Theorem.

·1. *Notation.* We shall now use $ABC \simeq A'B'C'$ to mean there is a relation of congruence between the points of $\triangle ABC$ and $\triangle A'B'C'$ *wherein* A *corresponds to* A', B *to* B' *and* C *to* C'. Hence the order of the letters in $ABC \simeq A'B'C'$ is important.

21. *If* ABC *and* $A'B'C'$ *are triangles and* $AB \simeq A'B'$, $BC \simeq B'C'$, $CA \simeq C'A'$ *then* $B\hat{A}C \simeq B'\hat{A}'C'$, $A\hat{B}C \simeq A'\hat{B}'C'$, $A\hat{C}B \simeq A'\hat{C}'B'$, $ABC \simeq A'B'C'$.

Dem. Make A correspond to A', and X on $[AB$ to X' on $[A'B'$ when $AX \simeq A'X'$; make Y on $[AC$ correspond to Y' on $[A'C'$ when $AY \simeq A'Y'$. Thus B corresponds to B' and C to C', and the correspondence between points on $B\hat{A}C$ and points on $B'\hat{A}'C'$ is (1, 1).

If X on $[AB$ and Y on $[AC$ correspond resp. to X' on $[A'B'$ and Y' on $[A'C'$ then $AX \simeq A'X'$, $AY \simeq A'Y'$.

When $Y = C$ then $Y' = C'$ and $AC, CB, BA, AX \simeq A'C', C'B', B'A', A'X'$. Hence $CX \simeq C'X'$ (15).

When $Y \neq C$ then $Y' \neq C'$ and $AX, XC, CA, AY \simeq A'X' X'C', C'A', A'Y'$. Hence $XY \simeq X'Y'$ (15).

Hence $B\hat{A}C \simeq B'\hat{A}'C'$. The same argument shews the remainder of the Theorem.

22. $B\hat{A}C \simeq C\hat{A}B$.

Dem. Let X be on $[AB$. There is Y on $[AC$ with $AX \simeq AY$. Hence since $XY \simeq YX$ (**C** IV) we have $AX, XY, YA \simeq AY, YX, XA$ and hence by 21, $X\hat{A}Y \simeq Y\hat{A}X$, that is, $B\hat{A}C \simeq C\hat{A}B$.

23. *If* $AB \simeq A'B', AC \simeq A'C', B\hat{A}C \simeq B'\hat{A}'C'$
then

$$BC \simeq B'C',\ A\hat{B}C \simeq A'\hat{B}'C',\ A\hat{C}B \simeq A'\hat{C}'B',\ ABC \simeq A'B'C'.$$

Dem. The hypothesis and 19·2 give $BC \simeq B'C'$. Whence the Theorem by 21.

·1. *Note.* If we try to shew the congruence Theorem which concerns one side and two angles of a triangle, we are held up by the fact that, so far, we might have $C\hat{A}B \simeq C\hat{A}B'$ with B, B' on the same side of AC and yet $[AB \neq [AB'$; cf. 15·2. This does not prevent 21 and 23 from being true.

24. *If ABC be a triangle and $AB \simeq AC$ then $A\hat{B}C \simeq A\hat{C}B$.*

Dem. $AB, BC, CA \simeq AC, CB, BA$ (**C** IV).

Hence $A\hat{B}C \simeq A\hat{C}B$ (21).

Or thus $AB, AC \simeq AC, AB$; $B\hat{A}C \simeq C\hat{A}B$ (22). Whence 23 gives the Theorem.

25. *Angles adjacent to congruent angles are congruent.*

Dem. Let $C\hat{A}B$, $C\hat{A}D$ be adjacent and $C'\hat{A}'B'$, $C'\hat{A}'D'$ be adjacent, and hence $[BAD]$ $[B'A'D']$ (III 4) and let $C\hat{A}B \simeq C'\hat{A}'B'$. We wish to shew $C\hat{A}D \simeq C'\hat{A}'D'$. Now if X, Y, Z be on $[AB, [AC, [AD$ resp. there are points X', Y', Z' on $[A'B', [A'C', [A'D'$ resp. such that $AY, YX, XA, AZ \simeq A'Y', Y'X', X'A', A'Z'$ (19·2, **C** I). Hence $YZ \simeq Y'Z'$ (15·1). But since $YA, AZ, ZY \simeq Y'A', A'Z', Z'Y'$ we have $Y\hat{A}Z \simeq Y'\hat{A}'Z'$ (21). Hence $C\hat{A}D \simeq C'\hat{A}'D'$.

·1. *Def.* Two angles congruent respectively to two adjacent angles are '*supplementary*.' Thus adjacent angles are themselves supplementary.

·2. *The supplements of congruent angles are congruent* (22 and 25).

26. *Opposite angles are congruent* (III 4).

Dem. If $[BAD]$ $[CAE]$ and A, B, C do not colline then we shew $B\hat{A}C \simeq D\hat{A}E$. For $B\hat{A}C$, $B\hat{A}E$ are adjacent and so are

$E\hat{A}B$, $E\hat{A}D$. But $E\hat{A}B \simeq B\hat{A}E$ (22). Therefore, by 25, $B\hat{A}C \simeq E\hat{A}D$. Thence $B\hat{A}C \simeq D\hat{A}E$.

27. If AB, $BC \simeq A'B'$, $B'C'$ and $B\hat{A}C \simeq B'\hat{A}'C'$ then $B\hat{C}A$ and $B'\hat{C}'A'$ are either congruent or supplementary.

Dem. If $AC \simeq A'C'$ then $B\hat{C}A \simeq B'\hat{C}'A'$ (21). If $AC \simeq A'C'$ is false, then either $\mu A'C' < \mu AC$ or $\mu AC < \mu A'C'$ (13). In the latter case, there is a point P with $[A'PC']$, $A'P \simeq AC$. Hence AB, $AC \simeq A'B'$, $A'P$ and $B\hat{A}C \simeq B'\hat{A}'P$; hence $BC \simeq B'P$, $B\hat{C}A \simeq B'\hat{P}A'$ (23). But since $BC \simeq B'C'$ we have $B'C' \simeq B'P$ and $B'\hat{C}'P \simeq B'\hat{P}C'$ (24). But since $[A'PC']$, therefore $B'\hat{C}'P = B'\hat{C}'A'$ (cf. I 4) while $B'\hat{P}A'$ and $B'\hat{P}C'$ are adjacent. Hence $B\hat{C}A$ and $B'\hat{C}'A'$ are supplementary (25·1). The case when $\mu A'C' < \mu AC$ is treated similarly.

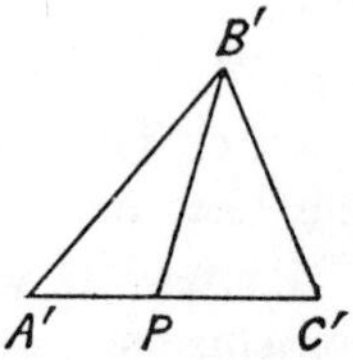

Fig. 23

28. If $A\hat{O}B \simeq A'\hat{O}'B'$ *and* $[OC$ *is in* $A\hat{O}B$ *then there is a ray* $[O'C'$ *in* $A'\hat{O}'B'$ *with* $A\hat{O}C \simeq A'\hat{O}'C'$ *and* $B\hat{O}C \simeq B'\hat{O}'C'$.

Dem. There are points F, D, F', D' on $[OA$, $[OB$, $[OA'$, $[OB'$ resp. such that OF, OD, $FD \simeq OF'$, OD', $F'D'$ (**C** I, 19·2) and

(*a*) $O\hat{F}D \simeq O'\hat{F}'D'$, $O\hat{D}F \simeq O'\hat{D}'F'$ (21).

Now $[OC$ meets F^-D in E say (III 7), and since $FD \simeq F'D'$, there is a point E' on $F'D'$ with $FE \simeq F'E'$ and $ED \simeq E'D'$ and $[F'E'D']$ (6·1). Since $[FED]$ $[F'E'D']$ therefore (*a*) gives $O\hat{F}E \simeq O'\hat{F}'E'$ and $O\hat{D}E \simeq O'\hat{D}'E'$.

Since OF, $FE \simeq O'F'$, $F'E'$ and $O\hat{F}E \simeq O'\hat{F}'E'$ we have $F\hat{O}E \simeq F'\hat{O}'E'$ (23). Similarly $D\hat{O}E \simeq D'\hat{O}'E'$, and thus $[O'E'$ is the ray required.

§ 4. **Ax. C VI. If $P\hat{Q}R$ be any angle, $[AC$ any ray, then there are not more than two rays $[AB$ in a plane containing $[AC$ such that $C\hat{A}B \simeq P\hat{Q}R$.**

As will be evident soon it would also suffice to assume that the number of such rays is finite.

29. *If* $[AB$, $[AB'$ *be two distinct rays satisfying the conditions of* **C** VI, *then* $[AB$, $[AB'$ *are on opposite sides of* AC.

*Dem.** If possible let them be on the same side of AC and let $AB \simeq AB'$. [We have omitted an obvious step so as not to bring in more letters; we do so in future without comment.]

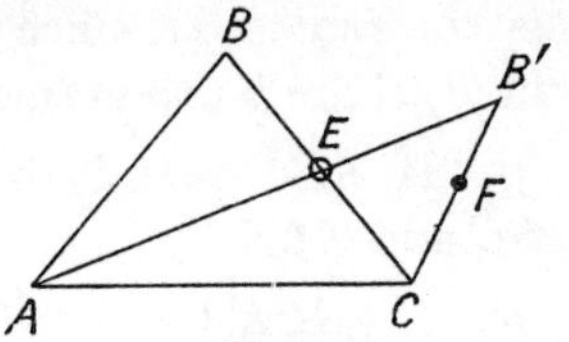

Fig. 24

Then $CB \simeq CB'$ and $A\hat{C}B \simeq A\hat{C}B'$ (23). Since B, B' are on the same side of AC therefore $[AB$ is in $C\hat{A}B'$ or $[AB'$ in $C\hat{A}B$ (III 9). Suppose the latter. Then $[AB'$ meets C^-B in E say (III 7). Since $CB \simeq CB'$ and $[CEB]$, there is a point F with $CF \simeq CE$, $[CFB']$ (6·1). Since $A\hat{C}B \simeq A\hat{C}B'$ we have $A\hat{C}E \simeq A\hat{C}F$ which with $AC, CE \simeq AC, CF$ gives $C\hat{A}E \simeq C\hat{A}F$ (23). Thus $C\hat{A}B \simeq C\hat{A}B' \simeq C\hat{A}F$. If $[AF$ is distinct from $[AB$ and $[AB'$ this will contradict **C** VI; and this is the case since $[CFB']$ and since $[AF$, being in $C\hat{A}B'$, is in $C\hat{A}B$ (III 8).

30. If PQR be a triangle, and if there are two points B in a plane through AC which satisfy $PQR \simeq CAB$ then they lie on opposite sides of AC (21, 29).

31. If B, B' be on the same side of AC and $[AB \neq [AB'$ then $C\hat{A}B \simeq C\hat{A}B'$ is impossible.

32. From 31 and **C** I—V follows **C** VI. Thus 31 could be substituted for **C** VI.

33. *If $C\hat{A}B$, $C\hat{A}D$ be supplementary, and B, D be on opposite sides of AC, then B, A, D colline.*

Dem. If not, let B' satisfy $[DAB']$. Then $[AB \neq [AB'$, and $C\hat{A}B \simeq C\hat{A}B'$ since both are supplements of $C\hat{A}D$ (25·2). But this contradicts 31.

34. *If $BC \simeq B'C'$, $A\hat{B}C \simeq A'\hat{B}'C'$, $A\hat{C}B \simeq A'\hat{C}'B'$ then $AB \simeq A'B'$, $AC \simeq A'C'$, $ABC \simeq A'B'C'$.*

Dem. If $AB \simeq A'B'$, the Theorem follows by 23. If $AB \simeq A'B'$ is false, suppose (13) $\mu A'B' < \mu AB$, then there is a point D with $[BDA]$ $BD \simeq B'A'$ (13·2). Then

$BC, BD \simeq B'C', B'A'$ and $D\hat{B}C \simeq A'\hat{B}'C'$

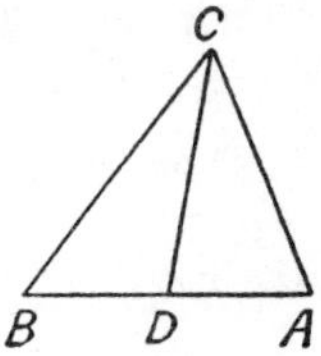

Fig. 25

give $D\hat{C}B \simeq A'\hat{C}'B'$. Thus $D\hat{C}B \simeq A\hat{C}B$, but

* Cf. Mollerup, *Math. Ann.* LVIII (1904), p. 479.

this contradicts 31, since $[BDA]$ implies that $[CD \neq [CA$ and that A, D are on the same side of BC. Hence $AB \simeq A'B'$.

35. If $A\hat{B}C \simeq A\hat{C}B$ then $AB \simeq AC$. Apply 34 to triangles ABC and ACB.

36. If $[ACK]$ and $C\hat{A}B \simeq K\hat{C}D$ and B, D are on the same side of AC then AB, CD do not meet.

Dem. First suppose AB, CD meet in E in the same half-plane as B, D. On DC there is a point F with $[DCF]$ and so $[ECF]$, and with $CF \simeq AE$. Since $[ACK]$ $[DCF]$ we have $K\hat{C}D \simeq A\hat{C}F$ (26) whence

$$C\hat{A}B \simeq A\hat{C}F,$$

that is, $C\hat{A}E \simeq A\hat{C}F$. This with

$$AC, AE \simeq CA, CF$$

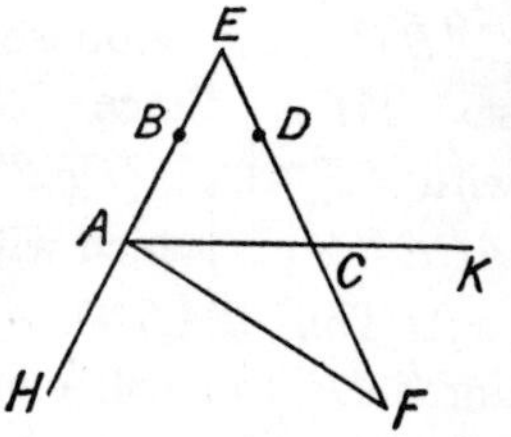

Fig. 26

gives $A\hat{C}E \simeq C\hat{A}F$. Now since $[ACK]$ therefore $K\hat{C}D, A\hat{C}E$ are adjacent and hence, since $C\hat{A}B \simeq K\hat{C}D$ and $C\hat{A}F \simeq A\hat{C}E$, therefore $C\hat{A}B$ and $C\hat{A}F$ will be supplementary. But B, F are on opposite sides of AC, hence B, A, F colline (33), and hence AB, CD meet in two points E, F (one on each side of AC) which is impossible.

Also if $[BAH]$ then $C\hat{A}H \simeq K\hat{C}F$ (25) and hence by the first part, AB, CD cannot meet on the other side of AC from that on which B, D lie.

·1. *Note.* Essential for the proof of 36 are (i) two lines cannot meet in two points; (ii) a line separates the other points of a plane in which it lies into two regions, so that E, F above cannot coincide. There are Geometries in which most of the Theorems in this chapter hold but in which 36 is false, owing to (i) or (ii) being false.

·2. *Note.* We cannot deduce from 36 the *existence* of lines which do not meet because we have not yet shewn the *existence* of congruent angles which are not identical and not opposite.

37. *If* $A\hat{B}C \simeq A'\hat{B}'C'$, $B\hat{A}C \simeq B'\hat{A}'C'$, $AC \simeq A'C'$ *then* $AB \simeq A'B'$, $BC \simeq B'C'$, $A\hat{C}B \simeq A'\hat{C}'B'$, $ABC \simeq A'B'C'$.

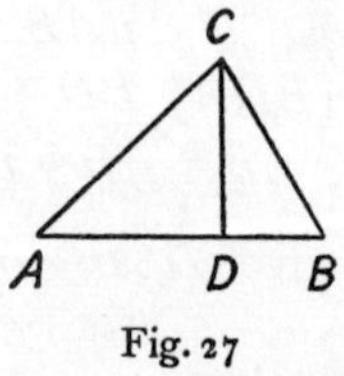

Fig. 27

Dem. If $AB \simeq A'B'$ the Theorem follows by 23. Otherwise, suppose (13) $\mu AB > \mu A'B'$, then there is a point D with $[ADB]$, $AD \simeq A'B'$

(13·2), and since $AC, AD \simeq A'C', A'B'$ and $B\hat{A}C \simeq B'\hat{A}'C'$ we have $A\hat{D}C \simeq A'\hat{B}'C'$ (23). Thus $A\hat{D}C \simeq A\hat{B}C$. But since $[ADB]$, this contradicts 36.

We have now all the Theorems on congruence of triangles save that relating to right-angled triangles.

Addition and Subtraction of Angles

38. *If $A\hat{O}C \simeq A'\hat{O}'C'$ and if $C\hat{O}B \simeq C'\hat{O}'B'$ and A, O, B do not colline and if there is no ray both in $A\hat{O}C$ and in $C\hat{O}B$ and if there is no ray both in $A'\hat{O}'C'$ and in $C'\hat{O}'B'$ then*

$$A\hat{O}B \simeq A'\hat{O}'B'.$$

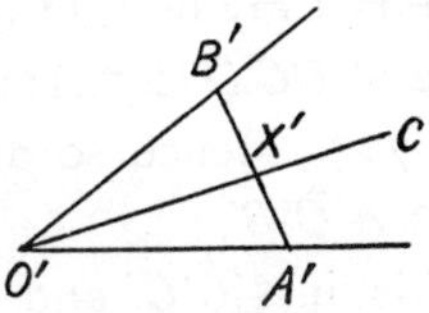

Fig. 28

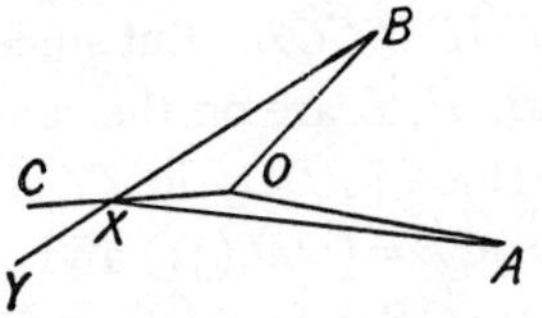

Fig. 29

Dem. Since there is no ray both in $A'\hat{O}'C'$ and in $C'\hat{O}'B'$, either $[O'C'$ is in $A'\hat{O}'B'$ or in $A_1'\hat{O}'B_1'$ where $[A_1'O'A']$ $[B_1'O'B']$ (III 10·2).

Case I. Let $[O'C'$ be in $A'\hat{O}'B'$, then $[O'C'$ meets $A'B'$ in X' say. Let $OA, OB, OX \simeq O'A', O'B', O'X'$ with X on $[OC$. Since $A\hat{O}X \simeq A'\hat{O}'X'$ we have then

$$AX \simeq A'X', \; O\hat{X}A \simeq O'\hat{X}'A' \; (23).$$

Similarly $BX \simeq B'X'$, $O\hat{X}B \simeq O'\hat{X}'B'$. But since $[A'X'B']$, $O'\hat{X}'A'$ and $O'\hat{X}'B'$ will be adjacent, and hence $O\hat{X}A$, $O\hat{X}B$ supplementary (25·1); and A, B are on opposite sides of OX (III 9·3). Hence A, X, B colline (33) and further $[OX$, *that is* $[OC$, *is in* $A\hat{O}B$ (III 2). Whence, since $AX, XB \simeq A'X', X'B'$ and $[AXB]$ $[A'X'B']$, we have $AB \simeq A'B'$ (**C** III) and this gives $A\hat{O}B \simeq A'\hat{O}'B'$ (21).

Case II. Let $[O'C'$ be in $A_1'\hat{O}'B_1'$. By Case I, if $[OC$ were in $A\hat{O}B$, then $[O'C'$ would be in $A'\hat{O}'B'$, but it is not (III 10). Hence $[OC$ is not in $A\hat{O}B$, and so is in $A_1\hat{O}B_1$ where $[AOA_1]$ $[BOB_1]$ (III 10·2). Then $A_1\hat{O}C \simeq A_1'\hat{O}'C'$, $B_1\hat{O}C \simeq B_1'\hat{O}'C'$ (25).

But by hyp. and III 9·7 there is no ray both in $A_1\hat{O}C$ and in $B_1\hat{O}C$, and similarly for $A_1'\hat{O}'C'$ and $B_1'\hat{O}'C'$. Hence by 26 and Case I, $A\hat{O}B \simeq A'\hat{O}'B'$.

38·1. If $[OC$ is in $A\hat{O}B$ and $[O'C'$ in $A'\hat{O}'B'$ and
$A\hat{O}C \simeq A'\hat{O}'C'$, $C\hat{O}B \simeq C'\hat{O}'B'$ then $A\hat{O}B \simeq A'\hat{O}'B'$.

39. *If* $A\hat{O}C \simeq A'\hat{O}'C'$ *and* $C\hat{O}B \simeq C'\hat{O}'B'$ *and if there is a ray both in* $A\hat{O}C$ *and in* $C\hat{O}B$ *and if there is a ray both in* $A'\hat{O}'C'$ *and in* $C'\hat{O}'B'$, *then* $A\hat{O}B \simeq A'\hat{O}'B'$ *unless* $[OA = [OB$.

Dem. By III 9·5 either $[O'A' = [O'B'$ or $[O'A'$ is in $C'\hat{O}'B'$ or $[O'B'$ is in $C'\hat{O}'A'$. Suppose the latter. Then there is a ray $[OD$ in $C\hat{O}A$ with $C\hat{O}D \simeq C'\hat{O}'B'$, $A\hat{O}D \simeq A'\hat{O}'B'$ (28). Thus $C\hat{O}D \simeq C\hat{O}B$. But since there is a ray both in $A\hat{O}C$ and in $C\hat{O}B$, A, B are on the same side of OC (III 7·4) and so are A, D since $[OD$ is in $C\hat{O}A$ (III 7·2). Hence so are B, D. Hence $[OB = [OD$ (31) and $A\hat{O}B \simeq A'\hat{O}'B'$.

·1. If $[OB$ is in $A\hat{O}C$, and $[O'B'$ is in $A'\hat{O}'C'$ and
$A\hat{O}C \simeq A'\hat{O}'C'$, $C\hat{O}B \simeq C'\hat{O}'B'$ then $A\hat{O}B \simeq A'\hat{O}'B'$.

Perpendiculars and Constructions

40. If $[AOC]$ $[BOD]$ and $A\hat{O}B \simeq D\hat{O}A$, then $A\hat{O}B$, $D\hat{O}A$, $C\hat{O}D$, $B\hat{O}C$ are all congruent.

41. *Def.* $[OA$ is '*perpendicular*' to $[OB$, written $[OA \perp [OB$, if and only if there is a point D with $[BOD]$ and $A\hat{O}B \simeq D\hat{O}A$ (we do not yet know if rays exist with such relations).

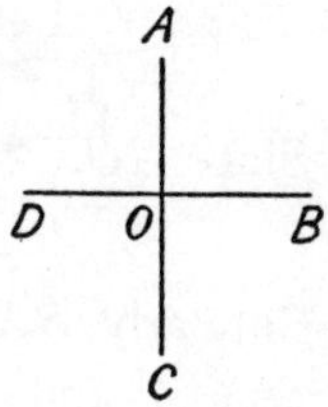

Fig. 30

·1. If $[OA \perp [OB$ and $[BOD']$ then
$A\hat{O}B \simeq D'\hat{O}A$.

42. If $[AOC]$ $[BOD]$ and $[OA \perp [OB$ then

·1. $[OB \perp [OA$, for there is a point C with $[AOC]$ and $C\hat{O}B \simeq B\hat{O}A$ (40, 22).

·2. And $[OA$ and $[OC$ are perpendicular to $[OB$ and $[OD$ and vice versâ (40, 22).

43. *Def.* The line OA is a '*perpendicular*' to the line OB written $OA \perp OB$, if each ray from O of OA is perpendicular to each ray from O of OB.

This definition is consistent by 42·1·2, provided perpendicular *rays* exist.

43·1. *Def.* $A\hat{O}B$ is a '*right angle*' provided $[OA \perp [OB$.

This definition is consistent by 42·1, with the proviso above.

44. *If* $A\hat{O}B$ *is a right angle and* $X\hat{Y}Z \simeq A\hat{O}B$ *then* $X\hat{Y}Z$ *is a right angle.*

Dem. If $[BOD]$ then $A\hat{O}B \simeq D\hat{O}A$. If $[ZYW]$ then $X\hat{Y}Z$, $W\hat{Y}Z$ are adjacent, and $X\hat{Y}Z \simeq A\hat{O}B$; hence $W\hat{Y}X \simeq D\hat{O}A$ (25), since $A\hat{O}B$, $D\hat{O}A$ are adjacent. Hence $X\hat{Y}Z \simeq W\hat{Y}X$.

Thus an angle congruent to a right angle is a right angle. We cannot yet affirm that all right angles are congruent.

45. *Def.* If $A\hat{O}B$ be any angle and $[OC$ be in $A\hat{O}B$ and $A\hat{O}C \simeq B\hat{O}C$ then $[OC$ is a '*bisector*' of $A\hat{O}B$.

46. *If* $A\hat{O}B$ *be any angle, there is one and only one ray in* $A\hat{O}B$ *which is a bisector of* $A\hat{O}B$ *and this ray can be constructed if the following constructions can be performed.*

a. *Any two distinct points can be joined by a line* (II 4).

b. *If two lines meet, their common point can be found* (II 4·3).

c. (i) *If* A, B *be distinct points a point* C *can be found with* $[ABC]$ (Ax. **O** IV);

(ii) *and a point can be found not on* AB (**O** V);

(iii) *hence a point* D *can be found with* $[ADB]$ (II 7).

$\mathbf{d}_1$. *If* $C \vdash D$ *be any interval,* $[AB$ *any ray, then a point* P *can be found on* $[AB$ *with* $AP \simeq CD$ (**C** I).

Note. We distinguish between an existence Theorem and a construction. The former asserts the existence of certain elements, the latter shews how they can be *isolated.* The references appended to the constructions give the corresponding existence Theorems. When the present proposition has been shewn, we shall know that some congruent angles, not identical and not opposite, exist. The Theory of Constructions is dealt with in Chapter IX.

Dem. Find C, C' on $[OA$, $[OB$ with $OC \simeq OC'$ ($\mathbf{d}_1$) and D with $[ODC]$ (**c**). Take D' on $[OC'$ with $OD' \simeq OD$ ($\mathbf{d}_1$). Then $[O'D'C']$, $D'C' \simeq DC$ (2). Then $C{-}D'$ and $C'{-}D$ meet in P say (II 11·6) and $[OP$ *is in* $A\hat{O}B$ (III 5).

Further P and $[OP$ can be found (**b**, **a**). By triangles COD', $C'OD$, we have

$$O\hat{D}'C \simeq O\hat{D}C',\ O\hat{C}'D \simeq O\hat{C}D'\ (22, 23).$$

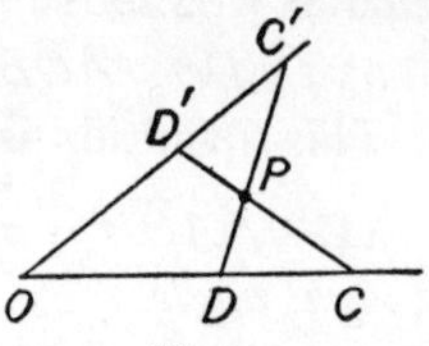

Fig. 31

But $[OD'C'][ODC]$ hence $C'\hat{D}'C \simeq C'\hat{D}C$ (25). Thus since $[D'PC]$ $[C'PD]$, we have $P\hat{D}C \simeq P\hat{D}'C'$, $P\hat{C}D \simeq P\hat{C}'D'$ and these with $CD \simeq C'D'$ give $DP \simeq D'P$ (34). Thus $OD, DP, PO \simeq OD', D'P, PO$, and hence $D\hat{O}P \simeq D'\hat{O}P$ (21), that is, $A\hat{O}P \simeq B\hat{O}P$.

Now suppose $[OQ$ is any bisector of $A\hat{O}B$; since it lies in $A\hat{O}B$ (45), it meets $C{-}C'$ in M say (III 7) and $CM \simeq C'M$ (23), whence M is mid CC'. Thus any bisector of $A\hat{O}B$ meets $C{-}C'$ in its mid-point and since CC' has not more than one mid-point (14·2), $A\hat{O}B$ cannot have more than one bisector.

46·1. *Def.* If $[OP$ bisects (i.e. is the bisector of) $A\hat{O}B$ then $A\hat{O}P$ is '*half*' $A\hat{O}B$.

·2. The halves of congruent angles are congruent (28, 46).

·3. If $OC \simeq OC'$ then the bisector of $C\hat{O}C'$ meets $C{-}C'$ in its mid-point M and OM is perpendicular to CC'.

47. *Right angles exist and can be constructed by* $\mathbf{abcd}_1$ (46, 46·3).

48. *If AB be any line in any plane ABC then there is a perpendicular to AB in this plane and it can be constructed by* $\mathbf{abcd}_1$.

Dem. Join AC (**a**), take E, F on $[AB$, $[AC$ resp. with $AE \simeq AF$ ($\mathbf{d}_1$) and draw the bisector $[AD$ of $B\hat{A}C$ (46). This meets $E{-}F$ in G say and $A\hat{G}E$ is a right angle (46·3). Take K, H on $[AD$, $[AB$ resp. with $AE \simeq AK$, $AG \simeq AH$, then $A\hat{G}E \simeq A\hat{H}K$ (22, 23) and thus $A\hat{H}K$ is a right angle (44).

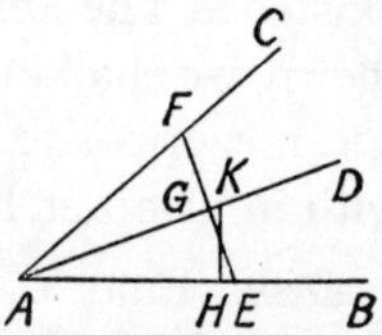

Fig. 32

·1. If $A\hat{G}E$ is a right angle, then a congruent right angle one of whose side-lines is AE, can be constructed by $\mathbf{abcd}_1$.

49. If P be any point on any line AB in any plane ABC, then there is a perpendicular to AB through P in ABC and it can be constructed by $\mathbf{abcd_1}$.

Dem. We can draw at any rate one perpendicular KH to AB, in ABC, with H on AB (48). If $H = P$ the construction is performed. If $H \neq P$ we can find E, F, B with $KH \simeq HE$, $[KHE][EPF][HPB]$ ($\mathbf{d_1}$, $\mathbf{c}$). Bisect $K\hat{P}F$ by $[PG$ (46). Then

$$K\hat{P}H \simeq E\hat{P}H \simeq F\hat{P}B \text{ (23, 26).}$$

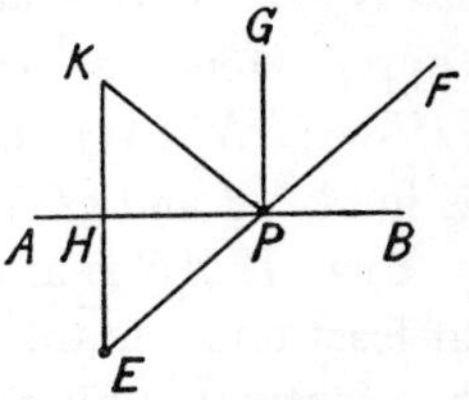

Fig. 33

Also $K\hat{P}G \simeq F\hat{P}G$. If then we shew there is no ray both in $K\hat{P}H$ and $K\hat{P}G$, and no ray both in $F\hat{P}B$ and $F\hat{P}G$, it will follow that $G\hat{P}H \simeq G\hat{P}B$ (38) and hence $GP \perp AB$.

Now since $[EPF]$ there are no rays both in $K\hat{P}E$ and in $K\hat{P}F$ (III 7·5), and since $[KHE]$ therefore $[PH$ is in $K\hat{P}E$ (III 5). Hence all rays in $K\hat{P}H$ are in $K\hat{P}E$ (III 8), and since $[PG$ is in $K\hat{P}F$ therefore all rays in $K\hat{P}G$ are in $K\hat{P}F$ (III 8). Hence there is no ray both in $K\hat{P}H$ and in $K\hat{P}G$.

Since $[KHE]$ $[HPB]$, therefore K, B are on opposite sides of PF and hence there is no ray both in $F\hat{P}B$ and in $F\hat{P}K$ (III 7·5). But since $[PG$ is in $F\hat{P}K$, therefore all rays in $F\hat{P}G$ are in $F\hat{P}K$ (III 8). Thus there is no ray both in $F\hat{P}B$ and in $F\hat{P}G$. The Theorem now follows.

·1. If P is any point on any line AB in any plane ABC, there are not two perpendiculars to AB through P in ABC*.

Dem. If possible, let PM, PN be perpendiculars to AB through P in the plane ABC with $PN \neq PM$. Let M, N be on the same side of AB and let $[APB]$. Then either $[PN$ is in $A\hat{P}M$ or $[PM$ is in $A\hat{P}N$ (III 9). Let $[PN$ be in $A\hat{P}M$. Since $[APB]$ we have $A\hat{P}M \simeq B\hat{P}M$ (41·1). Hence there is a ray $[PN'$ in $B\hat{P}M$

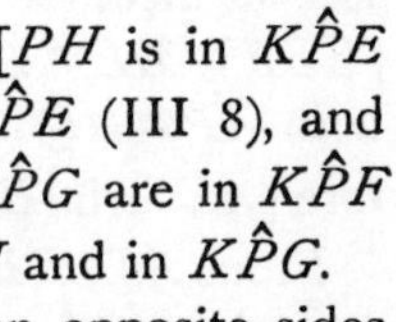

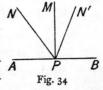

Fig. 34

* Coolidge remarks (*Non-Euclidean Geometry*, p. 36) that it is truly astonishing how much geometers, ancient and modern, have worried over this Theorem. Compare *Dem.* with 14·2 *Dem.*

with $A\hat{P}N \simeq B\hat{P}N'$ (28). Again since $[APB]$, we have

$$A\hat{P}N \simeq B\hat{P}N \ (41\cdot1).$$

Hence $B\hat{P}N \simeq B\hat{P}N'$. Now since $[PN'$ is in $B\hat{P}M$ therefore M, N' are on the same side of PB (III 7·2), and so are M, N (hyp.). Hence so are N, N'. But $B\hat{P}N \simeq B\hat{P}N'$. Therefore $[PN = [PN'$ (31). But this is contrary to III 7·5, since $[PN$ is in $A\hat{P}M$ and $[PN'$ is in $B\hat{P}M$ and also $[APB]$.

49·2. If AB is any line, P any point not on it, then there is at least one line through P perpendicular to AB and this can be constructed by **abcd**$_1$.

Dem. Let D be on AB, draw $DX \perp AB$ in the plane ABP (49). If D, X, P colline then DX is the line required. If not, let $[ADB]$ be true. Then DX meets $A\text{-}P$ or $B\text{-}P$ (II 16·1). Let it meet $A\text{-}P$ in E. Find F with $[EDF]$, $DE \simeq DF$ ($\mathbf{d}_1$) and Q on $[AF$ with $AP \simeq AQ$ ($\mathbf{d}_1$). Since $[EDF]$ therefore $[AD$ is in $E\hat{A}F$ (III 5).

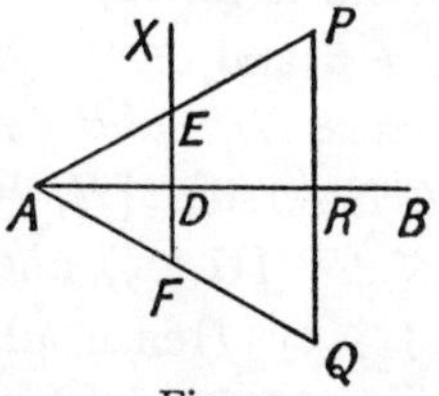

Fig. 35

From AD, $DE \simeq AD$, DF and $A\hat{D}E \simeq A\hat{D}F$ (41·1) we have $E\hat{A}D \simeq F\hat{A}D$, (23) that is $[AD$ is the bisector of $E\hat{A}F$. Whence since $AP \simeq PQ$ therefore $PQ \perp AD$ (46·3).

·3. If AB be any line, P a point not on it, then there are not two lines through P perpendicular to AB.

Dem. If possible let PM, PM' be both $\perp AB$ with M, M' on AB and $M \neq M'$. There are points Q, R with $[PMQ]$ $[PM'R]$, $PM \simeq MQ$. Then since PM, $MM' \simeq QM$, MM' and $P\hat{M}M' \simeq Q\hat{M}M'$ (41·1) we have $P\hat{M}'M \simeq Q\hat{M}'M$ (23). But as $[PM'R]$ and $PM' \perp M'M$ we have

$$P\hat{M}'M \simeq R\hat{M}'M \ (41\cdot1)$$

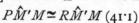

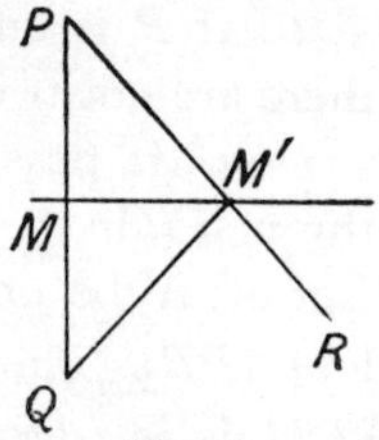

Fig. 36

and so $Q\hat{M}'M \simeq R\hat{M}'M$. But since $[PMQ]$ $[PM'R]$ therefore Q, R are on the same side of MM'. Hence since $Q\hat{M}'M \simeq R\hat{M}'M$, Q must lie on $M'R$ (31). Hence PM, PM' meet at $Q \neq P$ which is impossible.

·4. *Note.* The conditions mentioned in 36·1 are essential for the proof of this Theorem and for the reasons there stated. There are

Geometries in which the conditions are violated and the Theorem false. We could not use 36 to shew 49·3 because we do not yet know that all right angles are congruent. Summing up 49 to 49·3 we have

50. *One and only one perpendicular can be drawn from any point to any straight line and it can be constructed by* **abcd$_1$**.

·1. *Note.* Although we know that an angle congruent to a right angle is itself a right angle (44) we do not yet know if all right angles are congruent. Virtually we defined a right angle as half a 'straight angle' and we know (10) that any two 'straight angles' are congruent and that the halves of congruent angles are congruent (46·2). But this has only been shewn for *our* angles, not for 'straight angles,' for the proof depends on 28 and the proof of 28 would break down, if we attempted to apply it to the 'straight angle.' We now introduce as a last Congruence Axiom, one which will enable us to shew that all right angles are congruent.

§ 5. Ax. C VII. If $C\hat{A}B$ and $D\hat{B}A$ are right angles then $C\hat{A}B \simeq D\hat{B}A$.

(Note that A, B, C, D need not coplane.)
The following Theorems are based on **O**, **C** I—VII.

51. *Any two right angles are congruent.*

Dem. (i) If a side-line of one is a side-line of the other this is **C** VII.

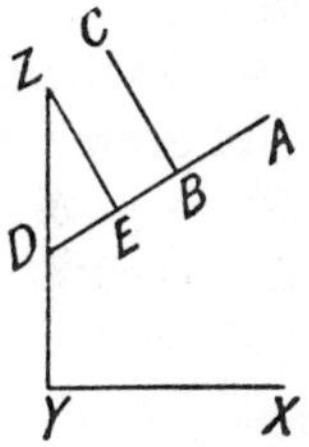

Fig. 37

(ii) If $A\hat{B}C$, $X\hat{Y}Z$ are the right angles (which may or may not coplane) and a side-line AB meets a side-line YZ in D say and $AB \neq YZ$ then by 50 draw $ZE \perp AD$, with E on AD. If $E = D$ then **C** VII gives $Z\hat{D}B \simeq A\hat{B}C$ and $Z\hat{D}B \simeq X\hat{Y}Z$ and hence $A\hat{B}C \simeq X\hat{Y}Z$. If $E \neq D$ then since $Z\hat{E}D$ is a right angle, therefore DZ is a side-line of a congruent right angle (48·1) which is also congruent to $X\hat{Y}Z$ by (i). Further $Z\hat{E}A \simeq A\hat{B}C$ by (i). Hence $A\hat{B}C \simeq X\hat{Y}Z$.

(iii) Finally if $A\hat{B}C$, $X\hat{Y}Z$ be any right angles, draw $CD \perp YZ$ (50) with D on YZ. Then by (i) $C\hat{D}Y \simeq X\hat{Y}Z$ and by (ii) $C\hat{D}Y \simeq A\hat{B}C$. Hence $A\hat{B}C \simeq X\hat{Y}Z$.

51·1. If **C** VII be assumed only when A, B, C, D coplane then the above shews that all right angles in their plane are congruent. *In any Theorem which involves one plane only we need only assume* **C** VII *in that plane.* This remark is of importance subsequently.

·2. Axioms **C** I—VI, and **C** VII assumed only for the case when A, B, C, D coplane, will be quoted as $\mathbf{C}_p$, even if all the points considered are not in one plane.

C I—VI and **C** VII will be quoted together as **C**.

52. *If* $A\hat{B}C$ *and* $A'\hat{B}'C'$ *be right angles and* $BC \simeq B'C'$, $AC \simeq A'C'$ *then* $AB \simeq A'B'$, $B\hat{A}C \simeq B'\hat{A}'C'$, $A\hat{C}B \simeq A'\hat{C}'B'$, $ABC \simeq A'B'C'$.

Dem. There is a point D with $[ABD]$, $BD \simeq B'A'$. Thus $[ABD]$, and $A\hat{B}C$ is a right angle, hence so is $D\hat{B}C$ (42·2). Hence $D\hat{B}C \simeq A'\hat{B}'C'$ (51) which with DB, $BC \simeq A'B'$, $B'C'$ gives $CD \simeq C'A'$ and $B\hat{D}C \simeq B'\hat{A}'C'$ (23). But $C'A' \simeq CA$, hence $CD \simeq CA$ and $A\hat{D}C \simeq D\hat{A}C$ (24) that is $B\hat{D}C \simeq B\hat{A}C$. Hence $B\hat{A}C \simeq B'\hat{A}'C'$ and the Theorem follows by 51 and 37.

53. *If* $B\hat{A}C$ *be any angle*, $[A'B'$ *any ray, then in any half plane* $\{A'B', D'\} = \zeta'$ *from* $A'B'$, *there is a ray* $[A'C'$ *such that* $B\hat{A}C \simeq B'\hat{A}'C'$; *and it can be constructed by* $\mathbf{abcd}_1$.

Dem. If $B\hat{A}C$ is a right angle, find E' in ζ' so that $A'E' \perp A'B'$ (50) then $B\hat{A}C \simeq B'\hat{A}'E'$ (51) and $[A'E'$ is the ray required. If $B\hat{A}C$ be not a right angle take G on $[AC$ and draw $GF \perp AB$, (50) with F on AB. Then $F \neq A$. Take F' on $[A'B'$ or on $A'B']$ according as F is on $[AB$ or $AB]$ and such that $A'F' \simeq AF$ ($\mathbf{d}_1$). Draw $F'G' \perp AB$, with G' in ζ' (50) and $F'G' \simeq FG$ ($\mathbf{d}_1$). Then AF, $FG \simeq A'F'$, $F'G'$ and $A\hat{F}G \simeq A'\hat{F}'G'$ (51). Hence $F\hat{A}G \simeq F'\hat{A}'G'$, $B\hat{A}C \simeq B'\hat{A}'C'$ (where we must use 25 if F is on $AB]$). Thus $[A'G'$ is the ray required.

54. *If we assume* 53 (*first part*) *and* **C** I—VI *then* 51 *and in particular* **C** VII *follow.*

Dem. If $A\hat{B}C$ and $X\hat{Y}Z$ be right angles, there is a ray $[YW$ in $\{XY, Z\}$ with $X\hat{Y}W \simeq A\hat{B}C$ (53). But $A\hat{B}C$ is a right angle, hence so is $X\hat{Y}W$ (44). Hence YZ, YW are both perpendicular to XY (43); whence $[YZ = [YW$ (49·1) and so $X\hat{Y}Z \simeq A\hat{B}C$. This shews 51 and in particular **C** VII.

54·1. *Note.* We might thus have introduced 53 as an Axiom instead of **C** VII and we might have assumed 31 instead of **C** VI (see 32). Combining 31 and 53 we have

·2. *If $B\hat{A}C$ be any angle, $[A'B'$ any ray, then in any half plane $\{A'B', D\}$ from $A'B'$, there is one and only one ray $[A'C'$ such that $B\hat{A}C \simeq B'\hat{A}'C'$.* This might have been taken as an Axiom*, but it is much stronger than **C** VI and VII combined. The course we have adopted is due to our desire to weaken Axioms as much as possible, so that they are only just sufficient to give us the results we deduce from them.

55. *If ABC be any triangle, $\{PQ, R\}$ any half plane, we can by* **abcd**$_1$ *construct a triangle XYZ where X is any point of PQ, Y is on $[PQ$, Z on $\{PQ, R\}$ and $ABC \simeq XYZ$.* This easily follows from 53.

It will be noted that we do not need to consider the intersection of circles in order to draw a triangle congruent to a given triangle. The case is different if we wish to draw a triangle with sides congruent to three given intervals, not fitted together to form a triangle.

The Measures of Angles as Magnitudes

56. *Def.* The '*measure*' of an angle $A\hat{O}B$, written $\mu A\hat{O}B$, is the set of all angles congruent to $A\hat{O}B$; or, alternatively, it may be regarded as a distinctive common property of these angles (I 9).

Thus $\mu A\hat{O}B = \mu X\hat{Y}Z$ and $A\hat{O}B \simeq X\hat{Y}Z$ assert the same fact.

·1. *Def.* $\mu A\hat{O}B + \mu C\hat{P}D$ means $\mu H\hat{X}K$ if there is a ray $[XL$ in $H\hat{X}K$ with $H\hat{X}L \simeq A\hat{O}B$ and $L\hat{X}K \simeq C\hat{P}D$.

This definition is consistent by 38·1.

·2. *The measures of angles satisfy the Axioms for a condensed*

* This is in fact the course adopted by Hilbert in his *Grundlagen.* Euclid on the other hand states 51 as an Axiom and also assumes implicitly that angles are a set of magnitudes except that the sum of two angles need not be an angle. Cf. 56.

set of magnitudes except that the sum of two measures need not be a measure (I 20).

Dem. (i) No angle has a measure equal to the sum of the measures of two right angles (·1 and 41·1, 51, 31).

(ii) If the sum of two measures (of angles) exist, it is unique (38·1).

In the following the expressions indicated are supposed to exist.

(iii) $\mu A\hat{O}B + \mu C\hat{P}D \neq \mu A\hat{O}B$ (31).

(iv) $(\mu A\hat{O}B + \mu A_1\hat{O}_1B_1) + \mu A_2\hat{O}_2B_2$

$= \mu A\hat{O}B + (\mu A_1\hat{O}_1B_1 + \mu A_2\hat{O}_2B_2)$ (28, III 8, 8·1).

(v) $\mu A\hat{O}B + \mu C\hat{P}D = \mu C\hat{P}D + \mu A\hat{O}B$ (28, 22).

(vi) *Def.* If a, b be the measures of angles then $a < b$, $b > a$ mean there is a measure x such that $a + x = b$ (see I 20·31).

(vii) *If a, b be measures of angles, either $a = b$ or $a < b$ or $a > b$, and only one of these is true*; for if $[OA$ be any ray we can find X, Y on the same side of OA such that $\mu A\hat{O}X = a$, $\mu A\hat{O}Y = b$ (53) and the Theorem follows by (vi) and III 9.

(viii) If a be the measure of an angle there is a measure $b < a$ (III 5·2). The Theorem ·2 now follows by I 20.

56·21. If $\mu X\hat{Y}Z < \mu A\hat{O}B$, there is a ray $[OC$ in $A\hat{O}B$ such that $\mu A\hat{O}C = \mu X\hat{Y}Z$. If $[OC$ is in $A\hat{O}B$, then $\mu A\hat{O}C < \mu A\hat{O}B$.

·3. *The measures of angles form a condensed class in linear order for* < (I 20·72·32).

·4. *Note.* The blemish that the sum of two measures need not be a measure is usually removed by introducing 'angles' greater than two or four right angles, and these are brought in by an appeal to the intuitive idea of rotation. Such a course is not open to us, and at first sight our method may well seem artificial in comparison, but it leads to the same results as the intuitive methods and is logical, while they avoid the main difficulties. We accordingly introduce a more general idea than the measure of an angle and for distinctness call it 'angular measure.'

57. *Def.* An '*angular measure*' is an ordered couple (n, σ) where n is a natural number and σ is the measure of an angle as defined in 56, or possibly o if $n > 0$, where o is a symbol obeying the laws $o + \sigma = \sigma + o = \sigma$ for all measures σ of angles, and $o + o = o$.

Note. (n, σ) corresponds to the intuitive idea of n half-turns plus a turn through an angle of measure σ. We have had to introduce o because our definition of angle does not provide for 'zero angles.' We now define the sum of two angular measures.

57·1. *Def.* If one or both of σ_1, σ_2 is o then

$$(n, \sigma_1) + (m, \sigma_2) = (n + m, \sigma_1 + \sigma_2).$$

If $\sigma_1 = \mu A\hat{O}B$ and $\sigma_2 = \mu B\hat{O}C$, and there is no ray both in $A\hat{O}B$ and in $B\hat{O}C$, then

$$\begin{aligned}(n, \sigma_1) + (m, \sigma_2) &= (n+m, \sigma) \text{ if } [OB \text{ is in } A\hat{O}C \text{ and } \sigma = \mu A\hat{O}C \\ &= (n+m+1, \sigma) \text{ if } [OB \text{ is not in } A\hat{O}C \text{ and } \\ &\qquad \sigma = \mu A_1\hat{O}C \text{ where } [AOA_1] \\ &= (n+m+1, o) \text{ if } [AOC].\end{aligned}$$

This definition is consistent by 25·2, 38.

·2. Comm+ clearly holds, and it is easy, though tedious, to shew Assoc+. (I 12·42·43.)

·3. *Angular measures are a condensed set of magnitudes* (I 20).

·4. We write $(1, o)$ defined in ·1, as π. It is usual to identify $(0, \alpha)$ with α whenever α is the measure of an angle, that is, to regard the measure of an angle as an angular measure (cf. I 28·4 for a similar situation). We shall do this and it then follows that

$$(n, \alpha) = (n, o) + (0, \alpha) = n(1, o) + (0, \alpha) = n\pi + \alpha,$$

where of course π is not the Ludolfian constant 3·14159... but merely the sum of the angular measures of two supplementary angles.

·5. With this identification, the *measure of a right angle is* $\pi/2$ (cf. 51).

·6. *The measure of any angle is* $< \pi$ (·1·3·4), the measure of the half of any angle is $< \pi/2$ (·3·4).

·7. *Note.* It will be noticed that we have *not* enlarged our idea of an angle and we shall not do so. It is rather awkward that an angular measure need not be the measure of any angle, but some awkwardness is inevitable somewhere, since the word 'angle' is commonly used in more than one sense, while we wish to adhere throughout to the definition in III 3.

·8. If two angles (not right angles) be supplementary, the measure of one is greater, of the other less than $\pi/2$.

57·9. We can define *subtraction* as in I 20·51, and as in similar cases in Chapter I we can also define '*signed angular measures*' and the '*zero angular measure*.' The signed angular measures form a fully ordered group for + as is easily shewn. Cf. I 22, 24.

Theorem **M**

58. (Cf. 14·5.) *Every interval AB has a mid-point.*

It can be constructed by **abcd**$_1$.

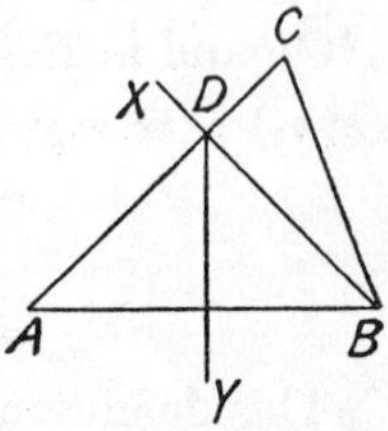

Fig. 38

Dem. Take a point C not on AB, then either $\mu A\hat{B}C <=$ or $> \mu B\hat{A}C$ (56·2). Find a point D thus: if $A\hat{B}C \simeq B\hat{A}C$, take $D=C$. If $\mu A\hat{B}C > \mu B\hat{A}C$, find X such that $[BX$ is in $A\hat{B}C$ and $A\hat{B}X \simeq B\hat{A}C$ (53, 56·21). Then $[BX$ meets $A^{-}C$ (III 5). Take the point of meeting as D. Bisect $A\hat{D}B$ by $[DY$ (46) then $[DY$ meets AB in mid AB (46·3, 35).

·1. If $B\hat{A}C \simeq A\hat{C}D$, $AB \simeq CD$ and B, D be on opposite sides of AC, then BD meets $A^{\vdash}C$ in its mid-point.

Dem. Let M be mid AC (58) and let D' satisfy $[BMD']$, $BM \simeq MD'$. Then $C\hat{A}B \simeq A\hat{C}D'$, $D=D'$.

Existence of Non-meeting Lines in a Plane. Inequalities

59. *If l be any line, A any point not on it, then through A by means of* **abcd**$_1$ *a line can be drawn in the plane (Al) which does not meet l* (36, 53).

·1. Hence there are 'parallel' lines; but the proof involves conditions (i), (ii) of 36·1.

·2. If AB, $CD \perp BC$ then AB, CD do not meet (36, 51, or 49·3).

60. *If ABC be a triangle and $[ACK]$ then $\mu B\hat{C}K > \mu B\hat{A}C$, and $\mu B\hat{C}K > \mu A\hat{B}C$.*

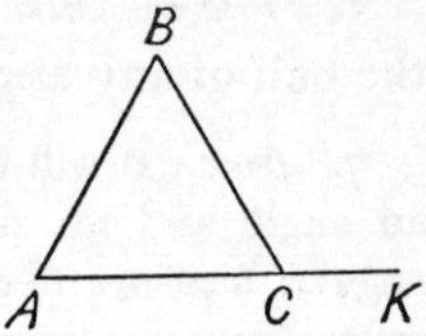

Fig. 39

Dem. If $\mu B\hat{C}K < \mu B\hat{A}C$ there is a ray $[AX$ in $B\hat{A}C$ such that $\mu C\hat{A}X = \mu K\hat{C}B$ and $[AX$ meets CB (III 7) contrary to 36. Also $B\hat{C}K \simeq B\hat{A}C$ contradicts 36. Hence $\mu B\hat{C}K > \mu B\hat{A}C$ (56·3). Similarly if $[BCY]$ then $\mu A\hat{C}Y > \mu A\hat{B}C$. But $A\hat{C}Y \simeq B\hat{C}K$ (26). Hence the Theorem.

·1. If $[ACK]$ and $\mu C\hat{A}B > \mu K\hat{C}D$ and B, D be on the same side of AC then $[AB$, $[CD$ do not meet (36).

61. If in a triangle ABC, $\mu BC < \mu BA$ then $\mu B\hat{A}C < \mu B\hat{C}A$.

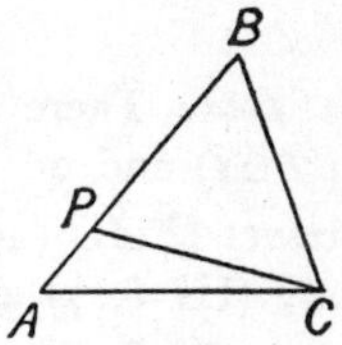

Fig. 40

Dem. Since $\mu BC < \mu BA$, there is a point P with $[APB]$, $BP \simeq BC$ (12·2). BPC is a triangle, hence $B\hat{P}C \simeq B\hat{C}P$ (24). Since $[APB]$ and ACP is a triangle, we have $\mu B\hat{A}C < \mu B\hat{P}C$ (60). And further $[CP$ is in $B\hat{C}A$ (III 5). Hence $\mu B\hat{C}P < \mu B\hat{C}A$ (56·21) and hence $\mu B\hat{A}C < \mu B\hat{C}A$ (56·3).

62. If $\mu B\hat{A}C < \mu B\hat{C}A$ then $\mu BC < \mu BA$ (13, 24, 61, 56·2).

63. If $B\hat{C}A$ be a right angle then $\mu B\hat{C}A > \mu B\hat{A}C$ and $\mu BC < \mu BA$.

Dem. Let $[ACK]$ then $\mu B\hat{C}A = \mu B\hat{C}K > \mu B\hat{A}C$ (42·1, 60). Hence by 62.

64. *If ABC be a triangle then $\mu AC < \mu AB + \mu BC$.*

Dem. There is a point D with $[ABD]$, $BD \simeq BC$ and BDC is a triangle. Hence $B\hat{D}C \simeq B\hat{C}D$ (24). But $[ABD]$, hence $[CB$ is in $A\hat{C}D$ (III 5) and $\mu B\hat{C}D < \mu A\hat{C}D$ (56·21). Hence $\mu B\hat{D}C < \mu A\hat{C}D$, that is $\mu A\hat{D}C < \mu A\hat{C}D$. Hence $\mu AC < \mu AD$ (62). But $[ABD]$ and $BD \simeq BC$. Hence $\mu AB + \mu BC = \mu AD$ (12·3). Hence

$$\mu AC < \mu AB + \mu BC.$$

65. If ABC be a triangle and $[BDC]$ then $\mu AD < \mu AB$ or $\mu AD < \mu AC$.

Dem. One of $\mu A\hat{D}B$, $\mu A\hat{D}C$ is not less than the other (56·2). Let $\mu A\hat{D}B \geqq \mu A\hat{D}C$. Now $[BDC]$, hence $\mu A\hat{D}C > \mu A\hat{B}D$ (60). Therefore $\mu A\hat{D}B > \mu A\hat{B}D$, $\mu AD < \mu AB$ (62).

·1. If $OA \perp AB$ and $[ABC]$ then $\mu OB < \mu OC$; for $\mu OB > \mu OA$ (63); hence by 65 on triangle OAC.

·2. If $OA \perp AB$ and C be on AB, then $\mu OB < \mu OC$ implies $\mu AB < \mu AC$ and conversely.

·3. If E, F be inside or on triangle ABC then $\mu EF \leqq$ greatest of μAB, μBC, μCA.

Dem. Suppose E, F not on the same side of the triangle, then EF meets $\triangle ABC$ in H, K say (II 16) and $\mu EF \leqq \mu HK$ (13·3). If H or K be at a vertex, the Theorem follows by 65. But if, say, H is on A^-B, K on A^-C then $\mu HK < \mu AH$ or $< \mu HC$ (65) since $[AKC]$, and $\mu AH < \mu AB$ since $[AHB]$, and $\mu HC < \mu BC$ or μCA (65). Hence the Theorem.

66. If $AB, AC \simeq A'B', A'C'$ and $\mu B\hat{A}C > \mu B'\hat{A}'C'$, then

$$\mu BC > \mu B'C'.$$

Dem. There is a ray $[AX$ in $B\hat{A}C$, such that $B\hat{A}X \simeq B'A'C'$ (56·21) and on the ray a point C'' such that $AC'' \simeq AC$. Let $[AX$ bisect $C''\hat{A}C$ (46). Since $[AX$ is in $C''\hat{A}C$ (45) it meets B^-C in D say (III 8, 7) and we have $DC \simeq DC''$ (23). If B, D, C'' colline, then B, C, C'' colline and since $[AC''$ is in $B\hat{A}C$ we have $[BC''C]$, $\mu BC > \mu BC''$. If B, D, C'' do not colline then $[BDC]$, $DC'' \simeq DC$ give $\mu BC = \mu BD + \mu DC'' > \mu BC''$ (64). Hence the Theorem.

·1. If $AB, AC \simeq A'B', A'C'$ and $\mu BC > \mu B'C'$ then

$$\mu B\hat{A}C > \mu B'\hat{A}'C' \text{ (56·3, 66).}$$

Congruence of Two Planes

67. *Any two planes are congruent in such a way that a given point A, a given ray $[AB$ from A, a given side $\{AB, C\}$ of AB on the first correspond to a given point A', ray $[A'B'$ from A', side $\{A'B', C'\}$ of $A'B'$ on the second.*

Dem. Make A and AB correspond to A' and $A'B'$ as in 10, so that $[AB$ corresponds to $[A'B'$. Then if X, Y on AB correspond to X', Y' on $A'B'$ we have $XY \simeq X'Y'$ (10). If E be any point on $\{AB, C\}$ or on the other side of AB, there is one and only one point E' on $\{A'B', C'\}$ or on the other side of $A'B'$ resp. so that $B'\hat{A}'E' \simeq B\hat{A}E$, $A'E' \simeq AE$ (55). Make E' correspond to E. The correspondence thus set up is (1, 1), and if E, F on ABC and not on AB correspond to E', F' on $A'B'C'$ (and not on $A'B'$), and if G on AB correspond to G' (on $A'B'$), then $EG \simeq E'G'$ (23, using 25 if necessary). Also $B\hat{A}E \simeq B'\hat{A}'E'$, $B\hat{A}F \simeq B'\hat{A}'F'$, and since E, F are on the same or opposite sides of AB in ABC according as E', F' are on the same or opposite sides of $A'B'$ in $A'B'C'$, there will be a ray both in $B\hat{A}E$ and in $B\hat{A}F$, or not, according as there is a ray both in $B'\hat{A}'E'$ and in $B'\hat{A}'F'$, or not (III 9·3 and 7·5). Hence $E\hat{A}F \simeq E'\hat{A}'F'$ (38, 39). But $AE, AF \simeq A'E', A'F'$. Hence $EF \simeq E'F'$ (23) and the Theorem follows.

The Isosceles Birectangle

68. If $[ADC]$, $AD \simeq DC$; $AH, CL \perp HL$, and H, D, L colline, then $[HDL]$ and $AH \simeq CL$, $AHD \simeq CLD$.

Dem. Take L' so that $[HDL']$, $DL' \simeq DH$, then we have

$$CL' \perp HL,\ L = L' \ (50).$$

68·1. *Def.* If M is mid KL and $MX \perp KL$, then MX is the '*right bisector*' of KL, (KL is here properly an interval but we omit the interval sign).

·2. If MX is the right bisector of KL then $KX \simeq XL$.

·3. If $KX \simeq XL$ and $XY \perp KL$ then XY is the right bisector of KL.

·4. If $KX \simeq XL$ and $KY \simeq YL$ then XY is the right bisector of KL.

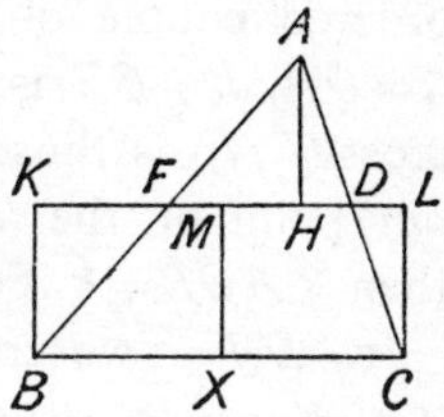

Fig. 41

69. If KB, $LC \perp KL$ and B, C be on the same side of KL and $KB \simeq LC$, then the right bisector of KL is the right bisector of BC and $K\hat{B}C \simeq L\hat{C}B$.

[It should be specially noted here that we do *not* use the properties of Euclidean parallels.]

Dem. Let MX be the right bisector of KL. It cannot meet KB (59·2), hence it meets $B-L$ (II 16·1). Similarly since it cannot meet LC, it meets $B-C$ in X say. Thus $KX \simeq LX$ (68·2), $M\hat{K}X \simeq M\hat{L}X$, $K\hat{X}M \simeq L\hat{X}M$. Since B, C are on the same side of KM, so are B, X since $[BXC]$ (III 2), hence $[KX$ is in $M\hat{K}B$ or $[KB$ in $M\hat{K}X$ or $[KB = [KX$ (III 9). In the two latter cases MX and KB would meet, hence $[KX$ is in $M\hat{K}B$; similarly $[LX$ is in $M\hat{L}C$. Hence $X\hat{K}B \simeq X\hat{L}C$ (39·1) and $XB \simeq XC$, $B\hat{X}K \simeq C\hat{X}L$. Similarly we can shew $[XK$ is in $B\hat{X}M$, and $[XL$ in $C\hat{X}M$ whence $B\hat{X}M \simeq C\hat{X}M$.

·1. With the hypothesis of 69, BC and KL do not meet (59·2).

·2. *Def.* A quadrilateral $KBCL$ satisfying the conditions of 69 is an '*isosceles birectangle*.'

70. If ABC be a triangle and F be mid AB and D be mid AC, then the right bisector of BC is perpendicular to FD.

Dem. Let AH, BK, $CL \perp FD$ and H, K, L be on FD. Then since $[AFB]$ $[ADC]$ (14·1) we have $KB \simeq HA$, $CL \simeq HA$ (68), and B, C are on the same side of KL. Hence by 69.

The Cross

71. *Def.* A '*cross*'* is an ordered couple of distinct lines which meet. (This def. will subsequently be extended to any ordered couple of lines, VI 22·2.) The cross (l_1, l_2) where $l_1 = OA$, $l_2 = OB$ is written $\measuredangle AOB$ or $\measuredangle l_1 l_2$. The '*opposite*' cross (l_2, l_1) is thus written $\measuredangle BOA$ or $\measuredangle l_2 l_1$. Hence if X be *any* point on the *line* OA and Y *any* point on the *line* OB, then $\measuredangle AOB = \measuredangle XOY$. (Cf. I 4.)

·1. *Def.* Two crosses $\measuredangle AOB$, $\measuredangle XPY$ are '*congruent*' ($\simeq$) if and only if *either* $A\hat{O}B \simeq X\hat{P}Y$ and $OA\hat{,}OB$ and $PX\hat{,}PY$ have the same sense (III 17) *or* $A\hat{O}B$ and $X\hat{P}Y$ are supplementary and $OA\hat{,}OB$ and $PX\hat{,}PY$ have opposite senses. Thus $A\hat{O}B \simeq X\hat{P}Y$ implies either

$$\measuredangle AOB \simeq \measuredangle XPY \text{ or } \measuredangle AOB \simeq \measuredangle YPX,$$

and each of the latter implies that $A\hat{O}B$, $X\hat{P}Y$ are congruent or supplementary.

·2. *Note.* The reader can acquire an intuitive idea of the congruence of crosses by noting that $\measuredangle AOB \simeq \measuredangle XOY$, if and only if the *line* OY is got from the *line* OX by the rotation equal in magnitude and sense to that which brings the *line* OA into the position of the *line* OB. It will be found later that the use of the cross instead of the angle leads to a great simplification in proofs. We omit the sign $\measuredangle$ when this is possible without ambiguity.

72. *If* $AB \simeq AC$ *then* $\measuredangle ABC \simeq BCA$ *and conversely* (III 17·9·93).

73. *If* B, C, D *colline then* $\measuredangle ABC \simeq ABD$ *and conversely.*

74. *If* $AB \perp BC$ *then* $\measuredangle ABC \simeq CBA$ *and conversely* (III 17·02·83).

75. *Def.* If $\measuredangle AOX \simeq XOB$ then OX '*bisects*' $\measuredangle AOB$.

·1. If OX bisects $\measuredangle AOB$ then [OX bisects one of $A\hat{O}B$, $A\hat{O}B'$, $A'\hat{O}B$, $A'\hat{O}B'$ where [AOA'] [BOB'].

76. *If* $\measuredangle AOB \simeq A'O'B'$, $\measuredangle BOC \simeq B'O'C'$ *and* A, O, C *do not colline then* $\measuredangle AOC \simeq A'O'C'$.

* Picken, *Math. Gazette*, Dec. 1922, p. 188; *Trans. London Math. Soc.* 1924, XXIII, p. 45. The word 'cross' was suggested in this connection by Prof. E. H. Neville.

Dem. Let X be on OB. There are points Y, X', Y' on OC, $O'B'$, $O'C'$ resp. such that $OA,\hat{}OX$, $OX,\hat{}OY$, $O'A',\hat{}O'X'$ and $O'X',\hat{}O'Y'$ have the same sense (III 17·95). Then

$$A\hat{O}X \simeq A'\hat{O}'X', \; X\hat{O}Y \simeq X'\hat{O}'Y',$$

and there is no ray both in $A\hat{O}X$ and in $X\hat{O}Y$ (III 17·86). Similarly for the dashed angles. Hence $A\hat{O}Y \simeq A'\hat{O}'Y'$ (38). Also by 38 *Dem.* $[O'X'$ is in $A'\hat{O}'Y'$ or not, according as $[OX$ is in $A\hat{O}Y$ or not. Hence $A\hat{O}Y, A'\hat{O}'Y'$ have the same sense (III 17·87·88). Hence $\measuredangle AOY \simeq A'O'Y'$ and the Theorem follows.

77. *If* $\measuredangle AOB \simeq B'O'A'$, $\measuredangle BOC \simeq C'O'B'$ *and* A, O, C *do not colline then* $\measuredangle AOC \simeq C'O'A'$.

Dem. Similar to 76.

78. If $\measuredangle AOB \simeq COD$ and A, O, C do not colline then $\measuredangle AOC \simeq BOD$.

Dem. Since $\measuredangle AOB \simeq COD$ and $\measuredangle BOC \simeq BOC$ the Theorem follows by 77.

·1. If $OA,\hat{}OB$ and $OC,\hat{}OD$ have the same sense and $A\hat{O}B \simeq C\hat{O}D$ then $OA,\hat{}OC$ and $OB,\hat{}OD$ have the same sense and $A\hat{O}C \simeq B\hat{O}D$, unless A, O, C colline and then B, O, D colline.

We now turn to solid Geometry. As we do not assume any parallel Axiom our proofs are usually quite different from those of Euclid Book XI.

Space. Perpendicular Lines and Planes

79. *If* O, A, B, C *coplane and* $OP \perp OA$, OC *and* $OA \ne OC$ *then* $OP \perp OB$.

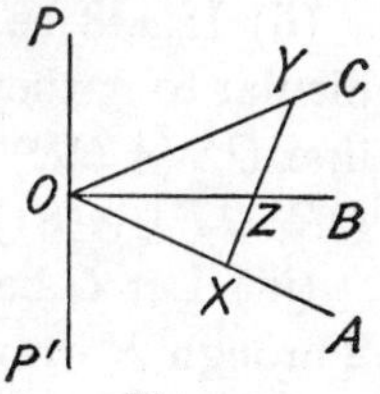

Fig. 42

Dem. We may suppose $OB \ne OA, OC$, then there is a line in the plane OAB which meets OA, OB, OC resp. in X, Z, Y, say, distinct from O (III 14). Suppose $[XZY]$. Take P' with $[POP']$, $OP' \simeq OP$. Then $PX \simeq P'X$, $PY \simeq P'Y$ (68·2). Hence

$$P\hat{X}Y \simeq P'\hat{X}Y, \text{ i.e. } P\hat{X}Z \simeq P'\hat{X}Z.$$

Hence $PZ \simeq P'Z$ and $OP \perp OZ$ (68·4).

·1. *Note.* That P is not in plane AOB follows by 49·1; we have not used this fact.

80. *If* $OP \perp OA, OB, OC$ *then* O, A, B, C *coplane.*

Dem. We may suppose OA, OB, OC distinct, then P is not in AOB (49·1). Hence OAB, OPC meet in a line through O, say in b (II 29). Since b is in plane AOB and through O, we have $OP \perp b$ (79). But $OP \perp OC$, and b, OC are in plane OPC. Hence $b = OC$ (49·1). Hence OC is in plane AOB.

·1. *Def.* If $OP \perp OA, OB$, and $OA \neq OB$, then we say OP and the plane OAB are '*perpendicular*' and write $OP \perp OAB$, $OAB \perp OP$.

81. If $OP \perp OAB$ and $C (\neq O)$ is in OAB then $OP \perp OC$ (79).

·1. *Notation.* We shall often denote planes by small Greek letters, lines by small Latin letters; $\alpha\beta$ means the line in which α, β meet; Pg the plane through P and g; if h, k coplane then (hk) means their plane.

82. *Through a given point* O *goes one and only one plane perpendicular to a given line* g *and this plane can be constructed by* **abcd**$_1$ and

e (i) *Given a plane, a point not on it can be found* (II 19).

(ii) *Given three non-collinear points, the plane through them can be found* (II 14).

(iii) *If two planes meet, the line in which they meet can be found* (II 29).

Dem. (i) Let O be on g. Through g draw two distinct planes β, γ and lines OP, OQ on β, γ resp. perpendicular to g (49). Then $OP \neq OQ$; $POQ \perp g$ (80·1). Hence there is at least one plane $\alpha = POQ$ through O perpendicular to g.

(ii) If α, δ be two distinct planes through O (on g) perpendicular to g, they meet in a line OR say (II 29) and there is a line $OS (\neq OR)$ on α and a line $OT (\neq OR)$ on β. Since OS, OR, $OT \perp g$ (81) they coplane (80) contrary to $\alpha \neq \delta$ (II 14).

(iii) Let O be not on g. Draw $OP \perp g$, with P on g (49·2). Through P draw $\alpha \perp g$ (i). Then if PA, PB be distinct lines $\neq OP$ and on α they are perpendicular to g (81). But $OP \perp g$, hence O is in $APB = \alpha$ (80). Hence α is a plane through O perpendicular to g.

(iv) If α, β be distinct planes through O (not on g) perpendicular to g, they meet g in distinct points P, Q say (by ii) and $OP, OQ \perp g$ (81) which is impossible (49·3) since OP, OQ lie in a plane.

83. *Through a given point O goes one and only one line perpendicular to a given plane α and this line can be constructed by* **abcd₁e**.

*Dem.** (i) Let O be on α, then not more than one line through O is perpendicular to α. For if $OP, OQ \perp \alpha$, $(OP \neq OQ)$, then OPQ meets α in OR say and $OP, OQ \perp OR$ (81) which is impossible since O, P, Q, R coplane (49·1).

(ii) If $\alpha = BOC$ (and thus B, O, C do not colline), through O draw planes $\beta \perp OB$ and $\gamma \perp OC$ (82). Then $\beta \neq \gamma$ by (i). Hence β, γ meet in OA say, and $OA \perp OB, OC$ (81). Hence $OA \perp OBC$ (80·1). Hence the Theorem when O is on α.

(iii) Let O be not on α, then there cannot be two perpendiculars OP, OQ from O to α; for if P, Q be on α then would $OP, OQ \perp PQ$ (81) contrary to 49·3.

(iv) Let O be not on α, and let AB be any line in α. Draw $OQ \perp AB$, with Q on AB (49·2). Draw $QR \perp AB$, with QR on α; $OP \perp RQ$, with P on RQ. If $P = Q$ then $OP \perp \alpha$ (80·1). If $P \neq Q$ then $OP \perp PQ$. Let $[OPO']$, $OP \simeq PO'$ then $OQ \simeq O'Q$ (68·2). Since $OQ, QP \perp AB$ therefore $O'Q \perp AB$ (79) and $A\hat{Q}O' \simeq A\hat{Q}O$. But $OQ \simeq O'Q$, hence $AO \simeq AO'$, $O\hat{P}A \simeq O'\hat{P}A$, $OP \perp PA$. But $OP \perp PQ$, hence $OP \perp APQ$ (60·1).

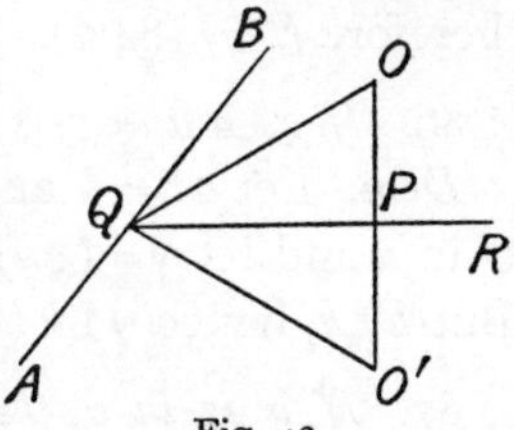

Fig. 43

84. *If planes OAB, $O'A_1B_1$ are perpendicular to OO' and meet $\alpha = OAA_1$ in OA, $O'A_1$ resp. and meet $\beta = OBB_1$ in OB, $O'B_1$ resp. where A, A_1 are on the same side of OO' in α and B, B_1 on the same side of OO' in β, then*

$$A\hat{O}B \simeq A_1\hat{O}'B_1.$$

Dem. Take A', B' so that $OA \simeq O'A'$, $OB \simeq O'B'$, $[A_1O'A']$, $[B_1O'B']$. Then since $A\hat{O}O' \simeq A'\hat{O}'O$, $B\hat{O}O' \simeq B'\hat{O}'O$, therefore

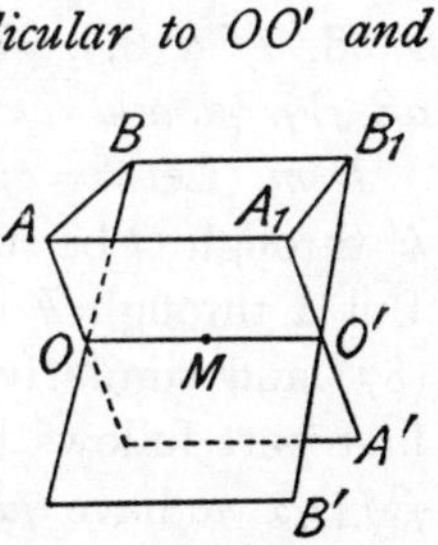

Fig. 44

* The proof given in Vahlen, *Abstrakte Geometrie* (1905), p. 244, is not sound, as it stands.

AA', BB' meet OO' at its mid-point M (58·1) and AM, $BM \simeq A'M, B'M$; $A\hat{M}B \simeq A'\hat{M}B'$. Whence $AB \simeq A'B'$, which with OA, $OB \simeq O'A'$, $O'B'$ gives the Theorem.

84·1. *Def.* With the hyp. of 84, if $\alpha_1 = \{OO', A\}$, $\beta_1 = \{OO', B\}$ then the '*measure*,' $\mu\widehat{\alpha_1\beta_1}$, of $\widehat{\alpha_1\beta_1}$ is $\mu A\hat{O}B$.

·2. *Def.* With the hyp. of 84, $\alpha \perp \beta$ means $OA \perp OB$.

·3. If α, β be half planes through O and $OP \perp \alpha$, $OQ \perp \beta$ then $\mu\widehat{\alpha\beta} = \mu P\hat{O}Q$ or $\pi - \mu P\hat{O}Q$ (39·1, 50).

85. If $\alpha \perp \beta$ then $\beta \perp \alpha$.

·1. If $\alpha \perp \beta$ and $\gamma \perp \alpha\beta$ (81·1) then $\alpha\beta$, $\beta\gamma$, $\gamma\alpha$ are mutually perpendicular (i.e. each is so to each) and so are α, β, γ. Also $\alpha \perp \beta\gamma$, and $\beta \perp \gamma\alpha$.

Dem. $\gamma \perp \alpha\beta$; hence $\beta\gamma \perp \alpha\beta$ and $\gamma\alpha \perp \alpha\beta$ (81). But $\alpha \perp \beta$, hence $\beta\gamma \perp \alpha\gamma$ (84·2). Thence $\alpha\beta, \beta\gamma, \gamma\alpha$ are mutually perpendicular. Since $\beta\gamma \perp \alpha\beta$ and $\beta\gamma \perp \alpha\gamma$, therefore $\beta\gamma \perp \alpha$ (80·1). Similarly $\gamma\alpha \perp \beta$. Since $\beta\gamma \perp \alpha$ and $\alpha\beta \perp \gamma\alpha$, therefore $\beta \perp \gamma$ (84·2). Similarly $\alpha \perp \gamma$.

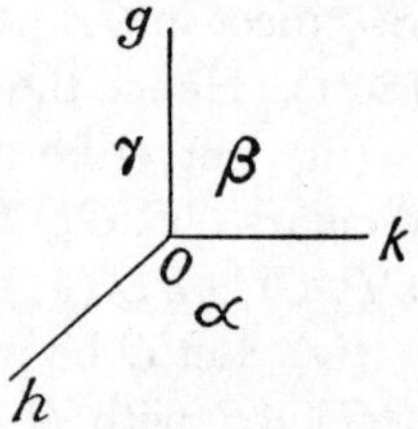

Fig. 45

86. *If $g \perp \alpha$ and g is on β then $\alpha \perp \beta$.*

Dem. Let $\alpha\beta = k$ and let g, α meet in O. Draw $h \perp k$ through O in α and let $\gamma = (gh)$. Then since $g \perp \alpha$ we have $g \perp h, k$ (81). But $h \perp k$, hence $\gamma \perp k$ (80·1). Hence $g \perp h$ gives $\alpha \perp \beta$ (84·2).

87. *If a is in α, there is one and only one plane through a perpendicular to α.*

Dem. There is one by 86, 83 and only one by 83, 84·2.

88. *If α, β, γ through O are mutually perpendicular so are $\alpha\beta$, $\beta\gamma$, $\gamma\alpha$, and conversely.*

Dem. Let $k = \alpha\beta$, $h = \gamma\alpha$. If k be not perpendicular to γ, let k' through O be such a line (83). Then $k \neq k'$ and $hk' \perp \gamma$ (86). But α through h is also perpendicular to γ. Hence k' is on α (87) and similarly on β. Thus $k = k'$. Hence $k \perp \gamma$ and the first part follows by 85·1. For the converse, since $\alpha\beta \perp \gamma\alpha$ and $\beta\gamma \perp \gamma\alpha$ we have $\gamma\alpha \perp \beta$ (80·1). Hence 84·2 gives the result.

(Orthogonal) Projection

89. *If k be a line in α then all lines g perpendicular to α through points of k lie in a plane perpendicular to α.*

Dem. Let $g_1 \perp \alpha$ through O_1 on k, then $(g_1 k) \perp \alpha$ (86). Let γ be perpendicular to k through a point O_2 on k, then γ meets $(g_1 k)$ on the sole perpendicular to α at O_2 (85·1). Hence all perpendicular lines to α through points of k lie on $(g_1 k)$.

90. *Two lines g, h perpendicular to α are coplanar* (89).

91. *If k be a line not on α and not perpendicular to α then all lines g perpendicular to α through points of k lie in a plane perpendicular to α* (90, 86).

·1. *Def.* If $[P]$ be a set of points and perpendiculars be drawn from them to a plane α or a line a, the points in which they meet α or a constitute the '*projection*' of $[P]$ on α or a.

·2. The projection on a plane of a line not on it or perpendicular to it, is a line.

·3. If h be the projection on α of the line k, the perpendiculars on h from points of k are perpendicular to α; the perpendiculars to α at points of h meet k; h and k lie in a plane perpendicular to α.

Congruence of Space Figures

92. *Space is congruent to itself in such a way that to a given point A, ray $[AB$ from A, side $\{AB,C\}$ of AB and side $\{ABC,D\}$ of ABC correspond resp. a given point A', ray $[A'B'$ from A', side $\{A'B',C'\}$ of $A'B'$ and side $\{A'B'C',D'\}$ of $A'B'C'$.*

Dem. Make A, $[AB$, $\{AB,C\}$ correspond to A', $[A'B'$, $\{A'B',C'\}$ by a congruence (67). Let P be any point not on ABC; $PF \perp ABC$; F on ABC. Let F' on $A'B'C'$ correspond to F, let $P'F' \perp A'B'C'$, P' on $\{A'B'C',D'\}$ or on the opposite side of $A'B'C'$ according as P is on $\{ABC,D\}$ or on the opposite side of ABC, and let $P'F' \simeq PF$. Make P' correspond to P. The correspondence is one-to-one (83, **C** I) and is easily shewn to be a congruence.

93. If O, A, B, C do not coplane then $\mu A\hat{O}B + \mu A\hat{O}C > \mu B\hat{O}C$.

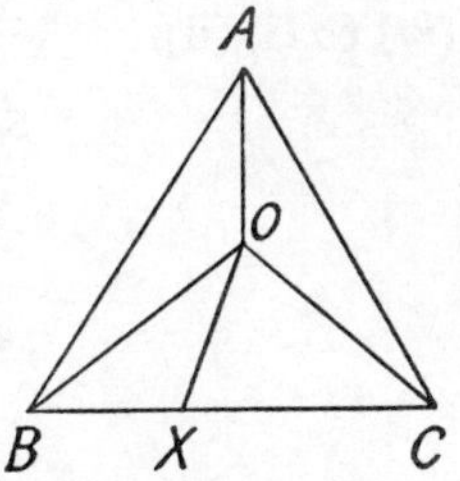

Fig. 46

Dem. If $\mu A\hat{O}B$ or $\mu A\hat{O}C$ is $\geqq \mu B\hat{O}C$, the Theorem is clear. If $\mu B\hat{O}C > \mu A\hat{O}B$, $\mu A\hat{O}C$

there is a ray $[OX$ in $B\hat{O}C$ with $B\hat{O}A \simeq B\hat{O}X$, and $[OX$ meets $B-C$ in X say. Let $OA \simeq OX$. Then $AB \simeq BX$.

But $$\mu AB + \mu AC > \mu BC = \mu BX + \mu XC \ (64).$$

Hence $$\mu AC > \mu XC,\ \mu A\hat{O}C > \mu X\hat{O}C \ (66\cdot 1).$$

But $$\mu B\hat{O}C = \mu B\hat{O}X + \mu X\hat{O}C.$$

Hence the Theorem.

94. If $A \neq B$, the set of points P such that $PA \simeq PB$ is the set of points on the plane perpendicular to AB through mid AB.

·1. *Def.* This plane is the '*right bisector*' plane of AB.

95. *Dihedral angles with the same measure are congruent* (92, 84·1).

96. *If in two trihedral angles* (III 25·3) (i) *two faces and their included angle or* (ii) *three faces or* (iii) *two angles and their common face or* (iv) *three angles of the one be congruent to the corresponding parts of the other, then the other angles and faces of the first are congruent to the corresponding parts of the other.*

Dem. (i) is equivalent to: If $\hat{\alpha\beta}$ with edge l and $\hat{\alpha'\beta'}$ with edge l' be congruent dihedral angles and a plane through a point P of l meets α, β resp. in rays r, s and similarly for the other figure, and if $\hat{rt} \simeq \hat{r't'}$, $\hat{st} \simeq \hat{s't'}$ for some rays t, t' of l, l' resp., then $\hat{rs} \simeq \hat{r's'}$. But this follows by 95.

(ii) If $O.A\hat{B}C$ and $O'.A'\hat{B'}C'$ are the trihedral angles, let $OA \simeq O'A'$; $ABC \perp OA$; $A'B'C' \perp O'A'$, then from the hyp. we easily shew $B\hat{A}C \simeq B'\hat{A'}C'$.

To shew (iii) and (iv) we may draw rays perpendicular to the faces of each trihedral angle at its vertex, the rays to be outside* the trihedral angle. Then by 84·3 we can reduce (iii) (iv) to (i) (ii).

* See XII 1·1 based on Axioms O.

CHAPTER V

THE CIRCLE AXIOMS

Introductory Remarks

This chapter may be considered as a continuation of the last, and its purpose is two-fold. First, we wish to deduce those properties of the circle and the sphere which do not depend on the Parallel Axiom. Among these, the most important are the properties of tangents. Secondly, we begin the process of reducing the number of Axioms.

The investigations of the last chapter shew that, given any plane figure we can make an exact copy of it in some other place. For instance we can make a triangle congruent to a given triangle (IV 55). But we cannot yet draw a triangle whose three sides have given measures. To do this, when possible, we need some Theorem which states that under certain conditions two circles intersect, and for this reason we introduce a new Axiom **Q**. This Axiom, as will be shewn in a later chapter, cannot be deduced from the earlier Axioms; but, as we shall see, it enables us to drop **C** VI and **C** VII, if we retain **C** I—V.

In deducing the properties of tangents, we may not use 'the method of limits' since we have not introduced any continuity considerations. Neither shall we in this chapter use any Parallel Axioms. Our Theorems are hence true in Hyperbolic Geometry.

§ 1. Basis $\mathbf{O}_p$ $\mathbf{C}_p$.

The Circle and its Tangents

1. *Defs.* If A, P be distinct points, the set of points $[X]$ in a plane α such that $OX \simeq AP$, where O is fixed in α, is a '*circle*,' of which O is the '*centre*' and $O \vdash X$ a '*radius*.' If $[XOY]$ and X, Y be on the circle, then $X \vdash Y$ is a '*diameter*.' A point Q is '*inside*' the circle, centre O, radius OX, if $\mu OQ < \mu OX$ or if $Q = O$. A point Q is '*outside*' that circle if $\mu OQ > \mu OX$.

2. If O be any point in any plane α and AP be any interval, then in α there is a circle centre O with radius congruent to AP (**C** I).

·1. Any given point in the plane α is either inside, outside, or on that circle, and only one of these statements is true for a given point (IV 13).

·2. Any ray from the centre of a circle, in its plane, meets the circle in one point only (**C** I).

·3. *Def.* If A, B, C, D be distinct points on a circle centre O, then B, D '*separate*' A, C, if and only if $[OB$, $[OD$ separate $[OA$, $[OC$ (III 24·1).

·4. The Theorems III 24·1 to ·6 can clearly be interpreted on the circle.

3. If A, B be on a circle centre O, and M $(\neq O)$ be the mid-point of AB then $OM \perp AB$; and if $OM \perp AB$ and M be on AB, then M is the mid-point of AB (IV 68·3·4).

·1. If two circles, centres O, P, with $O \neq P$, have common points A, B then OP is the right bisector of AB (IV 68·4).

4. *Two distinct circles cannot meet in more than two points* (**C** VI, I and IV 17).

·1. *A line and a circle cannot meet in more than two points.*

Dem. Suppose P, Q, S be on a circle centre O and let $[PQS]$. If O be not on PS then $\mu OQ < \mu OP$ or $\mu OQ < \mu OS$ (IV 65). If O is on PS the Theorem follows by **C** I.

·2. If P, S be on or inside a circle, centre O and $[PQS]$ then Q is inside the circle (IV 65).

·3. If P, S be on a circle, centre O and $[PSQ]$ then Q is outside the circle.

·4. *A line which has a point P on, and a point Q inside a circle, centre O, has one other point on the circle.*

Dem. Let $OR \perp PQ$, R on PQ. Then $R \neq P$, since $R = P$ gives $\mu OP < \mu OQ$ (IV 63). Take S so that $RS \simeq PR$, $[PRS]$, then $OP \simeq OS$; thus S is on the circle.

·5. *Note.* We do not yet know whether a line through an inside and an outside point of a circle must meet the circle.

·6. *Def.* A set of points on a circle is called '*cyclic.*' If

$ABCD$ be a quadrilateral (III 11·1) and A, B, C, D be cyclic then $ABCD$ is a '*cyclic quadrilateral.*'

5. If A, B, C, D be cyclic points and A, C be on opposite sides of BD then the polygon $ABCD$ is simple (III 12·1) and hence a cyclic quadrilateral. Conversely if $ABCD$ is a cyclic quadrilateral, then A, C are on opposite sides of BD and A^-C, B^-D meet.

Dem. To shew the second part, suppose, if possible that A, C were on the same side of BD, then since $BA \neq BC$, either $[BA$ is in $D\hat{B}C$ or $[BC$ in $D\hat{B}A$ (III 9). Suppose the latter, then $[BC$ meets A^-D in X say (III 7) and X is inside the circle (4·2) and hence $[BXC]$ (4·3). Hence B^-C meets A^-D, and the polygon is not simple, cont. hyp. Similarly $[BA$ is not in $D\hat{B}C$ and hence A, C are on opposite sides of BD. Whence A^-C meets BD (III 2). Similarly B^-D meets AC.

6*. If P be a point on a circle centre O and $O\hat{P}X$ be a right angle, then PX meets the circle in P only. (O, P, X and the circle are supposed coplanar.)

Dem. If PX and the circle met also in Q then $OP \simeq OQ$. But since $O\hat{P}Q$ is a right angle, $\mu OP < \mu OQ$ (IV 63).

·1. *Def.* A line which meets a coplanar circle in one point only, is called a '*tangent*' to the circle at that point and is said to '*touch*' the circle there.

·2. If PX touch a circle at P, no point of PX is inside the circle (4·4).

·3. If PX meet a circle, centre O, at P and no point of PX is inside the circle, then PX is a tangent at P. (O, P, X and the circle are supposed coplanar.)

Dem. If PX meet the circle also in S and $[PQS]$ then Q is inside the circle (4·2).

·4. If PX touch a circle, centre O, at P then $O\hat{P}X$ is a right angle.

Dem. If not, let $OQ \perp PX$, Q on PX. Then $Q \neq P$,

$$\mu OQ < \mu OP \quad \text{(IV 63)}$$

and hence Q is inside the circle, contrary to ·2.

* In a great many school texts, the proofs of these simple propositions are fallacious.

6·5. *If P be a point on a circle, there is one and only one tangent to the circle at P* (6, 6·4, IV 50).

·6. If PX be a tangent to a circle at P, then all points on the circle, save P, are on the same side of PX.

Dem. If A, B were on the circle and on opposite sides of PX, then $A{-}B$ would meet PX (III 2) in a point inside the circle (4·2) contrary to ·2.

7. If $XY \perp OA$, and $XZ \perp OB$ and Y, Z be on OA, OB resp. and if $XY \simeq XZ$, then $[OX$ bisects $A\hat{O}B$ or $A_1\hat{O}B$ or $A\hat{O}B_1$ or $A_1\hat{O}B_1$ where $[AOA_1]$ $[BOB_1]$. (Use III 9·1.)

·1. And if $[OX$ bisects any of these angles then $XY \simeq XZ$.

·2. *The. and Def.* If ABC be a triangle there is a point I inside $\triangle ABC$ such that, if IX, IY, IZ be perpendicular to BC, CA, AB resp. and X, Y, Z be on these lines, then $IX \simeq IY \simeq IZ$. Such a point is unique and is the '*incentre*' of the triangle.

Dem. The bisectors of $A\hat{B}C$, $B\hat{C}A$ lie in their respective angles and hence they meet $C{-}A$, $C{-}B$ resp. in M, N say, and hence they meet each other in a point I inside the triangle (II 11·6). Thence by ·1.

·3. The three bisectors of the three angles of a triangle concur.

·4. If $IX \perp BC$, X on BC, and I be the incentre of $\triangle ABC$ then $[BXC]$.

Dem. $[BCX]$ or $C = X$ gives $\mu B\hat{C}I \geqq \pi/2$ (IV 60). Similarly if $[XBC]$ or $X = B$. But the measure of the half of any angle is $< \pi/2$ (IV 57·6).

·5. The circle centre I, radius IX, (above notation) touches BC, CA, AB resp. in X, Y, Z.

8. If O, P, Q colline, and $O \neq P$, the circles through Q with centres O, P meet in Q only (IV 17).

·1. *Def.* Two circles which meet in one point only, are said to '*touch*' there.

·2. If two coplanar circles, centres O, P, touch at Q, the tangent QX at Q to the circle, centre O, is the tangent at Q to the circle, centre P.

Dem. If QX is not tangent to the circle, centre P, then since $O\hat{Q}X$ is a right angle while $P\hat{Q}X$ is not (6, 6·4), therefore O, P, Q do not colline. Take S so that $P\hat{O}S \simeq P\hat{O}Q$, $OS \simeq OQ$; S, Q

on opposite sides of OP, then $PS \simeq PQ$ and $S \neq Q$. Thus S is on both circles, cont. hyp.

8·3. If two coplanar circles, centres O, P, touch at Q, then O, P, Q are collinear.

Dem. The perpendicular to their common tangent at Q (·2) goes through O, P (6·4).

§ 2. *A Circle Axiom and the reduction of the Congruence Axioms*

9. *Note.* We do not yet know whether a line through a point inside a coplanar circle must meet it, or if a circle through a point inside a coplanar circle and a point outside it, must meet the latter circle. To secure these properties we introduce an Axiom which, as we shall see later, does not follow from **O, C**.

Ax. Q. If a circle, centre *A*, has a point inside and a point outside a circle, centre *C*, which lies in the same plane as the first circle, and the two points are on *AC* then the circles meet in at least one point on each side of *AC*.

We shall soon remove the restriction that the points are on *AC*.

Construction q. *If two circles meet and lie in the same plane, and their centres and a point on each be given, then their points of meeting can be found.*

·1. *Note.* In the presence of $\mathbf{O}_p$, $\mathbf{C}_p$ we need only assume one point of meeting can be found, the other can then be constructed by $\mathbf{abcd}_1$, using 3. On the other hand, we now shew that if Ax. **Q** be assumed we can shew **C** VI, VII from our other Axioms **O, C**.

10. **O, C** I—V, **Q** *imply* **C** VI, VII (re-quoted below). We shew this in 10·1 to 16.

·1. *Def.* A triangle of which every two sides are congruent is called '*equilateral.*'

11. (**O, C** I—IV, **Q**.) *Given any interval AB we can find a point C on a given side of AB, by means of* **q**, *such that ABC is an equilateral triangle.*

12. **O**, **C** I—V, **Q** *imply* **M**: *Every interval AB has at least one mid-point O.*

Dem. We can find C, C' on opposite sides of AB so that ABC, ABC' are equilateral triangles (11). Then C-C' meets AB in O, say (III 2), and $O \neq A, B$ (IV 17). Apply IV 21 to triangles ACC', BCC' and we find $A\hat{C}O \simeq B\hat{C}O$; then IV 23 on triangles ACO, BCO gives $AO \simeq BO$, whence O is a mid-point of AB. (Note that IV 17, 21, 23 follow from **O**, **C** I—V.)

That AB *has only one mid-point* O *and that* $[AOB]$ follows from **O**, **C** I—IV (IV 14·1·2).

13. **O**, **C** I—V, **M** *imply* **C** VI: *If $P\hat{Q}R$ be any angle, $[AC$ any ray, there are not more than two rays $[AB$ in a plane containing $[AC$ such that $C\hat{A}B \simeq P\hat{Q}R$.*

Dem. Suppose if possible that $[AB$, $[AB_1$, $[AB_2$ be distinct coplanar rays with $C\hat{A}B$, $C\hat{A}B_1$, $C\hat{A}B_2$ all congruent to $P\hat{Q}R$. None of B, B_1, B_2 can be on AC (IV 17), hence at least two, say B, B_1, are on the same side of AC. Let $AB \simeq AB_1$ then $CB \simeq CB_1$ (IV 23) and BB_1 cannot meet AC (IV 16). By **M**, BB_1 has a mid-point O, and $[BOB_1]$ (IV 14·1). Take E so that $[AOE]$. Since BB_1 meets A-E and not $A \vdash C$ it meets C-E in F, say (II 16·1). Thus AB, BO, OA, $AE \simeq AB_1$, B_1O, OA, AE and $[AOE]$. Hence $BE \simeq B_1E$ (IV 15). And CB, BE, EC, $CF \simeq CB_1$, B_1E, EC, CF and $[CFE]$. Hence $BF \simeq B_1F$ (IV 15, 17). Hence F is mid BB_1 and thus $F = O$ (12). But since $[AOE]$ $[CFE]$, therefore A, C, O colline and BB_1 meets AC contrary to IV 16. Hence **C** VI.

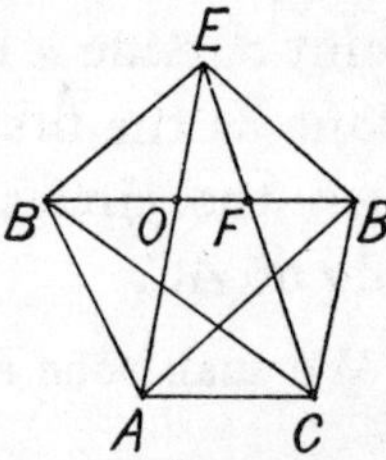

Fig. 47

·1. (**O**, **C** I—V, **Q**.) *The circles in* Ax. **Q** *meet in only one point on each side of* AC.

14. **O**, **C** I—V, **M** *imply* **C** VII *in a plane*; that is they imply: *if CA, DB coplane and be perpendicular to AB then $C\hat{A}B \simeq D\hat{B}A$.*

Dem. AB has a mid-point O (**M**) and $[AOB]$; there is a point T with $[COT]$, $CO \simeq OT$. Then by IV 26, 23 we find $O\hat{A}C \simeq O\hat{B}T$, whence $O\hat{B}T$

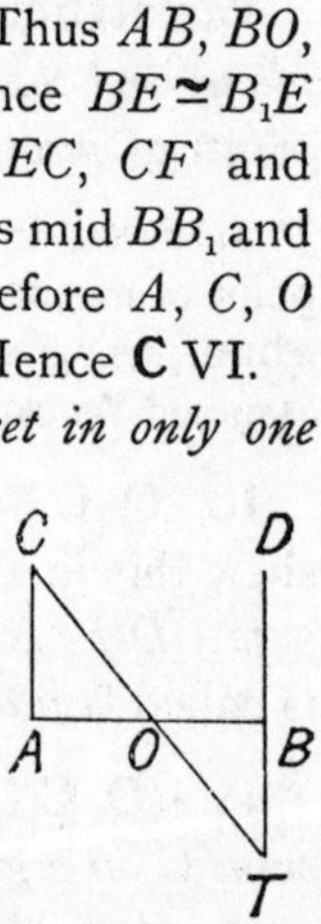

Fig. 48

is a right angle (IV 44). We may use this Theorem since it follows from **C** VI, without **C** VII, and since **C** VI holds by 13. Thus BT, $BD \perp OB$ and hence D, B, T colline (IV 50). But $DB \perp OB$, hence $O\hat{B}D \simeq O\hat{B}T$. Whence $O\hat{A}C \simeq O\hat{B}D$ and **C** VII is true in a plane.

15. **O, C** I—V, **Q** *imply: If* $B\hat{A}C$ *be any angle and* $\{A'Y, Z\}$ *any half plane, there is a point* X *on* $\{A'Y, Z\}$ *with* $B\hat{A}C \simeq Y\hat{A}'X$ *and it can be constructed by* **abcd₁q**.

Dem. Let $A'B' \simeq AB$, B' on $[A'Y$, and $B'D_1 \simeq B'D_2 \simeq BC$ and $A'E \simeq AC$ with D_1 on $[B'A'$, $[A'B'D_2]$ and E on $[A'B'$. Since $\mathbf{C}_p$ hold (14) we have $\mu AB + \mu BC > \mu AC$ (IV 64), and hence

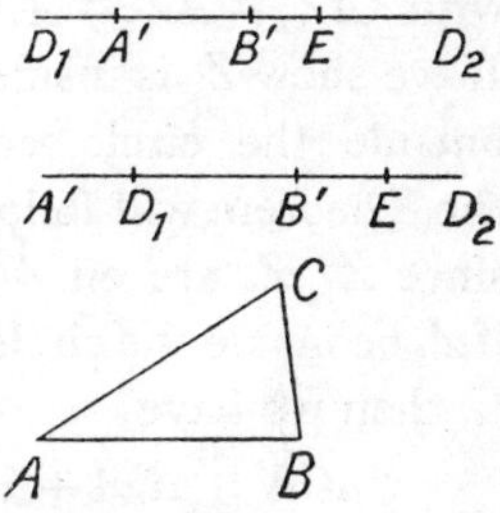

Fig. 49

$$\mu A'B' + \mu B'D_2 > \mu A'E ;$$

but $[A'B'D_2]$, hence $\mu A'D_2 > \mu A'E$; thus D_2 is *outside* the circle centre A', radius $A'E$.

Again if $\mu AB < \mu BC$, then

$$\mu A'B' < \mu B'D_1 \text{ and } [B'A'D_1].$$

Since $\mu BC < \mu AC + \mu AB$ we have $\mu B'D_1 < \mu A'E + \mu A'B'$. But $[B'A'D_1]$ gives $\mu B'D_1 = \mu A'D_1 + \mu A'B'$. Hence $\mu A'D_1 < \mu A'E$.

While if $\mu AB > \mu BC$ then $[A'D_1B']$; and since

$$\mu AB < \mu AC + \mu CB$$

we have $\mu A'B' < \mu A'E + \mu B'D_1$. But $[A'D_1B']$ gives

$$\mu A'B' = \mu A'D_1 + \mu B'D_1 .$$

Hence again $\mu A'D_1 < \mu A'E$.

Finally if $AB \simeq BC$ then $D_1 = A'$. Hence in all these cases, D_1 is *inside* the circle centre A', radius $A'E$. Hence by **Q** and 13·1, the circle centre B', radius $B'D_1$, meets the previous circle in just one point on each side of $A'B'$, and hence in just one point X on $\{A'Y, Z\}$. Then $B\hat{A}C \simeq Y\hat{A}'X$ (IV 21).

16. **O, C** I—V, **Q** *imply*: *Any two right angles* (coplanar or not) *are congruent* (15 and IV 54). *In particular they imply* **C** VII.

And now 10 follows from 12 to 16. In connection with this

deduction, the reader should note carefully the italicised statement in IV 51·1.

17. (A generalisation of **Q**.) *If a circle has a point outside and a point inside another circle in the same plane, the circles meet in just two points.*

Dem. Let the circle, centre A, have the point X outside and the point Y inside the circle centre C, radius CB. Take points Z_1 on $[AC$, Z_2 on $AC]$, with $AZ_1 \simeq AZ_2 \simeq AX \simeq AY$. If we shew Z_1 is inside and Z_2 outside the circle, centre C, the Theorem will follow by **Q**, since Z_1, Z_2 are on AC. Now if Z_2 be inside the circle, centre C, then we have

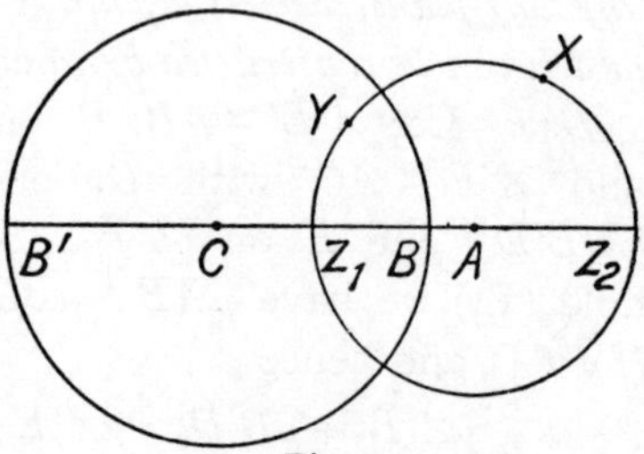

Fig. 50

$$\mu CX \leqq \mu CA + \mu AX = \mu CA + \mu AZ_2 = \mu CZ_2 < \mu CB;$$

hence X would be inside the circle centre C.

Similarly if Z_1 be outside the circle centre C, then considering the cases $[AZ_1C]$ and $[ACZ_1]$, we can shew that Y would be outside the circle. Hence the Theorem follows.

The Intersections of Lines and Circles

18. Instead of considering Axiom **Q** we might have considered

Ax. Q_1. A line which goes through a point inside a circle, and which lies in its plane, meets the circle.

Construction q_1. *If a line and a coplanar circle meet and the centre of the circle and a point on it are known, the points of meeting can be found.*

·1. By **O, C** I—VII, **Q_1** we can shew that the line and circle of Ax. **Q_1** meet in just two points (4·1·4).

·2. In the presence of **O, C** we need only assume that one point of meeting is found by **q_1**, the other can then be found by **abcd$_1$** (see 4·4).

·3. Note also that given the centre of a circle and a point

on it, the point where any ray *from the centre* meets the circle can be found by $\mathbf{abcd}_1$.

19. **O**, **C** I—V, **Q** *imply* $\mathbf{Q}_1$ *and imply also: A line l which goes through a point A inside a circle centre O, radius OX, and which is in the plane of the circle, meets the circle in just two points.*

Further relations between **O**, **C**, **Q**, $\mathbf{Q}_1$ will be considered later.

Dem. By 10 we can assume **C** VI, VII. Let $OB \perp l$, B on l. Then B is inside the circle, since $\mu OB \leqq \mu OA < \mu OX$. Now the circle meets $[OB$ in D say and $OB]$ in D' say. Take C, E with $[OBCE]$, $BC \simeq OB$, $CE \simeq OD$ and take E' on $[CB$ with $CE' \simeq OD$. Then E is outside the circle, since

$$\mu OE > \mu CE = \mu OD.$$

Further $\mu OD > \mu OB$ gives $\mu CE' > \mu CB$ and thus $[CBE']$. Also $[D'OC]$, E' is on $[CO$ and $CE' \simeq OD'$, hence $[CE'D']$, (IV 6) and this with $[CBE']$ $[DBD']$ gives $[DE'D']$, and thus

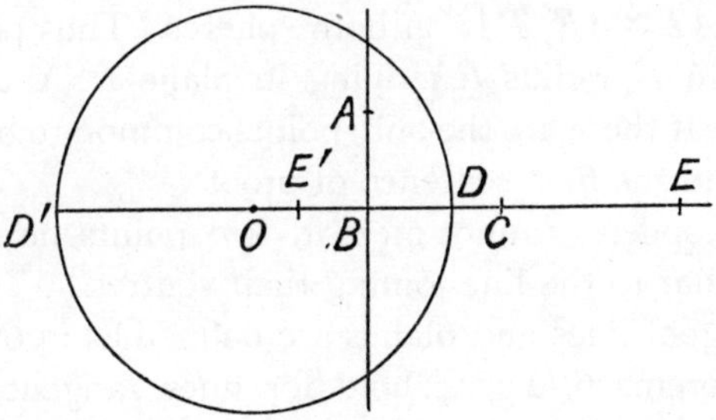

Fig. 51

E' is inside the circle. Hence the circle, centre C radius $CE \simeq CE'$, meets the original circle in two points P, Q, and $OP \simeq OQ \simeq CP \simeq CQ$. But since l is the right bisector of OC, therefore P, Q are on l (IV 68·4) and hence l meets the original circle in P, Q and there only (4·1).

The Sphere

§ 3. **Basis O C.**

20. *Defs.* If A, P be distinct points the set of points $[X]$ such that $OX \simeq AP$ is a '*sphere*' of which O is the '*centre*' and OX a '*radius*.' We define '*diameter*,' '*inside*,' '*outside*' as in 1.

20·1. A sphere and a plane through its centre meet in a circle with the same centre.

·2. Theorems 4·1·2·3·4 hold for a sphere.

·3. A plane α through a point Q on and a point P inside a sphere, centre O, meets the sphere in a circle, and P is inside the circle; all points inside the circle are inside the sphere.

Dem. If the plane goes through O, the Theorem is ·1. If not, then PQ meets the sphere again in R say (·2). Let $OF \perp \alpha$, F on α; let $OG \perp PQ$, G on PQ, then $O\hat{F}Q$, $O\hat{F}R$ are right angles and $OQ \simeq OR$. Hence $FQ \simeq FR$. Again if $FS \simeq FQ$ with S on α, then $OS \simeq OQ$. Thus the plane meets the sphere in a circle, centre F.

Also $\mu OP < \mu OQ$, hence $\mu FP < \mu FQ$ (IV 65·2, 83 iv).

·4. Two spheres, centres O, A with two points R, S common, meet in a circle lying in a plane perpendicular to OA.

Dem. If RX, $SY \perp OA$ and X, Y be on OA, then by congruence $X = Y$, $RX \simeq SX$. And if $TX \perp OA$ and $TX \simeq RX$, then T is in the plane $RSX \perp OA$, and since by congruence, $OT \simeq OR$, $AT \simeq AR$, T is on both spheres. Thus points on the circle centre X, radius RX, lying in plane RSX are on both spheres; that these are the only points common to both spheres follows from the first sentence of proof.

·5. Two spheres cannot meet in two points not in a plane perpendicular to the line joining their centres.

·6. Tangent lines and planes are defined as in 6·1.

·7. Theorems 6, 6·2·3·4 hold for lines tangent to spheres and 6·5·6 for tangent planes.

·8. The tangent lines to a sphere at P all lie in the tangent plane at P.

·81. *Def.* Two spheres which meet in one point only, are said to '*touch*' there.

·9. If two spheres touch at Q, they have the same tangent plane there.

·91. Theorems 8, 8·3 hold for spheres.

§ 4. **Basis O, C I—V, Q.**

21. *A plane α through a point P inside a sphere, centre O, meets it in a circle.*

Dem. A plane $\neq \alpha$, through OP meets the sphere in a circle C (20·1) and meets α in a line l say. Now l and C meet (19) since P is on l and inside C (20·3). Hence by 20·3.

22. *A sphere centre O, which goes through a point Q inside and a point P outside another sphere, centre A, meets it in a circle.*

Dem. The plane OPQ meets the sphere, centre O, in a circle (20·1) and the sphere, centre A, in a circle (21). These circles meet in two points (17) since Q is inside the latter circle and P outside (20·3). Hence by 20·4.

CHAPTER VI

THE PARALLEL AXIOMS

Introductory Remarks

The Theorem which distinguishes Euclidean Geometry from the other Geometries in which a congruence Theory holds is:

One and only one parallel to a given line goes through a given point not on the line.

We shall quote this as Axiom **P**. We saw in Chapter IV that from Axioms **O**, **C**, we could shew the existence of at least one parallel, so that with those Axioms it suffices to assume the parallel is unique. We shall weaken this statement as much as possible, and then proceed to deduce the elementary Theorems on parallels and parallelograms, and the rest of the elementary theory of the circle.

Two Theorems of great importance are considered in this chapter, viz. Pappus' Theorem and Desargues' Theorem. We shew the first from Theorems on the circle, using the 'cross' to avoid tedious enumeration of cases. The second is shewn from the consideration of parallels in space. As these Theorems are outstanding in Projective Geometry, we consider the relation of Euclidean Geometry to Projective Geometry, and give a logical treatment of ideas associated with the phrase 'parallel lines meet at infinity.'*

The Parallel Axioms and their first consequences

§ 1. 1. *Def.* Two distinct lines a, b in the same plane which do not meet are '*parallel*,' written $a \parallel b$. A line is also considered to be parallel to itself.

We now consider several 'Euclidean parallel Axioms' which differ in strength only.

Ax. P_0. There is *at least one* **line a and** *at least one* **point A not on a, such that not more than one parallel to a goes through A.**

* For a fuller treatment see Neville, "Prolegomena to Analytical Geometry" (1922), p. 247.

Ax. P_1. There is *at least one* plane α containing *at least one* line a such that, if A be *any* point of α not on a, then not more than one parallel to a goes through A.

We may vary this Axiom by affirming it for *any* plane or *any* line or *at least one point* for each line. Combining these variations we get the following Axioms, written in an easily understood form.

	P_1	P_2	P_3	P_0'	P_1'	P_2'	P_3'
Plane	One	One	One	Any	Any	Any	Any
Line	One	Any	Any	One	One	Any	Any
Point	Any	One	Any	One	Any	One	Any

Thus P_2 is: *There is at least one plane α, such that if a be any line on it, there is a point A not on a, but on α, such that not more than one parallel to a goes through A.* (Of course A need not be the same point for all the lines a.)

The strongest possible (Euclidean) parallel Axiom is:

Ax. P. One and only one parallel to a given line goes through a given point, not on the line.

We have seen that the part of this that asserts the existence of at least one parallel can be deduced from **O**, **C** (IV 59). We now investigate the part that asserts the uniqueness of this parallel.

1·1. *Axioms* **O**, **C**, P_1 *imply* **P**.

Dem. Let a' be any line, A' any point not on it, then in the plane $\alpha' = A'a'$ there is at least one line through A' not meeting a (IV 59). There is a congruence between α' and the plane α of Ax. P_1 wherein a' corresponds to the line a of that Ax. (IV 67). Suppose it is A on α that corresponds to A' on α'. If there were two distinct lines through A' in α' not meeting a', these would correspond in the congruence to two distinct lines through A in α not meeting a, contrary to P_1.

·2. Axioms **O**, **C**, P_0 or P_0' imply P_2'; **O**, **C**, P_2 imply P_2'; **O**, **C**, P_3 imply P_3' and hence **P**. (Shewn like ·1.)

·3. Thus it appears that Axioms which involve the assertion for *one* point only, e.g. P_0, P_0', P_2, P_2', while equivalent in the face of **O**, **C**, do not suffice to shew **P**; but the weakest Axiom which involves the assertion for *any* point, viz. $\mathbf{P}_1$, suffices to shew $\mathbf{P}$ in the presence of $\mathbf{O}$, $\mathbf{C}$.

2·1. If a, b are lines and $a \parallel b$ then $b \parallel a$ (Def.).

·2. ($\mathbf{O}$, $\mathbf{P}_3'$.) If a, b, c are lines and $a \parallel b$, $b \parallel c$ then $a \parallel c$*. (The three lines need not be coplanar.)

Dem. Since $a \parallel b$, therefore a, b coplane. Similarly b, c coplane. If a, b, c be all in the same plane and a, c met in X then two parallels to b would go through X, contrary to $\mathbf{P}_3'$. If a, b, c are not in the same plane, let $\boldsymbol{\alpha}$ be the plane through a and a point C on c; then $\boldsymbol{\alpha}$ meets the plane bC in a line c' say (II 29). If b, c' met, then a, b would meet (II 27). Hence $b \parallel c'$, hence $c = c'$ ($\mathbf{P}_3'$). Thus a, c coplane and if they met, a and b would meet (II 27). Hence $a \parallel c$.

·3. ($\mathbf{O}$, $\mathbf{P}_3'$.) *The relation* $\parallel$ *between lines is equable* (1, 2·1·2 and I 9).

·4. *Def.* If $ABCD$ is a polygon and $AB \parallel CD$, $BC \parallel AD$ then $ABCD$ is a '*parallelogram.*' The last phrase shall always mean $AB \parallel CD$ and $BC \parallel AD$, and A, B, C, D are not collinear.

3. ($\mathbf{O}_p$.) *If* $[AXY]$ *and* $XB \parallel YC$ *and* A, B, C *colline, then* $[ABC]$.

Dem. XB must meet either A–C or C⊢Y (II 16·1).

·1. ($\mathbf{O}_p$.) *If* $[XAY]$ *and* $XB \parallel YC$ *and* A, B, C *colline then* $[BAC]$.

Dem. If $[ABC]$ or $[ACB]$, Ax. $\mathbf{O}$ VI shews XB, YC meet.

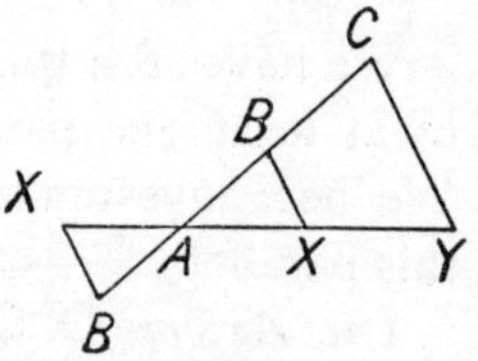

Fig. 52

·2. ($\mathbf{O}_p$.) If $[ABC]$ and $AX \parallel BY \parallel CZ$ and if X, Y, Z colline then $[XYZ]$.

Dem. A, X are on the same side of BY; so are C, Z. Thus $[ABC]$ gives $[XYZ]$ (III 2).

·3. ($\mathbf{O}_p$.) If $ABCD$ be a parallelogram, then B, D are on opposite sides of AC, and B–D, A–C meet.

Dem. A–B does not meet CD, nor does C–D meet AB, nor does A–D meet B–C. Hence by III 13.

·4. ($\mathbf{O}_p$.) A parallelogram is a quadrilateral (·3 and III 12·1).

* It is rather surprising that Euclid uses congruence Theorems to shew this, *Euclid* I, 30; XI, 9.

[The point to notice here is that a quadrilateral is a *simple* polygon (III 11·1).]

3·5. ($\mathbf{O}_p$.) If $ABCD$ be a parallelogram and X be on $[AB$ then $A{-}C$, $D{-}X$ meet. [As for ·3.]

·6. ($\mathbf{O}_p$.) If $ABCD$ be a parallelogram and X be on $[AB$ then X, D are on opposite sides of AC and A, C on opposite sides of XD.

·7. ($\mathbf{O}_p$.) If $CAYX$ be a parallelogram and $[COA]$ and $OY \parallel XB$ with B on CA then $[BOA]$.

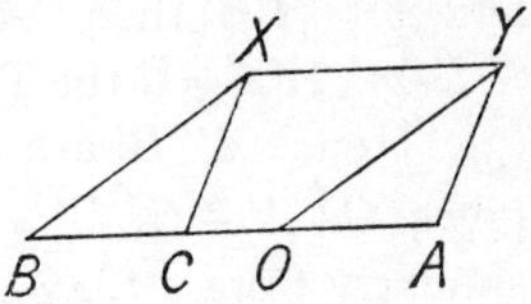

Fig. 53

Dem. If $[BOA]$ is false, and $B \neq O$, then B will be on $[OA$. Hence $[COB]$ (II 10·52) and B is on $[CA$ (II 10·58), wherefore $X{-}B$ meets $C{-}Y$ (·5). Thus since XB meets $C{-}Y$ and CO, but not $C{\vdash}O$, (since $[COB]$) therefore XB meets $O{-}Y$ (II 12), cont. hyp.

Metrical Properties connected with Parallels

4. ($\mathbf{O}_p$, $\mathbf{C}_p$.) *If B, D be on the same side of AC and $[ACE]$ and $B\hat{A}C \simeq D\hat{C}E$ then $AB \parallel CD$* (IV 36).

·1. ($\mathbf{O}_p$, $\mathbf{C}_p$.) If $AB, CD \perp AC$ and A, B, C, D coplane then $AB \parallel CD$ (IV 59·2).

·2. ($\mathbf{O}_p$, $\mathbf{C}_p$.) If B, D be on the same side of AC and $B\hat{A}C$, $D\hat{C}A$ are supplementary then $AB \parallel CD$ (4, IV 25·2).

·3. ($\mathbf{O}_p$, $\mathbf{C}_p$.) If B, F be on opposite sides of AC and $B\hat{A}C \simeq A\hat{C}F$ then $AB \parallel CF$ (4, IV 26).

§ 2. Basis $\mathbf{O}_p$ $\mathbf{C}_p$ $\mathbf{P}_1$.

·4. *If B, D be on the same side of AC and $[ACE]$ and $AB \parallel CD$ then $B\hat{A}C \simeq D\hat{C}E$.*

Dem. Let F be such that $F\hat{C}E \simeq B\hat{A}C$ with F, B and hence F, D on the same side of AE (IV 53). Then $CF \parallel AB$ (4). But $CD \parallel AB$. Hence successively $CD = CF$ (1·1), $[CD = [CF$, $B\hat{A}C \simeq D\hat{C}E$.

·41. If B, D be on the same side of AC and $[ACE]$ and $\mu D\hat{C}E < \mu B\hat{A}C$ then $AB]$, $CD]$ meet (1·1 and ·4 and IV 60·1).

·5. If $AB \perp AC$ and $AB \parallel CD$ then $CD \perp AC$.

·6. If $AB \parallel CD$, and $AB \perp XY$, and $CD \perp ZW$ and all the lines coplane then $XY \parallel ZW$ (·5·1).

4·7. If B, D be on the same side of AC and $AB \parallel CD$ then $B\hat{A}C, D\hat{C}A$ are supplementary (·4).

·8. If B, F be on opposite sides of AC and $AB \parallel CF$ then $B\hat{A}C \simeq F\hat{C}A$ (·4).

·9. If O, A, B colline and O, A', B' colline and $OA \neq OA'$ and $AA' \parallel BB'$ then $O\hat{A}A' \simeq O\hat{B}B'$.

Dem. If $A = B$ the Theorem is clear. If $[OAB]$ then $[OA'B']$ (3). Hence A', B' are on the same side of AB. Thus $[OAB]$ gives $O\hat{A}A' \simeq O\hat{B}B'$ (·4). If $[AOB]$ the Theorem follows similarly from 3·1, 4·8.

5. *If $ABCD$ be a parallelogram then $AB \simeq CD$, $BC \simeq DA$, $A\hat{B}C \simeq A\hat{D}C$ and $B\hat{A}D \simeq B\hat{C}D$.*

Dem. B, D are on opposite sides of AC (3·3) and $AB \parallel CD$. Hence $B\hat{A}C \simeq D\hat{C}A$ (4·8). And $CB \parallel AD$, hence $B\hat{C}A \simeq D\hat{A}C$ (4·8). Hence $BAC \simeq DCA$ and the Theorem follows.

·1. If $ABCD$ be a parallelogram and BD, AC meet in X then X is mid BD and mid AC.

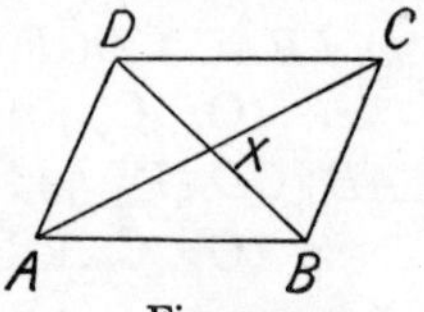

Fig. 54

Dem. B–D, A–C meet in X (3·3). As in 5, $B\hat{C}A \simeq D\hat{A}C$, $C\hat{B}D \simeq A\hat{D}B$. But $[BXD]$ $[AXC]$. Hence $B\hat{C}X \simeq D\hat{A}X$, $C\hat{B}X \simeq A\hat{D}X$, and $BC \simeq DA$ (5). Hence $BCX \simeq DAX$, $BX \simeq DX$, $CX \simeq AX$ (IV 34). (Or by IV 58·1.)

·2. If $ABCD$ be a (plane) quadrilateral and $AB \simeq CD$, $BC \simeq DA$ then $ABCD$ is a parallelogram*.

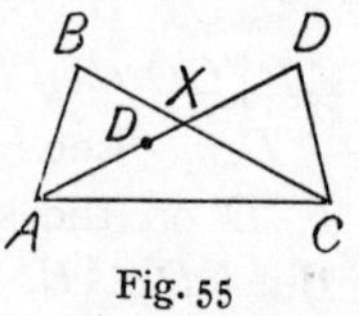

Fig. 55

Dem. AB, BC, $CA \simeq CD$, DA, AC give $ABC \simeq CDA$, $B\hat{A}C \simeq D\hat{C}A$, $B\hat{C}A \simeq D\hat{A}C$. If B, D be on the same side of AC then since A, B, D do not colline, either $[AD$ is in $C\hat{A}B$ or $[AB$ is in $C\hat{A}D$ (III 9). In the first case $[AD$ meets C–B in X say. But a quadrilateral is a *simple* polygon (III 11·1). Hence $[ADX]$. Thus $[CD$ is in $A\hat{C}B$; hence $\mu D\hat{C}A < \mu B\hat{C}A = \mu D\hat{A}C < \mu B\hat{A}C$ (IV 56·21). But $B\hat{A}C \simeq D\hat{C}A$. Hence $\mu B\hat{A}C < \mu B\hat{A}C$ contrary to IV 56·3. Similarly if $[AB$ is in $C\hat{A}D$ we get a contradiction. Thus B, D are

* It will be noticed how in this and many other Theorems, order considerations are essential for a sound proof. Yet these are always neglected.

not on the same side of AC, and since they are not on AC, they are on opposite sides of that line and hence 4·3 gives the Theorem.

5·3. If $AB \parallel CD$ and $AB \simeq CD$ then $ABCD$ is a parallelogram, *provided that B, C are on the same side of AD**.

Dem. If A, C be on the same side of BD, then either $[DC$ is in $A\hat{D}B$, or $[DA$ is in $C\hat{D}B$, or $[DA = [DC$ (III 9). Thus either $[DC$ meets A^-B, or $[DA$ meets C^-B, or A, C, D colline (III 7), all of which are impossible since $DC \parallel AB$ and B, C are on the same side of AD. Hence A, C are on opposite sides of BD and $A\hat{B}D \simeq C\hat{D}B$ (4·8). But $AB, BD \simeq CD, DB$. Hence $AD \simeq CB$. But by the above, $ABCD$ is a simple polygon, and the Theorem now follows by ·2.

·4. If $AB \parallel CD$, $AB \nparallel CD$; $AX, BY \perp CD$, with X, Y on CD then $AX \simeq BY$ (4·1, 5).

·5. If $[AXC]$ $[BXD]$, $AX \simeq XC$, $BX \simeq XD$ then $AB \parallel CD$.

·51. *Def.* If $ABCD$ be a parallelogram and $A\hat{B}C$ a right angle, then $ABCD$ is a '*rectangle*'; $C^{\vdash\dashv}D$ is the '*altitude*' with respect to the '*base*' $B^{\vdash\dashv}C$.

·6. An isosceles birectangle (IV 69·2) is a rectangle.

·7. All the angles of a rectangle are right angles.

·8. If $X^{\vdash\dashv}Y$ is the projection of $A^{\vdash\dashv}B$ on XY (IV 91·1), then $\mu XY < \mu AB$.

·9. Rectangles with congruent bases and congruent altitudes are congruent.

·91. *Def.* A '*square*' is a rectangle with two adjacent sides congruent.

·92. Any two sides of a square are congruent.

Division of an Interval into Congruent Intervals

6. *If B, C be on [OA and O, X, Y, Z colline and* $O \neq X, Y, Z$ *and* $OA \nparallel OX$ *and* $OA \simeq BC$ *and AX, BY, CZ are parallel then* $OX \simeq YZ$.

Dem. We can take the letters so that $[OBC]$. Then $[OYZ]$ (3). Let $YW \parallel BC$, W on ZC (W exists by II 16·1). Then $[ZWC]$ (3). Since B is on $[OA$ and $[OBC]$ $[ZWC]$, W, A will

* See footnote, page 142.

be on the same side of OZ. Hence $O\hat{X}A \simeq O\hat{Z}W \simeq Y\hat{Z}W$ (since $[OYZ]$) and $X\hat{O}A \simeq Z\hat{Y}W$ (4·4). Since $YB \parallel WC$, $BC \parallel YW$ we have $BC \simeq YW$ (5). But $OA \simeq BC$, hence $OA \simeq YW$ and congruence gives $OX \simeq YZ$.

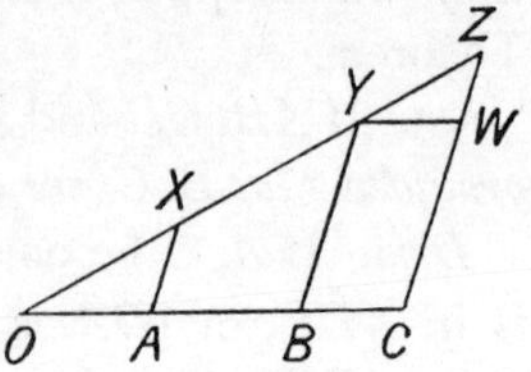

Fig. 56

6·1. If C, D, E be on $[OB$ and O, Y, Z, S, T colline and $O \neq Y, Z, S, T$ and $OB \neq OY$ and $BC \simeq DE$ and BY, CZ, DS, ET are parallel then $YZ \simeq ST$.

·2. If $[ABC]$ and $XA \parallel YB \parallel ZC$ and X, Y, Z colline and $AB \simeq BC$ then $XY \simeq YZ$ (·1 or 5).

·3. If $[OAB]$ and $XA \parallel YB$ and O, X, Y colline and $OA \simeq AB$ then $OX \simeq XY$ (6).

·4. If $[OAB]$ $[OXY]$, $OA \simeq AB$, $OX \simeq XY$ then $AX \parallel BY$ (·3, IV 14·2).

·5. *The. and Def.* If AB be an interval and n any natural number there are points

$$X_1, X_2, \ldots, X_{n-1} \text{ with } [AX_1X_2 \ldots X_{n-1}B]$$

such that $AX_1 \simeq X_1X_2 \simeq \ldots \simeq X_{n-2}X_{n-1} \simeq X_{n-1}B$. The interval AB is said to be '*divided into* $\simeq$ *congruent intervals*.'

Dem. There is a point Y_1 not on AB and points $Y_2, \ldots, Y_n$ such that $[AY_1Y_2 \ldots Y_n]$ and $AY_1 \simeq Y_1Y_2 \simeq \ldots \simeq Y_{n-1}Y_n$. There are points $Z_1, \ldots, Z_{n-1}$ on AB such that

$$Y_1Z_1 \parallel Y_2Z_2 \parallel \ldots \parallel Y_{n-1}Z_{n-1} \parallel Y_nB.$$

Then by 6 and 3 the points Z satisfy the requirements on the X.

·6. *Def.* If $a = \mu AB$, and X_1 satisfy the conditions of ·5 we write $\frac{1}{n}a$ for μAX_1.

·7. *If a is the measure of an interval then $\frac{1}{n}a$ exists* (·5).

If $\frac{1}{n}a = b$ then $a = nb$ and conversely.

·8. If B is on $[OA$, J on OI, and $BJ \parallel AI$ and $\mu OJ = n \,.\, \mu OI$, then $\mu OB = n \,.\, \mu OA$ and if $\mu OJ = \frac{1}{n} \,.\, \mu OI$ then $\mu OB = \frac{1}{n} \,.\, \mu OA$.

·9. If $a_1, a_2, \ldots, a_p$ be measures of intervals and n be a natural number then $n(a_1 + a_2 + \ldots + a_p) = na_1 + na_2 + \ldots + na_p$,

$$\frac{1}{n}(a_1 + a_2 + \ldots + a_p) = \frac{1}{n}a_1 + \frac{1}{n}a_2 + \ldots + \frac{1}{n}a_p$$

(IV 13, I 20·82, 21·7).

7. If $AX \parallel BY$ and $AH \parallel BK$ and X, Y be on the same side of AB, and H, K on the same side of AB, and $AX \neq AH$ then

$$X\hat{A}H \simeq Y\hat{B}K.$$

(Draw *all* the figures.)

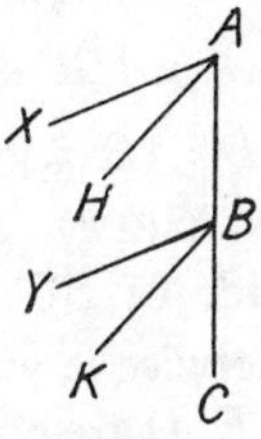

Fig. 57

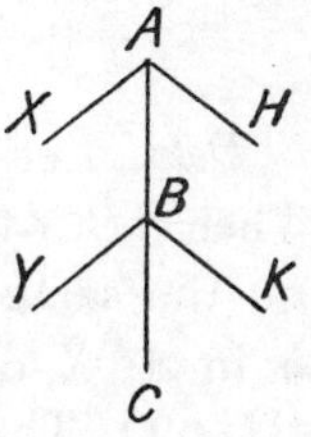

Fig. 58

Dem. If $A = B$ the Theorem is clear. If $A \neq B$ let C satisfy $[ABC]$, then $X\hat{A}C \simeq Y\hat{B}C$, $H\hat{A}C \simeq K\hat{B}C$ (4·4). If H, K are on the same side of AB as X, Y then there are rays both in $X\hat{A}B$ and in $H\hat{A}B$ and rays both in $Y\hat{B}C$ and in $K\hat{B}C$ (III 9·2). If H, K be on the opposite side of AB from X, Y then there is no ray both in $X\hat{A}B$ and in $H\hat{A}B$ and no ray both in $Y\hat{B}C$ and in $K\hat{B}C$ (III 7·5). Hence in both cases $X\hat{A}H \simeq Y\hat{B}K$ (IV 39, 38).

·1. If $AE \parallel BF$, $EC \parallel FD$, $AD \parallel EF$ and A, B, C, D colline then $AC \simeq BD$.

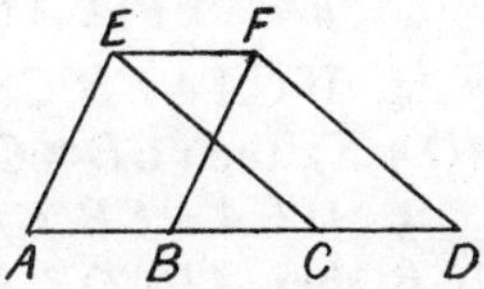

Fig. 59

Dem. A, B, C, D are on the same side of EF. Hence $A\hat{E}C \simeq B\hat{F}D$ (7) and $AE \simeq BF$, $EC \simeq FD$ (5). Hence $AC \simeq BD$.

·2. If O, X, Y colline and O, A, B colline and $OA \neq OX$ and $AX \nparallel BY$, $XM \parallel YL \parallel OB$ and $MB \parallel LA \parallel OX$ and if YB meet XM, AL in Q, P resp. then $PYL \simeq BQM$, where P, Q may coincide. (We need this Theorem in one place subsequently.)

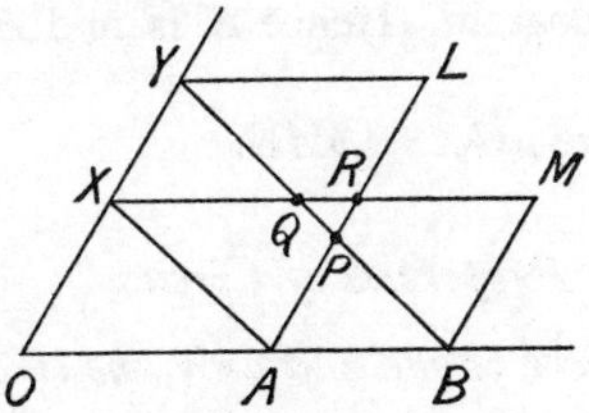

Fig. 60

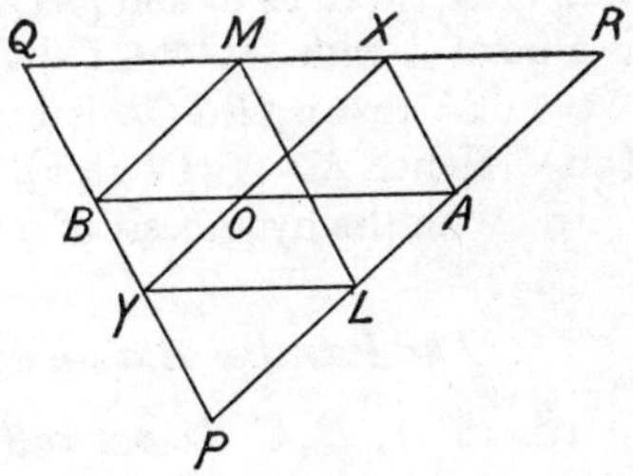

Fig. 61

Dem. XM meets AL in R, say. Then $XR \simeq QM$ ($\cdot 1$). But $XR \simeq YL$ (5). Hence $YL \simeq QM$. Similarly $LP \simeq MB$, $PY \simeq BQ$. Hence $PYL \simeq BQM$.

The Angle-Sum in a Triangle

8. *If ABC be a triangle and $[BCX]$ then*

$$\mu A\hat{B}C + \mu C\hat{A}B = \mu A\hat{C}X.$$

Dem. Let $CD \parallel AB$ with D, A on the same side of BC. Then $A\hat{B}C \simeq D\hat{C}X$ (4·4). Since D, A are on the same side of BC, therefore $[CD$ is in $A\hat{C}X$, otherwise it would meet AB (III 9·1). Thus B, D are on opposite sides of AC (III 7·1) and hence $B\hat{A}C \simeq A\hat{C}D$ (4·8). Hence by IV 56·1.

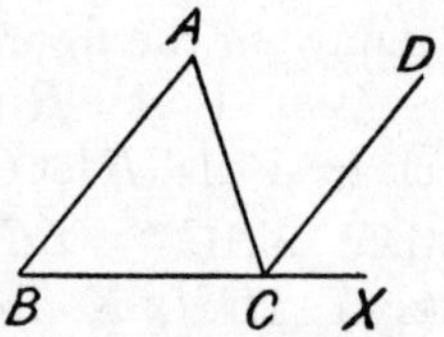

Fig. 62

·1. If in triangles ABC, $A'B'C'$ we have $\hat{A} \simeq \hat{A}'$, $\hat{B} \simeq \hat{B}'$, then $\hat{C} \simeq \hat{C}'$ (8, IV 25·2).

·2. If ABC be a triangle, then $\mu A\hat{B}C + \mu B\hat{C}A + \mu C\hat{A}B = \pi$ (8, IV 57·4).

·3. If $A\hat{C}B$ is a right angle then

$$\mu A\hat{B}C + \mu C\hat{A}B = \pi/2, \quad \mu A\hat{B}C < \pi/2 \text{ (8, IV 57·5)}.$$

·4. If $CA \neq CB$, $CA \simeq CB$, $AB \parallel DE$ with D on CA, E on CB $(D \neq E)$, then $CD \simeq CE$.

·5. If $CA \neq CB$, $CA \simeq CB$, $CD \simeq CE$, with D on $[CA$, E on $[CB$, then $AB \parallel DE$.

9. If ABC be a triangle and X, Y, Z be the mid-points of BC, CA, AB resp. then AX, BY, CZ concur.

Dem. Since $[AZB]$ $[AYC]$ (IV 14·1), $C{-}Z$, $B{-}Y$ meet in G, say with $[CGZ]$ (II 11·6) and $[AG$ meets $B{-}C$ in K say (II 5). There is a point L with $AG \simeq GL$, $[AGL]$. Then 6·4 gives $ZG \parallel BL$ and $YG \parallel CL$; that is, $BGCL$ is a parallelogram. Hence K is mid BC (5·1). Hence $K = X$ (IV 14·2).

·1. With the hypothesis of 9 we have $\mu GX = \frac{1}{2}\mu AG$.

The Parallel Axiom and the Properties of Circles

10. *If A, B, C do not colline there is one and only one circle through A, B, C.* (Cf. V 4.)

Dem. There cannot be two circles through A, B, C (V 4). Now the right bisectors of AB and BC meet, for if they were parallel then would $AB \parallel BC$ (4·6) and hence $AB = BC$, cont. hyp. Let them meet in X then $XA \simeq XB \simeq XC$ (IV 68·2).

Note. $\mathbf{P}_1$ is essential for the proof of the existence of the circle. We could replace the parallel Axiom by the assertion that such a circle always exists.

10·1. *The. and Def.* The right bisectors of the sides of a triangle meet in a point, the '*circumcentre*' of the triangle.

11. If ABC be a triangle and AX, BY, CZ be perpendicular to BC, CA, AB resp. then AX, BY, CZ concur.

Dem. Through A, B, C draw lines parallel to BC, CA, AB resp. These lines meet by 2·2 since AB, BC, CA are not parallel. Let them meet in L, M, N; these are distinct points by 3·3. Suppose A, B, C on MN, NL, LM resp. The parallelograms in the figure shew that A, B, C are the mid-points of the intervals MN, NL, LM and the Theorem follows from 4·5 and 10·1.

·1. *Def.* If $AX \perp BC$ with X on BC then $A \vdash\!\dashv X$ is the '*altitude*' of $\triangle ABC$ with respect to the base $B \vdash\!\dashv C$.

·2. *Note.* 9 is true in the absence of a parallel Axiom: so is 11 in the sense that if two of the lines in question meet, they all concur; but no proof depending on simple considerations of congruence in two dimensions (without parallels) seems to be known. The existence of a mid-point of each interval follows from $\mathbf{O}_p$ $\mathbf{C}_p$ (IV 58). The proof given of 10·1, modified in the way just mentioned for 11, does not depend on the parallel Axiom.

We now take up the question of angles in the same segment, and we shall make a detour to avoid bringing in the full theory of angular measure of IV 57, as we wish to avoid 'reflex' angles.

12. *Let A, B, C be on a circle centre O, and let O, C be on the same side of AB then* $A\hat{C}B \simeq$ half $A\hat{O}B$.

*Dem.** Let $[COX]$, and let X be inside the circle.

(i) If X be on OA then since O, C are not on AB (V 4·1), we have $[COA]$. Whence $OB \simeq OC$ gives by 8,

$$\mu A\hat{O}B = \mu O\hat{C}B + \mu O\hat{B}C = 2\mu A\hat{C}B$$

and the Theorem follows by IV 46·2.

* We give a conventional proof of this Theorem to shew what considerations are necessary concerning order and the magnitudes of angles.

(ii) If X be not on OA or on OB, we have as in (i)

$$\mu A\hat{O}X = 2\mu O\hat{C}A, \quad \mu B\hat{O}X = 2\mu O\hat{C}B.$$

If now A, B are on opposite sides of OX then OX meets $A^{-}B$ in Y say (III 2), and $\mu OY < \mu OC$ (V 4·2). Hence $[COY]$, for $[CYO]$ would imply that O, C were on opposite sides of AB. Thus $[OX$ is in $A\hat{O}B$ and $[CX$ in $A\hat{C}B$ (III 5). Therefore

$$\mu A\hat{O}B = \mu A\hat{O}X + \mu B\hat{O}X \text{ (IV 56·1)} = 2\mu O\hat{C}A + 2\mu O\hat{C}B$$
$$= 2\,(\mu O\hat{C}A + \mu O\hat{C}B) \text{ (IV 56·2, I 20·82)} = 2\mu A\hat{C}B.$$

Hence by IV 46·2.

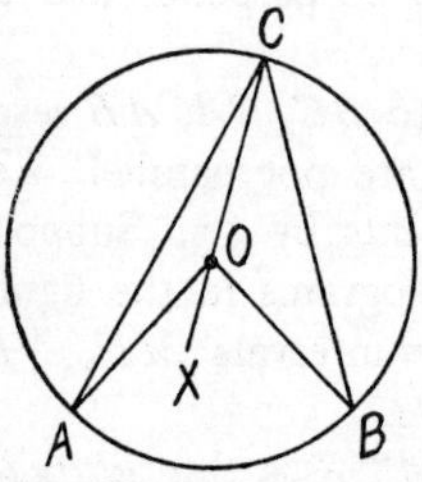

Fig. 63

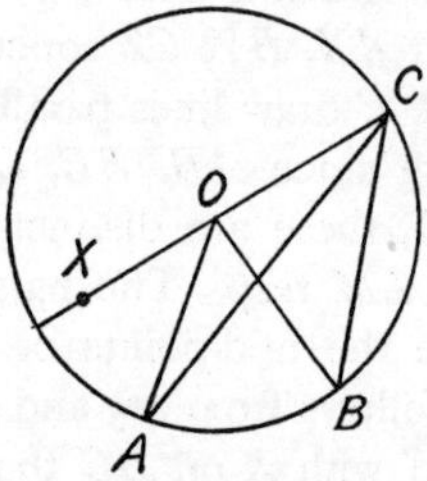

Fig. 64

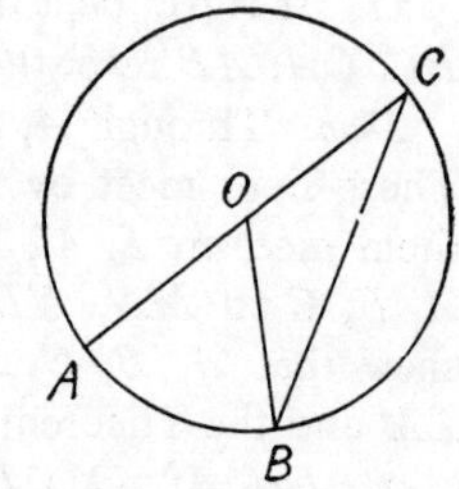

Fig. 65

But if A, B be on the same side of OX then $[OA$ is in $B\hat{O}X$ or $[OB$ in $A\hat{O}X$ (III 9). Suppose the former, then $O^{-}A$ meets $B^{-}X$ (III 7, V 4·2), whence BX meets $A^{-}C$, since it cannot meet $O\vdash C$. Hence (using V 4·2·3), we find that $[CA$ is in $X\hat{C}B$, i.e. in $O\hat{C}B$. Hence by IV 57·9 and I 20·83 we get

$$\mu A\hat{O}B = \mu B\hat{O}X - \mu A\hat{O}X = 2\mu O\hat{C}B - 2\mu O\hat{C}A$$
$$= 2\,(\mu O\hat{C}B - \mu O\hat{C}A) = 2\mu A\hat{C}B,$$

and the Theorem follows by IV 46·2.

12·1. If C, D, O be on the same side of AB and A, B, C, D be on a circle centre O then $A\hat{C}B \simeq A\hat{D}B$ (12 and IV 46·2).

13. *If AC be a diameter of a circle through $B \neq A, C$ then $A\hat{B}C$ is a right angle.*

*Dem.** Let O be the centre of the circle then $OA \simeq OB \simeq OC$, and A, O, B do not colline, hence $O\hat{A}B \simeq O\hat{B}A$, i.e. $C\hat{A}B \simeq O\hat{B}A$ and similarly $A\hat{C}B \simeq O\hat{B}C$. But since $[AOC]$ therefore $[BO$ is in $A\hat{B}C$ and hence $\mu O\hat{B}A + \mu O\hat{B}C = \mu A\hat{B}C$. Let $[CBX]$ then

* See footnote on page 147.

$\mu C\hat{A}B + \mu A\hat{C}B = \mu A\hat{B}X$. Hence $A\hat{B}X \simeq A\hat{B}C$ and the Theorem follows.

13·1. Conversely if $A\hat{B}C$ is a right angle, the circle on AC as diameter goes through B (13, IV 50 and V 6·4).

14. If A, B, C, D be on a circle centre O and $[AOC]$, and B, D be on opposite sides of AC then

$$\mu B\hat{A}D + \mu B\hat{C}D = \pi.$$

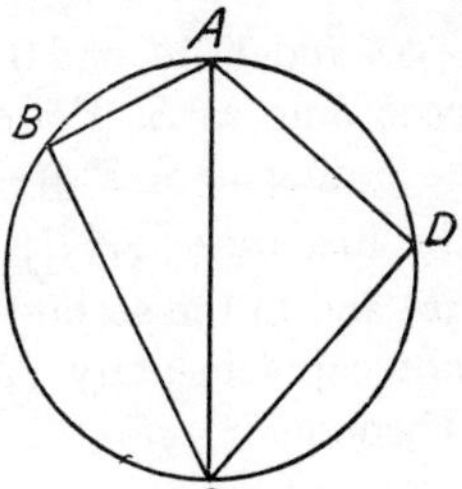

Fig. 66

Dem. $\mu C\hat{A}B + \mu A\hat{C}B = \pi/2$ (13, 8·3). Similarly $\mu C\hat{A}D + \mu A\hat{C}D = \pi/2$. But B^-D, A^-C meet (V 5). Hence $[AC$ is in $B\hat{A}D$ and $[CA$ in $B\hat{C}D$. Hence

$$\mu C\hat{A}B + \mu C\hat{A}D = \mu B\hat{A}D$$

and $\qquad \mu A\hat{C}B + \mu A\hat{C}D = \mu B\hat{C}D.$

Whence by IV 57·3.

15. *If $ABCD$ be a cyclic quadrilateral then*

$$\mu B\hat{A}D + \mu B\hat{C}D = \pi.$$

Dem. A, C are on opposite sides of BD (V 5). Let O be the centre of the circle. If $[BOD]$ the Theorem follows from 13. If O be not on BD, then since A, C are on opposite sides of BD either O, A or O, C are on the same side. Suppose this so for O, C and let $[AOE]$ with E on the circle, then C, O, E are on the same side of BD and A, E on opposite sides. Hence B, D are on opposite sides of AE (V 5). Thus $B\hat{E}D \simeq B\hat{C}D$ (12·1) and $\mu B\hat{A}D + \mu B\hat{E}D = \pi$ (14), whence

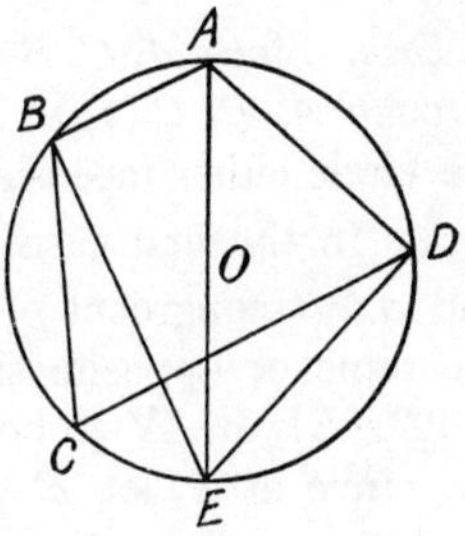

Fig. 67

$$\mu B\hat{A}D + \mu B\hat{C}D = \pi.$$

·1. If $ABCD$ be a cyclic quadrilateral and $[ADF]$ then $C\hat{D}F \simeq A\hat{B}C$.

16. *If A, B, C, D be on a circle, centre O, and C, D be on opposite sides of AB then $A\hat{C}B$, $A\hat{D}B$ are supplementary, but if C, D be on the same side of AB, these angles are congruent.*

Dem. The first part follows by 15 since $ACBD$ is a cyclic quadrilateral (V 5). For the second part; if C, O and hence D, O be on the same side of AB the Theorem is 12·1; if C, O and hence D, O

be on opposite sides of AB, let X be on the circle so that C, X and hence D, X are on opposite sides of AB, then $A\hat{C}B$, $A\hat{X}B$ are supplementary and so are $A\hat{D}B$, $A\hat{X}B$. Hence $A\hat{C}B \simeq A\hat{D}B$.

17. *If $X\hat{A}T \simeq X\hat{Y}A$ and Y, T are on opposite sides of AX then the circle XAY touches AT at A.*

Dem. If not, AT will meet the circle in a point $S \neq A$. Hence $X\hat{S}A$ and $X\hat{Y}A$, and thus $X\hat{S}A$, $X\hat{A}T$ are congruent or supplementary, according as S, Y are on the same or opposite sides of AX, i.e. according as S, T are on opposite or the same sides of AX. But in the first case $[SAT]$ and hence $X\hat{S}A$, $X\hat{A}T$ are not congruent (IV 36) and in the second case $X\hat{A}S = X\hat{A}T$ and hence $X\hat{S}A$, $X\hat{A}T$ are not supplementary (IV 36, 25·2). This contradiction proves the Theorem.

18. *If AT is tangent to the circle XAY at A and if T, Y are on opposite sides of AX then $X\hat{A}T \simeq X\hat{Y}A$.*

Dem. This follows by 17 and V 6·5, if we take AT' so that $XAT' \simeq XYA$ with T, T' on the same side of AX.

19. *If C, D be on the same side of AB and $A\hat{C}B \simeq A\hat{D}B$ then A, B, C, D are cyclic.*

Dem. Since A, C, B do not colline (def. of angle) there is a circle through A, B, C (10). If D is on it, the Theorem is proved; if not, the circle either meets AD in $E \neq D, A$, or AD touches* the circle at A. In the first case we have $A\hat{E}B$ and $A\hat{C}B$, and hence $A\hat{E}B$ and $A\hat{D}B$ congruent or supplementary* according as C, E are on the same or opposite sides of AB, i.e. according as E is on $[AD$ or $[DAE]$. By IV 36 both cases are impossible. And if AD touches the circle at A, let E be on AD and on the opposite side of AB from C, then $[DAE]$ and $B\hat{A}E \simeq A\hat{C}B$ (18) and hence $B\hat{A}E \simeq A\hat{D}B$ contrary to IV 36. Hence the Theorem.

20. *If C, D be on opposite sides of AB and $A\hat{C}B$, $A\hat{D}B$ are supplementary then $ACBD$ is a cyclic quadrilateral.*

Dem. Let E be on $\{AB, C\}$ and on the circle ABD. Then by 16 we have $A\hat{E}B$ and $A\hat{D}B$ supplementary and hence $A\hat{C}B \simeq A\hat{E}B$. Hence E is on the circle ABC and on the circle ADB, and hence these circles coincide (V 4).

·1. If $AB \perp BC$ and $AD \perp DC$ then A, B, C, D are cyclic.

* This possibility is usually overlooked.

21. If $ACBD$ be a polygon and C, D on opposite sides of AB and $[ADX]$ and $B\hat{D}X \simeq A\hat{C}B$, then $ACBD$ is a cyclic quadrilateral.

·1. *Note.* In order to avoid the troublesome consideration of 'cases' we now introduce the cross* (IV 71). The reader will not fail to note the simplicity and generality of the proofs constructed when this idea is used. An intuitive introduction of the cross would be an improvement in the Geometry of the Schools.

The Cross

22. *If* $AB \parallel CD$ *then*

$\times ABC \simeq DCB$, $\times ABD \simeq CDB$, $\times BAC \simeq DCA$, $\times BAD \simeq CDA$

and any one of these implies $AB \parallel CD$.

Dem. The first and its converse is simply 4, 4·3 and 4·4·8 using III 17. The others then follow formally since $AB \parallel CD$, $AB \parallel DC$, $BA \parallel CD$, $BA \parallel DC$ all mean the same thing.

·1. *If* $AB \parallel CD$ *and* O *be on* AC *and* $O \neq A$, C *then* $\times OAB \simeq OCD$ *and conversely* (4, 4·3·4·8).

·2. *Extension of definition of cross.* Cf. IV 71·1.

Any ordered couple of coplanar lines, whether they meet or not, or coincide or not, is a '*cross.*'

·21. *Def.* If $l_1 \parallel l_2$ then $\times l_1 l_2 \simeq l_3 l_4$ if and only if $l_3 \parallel l_4$.

23. If $l_1 \parallel l_2$ then $\times l_1 l_3 \simeq l_2 l_3$ and conversely (22·1·21 and 2·2).

·1. If $l_1 \parallel l_2$ and $l_3 \parallel l_4$ then $\times l_1 l_3 \simeq l_2 l_4$ (23; cf. 7).

·2. If $\times l_1 l_2 \simeq l_1' l_2'$ and $\times l_2 l_3 \simeq l_2' l_3'$ then $\times l_1 l_3 \simeq l_1' l_3'$.

Dem. Let l_4, l_4' be parallel to l_3, l_3' resp. and through the meets (if any) of l_1, l_2 and of l_1', l_2' resp. then $\times l_2 l_4 \simeq l_2' l_4'$ (23). Hence by IV 76 we have $\times l_1 l_4 \simeq l_1' l_4'$ provided $l_1 \neq l_4$. But by (23) $\times l_1 l_4 \simeq l_1 l_3$ and $\times l_1' l_4' \simeq l_1' l_3'$. Hence $\times l_1 l_3 \simeq l_1' l_3'$. And if $l_1 = l_4$ then $l_1 \parallel l_3$, $l_1' \parallel l_3'$ and the Theorem is 22·21. If $l_1 \parallel l_2$ then $l_1' \parallel l_2'$, and 23 gives the Theorem.

·3. If $\times l_1 l_2 \simeq l_2' l_1'$ and $\times l_2 l_3 \simeq l_3' l_2'$ then $\times l_1 l_3 \simeq l_3' l_1'$. (By IV 77 as for ·2.)

24. *If* $\times l_1 l_2 \simeq l_3 l_4$ *then* $\times l_1 l_3 \simeq l_2 l_4$. (This Theorem is of great use. Cf. IV 78.)

Dem. Since $\times l_1 l_2 \simeq l_3 l_4$ and $\times l_2 l_3 \simeq l_2 l_3$ we have the conclusion by 23·3.

* Picken, *loc. cit.* on page 120.

25. *If A, B, C, D be cyclic then* $\measuredangle\, ABC \simeq ADC$ *and conversely.*

Dem. First let B, D be on the same side of AC then $BA, \hat{}BC$ and $AC, \hat{}AB$ have the same sense (III 17·9·93), so have $DA, \hat{}DC$ and $AC, \hat{}AD$ and so have $AC, \hat{}AB$ and $AC, \hat{}AD$; hence so have $BA, \hat{}BC$ and $DA, \hat{}DC$ (III 17 *et seq.*). Also $A\hat{B}C \simeq A\hat{D}C$ (16).

Similarly (using III 17) if B, D be on opposite sides of AC then $BA, \hat{}BC$ and $DA, \hat{}DC$ have opposite senses and $A\hat{B}C, A\hat{D}C$ are supplementary. Hence the first part of the Theorem follows by IV 71·1. The converse comes from 19, 20.

26. *If AT is tangent to the circle XAY at A then*

$$\measuredangle\, XAT \simeq XYA$$

and conversely.

Dem. If T, Y be on opposite sides of AX then $AX, \hat{}AT$ and $AY, \hat{}AX$ have the same sense, and thus $YX, \hat{}YA$ and $AX, \hat{}AT$ also (III 17·9), and $X\hat{A}T \simeq X\hat{Y}A$ (18). Similarly if T, Y be on the same side of AX.

27. As an illustration of the use of the cross we give another proof of 11. If ABC be a triangle then the perpendiculars AX, BY, CZ to BC, CA, AB resp. concur. (Our proof of course applies to *all* figures.)

Dem. BY, CZ meet in O (say), for $BY \parallel CZ$ would give $AC \parallel AB$ (4·6). If $A = O$ the Theorem is clear. Let $A \neq O$ then B, C, Y, Z are cyclic and A, O, Y, Z are cyclic (20·1). Hence

$$\measuredangle\, YAO \simeq YZO \simeq YZC \simeq YBC \text{ (25, IV 73).}$$

Now AO, BC meet, for if $AO \parallel BC$ then $\measuredangle\, OAC \simeq BCA$ (22) that is $\measuredangle\, YAO \simeq ACB$ (IV 73). Hence, by above, $\measuredangle\, YBC \simeq ACB$, and so $YB \parallel AC$ (22) cont. hyp.

Let then AO, BC meet in W, then

$$\measuredangle\, YAO \simeq YAW, \quad \measuredangle\, YBC \simeq YBW,$$

hence $\measuredangle\, YAW \simeq YBW$ and thus A, B, W, Y are cyclic (25) and $\measuredangle\, AYB \simeq AWB$ (25). Hence $AW \perp BC$ and $W = X$.

·1. With the notation of 27, AX meets the circle ABC in Q where $OX \simeq XQ$.

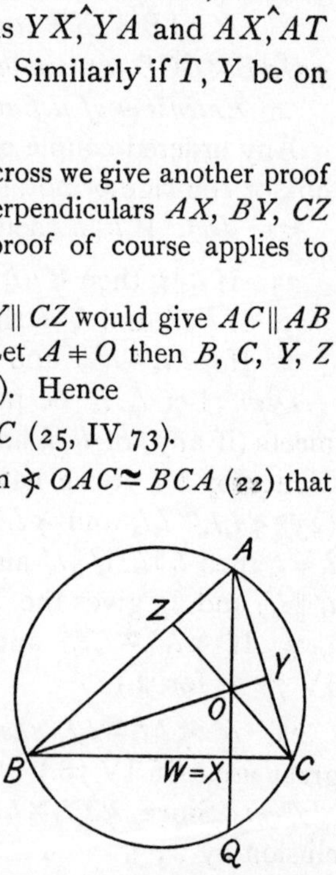

Fig. 68

Dem. If AX touches the circle at A, let $A = Q$ then

$$\sphericalangle\, CBA \simeq CAX \simeq YAO \simeq YBC \simeq OBC \quad (26,\ 27).$$

If AX meets the circle again, let it do so in Q then

$$\sphericalangle\, CBQ \simeq CAQ \simeq CAX \simeq CZX \simeq OZX \simeq OBX \simeq OBC$$

using 25 and IV 73. Thus in both cases BC bisects $\sphericalangle\, OBQ$ (IV 75) and since $BC \perp OQ$ it follows that $OX \simeq XQ$.

28. (Simson Line.) If P, A, B, C be cyclic and L, M, N be on BC, CA, AB resp. and PL, PM, PN be perpendicular to these lines resp. then L, M, N colline.

Dem. By repeated use of 25 we have

$$\sphericalangle\, PLM \simeq PCM \simeq PCA \simeq PBA \simeq PBN \simeq PLN;$$

whence the Theorem follows by IV 73.

·1. If ABC be a triangle and $[CAX]\ [CBY]$, then the bisectors of $A\hat{C}B$, $B\hat{A}X$, $A\hat{B}Y$ concur. (The real difficulty is to shew that two of them meet.)

Dem. If $[AL$, $[BM$, $[CN$ bisect $X\hat{A}B$, $A\hat{B}Y$, $A\hat{C}B$ resp., then X, L are on the same side of AB (III 7·2) and similarly so are Y, M, and so are X, Y since $[CAX]\ [CBY]$. Hence so are L, M.

Now $\mu A\hat{B}M$, $\mu B\hat{A}L < \pi/2$ (IV 57·6) whence $\mu B\hat{A}K > \pi/2$, where $[LAK]$ (IV 57·8). Hence $\mu A\hat{B}M < \mu B\hat{A}K$ and therefore by 4·41 and IV 26 we find $[AL$ $[BM$ meet in E, say.

Then E, A are on the same side of CB, since $[BE$ is in $A\hat{B}Y$; and E, B are on the same side of CA, since $[AE$ is in $B\hat{A}X$ (III 7·2).

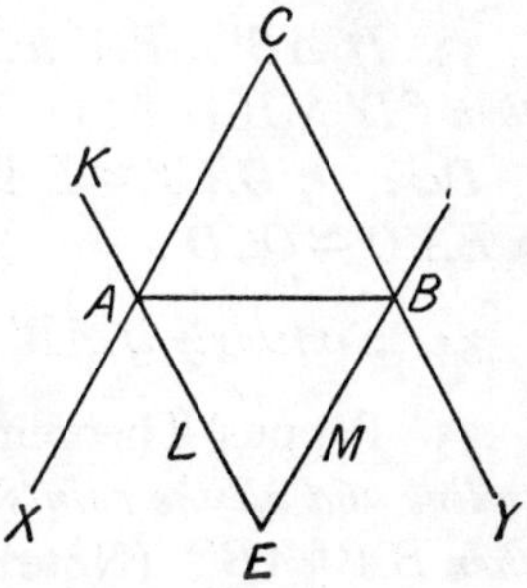

Fig. 69

Hence $[CE$ is in $A\hat{C}B$ (III 9·6). But the perpendicular intervals from E to CA, AB, CB are congruent (V 7·1) and hence $[CE$ bisects $A\hat{C}B$ (V 7).

·2. *Def.* The point E is an '*ecentre*' of triangle ABC.

·3. Thus each triangle has three ecentres.

Pappus' Theorem and Anti-parallels*

29. *Def.* If O, A, B colline and O', A', B' colline and $OA \nparallel O'A'$, then AB' and $A'B$ are '*anti-parallel lines, with*

* The Theorems we call Pappus' and Desargues' Theorems are special cases of those usually known by these names.

respect to the base lines $OA, O'A'$' if and only if A, B, A', B' are cyclic, where if $A=B$ the latter phrase means the circle $A'B'A$ touches OA at A, and similarly if $A'=B'$ the circle ABA' touches $O'A'$ at A'.

29·1. OA, $O'A'$ may be parallel or not. As our base lines will always be OA, $O'A'$ we omit mention of them and use the notation of 29 throughout, writing $AB' \wedge A'B$ for 'AB' and $A'B$ are anti-parallel.'

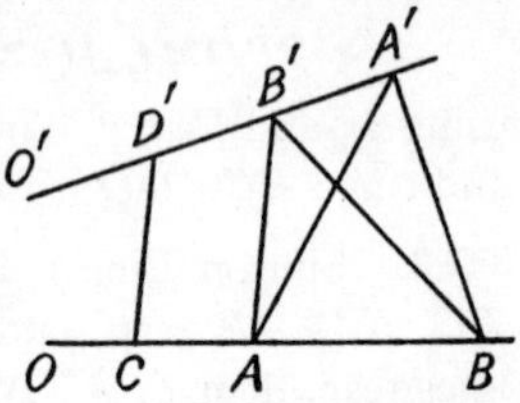

Fig. 70

30. If X is on OA and not on $O'A'$, then through X goes one and only one line XB' anti-parallel to $A'B$.

31. $AB' \wedge BA'$ implies $BA' \wedge AB'$ and $AA' \wedge BB'$ (29).

32. $AB' \wedge BA'$ *implies* $\sphericalangle OAB' \simeq BA'O'$ *and conversely* (25, 26).

33. *If* $AB' \wedge BA'$ *and* $CD' \parallel AB'$ *with* C *on* OA, D' *on* OA' *then* $CD' \wedge BA'$.

Dem. $\sphericalangle OAB' \simeq BA'O'$, $\sphericalangle OCD' \simeq OAB'$ (22·1). Hence $\sphericalangle BA'O' \simeq OCD'$.

34. *Similarly if* $AB' \wedge A'B$ *and* $CD' \wedge A'B$ *then* $AB' \parallel CD'$.

35. Pappus' Theorem*: *If* A, B, C *colline and* A', B', C' *colline and all the points do not colline, and* $CB' \parallel BC', CA' \parallel AC'$ *then* $BA' \parallel AB'$. (Note that some of the points may coincide.)

Dem. With respect to the base ines $AB, A'B'$ let $BD' \wedge CA'$. (D' on $A'B'$.) Then $BA' \wedge CD'$ (31). Now $CA' \parallel AC'$. Hence $BD' \wedge AC'$ (33) and $BC' \wedge AD'$ (31). Again

$$CB' \parallel BC';$$

hence $CB' \wedge AD'$ (33) and

$$AB' \wedge CD' \text{ (31).}$$

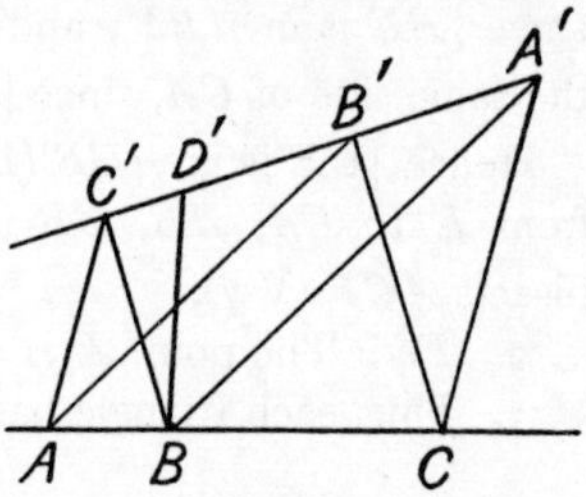

Fig. 71

But we have seen that $BA' \wedge CD'$. Hence $BA' \parallel AB'$ (34).

* Hessenberg, "Begründung der elliptischen Geometrie," *Math. Ann.* 1904, LXI, p. 173. In continental literature this Theorem is referred to as Pascal's Theorem.

35·1. This Theorem is of great importance subsequently. We have used Axioms $\mathbf{O}_p\ \mathbf{C}_p\ \mathbf{P}_1$ in proving it. How far these are essential will be seen later.

Space

§ 3. Basis O.

36. *Def.* If a line and a plane do not meet they are '*parallel*'; if two planes do not meet they are '*parallel.*' A plane is taken to be parallel to itself and to any line on it.

As usual we use small Greek letters for planes, small Latin letters for lines, and $\|$ for the relation '*parallel to.*'

·1. If $\alpha \| \beta$ then $\beta \| \alpha$; if $a \| \alpha$ then $\alpha \| a$.

·2. If $\alpha \| \beta$, and γ meet α, β in a, b resp. then $a \| b$.

·3. If $a \| \alpha$, and β is any plane through a meeting α in b say, then $a \| b$. If γ is another plane through a meeting α in c, then $b \| c$ (II 27).

·4. If $\alpha \| \beta$, and b is on β, then $b \| \alpha$.

·5. If $a \| b$, and a is on α, then $\alpha \| b$.

·6. If α, β, γ are planes and $(\alpha\beta) = c$, $(\beta\gamma) = a$, $(\gamma\alpha) = b$, and $a \| b$ then a, b, c are parallel (II 27).

·7. *Def.* A '*parallelepiped*' is a figure formed by six quadrilaterals, no two being in the same plane, but lying in pairs and in pairs only, in parallel planes, each side of each quadrilateral being common to two quadrilaterals only.

·8. If OAB, OBC, OCA be distinct planes through O, we get a parallelepiped by drawing planes through A, B, C resp. parallel to OBC, OCA, OAB.

§ 4. Basis O $\mathbf{P}_3'$.

37·1. If $a \neq b$ and a, b meet in O and $a, b \| \alpha$, then the plane $(ab) \| \alpha$.

Dem. If (ab) meet α in c, say, then since $a \neq b$ and a, b go through O one of them, say a, meets c ($\mathbf{P}_3'$). Hence α meets a, cont. hyp.

·2. *The set of lines through O parallel to α are on a plane parallel to α.*

Dem. Let O be not on α and a, b, c be distinct lines through O parallel to α. If c is not on the plane (ab) let P be on the plane α then the plane (Pc) meets α in a line d say (II 29) and since (Pc) goes through O, it meets (ab) in a line e say. Now $(ab) \parallel \alpha$ (·1). Hence $e \parallel d$ (36·2) and $c \parallel d$ (36·3). But e, c meet in O contrary to $\mathbf{P}_3'$.

37·3. If $\alpha \parallel \beta$, and $\gamma \parallel \beta$ then $\alpha \parallel \gamma$.

Dem. If not, then α, γ meet in O say. Through O and any point of β and any point of α, not on γ, draw a plane δ. Then $(\alpha\delta) \parallel (\beta\delta)$; $(\gamma\delta) \parallel (\beta\delta)$ (36·2) and $(\alpha\delta)$, $(\beta\delta)$ are distinct lines through O, contrary to $\mathbf{P}_3'$.

·4. Through O, not on α, goes not more than one plane parallel to α.

·5. If $a \parallel b$, $c \parallel d$, and a, c meet and b, d coplane, then plane $(ac) \parallel$ plane (bd).

Dem. We may assume a, b, c, d distinct and $(ac) \neq (bd)$. Since $a \parallel b$, therefore $a \parallel (bd)$ (36·5). Since $c \parallel d$, therefore $c \parallel (bd)$ (36·5). Hence $(ac) \parallel (bd)$ (·1).

·6. If $a \parallel \beta$ and $\beta \parallel \gamma$ then $a \parallel \gamma$.

Dem. Through a and a point on β goes a plane which meets β and γ (·3) in b and c, say. Then $a \parallel b$ (36·3), $b \parallel c$ (36·2). Hence $a \parallel c$ (2·2) and $a \parallel \gamma$ (36·5).

·7. *Note.* In the proofs of the Theorems of this and the preceding section, we have not actually used the idea of order, typified by the proposition $[ABC]$, but only certain consequences deduced from this idea. See 39·5 below.

§ 5. **Basis O P.**

38. Through a point O goes one and only one plane parallel to α.

Dem. Let PA, PB be two lines in α. There are lines $OC \parallel PA$, $OD \parallel PB$ and OC, OD are unique ($\mathbf{P}$). Hence plane $COD \parallel \alpha$ (37·2). Hence Theorem by 37·4.

Desargues' Theorem

39. *If ABC, XYZ be triangles not in the same plane and AB, BC, CA be parallel resp. to XY, YZ, ZX then AX, BY, CZ are parallel or concurrent.*

Dem. By hyp. A, B, C, X, Y, Z are all distinct and since $AB \parallel XY$ therefore A, B, X, Y coplane in γ, say. Similarly

B, C, Y, Z coplane in α, say, and C, A, Z, X in β, say. Hence $(\gamma\alpha)=BY$, $(\alpha\beta)=CZ$, $(\beta\gamma)=AX$. And since BY, CZ coplane (in α) either they meet and then BY, CZ, AX concur (II 27), or $BY \parallel CZ$ and then BY, CZ, AX are parallel (36·6).

39·1. If ABC, XYZ be triangles not in the same plane and AB, BC be parallel to XY, YZ resp. and if AX, CZ are parallel or concurrent, then $CA \parallel ZX$, and AX, BY, CZ are parallel or concurrent.

Dem. Since AB, BC are parallel to XY, YZ resp. we have $ABC \parallel XYZ$ (37·5). Now AX, CZ coplane and their plane meets ABC in CA and XYZ in ZX. Hence $CA \parallel ZX$ (36·2). Hence Theorem by 39.

·11. *Note.* In 39, 39·1 we have used $\mathbf{P}_3'$ only, not $\mathbf{P}$.

·2. *If A, B, C, X, Y, Z be distinct and coplanar and if AX, BY, CZ are distinct and either parallel or concurrent and AB, BC are parallel resp. to XY, YZ then $CA \parallel ZX$.*

Dem. If AX, BY, CZ concur in O say, let l be a line through O not in plane ABC. If AX, BY, CZ are parallel, let l be a line parallel to them ($\mathbf{P}$). Let P be on l, and not on ABC. Let $XQ \parallel AP$ ($\mathbf{P}$). Then XQ, l are in plane PAX and since PA is not parallel to l, neither is XQ which thus meets l in Q say. Hence BY, PQ are either parallel or they meet in O and $AP \parallel XQ$ and $AB \parallel XY$ and $ABP \nparallel XYQ$ (since P is not on ABC and $AX \nparallel BY$). Hence $BP \parallel YQ$ (·1).

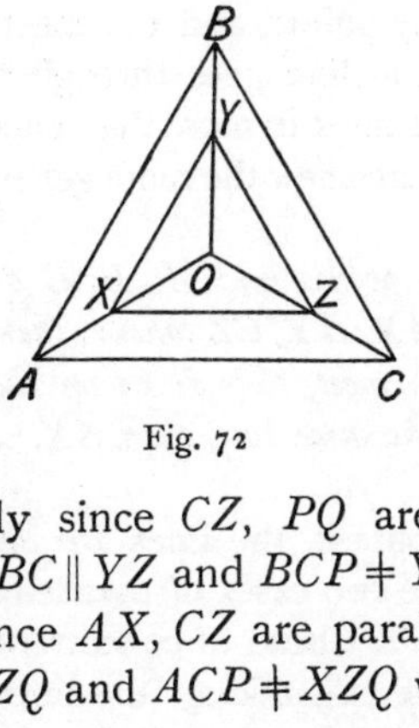

Fig. 72

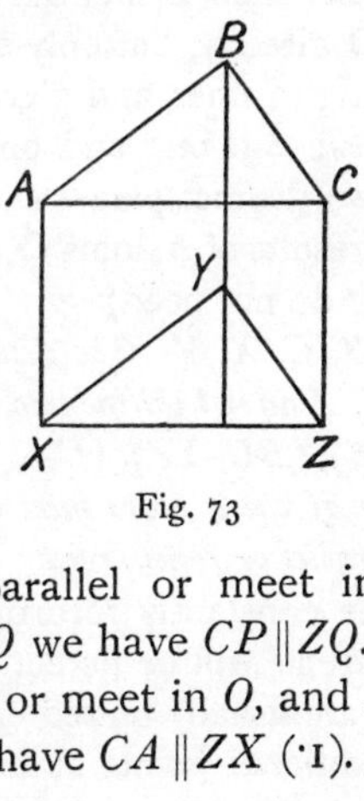

Fig. 73

Similarly since CZ, PQ are parallel or meet in O and $BP \parallel YQ$, $BC \parallel YZ$ and $BCP \nparallel YZQ$ we have $CP \parallel ZQ$.

And since AX, CZ are parallel or meet in O, and $AP \parallel XQ$ and $CP \parallel ZQ$ and $ACP \nparallel XZQ$ we have $CA \parallel ZX$ (·1).

39·3. *If* A, B, C, X, Y, Z *be distinct and coplanar and* A, B, C *do not colline, and* AB, BC, CA *be parallel resp. to* XY, YZ, ZX *then* AX, BY, CZ *(assumed distinct) are either parallel or concurrent.*

Dem. If no two be parallel then AX, BY meet in O say, and O is not on YZ since $YZ \parallel BC$ but OY meets BC. Hence $OZ \nparallel YZ$ and thus OZ, BC meet in C' say. Hence AX, BY, $C'Z$ meet in O and $XY \parallel AB$ and $YZ \parallel BC'$ and A, B, C', X, Y, Z are distinct and AX, BY, $C'Z$ are distinct (for if, e.g. $AX = C'Z$ then $XZ \parallel AC$ would be false). Hence $C'A \parallel XZ$ (·2). Hence $C = C'$.

And if $AX \parallel BY$ then BY, CZ cannot meet, by the first case.

·4. *The following special case of Pappus' Theorem can be deduced from the above Theorems:*

If $AB \parallel A'B'$, $AB \nparallel A'B'$, and A, B, C colline and A', B', C' colline and $AB' \parallel A'B$, $BC' \parallel B'C$ then $CA' \parallel C'A$. (The special hypothesis is that $AB \parallel A'B'$.)

Dem. We may assume A, B, C, A', B', C' all distinct; then AB', $B'C$, CA are parallel to $A'B$, BC', $C'A'$ resp. and AA', BB', CC' are distinct; hence they are parallel or concurrent (·3). But $AB \parallel A'B'$ and $BC' \parallel B'C$, hence $CA' \parallel C'A$ (·2).

·5. Theorems 39 to 39·3 will be quoted as Desargues' Theorem. Like Pappus' Theorem they are of great importance subsequently. We have shewn them from Axioms **O**, **P**, and we shall see later that we could *not* shew them from Axioms $\mathbf{O}_p$, **P**. But we have not used Axioms **O** directly, but only such results from them as concern the determining of lines and planes by points, and the meeting of lines and planes; e.g. one and only one line goes through two distinct points: two distinct planes cannot meet in more than one line. From the same results of Axioms **O**, we can shew the more general Theorem (which we do not need).

If A, B, C, X, Y, Z *be distinct points and* A, B, C *do not colline and* X, Y, Z *do not colline and if* AX, BY, CZ *concur, then if the pairs* (AB, XY), (BC, YZ), (CA, ZX) *meet, they do so on the same line: conversely, if these pairs meet on the same line, then* AX, BY, CZ *are either parallel or concurrent.*

·6. The constantly recurring phrase 'the lines are either parallel or concurrent' will be noted. The two cases of parallelism and concurrency are usually united under the head of concurrency by postulating additional points at infinity and taking 'the lines meet in a point at infinity' to mean 'the lines are parallel.' This might be regarded as a mere *façon de parler* designed to secure brevity in enunciations and proofs; but the fact that it is so successful in doing this, shews that it is more than a mere verbal convenience. We will now try to explain how these points at infinity can be introduced. But first we will shew what is meant by a Projective Geometry.

§ 6. *Axioms of Projective Geometry**

40. As undefined entities we take a class of elements called '*points*' and sub-classes of this class called '*lines*.'

Ax. A 1. *If A, B be distinct points there is at least one line on which they both lie.*

Ax. A 2. *If A, B be distinct points, there is at most one line on which they both lie.*

·1. *Def.* If A, B be distinct points, the line on which they both lie is denoted by AB.

Ax. A 3. *If A, B, C be distinct points and A is not on BC, and D, E are on BC, CA resp. and $D \neq E$, then there is a point F on DE and on AB.* (Cf. **O** VI.)

·11. If A, B, C be distinct and do not colline, the '*plane*' ABC is the set of all points on all lines joining A to points of BC. (Cf. II 13·1.)

·12. *Def.* If A, B, C, D be distinct and do not coplane the '*space*' $ABCD$ is the set of all points on all lines joining A to points of a plane through B, C, D. (Cf. II 20·1.)

Ax. A 4. *There are at least three points on any line and there is at least one line.*

Ax. A 5. *All points are not on the same line.* (Cf. **O** V.)

Ax. A 6. *All points are not on the same plane.* (Cf. **O** VII.)

Ax. A 7. *All points are on the same space.* (Cf. **O** VIII.)

From these Axioms, somewhat as in Chapter II, only the proofs are simpler, we can shew:—

·2. If A, B lie on a plane α, so do all points of AB.

* Veblen and Young, *Projective Geometry*, vol. I (1910). We may take the relation 'lies on' in the phrase 'A lies on the line BC' *either* as the logical relation between an element of a class and that class, *or* as undefined, in which case a 'line' need not be a class of 'points.'

40·3. Two distinct points of a line determine it.

·31. Two distinct lines on the same plane meet in just one point.

·32. Thus parallel lines *do not exist* in projective space.

·4. Three distinct non-collinear points of a plane determine it.

·41. Two distinct planes meet in just one line; a plane and a line not on it meet in just one point.

·42. Thus parallel planes *do not exist* in projective space.

·5. Three distinct planes meet in just one point.

·6. Desargues' Theorem in projective space takes the form: *If* A, B, C, X, Y, Z *be distinct* (*and coplanar or not*) *and* A, B, C *do not colline and* X, Y, Z *do not colline, then if* AX, BY, CZ *concur, the pairs* (AB, XY), (BC, YZ), (CA, ZX) *meet on the same line, and conversely.*

This has virtually been shewn above. For we can take any plane α in the space and call lines which meet on it '*pseudo-parallel*'; then Ax. **P** holds for points and lines not on α, if we replace 'parallel' by 'pseudo-parallel.' The proofs of 39 to 39·4 hold, practically unchanged, the exceptional plane α being suitably chosen in each case.

This artifice is actually quite unnecessary and automatically drops out of the proof, but it exhibits the relation of the Theorem in projective space to that in Euclidean space.

A proof from Axioms **A** will be found in any text-book of Projective Geometry.

·7. Desargues' Theorem in its Euclidean form can be deduced from Axioms **A**, replacing **A** 3 by **P**, and defining plane and space as in Chapter II, treating 'point' and 'line' as undefined entities, a line being a class of points.

This has been done in 39 to 39·3.

When the definitions of plane and space are taken as in Chapter II we shall call the Axioms **A**, with **A** 3 omitted, the Axioms **A**′; and we shall call the set **A** 1, 2, 4, 5 the set $\mathbf{A}_p'$.

41. We will now construct a Projective Geometry from our Euclidean Geometry; as we shall say, we will make our Euclidean Geometry projective. Instead of *postulating* points at infinity where the parallel lines of the earlier theory may be supposed to meet, we shall adjoin to the points, lines

and planes of Euclidean Geometry certain 'ideal' entities *constructed* from them.

41·1. *Defs.** An '*ideal point*' is the set of all lines parallel to a given line, the ideal point is '*on*' each of these lines and they '*go through*' it. An '*ideal line*' is the set of all planes parallel to a given plane, the ideal line is '*on*' each of these planes and they '*go through*' it. '*The ideal plane*' is the set of all ideal points (i.e. the set of all sets of parallel lines). An ideal point is '*on*' an ideal line if the set of parallel lines which give the ideal point is parallel to the set of parallel planes which give the ideal line. All ideal points are points of the ideal plane.

·2. *The set of ideal and other points, lines and planes satisfy the Axioms and definitions of Projective Space.* This is easily shewn. For instance, to shew that one and only one line goes through two points: If both points are ordinary this is known: if P is an ordinary point and Q ideal, then the line PQ is the (ordinary) line through P which is one of the lines that constitute Q: if P and Q are both ideal, then PQ is the ideal line constituted by the set of parallel planes each containing a line of P and a line of Q.

·3. The introduction of ideal entities serves the same purpose as postulating points at infinity.

Consider now any Theorem in Euclidean space which can be shewn from Axioms **A**′, **P** alone, for instance 39. Introducing ideal entities this becomes:

If ABC, XYZ be triangles not in the same plane and AB, BC, CA meet XY, YZ, ZX resp. in an ideal line then AX, BY, CZ meet in a point (ordinary or ideal).

Dem. AB, XY meet and therefore A, B, X, Y coplane in γ, say. Similarly B, C, Y, Z coplane in α, say, and C, A, Z, X coplane in β, say. Hence $(\gamma\alpha) = BY$, $(\alpha\beta) = CZ$, $(\beta\gamma) = AX$. Thus BY, CZ, AX meet in the point common to α, β, γ.

We see that in this proof no use is made of the given fact that certain lines meet on an ideal line. The fact that they meet is alone

* Since the relation 'parallel to' between lines is equable, parallel lines may be supposed to have a common property (I 8). Instead of doing this, we put such lines in one class and give such classes a name. Cf. also footnotes, pp. 138, 159.

used, and we have really shewn the projective generalisation in Euclidean space made projective, viz.:

If ABC, XYZ be triangles not on the same plane and AB, BC, CA meet XY, YZ, ZX resp., then AX, BY, CZ concur.

Quite generally, if we have a Theorem in Euclidean space, proved from Axioms **A′**, **P** alone, then if it be stated and proved in Euclidean space made projective, this statement and proof still hold for its projective generalisation, i.e. when the distinction between ideal and ordinary entities is ignored. We are in fact then deducing the projective generalisation from Axs. **A**.

41·4. If we isolate a plane α in Euclidean space made projective and call those lines which meet on it '*pseudo-parallel*' we accomplish the same end as is usually achieved by projecting the plane α to infinity. *Any* plane in projective space may be regarded as the 'plane at infinity.' In this way we can pass from a projective generalisation of a theorem to a special case in which certain lines are parallel.

·5. In projective space Pappus' Theorem is as follows:

If A, B, C colline and A_1, B_1, C_1 colline and $AB \neq A_1B_1$ the points of meeting of the pairs (AB_1, A_1B), (BC_1, B_1C), (CA_1, C_1A) colline. We shall see that this cannot be deduced from Axioms **A** alone and accordingly the above considerations do not apply. We have deduced the special form in 35 for Euclidean space from Axs. **O**, **P** *and* **C**. If now we wish to deduce the projective form of Pappus' Theorem in Euclidean space made projective (where it is indeed true) our simplest plan is actually to project from one plane to another in the accustomed way. (We cannot do this sort of thing for Theorems in *space*, without assuming points *outside* our space.)

·6. Let us call '*graphical Theorems*' those which involve only the determination of lines and planes and their intersections (including the properties of parallels when we are dealing with Euclidean space), but which do not involve order or congruence relations.

We shall see that all graphical Theorems in Euclidean space follow from **A′**, **P** and Pappus' Theorem 35, and all graphical Theorems in projective space from **A** and Pappus' Theorem in ·5. Having then assured ourselves of the truth of 35 in

Euclidean space and so of ·5 in Euclidean space made projective, it will follow that if any graphical Theorem be true in Euclidean space, its projective generalisation is true in that space made projective.

41·61. We *could* assume that our order Axioms **O** held for all entities, ideal or not, of our Euclidean space made projective. There is no advantage in doing so at present, and later when a continuity Axiom is introduced it would lead to contradiction (XIII 13, 8·6).

·7. The consistency of the Axioms **A** follows from the consistency of the Axioms of Euclidean Geometry (which will be shewn hereafter) since from the points, lines and planes of Euclidean space we have constructed entities which together with the original entities satisfy Axioms **A**.

·71. The consistency of Axioms **A** can also be shewn as follows: Let 1, 2, 3, 4, 5, 6, 7 be 'points' and let points in vertical columns in the following scheme constitute the same 'line'

1	2	3	4	5	6	7
2	3	4	5	6	7	1
4	5	6	7	1	2	3

It is easily verified that two points are on just one line and that two lines have just one point common. The points 1...7 form a projective 'plane.'

To get a projective 'space' take in addition the 'points' 0, 1′, 2′, 3′, 4′, 5′, 6′, 7′ and let the triads of points 124, 17′3′, 14′2′, 15′6′, 011′ and the triads got from them by replacing 1 by 2, 2 by 3, 1′ by 2′, and so on, constitute each a line. All Axioms **A** are satisfied by this set. This was first obtained in connection with Kirkman's school-girl problem: To arrange 15 girls in 5 rows of 3 each for 7 days so that no two girls are in the same row more than once. If the Sunday arrangement is 011′, 235, 43′6′, 62′7′, 74′5′ (these are five 'lines') the arrangements for the other days can be got by replacing 1 by 2, 2 by 3, 1′ by 2′, and so on.

It will be noted that a *finite** set of 'points' and 'lines' can satisfy Axs. **A**; this is not the case with Axs. **O** by II 8.

·8. Ax. **P** is equivalent to: In Euclidean space made projective, there is just one ideal point on each ordinary line.

* Veblen and Bussey, "Finite Projective Geometries," *Trans. Amer. Math. Soc.* 1906, VII, p. 241.

41·9. It is a highly remarkable and very important fact that not merely Euclidean space but any space satisfying Axioms **O** can be made projective, but the argument is longer*. This is one of the reasons why Projective Geometry is of fundamental importance.

§ 7. Basis O C P_1.

42. *If AB, $CD \perp \alpha$, then $AB \parallel CD$.*

Dem. Let A, C be on α. Now AB, CD coplane (IV 90) and both are perpendicular to AC (IV 81). Hence the Theorem by 4·1.

·1. If $AB \perp \alpha$ and $AB \parallel CD$, then $CD \perp \alpha$.

43. *If planes α, β be perpendicular to the line c, then $\alpha \parallel \beta$.*

Dem. If α, β met in E, then the plane cE would meet α, β resp. in lines a, b which meet in E and are yet parallel (4·1, IV 81).

·1. If $\alpha \perp a$ and $\alpha \parallel \beta$, then $\beta \perp a$.

Dem. β and a cannot be parallel (37·6). Thence by 43.

44. *If $\alpha \parallel \beta$ and $\alpha \perp \gamma$, then $\beta \perp \gamma$.*

Dem. β and γ meet (37·3) in a line parallel to $(\alpha\gamma)$ (36·2). From A on $(\alpha\gamma)$ draw the line AB perpendicular to α, then AB lies in γ (IV 87, 89) and $AB \perp \beta$ (43·1). Hence $\beta \perp \gamma$ (IV 86).

45. *The projection on a plane of a set of parallel lines (not perpendicular to the plane) is a set of parallel lines.*

Dem. If $g \parallel h$ and if g_1, h_1, their projections on the plane α, meet in P then the perpendicular to α at P meets both g and h (IV 91·3) and since $g \parallel h$ we have $Pg = Ph$. But Pg, Ph meet α in g_1, h_1 (IV 91). Hence either $g_1 = h_1$ or g_1, h_1 do not meet.

46. An interval AB of a line parallel to α, projects on α into a congruent interval $A'B'$, and if $AC \perp AB$, and AC is not perpendicular to α, then AC projects into $A'C' \perp A'B'$.

Dem. We shew the second part. AB, $A'B'$ are coplanar (IV 91·3) and so parallel (36·3). Since A' is the projection of A, therefore $AA' \perp \alpha$. Hence $AA' \perp A'B'$ and $AA' \perp AB$. But $AC \perp AB$, hence $AB \perp AA'C$ (IV 80·1). Hence $A'B' \perp AA'C$ (42·1), that is $A'B' \perp AA'C'$ (IV 91·3) and hence $A'B' \perp A'C'$ (IV 81).

* Baker, *Principles of Geometry*, I, p. 107; Whitehead, "Descriptive Geometry" (*Cambridge Tracts*, No. 5).

47. *Two lines a, b, not coplanar, have one and only one common perpendicular line.* (Fig. 74.)

Dem. Through a point X on a draw the line $c \parallel b$. Then the plane $(ac) \parallel b$ (36·5). Let AB be the projection of b on (ac). Since $AB \parallel b$ (36·3), therefore AB is not parallel to a (2·2) for a, b do not coplane. Let AB meet a in A. The perpendicular line to (ac) at A is perpendicular to a (IV 81) and meets b (IV 91·3), and since it is perpendicular to AB, and $AB \parallel b$, it is perpendicular to b.

47·1. This Theorem depends on the existence of parallels since it is false in Elliptic Space.

48. If $AD \perp DF$, AC and D, F, A, C do not coplane, then $\mu AD < \mu CF$, that is, the common perpendicular interval of two non-coplanar lines is the shortest interval joining a point of one to a point of the other.

Dem. Let $AC = a$, $DF = b$ and use the figure of 47. Let AB be the projection of DF on the plane (ac), then $DF \parallel AB$. Let $FB \perp AB$. Then $FB \perp ABC$ (IV 91·3), $FB \perp BC$ (IV 81), $\mu AD = \mu FB$ (5), $\mu FB < \mu CF$ (IV 63). Hence $\mu AD < \mu CF$.

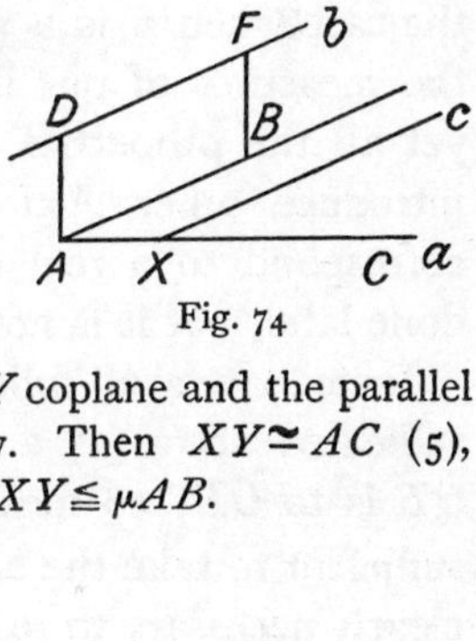

Fig. 74

49. If $X \vdash\!\dashv Y$ be the projection of $A \vdash\!\dashv B$ on a plane α, then $\mu XY \leqq \mu AB$.

Dem. $AX \parallel BY$ (42). Hence A, X, B, Y coplane and the parallel through A to XY meets BY in C, say. Then $XY \simeq AC$ (5), $AC \perp BY$, $\mu AC \leqq \mu AB$ (IV 63). Hence $\mu XY \leqq \mu AB$.

[Note that B, C may coincide.]

CHAPTER VII

PROPORTION AND THE ALGEBRA OF INTERVALS

Introductory Remarks

We have shewn in VI 6·8 that if T is on $[OS$ and T' on $[OS'$ and $TT' \parallel SS'$, then if $\mu OT = n \,.\, \mu OS$ and n is a natural number, it follows that $\mu OT' = n \,.\, \mu OS'$. It is an easy step to shew that this is also true when n is a ratio (I 15). Unfortunately the measures of some intervals are incommensurable with each other, for instance, the side of a square and its diagonal; and we cannot extend the above Theorem to the case when n is a real number, because the measures of our intervals have not as yet all the properties of real numbers. We could, of course, introduce other Axioms designed to make each interval correspond to a real number, and conversely. This will be done later, but it is not necessary for our present purpose.

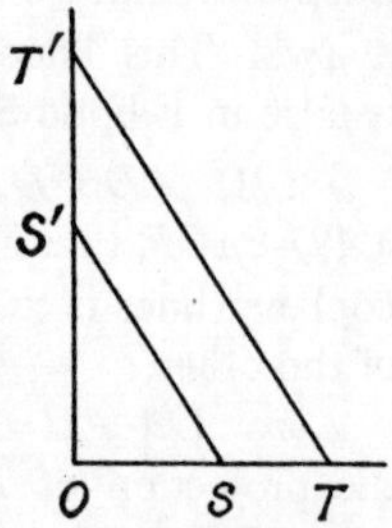

Fig. 75

Instead we shall, following Hilbert*, use the general Theorem indicated above as a definition, and define 'OS is to OS' as OT is to OT'' to mean that SS' and TT' are parallel. It is sufficient to take the case when $S\hat{O}S'$ is a right angle and it is clearly necessary to restrict ourselves to some such case, if the statement is to be used as a *definition*. The Theorems on proportion and similar triangles follow.

To pass from 'a is to b as c is to d' to the equation $ad = bc$, where a, b, c, d are not ordinary numbers but the measures of intervals, we erect an algebra of intervals; in particular we define the multiplication of such measures. We may not use the Theory of Areas here since that is still to come.

We are then able to shew the Theorem of Pythagoras and the 'rectangle' properties of the circle. These lead to the

* *Grundlagen*, Chapter III. See also F. Schur, *Grundlagen der Geometrie*, p. 135.

Theory of the Inversion Plane needed to complete the Theory of Constructions.

This Inversion Geometry, like the Projective, though deduced from the Euclidean is capable of being founded independently.

The first Properties of Proportion

§ 1. **Basis O_p C_p P_1.** *All our figures are in one plane.*

1. *Def.* If s, t, s', t' be measures of intervals then $s|s' \sim t|t'$ is a relation between those measures, which means that there are points O, S, T, S', T' such that the intervals OS, OT, OS', OT' have resp. measures s, t, s', t' and $S\hat{O}S'$ is a right angle and T, T' are on $[OS$, OS' resp. and $SS' \parallel TT'$.

·01. T' in 1 is on $[OS'$ (VI 3).

·02. Note that $s|s' \sim t|t'$ is a four-termed relation between measures of intervals, whose properties are now to be investigated. The symbolism is, of course, chosen in view of those properties, but it must not induce us to *assume* them.

·03. If $S\hat{O}S'$ is a right angle and T, T' be on $[OS$, $[OS'$ resp., then $s|s' \sim t|t'$ (where s, s', t, t' are the measures of the intervals OS, OS', OT, OT' resp.) holds if and only if $SS' \parallel TT'$. (By 1 and congruence.)

·1. If any three of s, s', t, t' be given, then a fourth measure satisfying $s|s' \sim t|t'$ exists and is unique.

·2. $s|s' \sim s|s'$.

·3. If $s|s' \sim t|t'$, then $t|t' \sim s|s'$ and $s'|s \sim t'|t$.

·4. If $s|s' \sim t|t'$ and $t|t' \sim v|v'$, then $s|s' \sim v|v'$ (VI 2·2).

·5. By ·2·3·4 we could consider a relation $s|s'$ between the measures of two intervals, regarding two such relations $s|s'$, $t|t'$ (defined by abstraction) as identical when $s|s' \sim t|t'$ and we should then write $s|s' = t|t'$. Such a relation is called a '*ratio.*' We shall not however do this, because it is not necessary and because of the logical difficulties of definition by abstraction. (I 9.)

2. If $s = t$ and $s' = t'$, then $s|s' \sim t|t'$.

·1. If $s|s' \sim t|t'$ and $s = t$, then $s' = t'$.

·11. If $s|s' \sim t|t'$ and $s' = t'$, then $s = t$.

The above properties follow from the def. and Ax. **P**, noting that a line is parallel to itself.

2·2. If $s=s'$ and $t=t'$, then $s|s' \sim t|t'$ (VI 8·5).

·21. If $s|s' \sim t|t'$ and $s=s'$, then $t=t'$ (VI 8·4).

·22. If $s|s' \sim t|t'$ and $t=t'$, then $s=s'$ (VI 8·4).

3. *If* $s|s' \sim t|t'$ *then* $s|t \sim s'|t'$.

Dem. By 1 there are points O, S, T, S', T' such that the intervals OS, OT, OS', OT' have measures s, t, s', t' resp. with $S\hat{O}S'$ a right angle, T on $[OS$, T' on $[OS'$, and $SS' \parallel TT'$. Let $OR' \simeq OT$, $OR \simeq OS'$ with R' on $[OS'$ and R on $[OS$. Then $R'T \parallel RS'$ (VI 8·5). Now O, S, T, R colline, O, S', T', R' colline and O, S, S' do not, whence by Pappus' Theorem, $TR' \parallel S'R$ and $TT' \parallel SS'$ imply $SR' \parallel RT'$. But $\mu OR = s'$, $\mu OR' = t$. Whence $s|t \sim s'|t'$.

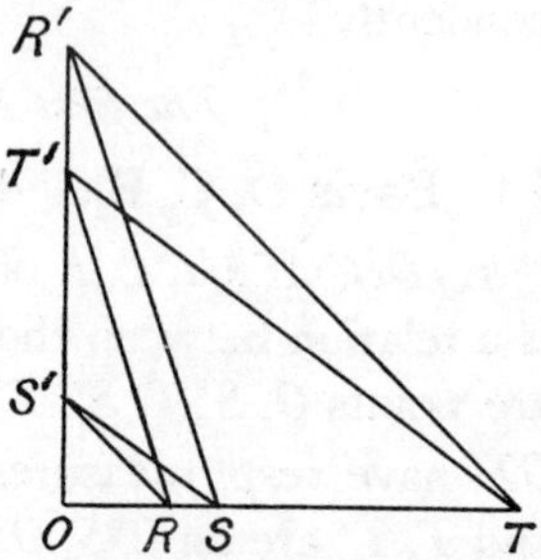

Fig. 76

·1. Note the use of Pappus' Theorem in the proof.

·2. If $s|s_1 \sim t|t_1$ and $s_1|s_2 \sim t_1|t_2$, then $s|s_2 \sim t|t_2$.

Dem. By 3 we have $s|t \sim s_1|t_1$ and $s_1|t_1 \sim s_2|t_2$. Whence by 1·4 and 3.

·3. If $s|s_1 \sim t|t_1$ and $s|s_2 \sim t|t_2$, then $s_1|s_2 \sim t_1|t_2$. (As for ·2.)

4. *If* $s|t \sim s'|t'$ *then* $(s+t)|t \sim (s'+t')|t'$.

Dem. Since $s|t \sim s'|t'$ we have $s|s' \sim t|t'$ (3) and with the construction of 1 this gives $SS' \parallel TT'$. Let $SR \simeq OT$, $[OSR]$ and $RR' \parallel SS'$ with R' on OS'. Since $OT \simeq SR$ we have $OT' \simeq S'R'$ (VI 6) and $[OSR]$ gives $[OS'R']$ (VI 3). Let $\mu OR = r$, $\mu OR' = r'$, then $r = s+t$ (IV 12·2), $r' = s'+t'$. But $RR' \parallel TT'$. Hence $r|r' \sim t|t'$, $(s+t)|t \sim (s'+t')|t'$.

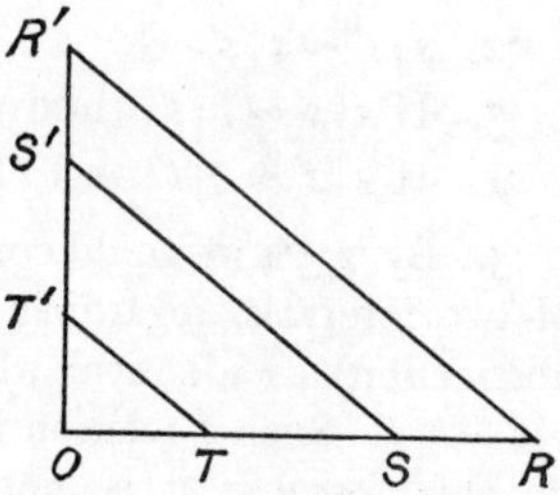

Fig. 77

·1. If $(s+t)|t \sim (s'+t')|t'$, then $s|t \sim s'|t'$.

·2. If $s > t$ and $s|t \sim s'|t'$, then $s' > t'$ and

$$(s-t)|t \sim (s'-t')|t'.$$

·3. And $(s+t)|(s-t) \sim (s'+t')|(s'-t')$ (1·3 and 3·3).

5. *If* $s\,|\,t \sim s'\,|\,t'$, *then* $s\,|\,t \sim (s+s')\,|\,(t+t')$.

Dem. Since $s\,|\,t \sim s'\,|\,t'$ we have successively $s\,|\,s' \sim t\,|\,t'$ (3), $(s+s')\,|\,s' \sim (t+t')\,|\,t'$ (4) and $(s+s')\,|\,(t+t') \sim s'\,|\,t'$ (3).

·1. If $s>s'$ and $s\,|\,t \sim s'\,|\,t'$, then $t>t'$ and

$$s\,|\,t \sim (s-s')\,|\,(t-t').$$

6. *If* $s\,|\,s' \sim t\,|\,t'$ *and* $s\,|\,r' \sim r\,|\,t'$, *then* $s'\,|\,r \sim r'\,|\,t$.

Dem. The usual construction gives $SS' \parallel TT'$, $SR' \parallel RT'$ and hence by Pappus' Theorem $S'R \parallel R'T$.

7. *If* $t\,|\,s \sim t'\,|\,s'$ *and* $r\,|\,s \sim r'\,|\,s'$, *then* $(t+r)\,|\,s \sim (t'+r')\,|\,s'$.

Dem. For $s\,|\,t \sim s'\,|\,t'$ and $s\,|\,r \sim s'\,|\,r'$ (1·3), whence $t\,|\,r \sim t'\,|\,r'$ (3·3), $(t+r)\,|\,r \sim (t'+r')\,|\,r'$ (4). But $r\,|\,s \sim r'\,|\,s'$, hence

$$(t+r)\,|\,s \sim (t'+r')\,|\,s' \text{ (3·2)}.$$

·1. If $t\,|\,s \sim t'\,|\,s'$ and $r\,|\,s \sim r'\,|\,s'$ and $t>r$, then $t'>r'$ and $(t-r)\,|\,s \sim (t'-r')\,|\,s'$.

·2. *Notation.* It will be convenient to write $AB\,|\,BC$ in future in place of $\mu AB\,|\,\mu BC$.

Similar Triangles

8. *Def.* If ABC, $A'B'C'$ be two triangles and $\hat{A} \simeq \hat{A}'$, $\hat{B} \simeq \hat{B}'$ (in which case also $\hat{C} \simeq \hat{C}'$ (VI 8·1)) then we say $\triangle ABC$ and $\triangle A'B'C'$ are '*similar*' and we write $ABC \sim A'B'C'$.

·1. Note that the order of the letters is important. Thus if $ABC \sim A'B'C'$ then $BCA \sim B'C'A'$, $CAB \sim C'A'B'$, etc.; but $ACB \sim A'B'C'$ need not be true.

9. *The relation* $\sim$ *between triangles is equable*, since the relation $\simeq$ between angles is equable.

·1. Congruent triangles are similar.

10. *If* $ABC \sim A'B'C'$, *then* $AB\,|\,A'B' \sim BC\,|\,B'C' \sim CA\,|\,C'A'$.

Dem. First let $A\hat{B}C$ and hence $A'\hat{B}'C'$ be a right angle (IV 44). There are points A'', C'' on $[BA$, $[BC$ resp. such that $BA'' \simeq B'A'$, $BC'' \simeq B'C'$, whence $A'B'C' \simeq A''BC''$, $B\hat{C''}A'' \simeq B\hat{C}A$; hence $CA \parallel C''A''$ (VI 4) and

$$BC\,|\,BA \sim BC''\,|\,BA'' \text{ (1)},$$

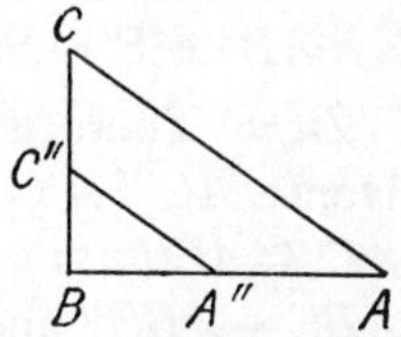

Fig. 78

i.e. $BC\,|\,BA \sim B'C'\,|\,B'A'$, and the Theorem follows by 3, for the sides containing the right angle in right-angled triangles.

Next let ABC be any triangle, I its incentre, IP, IQ, IR perpendiculars to BC, CA, AB resp. Then $IP \simeq IQ \simeq IR$ (V 7·2). Let corresponding dashed letters refer to $\triangle A'B'C'$. Since $I\hat{B}P$, $I'\hat{B}'P'$ are halves of $A\hat{B}C$, $A'\hat{B}'C'$ resp. we have $I\hat{B}P \simeq I'\hat{B}'P'$ (IV 46·2). Also $I\hat{P}B$, $I'\hat{P}'B'$ are right angles, hence by the first case $BP|PI \sim B'P'|P'I'$. Similarly

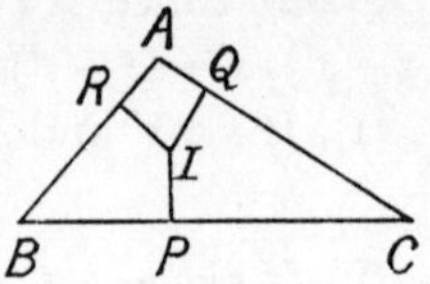

Fig. 79

$$CP|PI \sim C'P'|P'I'.$$

Now I is the incentre of $\triangle ABC$ and $IP \perp BC$, hence $[BPC]$ (V 7·4) and $\mu BP + \mu PC = \mu BC$. Hence by 7,

$$BC|PI \sim B'C'|P'I', \text{ and by 3, } BC|B'C' \sim PI|P'I'.$$

Similarly $CA|C'A' \sim QI|Q'I' \sim PI|P'I'$ (2). Hence the Theorem.

10·1. If $ABC \sim A'B'C'$ then $AB|BC \sim A'B'|B'C'$ (10, 3).

11. *If O, A, B colline and $A, B \neq O$ and O, A', B' colline and $OA \neq OA'$ and $AA' \| BB'$, then $OA|OA' \sim OB|OB'$* (VI 4·9).

·1. *If $[OAB]$ $[OA'B']$ or $[BOA]$ $[B'OA']$ or $[OBA]$ $[OB'A']$ and $OA|OA' \simeq OB|OB'$ and $OA \neq OA'$ then $AA' \| BB'$.* (Use VI 3, 3·1.)

·2. *If a, b be measures of intervals, and n a natural number, then $na|nb \sim a|b$ and $\frac{1}{n}a \,\Big|\, \frac{1}{n}b \sim a|b$* (VI 6·8).

·3. *If in triangles OAB, $O'A'B'$ we have $\hat{O} \simeq \hat{O}'$,*

$$OA|OA' \sim OB|OB', \textit{ then } OAB \sim OA'B'$$

(11·1 and congruence).

12. *If in triangles ABC, $A'B'C'$ we have*

$$AB|A'B' \sim BC|B'C' \sim CA|C'A', \textit{ then } ABC \sim A'B'C'.$$

Dem. There is a point C'' with $ABC'' \sim A'B'C'$ (IV 53). Hence $AC''|A'C' \sim AB|A'B'$ (10) $\sim CA|C'A'$ (hyp.). Hence $AC'' \simeq AC$ (2·11). Similarly $BC'' \simeq BC$, $ABC \simeq ABC''$. Hence $ABC \sim ABC''$ and the Theorem follows.

13. *If in triangles ABC, $A'B'C'$ we have $\hat{A} \simeq \hat{A}'$ and $AB|A'B' \sim BC|B'C'$, then $\hat{C}$, $\hat{C}'$ are congruent or supplementary.*

Dem. If also $AB \mid A'B' \sim AC \mid A'C'$ then $ABC \sim A'B'C'$ (12) and $\hat{C} \simeq \hat{C}'$. But if this is false there is a point $D \neq C$ on $[AC$ such that $AB \mid A'B' \sim AD \mid A'C'$ (1·1). By 11·3 and 2·11 we find $BD \simeq BC$ and the Theorem follows as in IV 27.

14. *If $B\hat{A}C$, $B'\hat{A}'C'$ be right angles and $AB \mid A'B' \sim BC \mid B'C'$, then $ABC \sim A'B'C'$.*

Dem. $\hat{C}$, $\hat{C}'$ cannot be supplementary since both are of measure $< \pi/2$ (VI 8·3, IV 57·8). Hence they are congruent (13).

·1. *Note.* We could not have shewn IV 52 by this method because then we had not introduced the parallel Axiom. There is no point in avoiding it here because, as we shall see, it is essential to the theory of similarity.

The Algebra of Intervals

15. *Defs.* Take any fixed measure of an interval, once for all. Denote this fixed measure by u, and call any interval with this measure a '*unit*' interval.

If a, b be measures of intervals and there are points O, I, A, B, C, such that O, I, B colline and O, A, C colline, $I\hat{O}A$ is a right angle, $BC \parallel IA$, $\mu OI = u$, $\mu OA = a$, $\mu OB = b$ then μOC is denoted by ab—the '*product*' of a and b.

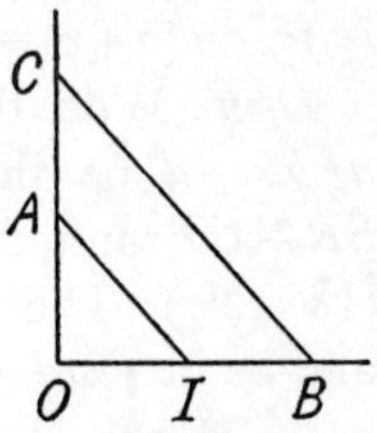

Fig. 80

·1. *If a, b be measures of intervals, then ab is also the measure of an interval.*

·2. $au = a$.

·3. *$ab = c$ implies $c \mid b \sim a \mid u$, and conversely* (1, 15).

·4. *If a, b be measures of intervals, ab is uniquely fixed* (1·1).

16. *If $ab = ad$ then $b = d$, and conversely.*

Dem. $ab = ad = c$ implies $c \mid b \sim a \mid u$ and $c \mid d = a \mid u$ (15·3). Now use 1·4, 2·1.

17. $ab = ba$.

Dem. $ab = c$ implies $c \mid b \sim a \mid u$, hence $c \mid a \sim b \mid u$ (3), $ba = c$ (15·3).

·1. If $ba = da$ then $b = d$, and conversely (16, 17).

17·2. *Note.* In the proof of 17 we have used 3 which involves Pappus' Theorem. We shall see later that Pappus' Theorem is essential to the proof (Chapter VIII).

18. $a(bc) = (ab)c$.

Dem. Let IOA' be a right angle, D, B, E on $[OI$, D', F', E', C' on $[OA'$. Let OA', OB, OC' have measures a, b, c resp. and let $\mu OI = u$. Let $BD' \parallel IA'$, $OD \simeq OD'$. Then $\mu OD = \mu OD' = ab = d$ (say). Let $DF' \parallel BE' \parallel IC'$; $OE \simeq OE'$. Then $\mu OF' = cd$, and $\mu OE = \mu OE' = cb = e$ (say). Hence $bc = e$ (17). Since OD, $OE \simeq OD'$, OE', we have $DD' \parallel EE'$ (VI 8·5) and thence by Pappus' Theorem $BD' \parallel EF'$. Hence $IA' \parallel EF'$, which gives $ae = \mu OF' = cd = dc$ (17). But $e = bc$, $d = ab$. Hence the Theorem.

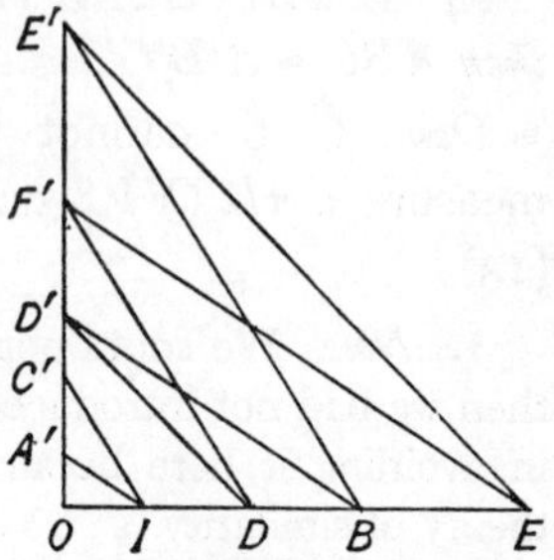

Fig. 81

19. $a(b+c) = ab + ac$.

Dem. With the figure of 4, let I be on $[OS$, A on $[OS'$; let a, b, c, d be the measures of OA, OT, OS, OR resp. Let $SR \simeq OT$ and IA, TT', SS', RR' be parallel. Then $d = b + c$ (IV 12·2). The measures of OT', OS', OR' resp. are ab, ac, ad and as in 4, $ad = ab + ac$.

·1. If $a, b_1, \ldots, b_n$ be the measures of intervals then

$$a(b_1 + b_2 + \ldots + b_n) = ab_1 + ab_2 + \ldots + ab_n \quad \text{(I 23·7)}.$$

·2. And $(b_1 + b_2 + \ldots + b_n)a = b_1 a + b_2 a + \ldots + b_n a$.

20. *If* $ad = bc$ *then* $a|c \sim b|d$, *and conversely.*

Dem. $ad = bc$ means there is a measure x with $ad = x$, $bc = x$. By 17 and 15·3, we have $x|a \sim d|u$ and $x|b \sim c|u$. Hence by 6.

·1. *Notation.* We shall often find it convenient to write AB instead of μAB. Thus we shall usually write $AB.CD$ for $\mu AB.\mu CD$, and $\frac{1}{n}AB$ for $\frac{1}{n}.\mu AB$, n being a natural number. If $a = \mu AB$, we write a^2 for aa, and AB^2 for $\mu AB.\mu AB$. Thus, again, if X is mid AB, we write $\frac{1}{2}AB$ for μAX.

·2. If a, b, x be measures of intervals then

$$(a+b)^2 = a^2 + 2ab + b^2.$$

20·3. And $(a-b)^2 = a^2 + b^2 - 2ab$ if $a > b$.

·4. And $a^2 - b^2 = (a-b)(a+b)$ if $a > b$.

·5. And $a < b$ implies $ax < bx$ and $a^2 < b^2$.

These all follow from the algebraical laws that we have established for the measures of intervals. It does *not* of course follow from these laws that these measures are real numbers; for instance these measures are not yet a continuous set. Note also that the measures are signless.

21. *If n be a natural number and a, b measures of intervals then* $na.b = a.nb = n(ab)$ (11·2, 20, 19·1).

·1. Also $a.\frac{1}{n}u = \frac{1}{n}a$ (11·2, 15·3).

·2. And $a.\frac{1}{n}b = \frac{1}{n}a.b = \frac{1}{n}(ab)$ (11·2, 20).

·3. If a, b, x are measures of intervals $a|b \sim ax|bx \sim xa|xb$.

Dem. There is y with $ax|bx \sim y|u$. Hence $y(bx) = ax$ (15·3), $(yb)x = ax$ (18), $yb = a$ (17·1), $a|b \sim y|u$.

·4. If $ab|cd \sim u|u$ then $a|c \sim d|b$, and conversely.

Dem. $ab|cd \sim u|u$ implies $ab = cd$ (2) whence by 17, 20.

·5. $a|b \sim x|y$ implies $ac|bd \sim xc|yd$ (·3, 3).

·6. If $a|b \sim x|y$ and $c|d \sim z|w$, then $ac|bd \sim xz|yw$ (·5).

·7. *If a be a measure of an interval, there is a measure, which may be denoted by a^{-1}, such that $a.a^{-1} = a^{-1}.a = u$.*

·8. *If $ad = bc$ then $a.c^{-1} = b.d^{-1}$ and conversely. Comparing with* 20 *we see that $a|c \sim b|d$ and $ac^{-1} = bd^{-1}$ imply each other.*

Thus we could have erected the Algebra of intervals first, and then have deduced the theory of proportion as a theory of equations of type $ac^{-1} = bd^{-1}$.

Applications. The Theorem of Pythagoras. Circles

22. *If $A\hat{B}C$ be a right angle and $BD \perp AC$, D on AC, then* $AB^2 = AD.AC$, and $BD^2 = AD.DC$.

Dem. $[ACD]$ is impossible since it gives $\mu B\hat{C}A > \mu B\hat{D}C = \pi/2$ (IV 60) which is impossible since $A\hat{B}C$ is a right angle (VI 8·3). Similarly $[DAC]$ and $D = A, C$ are impossible, and hence $[ADC]$. From this it easily follows that $DAB \sim BAC$ and $BDA \sim CDB$. The first gives $AD|AB \sim AB|AC$ (10) and so $AB^2 = AD.AC$ (20). Similarly for the second.

23. Pythagoras' Theorem. *If $A\hat{B}C$ is a right angle then*

$$AB^2 + BC^2 = AC^2.$$

Dem. With the construction of 22 we have $AB^2 = AD.AC$ and similarly $CB^2 = CD.CA$. But since $[ADC]$ we have $\mu AD + \mu CD = \mu AC$ (IV 12·3). Then 19 gives the Theorem.

Note. It is hardly necessary to remark that no question of *areas* has yet arisen. AB^2 is the measure of an *interval.*

·1. If A, B be fixed points, the set of points X such that $AX^2 - BX^2$ is a fixed measure, is a line perpendicular to AB.

Dem. If $XY \perp AB$, Y on AB then, by 20·4·5, 23

$$AX^2 - BX^2 = AY^2 + YX^2 - (BY^2 + YX^2)$$
$$= AY^2 - BY^2 = (AY + BY)(AY - BY) = AB.2MY,$$

where M is mid AB, by IV 14·4 and the theory of addition and subtraction (IV 13, I 20). Hence μMY is a fixed measure (17·1) and since $AY > BY$ (by hyp.), therefore Y is a fixed point.

24. *The. and Def.* If in triangles ABC, $A'B'C'$ we have $\measuredangle ABC \simeq A'B'C'$, $\measuredangle BCA \simeq B'C'A'$ or if we have

$$\measuredangle ABC \simeq C'B'A', \quad \measuredangle BCA \simeq A'C'B'$$

then the triangles are similar, in the first case '*directly*,' in the second '*indirectly*.'

25. *If A, B, C, D be cyclic and BC, AD meet in O then $AO.DO = BO.CO$. Conversely, if $[AOD]\,[BOC]$ or $[ADO]\,[BCO]$ or $[OAD]\,[OBC]$ and $AO.DO = BO.CO$ then A, B, C, D are cyclic.*

Dem. For the first part, $\measuredangle ABC \simeq ADC$ (VI 25). Hence $\measuredangle ABO \simeq ODC$. Also $\measuredangle BOA \simeq COD$. Hence $ABO \sim CDO$, $AO|BO \sim CO|DO$, $AO.DO = BO.CO$. The second part follows from 11·3, or indirectly.

·1. If OA touches the circle ABC at A, and O, C, B colline then $OA^2 = OB.OC$. Conversely if $OA^2 = OB.OC$ and B is on $[OC$ then OA touches the circle ABC at A.

Dem. For the first part $\measuredangle CBA \simeq CAO$ (VI 26), $\measuredangle BOA \simeq COA$. Hence $OBA \sim OAC$, $OB|OA \sim OA|OC$, $OA^2 = OB.OC$. The second part by 11·3, or indirectly. (Here again we see the advantages of the cross.)

Harmonic Ranges

26. If r, s be measures of intervals and AB a given interval, there is a point F with $[AFB]$ and $AF|FB \sim r|s$, and if $r > s$ there is a point G with $[ABG]$ and $AG|GB \sim r|s$.

Dem. Let Z be a point not on AB and let C, D be on $[AZ$ with $\mu AC = r$, $\mu CD = s$, $[ACD]$. Let $CF \| DB$, F on AB. Then by 11 and VI 3, F satisfies the conditions. For the second part, since $r > s$ there is a point W on A^-C with $\mu CW = s$; let $CK \| WB$, then CK meets AB in a point G satisfying the conditions.

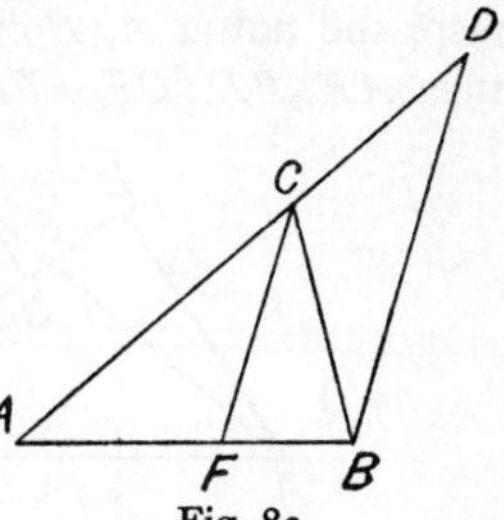

Fig. 82

27. Let ACB be a triangle and $[ACX]$. Let $[CY$ bisect $A\hat{C}B$ or $X\hat{C}B$ and meet AB in F then $AC|CB \sim AF|FB$.

Dem. Let $DB \| CF$ then DB meets AC in D, say, and (using the cross) $\measuredangle DBC \simeq FCB \simeq ACF \simeq ADB \simeq CDB$. Hence $CD \simeq CB$ and by 11,

$$AC|CD \sim AF|FB.$$

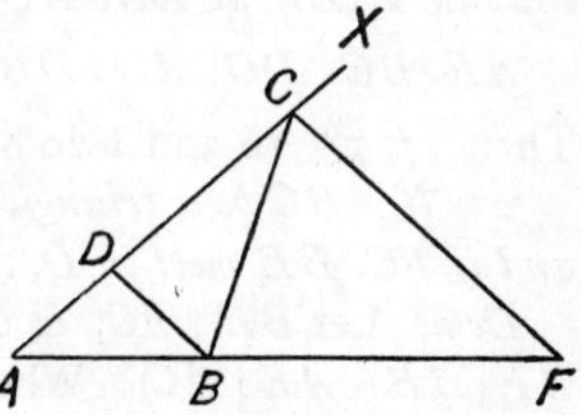

Fig. 83

·1. *Def.* If A, F, B, G colline, and $AG|GB \sim AF|FB$ and $F \neq G$, then the ordered set of points (A, F, B, G) is called a '*harmonic range*' and F, G are said to '*separate A, B harmonically*.' We have orders $[AFBG]$ or $[AGBF]$.

·2. There are points which separate two given points harmonically (26).

·3. If F, G separate A, B harmonically, then A, B do so for F, G.

Dem. $AF|FB \sim AG|GB$ implies $FA|AG \sim FB|BG$.

·4. If ACB be a triangle, F, G on AB and $[CF$, $[CG$ bisect $A\hat{C}B$, $X\hat{C}B$ where $[ACX]$, then A, B separate F, G harmonically. (27, 27·1.)

The Theorems of Menelaus and Ceva

28. If ABC be a triangle and D, E, F be on BC, CA, AB resp. and not at A, B or C and if DEF colline, then

$$AF.BD.CE = FB.DC.EA.$$

Dem. Let $AL, BM, CN \perp DF$ with L, M, N on DF. Then $AF|FB \sim AL|BM$, $BD|DC \sim BM|CN$, $CE|EA \sim CN|AL$ (10).

Hence

$$AF.BD.CE \mid FB.DC.EA \sim AL.BM.CN \mid BM.CN.AL \sim u \mid u$$

by 21·6, 17, 2·2, and the Theorem follows by 2·22.

28·1. If ABC be a triangle and D, E, F be on BC, CA, AB resp. and not at A, B or C and if AD, BE, CF concur (in O say), then $AF.BD.CE = FB.DC.EA$.

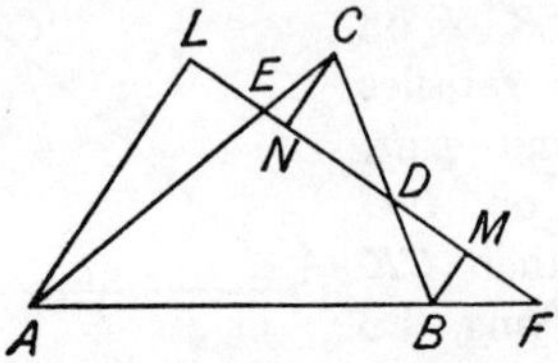

Fig. 84

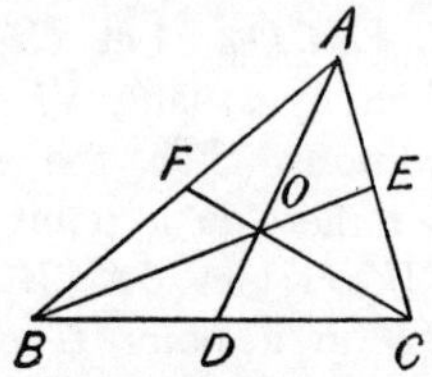

Fig. 85

Dem. By 28 applied to the triangle ABD and the line FOC, we have $AF.BC.DO = FB.CD.OA$. By the triangle ACD and the line EOB, we have $AO.DB.CE = OD.BC.EA$. Whence

$$AF.BC.DO.AO.DB.CE = FB.CD.OA.OD.BC.EA.$$

Then 17, 18, 16 and I 20·81 give the Theorem.

·2. *If ABC be a triangle and F be on $[AB$, E on AC and $FE \parallel BC$, and if FC, BE meet in O, then AO meets BC in its mid-point D, say.*

Dem. Let $BH \parallel FO$, H on AO. Then easily $AF \mid AB \sim AO \mid AH$, $AF \mid AB \sim AE \mid AC$. Whence $BOCH$ is a parallelogram, and the Theorem follows.

·3. *If ABC be a triangle and D the mid-point of BC and O be on $[DA$ then CO, BO meet AB, AC resp. in points F, E such that $FE \parallel BC$.*

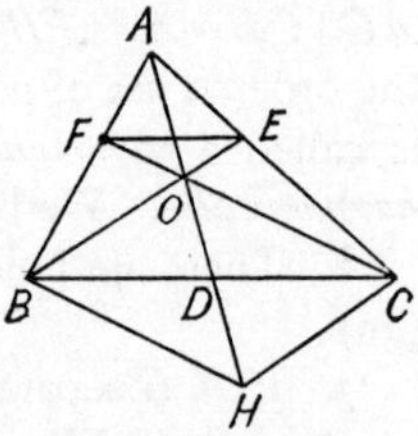

Fig. 86

Note. These Theorems are important in the theory of constructions. They could be shewn like the next from 28, 28·1.

29. If ABC be a triangle and D, E, F be on BC, CA, AB resp., and AD, BE, CF meet in O, and FE meet BC in G, then D, G separate B, C harmonically. (Apply 28, 28·1 to triangle ABC, using the method of 28·1.)

·1. *Note.* This Theorem is of great importance in projective geometry where it figures as the harmonic property of the complete quadrilateral. Suppose we make our Euclidean space projective, then in 28·2 the lines FE, BC meet in an ideal point X. If then the mid-point of BC and the ideal point X on BC be taken to separate B, C harmonically (by extending the definition), 28·2 will be a special case of 29. If we attempt to reconcile this extension with 27·1 we shall have to put $BX \mid XC \sim u \mid u$, but *as we have not defined* $B \vdash\!\dashv X$, this will have to be regarded as a pure convention.

30. *Desargues' Theorem in a plane*, VI 39·2·3, *follows from* $\mathbf{O}_p\, \mathbf{C}_p\, \mathbf{P}_1$. (We shew VI 39·2.)

Dem. If AX, BY, CZ concur in O then since $AB \parallel XY$ and $BC \parallel YZ$ we have $OA \mid OX \sim OB \mid OY$ (11, 3), $OB \mid OY \sim OC \mid OZ$. Hence $OA \mid OX \sim OC \mid OZ$ and $AC \parallel XZ$. If AX, BY, CZ are parallel we have $AB \simeq XY$, $BC \simeq YZ$ (VI 5) and $A\hat{B}C \simeq X\hat{Y}Z$ (VI 7, 3·4). Hence $AC \simeq XZ$. Also $AX \simeq BY \simeq CZ$. Hence

$$AC \parallel XZ \text{ (VI 5·2)}.$$

(We have not used VI 5·3 because the proviso raises difficulties.)

Homotheties and Translations

§ 2. **Basis O P** or **A′ P** or, if the figures are all in one plane, then *Desargues' Theorem* and $\mathbf{O}_p$ **P** or $\mathbf{A}_p'$ **P**.

31. *If* DA, AB, BC *go not through* O *and be parallel to* $D'A'$, $A'B'$, $B'C'$ *resp. where* D', A', B', C' *are on* OD, OA, OB, OC *resp. then* $CD \parallel C'D'$.

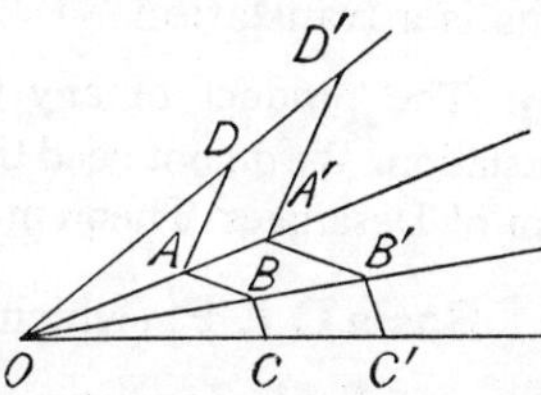

Fig. 87

Dem. If B be not on OD, then Desargues' Theorem on triangles DAB, $D'A'B'$ gives $DB \parallel D'B'$ and then on triangles DBC, $D'B'C'$ gives $CD \parallel C'D'$. (The cases when $BD = AB$ or BC are trivial.) If B be on OD, let E be not on OD or on OC and let $AE \parallel A'E'$ with E' on OE. Then as above, $EC \parallel E'C'$, and $ED \parallel E'D'$ by triangles EDA, $E'D'A'$. Hence $CD \parallel C'D'$ by triangles ECD, $E'C'D'$. Note that C may be on OA.

·1. If DD', AA', BB', CC' are parallel and $DD' \ddagger AA'$, $AA' \ddagger BB'$, $BB' \ddagger CC'$ and DA, AB, BC are parallel to $D'A'$, $A'B'$, $B'C'$ resp. then $CD \parallel C'D'$.

32. *Defs.* If A' is on OA, the '*homothety*' (O, AA') is a (1, 1) transformation of points of a plane or space into points of the same plane or space, in which the '*centre*' O corresponds to itself, A is transformed into A', and a point B not on OA

into a point B' on OB such that $AB \parallel A'B'$, and a point $C \neq O$, A, on OA, is transformed into a point C' on OA such that $BC \parallel B'C'$.

If $A \neq A'$, the '*translation*' AA' is a (1, 1) transformation of points of a plane or space into points of the same plane or space, in which A is transformed to A', and a point B not on AA' into a point B' such that $AB \parallel A'B'$ and $AA' \parallel BB'$, and a point C on AA' is transformed to a point C' on AA' such that $BC \parallel B'C'$.

The position of C' in both the homothety and the translation is determined by C alone and is independent of B (31, 31·1).

If $A = A'$ the '*translation*' AA' is identity.

33. A homothety or a translation transforms a line (plane) into a parallel line (plane).

·1. And if A, B, C be transformed into A', B', C' then $AB \parallel A'B'$, and $[ABC]$ implies $[A'B'C']$.

·2. The product of two homotheties with the same centre is a homothety with that centre. The product of two translations is a translation.

·3. The product of any two homotheties is a homothety or a translation. We do not need this. It is easily shewn from the projective form of Desargues' Theorem.

§ 3. **Basis O C P$_1$** (which implies *Desargues' Theorem*).

34. *If X, Y, Z are transformed to X', Y', Z' by the homothety (O, AA') then* $XO\hat{,}XY \simeq X'O\hat{,}X'Y'$; $YX\hat{,}YZ \simeq Y'X'\hat{,}Y'Z'$; $X'Y' \mid XY \sim OA' \mid OA$; $X'Y' \mid Y'Z' \sim XY \mid YZ$.

Dem. VI 3, 3·1, 7; IV 96 (for space), VII 10, 3.

Note that in the homothety we can have either $[AOA']$ or $[OAA']$.

·1. If X, Y, Z are transformed to X', Y', Z' by the translation AA' then

$$XX' \parallel AA',\ XX' \simeq AA' \text{ (VI 5)},\ YX\hat{,}YZ \simeq Y'X'\hat{,}Y'Z' \text{ (30)}.$$

·2. A transformation of points into points whereby O is unchanged and A becomes A' on OA, and B becomes B' on $[OB$ or $OB]$ according as A' is on $[OA$ or $OA]$, and where $OA \mid OA' \sim OB \mid OB'$, is the homothety (O, AA').

35. *By a homothety (centre O) or a translation, a circle becomes a circle, a sphere a sphere, whose centre P′ is the transform of the original centre P by the homothety or translation.*

Dem. For a circle in a plane through O and for a sphere this follows by 34, 34·1. For a circle in a plane not through O, we can draw two spheres meeting in the circle; these transform into spheres with at least two common points, and hence which meet in a circle (V 20·4). That the centres correspond is easy to shew.

·1. *A circle or sphere with a tangent line or plane is transformed into such by a homothety, or translation.*

Dem. Centres become centres (35) and the angle between any two rays is congruent to the angle between the transformed rays (34).

Crosses between Coplanar Circles

36. *Defs.* If two circles C_1, C_2 meet in P the '*cross*' (C_1, C_2) at P is $\measuredangle (PT_1, PT_2)$, where PT_1, PT_2 are the tangents at P to C_1, C_2 resp. If C_1, C_2 also meet at Q, it is easy to shew that $\measuredangle (PT_1, PT_2)$ is congruent to the cross opposite to $\measuredangle (QT_1', QT_2')$ where QT_1', QT_2' are the tangents at Q to C_1, C_2. (Join the centres of the circles to P and Q and use IV 72, 76, 77.)

If a line l and a circle C meet at P, the cross (l, C) at P is $\measuredangle (l, PT)$ where PT touches C at P. Similarly for (C, l). If a cross between two circles, or a line and a circle, is a right-angled cross the figures are '*orthogonal*' to one another.

·1. If two circles are orthogonal, the radius of one to a point of meeting touches the other there.

·2. If the radius of one circle to a point where it meets a second circle touches the latter, the circles are orthogonal.

·3. If two circles are orthogonal, the centre of each is outside the other (V 6·1).

·4. If circles C_1, C_2 meeting at P become by a homothety circles C_1', C_2' meeting at P' (corresponding to P), the cross (C_1, C_2) at P is congruent to the cross (C_1', C_2') at P'. (Cf. VI 22·2.)

·5. By a homothety orthogonal circles become orthogonal circles.

Inversion and the Inversion Plane

37. *Defs. and Thes.* An '*inversion*' with respect to a given circle or sphere, centre O and radius of measure k, is a transformation which transforms a point $P \neq O$ into P' on $[OP$ with $OP \,.\, OP' = k^2$. Thus O has *no* corresponding point, and points on the given circle or sphere correspond to themselves.

If P is transformed to P', then P' is transformed to P and P, P' are '*inverse*' points with respect to the circle or sphere.

P, P' are '*inverse*' points with respect to a line or plane if the latter is the right bisector of PP'. For the present we denote the inverse point of X, etc., by X', etc.

·1. *The inverse of a line AB with respect to a (coplanar) circle, centre O, is a circle through O, omitting O, which is supposed not on AB.*

Dem. Let $OP \perp AB$, with P on AB and let $OP \,.\, OP' = OA \,.\, OA' = k^2$ with P' on $[OP$ and A' on $[OA$. Then A, A', P, P' are cyclic, hence

$$\measuredangle OA'P' \simeq AA'P' \simeq APP' \text{ (VI 25).}$$

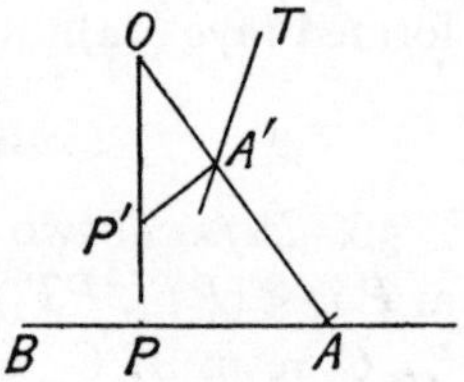

Fig. 88

Hence $O\hat{A}'P'$ is a right angle and A' lies on a circle with diameter OP'. Conversely every point save O on this circle is on the inverse of the line. (Cf. ·5.)

·2. *The inverse of a plane with respect to a sphere, centre O, (O not on the plane) is a sphere through O, omitting O.*

·3. *The inverse of a circle centre P, not through O, with respect to a sphere, centre O, is a circle.*

·4. *The inverse of a sphere centre P, not through O, with respect to a sphere, centre O, is a sphere.*

Dems. ·3, ·4. First let the circle, centre P, lie on a plane through O and let A, B and likewise C, D be points on the circle collinear with O, then

$$OA \,.\, OB = OC \,.\, OD, \quad OB \,.\, OB' = OC \,.\, OC' = OD \,.\, OD',$$

$$OA \,|\, OB' \sim OA \,.\, OB \,|\, OB \,.\, OB' \sim OC \,.\, OD \,|\, OD \,.\, OD' \sim OC \,|\, OD'$$

(21·3) and A is on $[OB = [OB'$ or on $OB] = OB']$ according as C is on $[OD = [OD'$ or on $OD] = OD']$ (V 4·2·3). Thus D' corresponds to C in the homothety (O, AB') (34·2). Hence as

C describes the circle centre P, D′ describes a circle whose centre P′ corresponds to P in that homothety (35). By considering planes through OP we now get ·4. Next, a circle is the meet of two spheres, and their inverses are spheres (·4) which meet in at least two points and hence in a circle. This gives ·3.

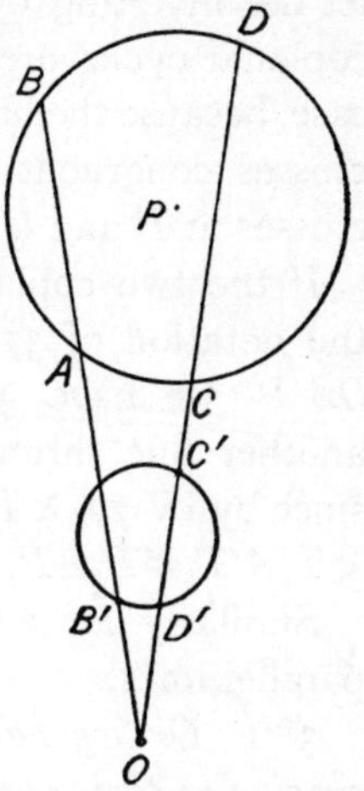

Fig. 89

37·5. The fact that the inverse of a line or plane is not a complete circle or sphere is extremely awkward if a succession of inversions is performed. It is ultimately due to the fact that in inverting with respect to a sphere, centre O, no point corresponds to O. We shall remedy this defect in the plane—a similar remedy serves for space—by adjoining to the previous points of the plane *one* ideal point only, which is not to have any relation of order with the ordinary points; i.e. [ABC] is meaningless, if A or B or C is the ideal point.

Defs. When this ideal point is adjoined, a plane so enlarged is called an '*inversion plane*.' A '*line*' of an inversion plane is a set of points satisfying II 3, together with the ideal point. Thus parallel lines in an inversion plane are those which have no common point save the ideal point. Lines and circles of an inversion plane are called '*cycles*.' The '*inverse*' of the ideal point with respect to a sphere, centre O, is to be taken as O whether O is or is not on the plane. The '*centre*' of every cycle which is a line, is the ideal point of the plane.

·6. *The inverse of an inversion plane* α *with respect to a sphere, centre O not on* α, *is a (complete) sphere through O, and the cycles on the inversion plane become circles on the sphere.*

·7. *The inverse of a cycle in an inversion plane* α *with respect to a cycle which lies on* α, *is a cycle of* α.

38. *If two coplanar cycles meet and be inverted with respect to a cycle, centre O, lying on their plane, then a cross between the cycles is congruent to the opposite of the corresponding cross between the inverted cycles.*

Dem. This is easily shewn when O is the ideal point. Next let the inverting cycle be a circle and first suppose the two coplanar cycles are also circles. The Theorem follows in this case, because the homothety of 37·4 *Dem.* makes corresponding crosses congruent, when we use the remark in 36 about the crosses at P and Q.

If the two coplanar cycles be non-parallel lines, then with the notation of 37·1, if $A'T$ be the tangent at A' to the circle $OA'P'$ we have $\measuredangle AA'T \simeq OA'T \simeq OP'A' \simeq PAA'$. Taking another line through A, we have the Theorem in this case, since by IV 77, $\measuredangle T_1A'A \simeq A'AP_1$ and $\measuredangle AA'T_2 \simeq P_2AA'$ imply $\measuredangle T_1A'T_2 \simeq P_2AP_1$.

Similarly for a line and a circle which meet, or for two parallel lines.

38·1. *Orthogonal cycles invert into orthogonal cycles by an inversion in their plane.*

·2. *If P, Q be on a circle, centre O', which meets a circle, centre O, orthogonally and O, P, Q colline, then P, Q are inverse with respect to the circle, centre O.*

Dem. O is outside the circle, centre O' (36·3), hence Q is on [OP and the Theorem follows by 36·1, 25·1.

·3. *If P, P' be distinct inverse points with respect to a cycle K then any cycle through P, P' meets K orthogonally.*

·4. *If two cycles through P, Q meet a cycle K orthogonally then P, Q are inverse points with respect to K.*

Dem. If K is a circle, centre O, then OP meets the two cycles in the same point, viz. the inverse of P with respect to K (·2). This point must be Q since two cycles cannot meet in three points.

·5. If a Theorem involves only the determination and intersection of lines and circles and the congruence of crosses between them, and it is shewn for the Euclidean plane, it will be true in the inversion plane when lines and circles are replaced by cycles, and thus it will be true in the Euclidean plane when lines are replaced by circles through a point; and a slight extension of the above theory shews it is true on the sphere when cycles are replaced by circles. This is the basis of the well-known generalisation by inversion.

39. *A cycle K and two inverse points P, Q become, by inversion with respect to a cycle of their plane, a cycle and two inverse points.*

Dem. Any cycle C through P, Q (supposed distinct) meets K orthogonally. Hence through P', Q' pass at least two cycles C' meeting K' orthogonally. Hence the Theorem (38·4). In particular—

·1. *If P, Q be inverse points with respect to a cycle K then by inversion with respect to a circle C, centre P, K becomes a cycle K′, and the inverse of Q with respect to C becomes the centre of K′.* (P and Q may coincide.)

·2. If E is the inverse of D with respect to a circle on diameter AB, and E be on AB then D, E separate A, B harmonically (20, 4·3).

·3. *Def.* If E ($\neq O$) is the inverse of D with respect to a circle C, centre O, the line through E perpendicular to OE is the '*polar*' of D with respect to C, and D is the '*pole*' of the line.

·4. If E is outside a circle C and EP, EQ be tangents to C from E touching C in P, Q then PQ is the polar of E (22). If E be on C, then the tangent at E is the polar of E.

·5. If the polar of X goes through Y, the polar of Y goes through X (25).

·6. If EX be the polar of D with respect to the circle C, centre O, and DX meets C in Y, Z then X, D separate Y, Z harmonically.

Dem. Let E be on OD then E, D are inverse points with respect to C. The circle C' on diameter XD goes through E and D and hence meets C orthogonally (38·3). Thus since C through Y, Z meets C' on diameter DX orthogonally, therefore Y, Z are inverse points with respect to C' (38·2). Hence by ·2.

·7. (Fig. 90.) *If two lines through a point E, not on a circle C, meet C in F, G and in H, K resp. and FK, GH meet in X and FH, KG meet in Y, then XY is the polar of E* (·6 and 29).

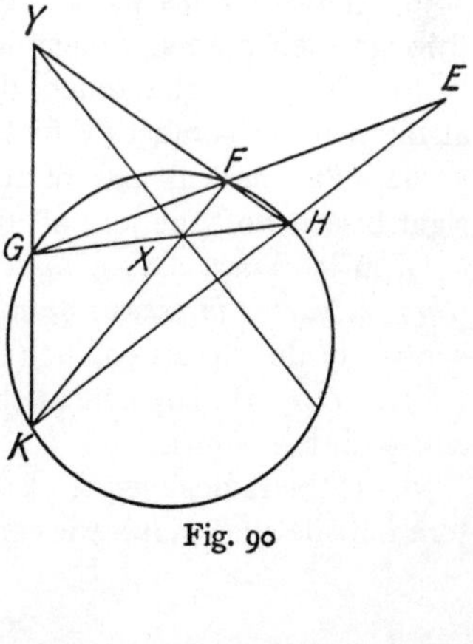

Fig. 90

Thus if we can construct the meets (if existent) of a line and a fixed given circle, we can by drawing lines alone, construct the tangents to that circle from an outside point. The theory of such constructions will be exhaustively dealt with later.

Radical Axes

40. *Def.* If P be not on a circle C, and a line through P meet C in R, S then the '*power*' of P with respect to C is $PR.PS$ if S is on $[PR$ and is $-PR.PS$ if $[RPS]$. As we shall not add powers the minus sign has no algebraic significance, but is merely a distinguishing mark like a dash.

The power of P depends on P and C only (25).

If two circles meet we shall adopt the convention that the power of a point of meeting shall be the same with respect to both circles.

·1. If P be outside a circle C and PT be a tangent to C at T, the power of P with respect to C is PT^2.

·2. The power of P with respect to a circle (O, k) i.e. *a circle of centre O and radius of measure k*, is apart from 'sign' the difference between OP^2 and k^2.

Dem. Let P be inside the circle and let PO meet it in R, S and suppose $[POR]$; then $PR.PS=(OR+OP)(OR-OP)=k^2-OP^2$ (20·4). Similarly if P be outside the circle.

·3. If a point have equal powers for two circles it is on both or outside both or inside both.

·4. *The locus of a point P whose powers with respect to two circles are equal, is a straight line perpendicular to the line joining the centres of the two circles, the centres being supposed distinct.*

Dem. Let (O, k) and (O', k') be the circles and let $k>k'$. If P be outside both circles (·3) then $OP^2-k^2=O'P^2-k'^2$; if P be inside both then $k^2-OP^2=k'^2-O'P^2$; if P be on both then $k=OP$, $k'=O'P$. Hence in all cases $OP^2-O'P^2=k^2-k'^2$ and 23·1 gives the Theorem. (The points P do not exist for concentric circles.)

·5. *Def.* This line is the '*radical axis*' of the two circles.

·6. If two circles meet in two points, their radical axis is the line through their points of meeting.

·61. If two circles touch, their radical axis is the tangent to each at the point of contact (V 8·2).

·62. The radical axis of two circles with congruent radii is the right bisector of (the join of) their centres.

·7. *The radical axes of three circles taken in pairs are either parallel (this includes coincidence) or concurrent* (·4). If they are parallel the centres of the circles colline (·4).

·71. *Def.* If they concur the point of concurrence is the '*radical centre*' of the circles.

·8. If the radical centre of three circles lies outside one and therefore outside all (·3), it is the centre of a circle meeting all orthogonally.

41. *If a set of parallel intervals be projected on a plane the measures of the projected intervals are obtained from those of the original intervals by multiplying them by a fixed measure less than or equal to u.*

(By similar triangles. Cf. VI 45, 49.)

·1. *Def.* If a line a be parallel to a plane β, and an interval b be perpendicular to a but not to β, and if b projects into b' on β with $b' \mid b \sim c \mid u$ then c is the '*parameter*' of the projection of the plane (ab) on β.

CHAPTER VIII

DESARGUES' AND PAPPUS' THEOREMS AND THE INTRODUCTION OF CONGRUENCE BY DEFINITION

Introductory Remarks

Our first object is to erect an algebra of points and an analytical geometry on the basis of Axioms **O**, **P**, using particularly Desargues' Theorem and Pappus' Theorem in the forms given in Chapter VI. We find that we can proceed a long way without Pappus' Theorem but that this Theorem is needed to complete the algebra of points in an important respect (commutativity of multiplication). The algebra we give is based on Hilbert's in his *Grundlagen*, but our proofs are much simpler. It may be profitably compared with the algebra of Projective Geometry elaborated in Baker's *Principles of Geometry* and Veblen and Young's *Projective Geometry*.

Having set up our coordinate geometry we can establish a Theory of Congruence on the basis of Axioms **O**, **P** together with Pappus' Theorem and an additional Axiom ($\mathbf{Q}_0$ in § 4) which secures the existence of a sufficient number of points. Our object is simply to get *some* relation between point-couples which has the properties enunciated in Axioms **C** I—VII of Chapter IV. It is easy to see that there may be more than one relation of this kind. For suppose we know already some such relation, so that we may significantly say one figure is congruent to another. Take two non-parallel planes α, β inside which this congruence relation holds. Project *orthogonally* all figures of β on to α. If then we call figures on α 'pseudo-congruent' when the corresponding figures on β are congruent, we easily see that if the congruence relation satisfies **C** I—VII, so does the 'pseudo-congruence' relation on α. An analogous statement holds for space.

The fact is that from a point O we can take *any* three non-coplanar rays and on them *any* three points A, B, C and treat the rays as perpendicular and the intervals OA, OB, OC as congruent, and still preserve all our Axioms **O**, **P**, **C**. For any other ray OX from O, the point D such that OA is 'congruent' to OD, is fully fixed by OA, OB, OC.

Another method, specially applicable to non-Euclidean geometry, by which congruence can be introduced on the basis of Axioms **O** *alone*, is the following: By introducing ideal points we make the space projective, and we consider transformations in this space which turn planes into planes; then, by requiring these transformations to possess certain properties, we arrive at congruent transformations. For this investigation we refer to the books quoted above and to Schur's *Grundlagen der Geometrie*.

It will be noted that in introducing congruence we use not only Axioms **O**, **P** but also Pappus' Theorem and an additional Axiom. In Chapter XIII we shall deduce the two latter assumptions from a continuity Axiom and **O**, $\mathbf{P}_2'$.

As we shall need in the next chapter the algebra of the Complex Variable, we give in the present a geometric foundation of that theory and use it at once to shew that the parallel Axiom is independent of Axioms **O**, **C**.

Since Desargues' and Pappus' Theorems are so important in our work we discuss their connection with the Axioms. We find that the latter (though deducible from $\mathbf{O}_p$, $\mathbf{C}_p$, $\mathbf{P}_1$) cannot be shewn from $\mathbf{O}_p$, **P** and the former, or from **O**, **P**; but that on the other hand Desargues' Theorem does follow from $\mathbf{O}_p$, **P** and Pappus' Theorem but not from $\mathbf{O}_p$, **P** alone, although (VI 39) it does follow from **O**, **P**. Roughly speaking, Desargues' Theorem involves space, and Pappus' Theorem (in our treatment) involves congruence.

The graphical properties of lines and planes in space can all be deduced from **O**, **P** and Pappus' Theorem; and those of lines in the plane from $\mathbf{O}_p$, **P** and Pappus' Theorem (49·2).

An Algebra of Points

§ 1. **Basis O P** or **A′ P** or, if all figures are in one plane, *Desargues' Theorem* and $\mathbf{O}_p$ **P** or $\mathbf{A}_p'$ **P**.

1. *Def.* If O be any point, then $(A+B)\,|\,O$ means the point

which A becomes by the translation OB (VII 32). We shall usually keep O fixed and then write $A+B$ instead of $(A+B)|O$. O is the '*zero point*.'

1·1. *If A, B are given, then $A+B$ is fixed and unique* (given O). (VII 31, 32.)

·2. $O+B=B$, $B+O=B$.

·3. *Given A, there is one and only one point B such that $A+B=O$ and it lies on OA**.

·4. *If $A+B=O$, then $B+A=O$.*

·5. *If $A\neq O$, then $A+A\neq O$.*

·6. *If $A+B=A$, then $B=O$.*

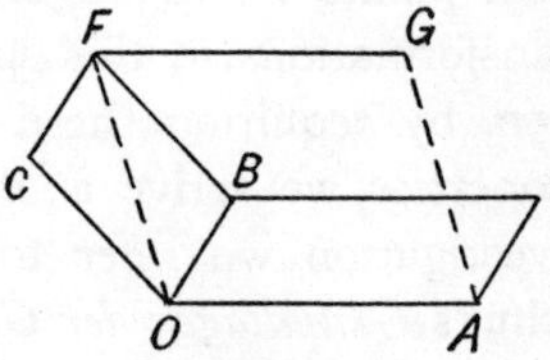

Fig. 91

2. $A+(B+C)=(A+B)+C$.

Dem. Suppose no three of O, A, B, C colline. Let $E=A+B$, $F=B+C$ and $G=A+F$. Then $OAEB$, $OBFC$, $OAGF$ are parallelograms and by Desargues' Theorem $GE \parallel FB$, $GC \parallel EO$. Hence $G=E+C$. If any three of O, A, B, C colline, all colline and the proof is simple (VII 31·1).

3. $A+B=B+A$.

Dem. If A, B do not colline with O the Theorem is clear. If A, B, O colline and $A+B=C$, then there are points X, Y not on OA with OX, XA, $XY \parallel BY$, YC, OA resp. (VII 32). Let $AZ \parallel OX$, then AZ meets XY in Z, say, and AZ, $AX \parallel BY$, YC and X, Y, Z and A, B, C lie on distinct parallel lines. Hence $XB \parallel ZC$ (VI 39·4). Hence OX, XB, $XZ \parallel AZ$, ZC, OB resp. Whence $B+A=C$.

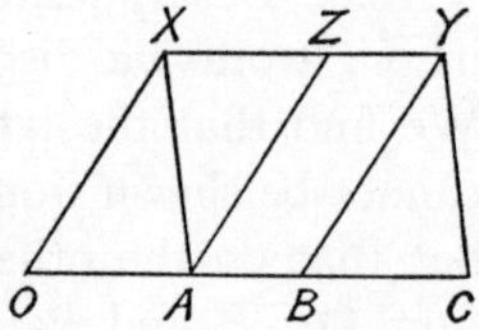

Fig. 92

4. *Hence the points of a plane or space form an abelian group under the operation* $+$, for compare 1·1·2·3, 2, 3 with I 22·1·3·4·2·42.

It should be carefully noted that we are not assuming any congruence axioms, but only the basis set forth above. It is also instructive to compare the above with the addition of vectors in statics.

* Hence our present algebra, unlike that in the last chapter, contains 'negative' elements.

5. *If* $A+B=C$ *and* O, A, B, C *colline and* AX, BY, CZ *are parallel and* X, Y, Z *colline* ($OX \neq OA$), *then* $X+Y=Z$. (Figs. 60, 61, p. 145.)

Dem. Let the parallels to OA through X, Y resp. meet CZ in M, L resp. Then since $A+B=C$ we have $BM \parallel OX$ and since $B+A=C$ we have $AL \parallel OY$. Since

$$OA,\ AX,\ AL \parallel YL,\ LZ,\ OZ \text{ resp.}$$

we have $X+Y=Z$.

6. *Def.* If O, U be distinct points and A be a point $\neq O$ on OU then $(X.A)|O,U$ is the point that X becomes by the homothety (O, UA) (VII 32). We shall usually keep O, U fixed and then write $X.A$ for $(X.A)|O,U$. If $A=O$ then shall $X.A=O$. U is the '*unit point*' on OU.

Note that $X.A$ is defined when X is *any* point and A *is on* OU.

·1. *If* X, A *be given points and* A *is on* OU, *then* $X.A$ *is fixed and unique* (VII 31, 32).

·2. *If* A *is on* OU, *then* $U.A=A.U=A$.

·3. *Given* $A \neq O$ *on* OU, *there is one and only one point* X *with* $X.A=U$ *and it lies on* OU.

·4. *If* $X.A=U$ *and* X, A *both lie on* OU, *then* $A.X=U$.

·5. *If* $X \neq U$ *be on* OU, *then* $X.X \neq X$.

·6. *If* A *be on* OU, *then* $O.A=O$.

7. *If* A, B, C *be on* OU *and* X, Y, Z *on* $OV \neq OU$ *and* UV, AX, BY, CZ *be parallel, then* $(A.B)|O,U=C$ *implies* $(X.Y)|O,V=Z$.

Dem. Since $UV \parallel BY$ and $(A.B)|O,U = C$, therefore $VA \parallel YC$ (VII 32). This with $AX \parallel CZ$ gives $(X.Y)|O,V=Z$.

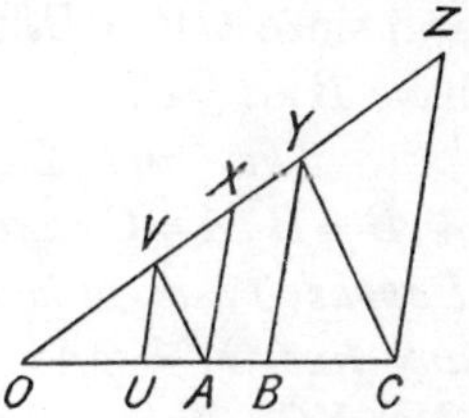

Fig. 93

8. *If* B, C *be on* OU, *then*

$$(A.B).C=A.(B.C).$$

Note that $A.B$ is only defined when B is on OU, and $(A.B)\,C$ only when C and hence $B.C$ are on OU. The Theorem follows from the Def. both when A is and when A is not on OU.

9. $E.(A+B)=E.A+E.B$ *when* A, B *and hence* $A+B$ *are on* OU.

Dem. Let $A+B=C$, $E.A=X'$, $E.B=Y'$, $E.C=Z'$ then if E is not on OU we have EU, AX', BY', CZ' parallel and hence $X'+Y'=Z'$ (5). If E is on OU, there are points E_1, X_1, Y_1, Z_1 collinear with O, and with UE_1, AX_1, BY_1, CZ_1 parallel and E_1E, X_1X', Y_1Y', Z_1Z' parallel, and the Theorem follows again by 5.

10. $(A+B).E=A.E+B.E$ *when E is on OU.*

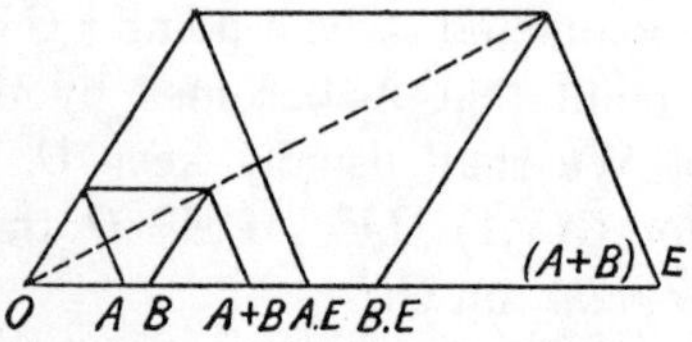

Fig. 94

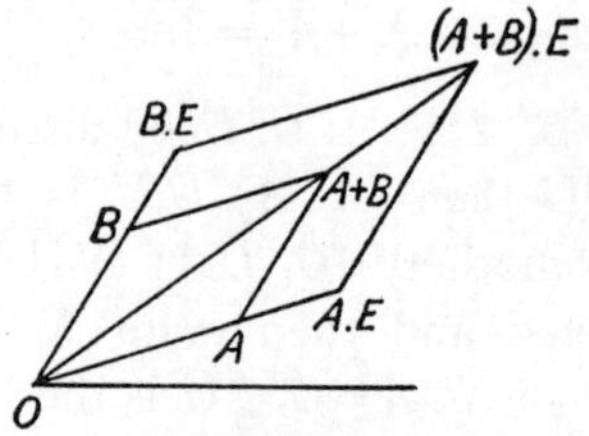

Fig. 95

Dem. A homothety transforms parallel lines into parallel lines (VII 33).

11. *If Pappus' Theorem be true, then* $A.B=B.A$ *for all points A, B on OU.*

Dem. If $A.B=C$ then there are points V, Y collinear with O such that $OV \neq OA$ and UV, $VA \parallel BY$, YC resp. Let $AX \parallel UV$ with X on OV. Thus XA, $AV \parallel BY$, YC resp. Hence $VB \parallel XC$ (Pappus' Theorem) and since UV, $VB \parallel AX$, XC resp. we have $B.A=C$.

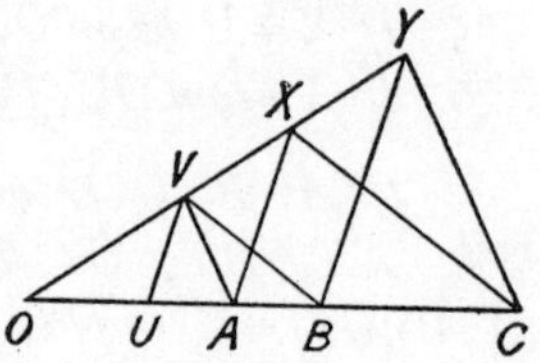

Fig. 96

·1. *The. and Def. Conversely if* $A.B=B.A=C$ *and A, B and hence C are on OU, then Pappus' Theorem holds for A, B, C and any points X, Y, Z on any line* $OV \neq OA$. *That is, if* XA, $AZ \parallel BY$, YC *resp. then* $ZB \parallel XC$. Three such points A, B, C will be called a '*Pappus triad.*'

12. *If Pappus' Theorem be true, the points on OU form a field for addition and multiplication wherein O, U play the part of* 0 *and* 1; *while if Pappus' Theorem be not assumed, the points on OU still form a quasi-field.*

Dem. Compare 4, 6·1·2·3, 8, 9, 10, 11 with I 23.

Coordinate Geometry

13. *The. and Def. If OU, OU′ be distinct lines, a* (1, 1) *correspondence can be set up between the points of OU and those of OU′, such that the fields or quasi-fields of points on OU, OU′* (with zero and unit points O, U and O, U' resp.) *are similar for addition and multiplication* (I 5), *and such that A on OU corresponds to A′ on OU′ if and only if* $AA' \parallel UU'$ (5, 7). *Thus the corresponding points can be represented, as far as their addition and multiplication are concerned, by the same element of the abstract field or quasi-field K.* This we shall henceforth do, and shall call the corresponding element of K the '*coordinate*' of the point '*in the scale*' OU or OU', and we shall usually denote it by the corresponding small letter. K represents the quasi-field of points *on a line.*

14. *Defs.* Take three distinct fixed concurrent lines Ox, Oy, Oz in space, not all coplanar, and any three fixed points distinct from O on them, say U_1, U_2, U_3, as unit points and consider the scales on these lines. If P be any point not on them, and the parallelopiped be drawn of which O, P are opposite vertices* and Ox, Oy, Oz edge-lines*, then if A, B, C be its vertices on Ox, Oy, Oz, and a, b, c their coordinates in the scales on these lines, then (a, b, c) are the '*coordinates*' of P with respect to the '*axes*' OU_1, OU_2, OU_3 or '*the frame*' $OU_1U_2U_3$. Points in the '*coordinate plane*' yOz have the first coordinate 0, and similarly for the other coordinate planes.

In the same way we can assign coordinates to points of a plane by drawing parallelograms.

If the coordinates of the points of any figure satisfy an equation, this is the '*equation of the figure.*'

It will be again noticed that no idea of congruence is assumed.

15. *The equation of a line in a plane Oxy is* $ax + by + c = 0$, *where* (x, y) *are the coordinates of any point on the line with respect to the axes* OU_1, OU_2, *and* a, b, c *are constants in our field or quasi-field K.*

* This ordinary term is defined in general in Chapter XII.

Dem. If the line be parallel to OU_1 or OU_2, its equation is clearly $x=$ const. or $y=$ const. resp. Next let it go through O, let C be a fixed point on it, and P any point on it, with coordinates (xy). Let $OAPB$, $ODCE$ be parallelograms with A, D on OU_1 and B, E on OU_2, then $AB \parallel DE$ (Desargues' Theorem). Let $U_1F \parallel DE$, $AA_1 \parallel U_1U_2$ with F, A_1 on OU_2. Then F is a fixed point on OU_2 with coordinate f, say, in the scale OU_2 and $U_1F \parallel AB$. Hence $F.A_1=B$, that is $fa_1=b$. But $a_1=a=x$ and $b=y$. Hence $fx=y$.

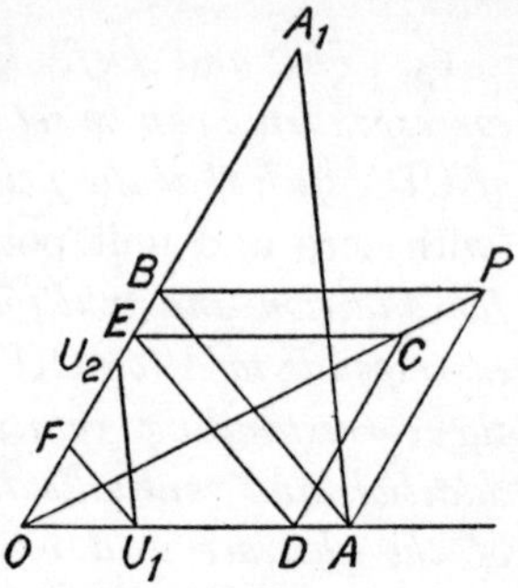

Fig. 97

Next let AP be any line meeting OU_1 in $C \neq O$ and let $OL \parallel AP$ and $OXPY$ be a parallelogram with X, Y on OU_1, OU_2 resp. Then PY meets OL in Q say. Let $QB \parallel PX$ with B on OX. Then since $PC \parallel OQ$ we have $x=b+c$. But $fb=y$ by the first part. Hence $fx=y+fc$ or $fx-y-fc=0$, which is of the required form.

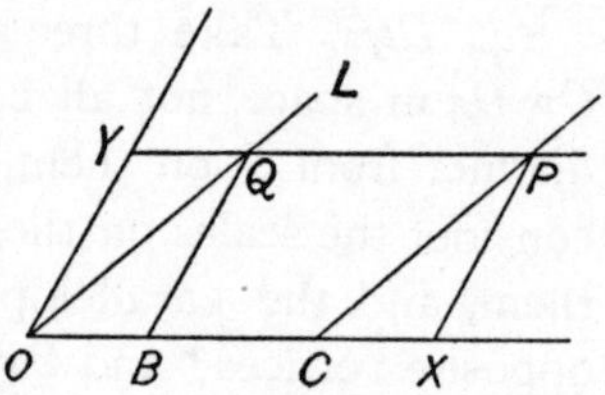

Fig. 98

15·1. *Conversely any equation of the form* $ax+by+c=0$, *where* a, b, c *are constants in our quasi-field* K, *is the equation of a line.*

Dem. If $b \neq 0$ we multiply on the left by b', where $b'b=-1$. Then
$$b'ax-y+b'c=0 \quad \text{or} \quad b'ax=y-b'c,$$
and the Theorem follows by the argument of 15.

·2. Unless Pappus' Theorem is assumed, it does *not* follow that $xa+yb+c=0$ is the equation of a line.

·3. The lines $fx-y-c_1=0$, $fx-y-c_2=0$ are parallel (15).

·4. If $ax+by+c=0$ and $a_1x+b_1y+c_1=0$ are the equations of parallel lines and $a, b, a_1, b_1 \neq 0$, then by ·1·3 and I 22·84.
$$b^{-1}a=b_1^{-1}a_1, \quad aa_1^{-1}=bb_1^{-1}, \quad a^{-1}b=a_1^{-1}b_1, \quad a_1a^{-1}=b_1b^{-1}.$$

·5. *Def.* The '*coordinates*' of the lines $ax+by+c=0$ $(c \neq 0)$ and $ax+by=0$ $(b \neq 0)$ and $x=0$ are respectively $(c^{-1}a, c^{-1}b)$ and $b^{-1}a$ and 0. (Cf. 26·1, 27.)

16. *If $OU_1U_2U_3$ be any frame in space, the equations of any line are of the form*
$z=ax+b=cy+d$ *or* $z=cy+d$, $x=$const. *or* $z=ax+b$, $y=$const. *or* $x=$const. $y=$const.

Dem. The parallels from points of the line l to OU_2 are parallel to one another and so coplane. The plane in which they lie is parallel to OU_2 (VI 36·5) and so meets U_1OU_3 in a line l'. The corresponding points on l, l' (in this projection) have the same (x, z) coordinates. Hence $z=ax+b$ or $x=$const. along both. A continuation of the same argument shews the Theorem.

·1. Conversely any equations of the above forms represent lines.

·2. The lines whose equations are

$$z=ax+b=cy+d \text{ and } z=ax+b_1=cy+d_1$$

are parallel. The lines whose equations are

$$z=cy+d_1,\ x=\text{const. and } z=cy+d_2,\ x=\text{const.}$$

are parallel. Similarly for other forms of the equations.

·3. Conversely the equations of parallel lines can be reduced to such forms.

17. *If the distinct points P_1, P_2, P_3 with coordinates $(x_1y_1z_1)$, $(x_2y_2z_2)$, $(x_3y_3z_3)$ colline, then there are two constants A, B in K, neither zero, such that*

$$\left.\begin{aligned} x_1A+x_2B=x_3,\quad y_1A+y_2B=y_3,\quad z_1A+z_2B=z_3,\\ A+B=1\end{aligned}\right\}\ldots(1).$$

Dem. Let the points be on the line $z=ax+b=cy+d$. Then $z_1=ax_1+b=cy_1+d$, etc.

Let $a\neq 0$, $c\neq 0$ then x_1, x_2, x_3 are unequal; for if e.g. we had $x_1=x_2$, then would $z_1=z_2$, $y_1=y_2$, $P_1=P_2$.

Our equations now give,

$$z_1-z_2=a(x_1-x_2),\quad z_1-z_3=a(x_1-x_3),\quad a=(z_1-z_2)(x_1-x_2)^{-1}.$$

Hence

$$\begin{aligned} z_1-z_3&=(z_1-z_2)(x_1-x_2)^{-1}(x_1-x_3)\\ &=z_1(x_1-x_2)^{-1}(x_1-x_3)-z_2(x_1-x_2)^{-1}(x_1-x_3)\end{aligned}$$

that is
$$z_1A+z_2B=z_3$$

where $A=1-(x_1-x_2)^{-1}(x_1-x_3)$, $B=(x_1-x_2)^{-1}(x_1-x_3)\ldots(2)$.

Thus $$A+B=1$$
and
$$x_1A+x_2B=a^{-1}(z_1-b)A+a^{-1}(z_2-b)B$$
$$=a^{-1}(z_1A+z_2B)-a^{-1}b(A+B)=a^{-1}z_3-a^{-1}b$$
$$=a^{-1}(z_3-b)=a^{-1}ax_3=x_3.$$
Similarly, $$y_1A+y_2B=y_3.$$

If $a=0$ or $c=0$, or the equation of the line is in one of the other forms, the Theorem is shewn in the same way.

17·1. *The first three relations in* (1) *will frequently be written together as*
$$P_1A+P_2B=P_3 \text{ or as } P_1A+P_2B-P_3=0 \quad\text{........(3).}$$

·11. In (1) we have regarded A, B as elements of K. But we could also treat them as points and use our earlier multiplication by points on OU. For then it is easily shewn that, if P_1, P_2, P_3 are distinct collinear points, there are distinct points C_1, C_2, C_3 on OU_1 and points B, A on P_1P_2 such that
$$P_1=B.C_1+A,\quad P_2=B.C_2+A,\quad P_3=B.C_3+A.$$
Then will $$P_3=P_1.A_1+P_2.A_2,$$
provided that $$A_1+A_2=1,$$
and $$C_3=C_1.A_1+C_2.A_2.$$
These give $$C_3=C_1+(C_2-C_1).A_2,$$
and hence $$A_2=(C_1-C_2)^{-1}.(C_1-C_3),\quad A_1=1-A_2.$$
The analogy with (2) is clear; but it is more convenient, seeing that C_1, C_2, C_3 are on OU, to replace them by elements of K.

·2. *Conversely if* $(x_1y_1z_1)$ *and* $(x_2y_2z_2)$ *be the coordinates of points* P_1, P_2, *then any point* P_3 *whose coordinates satisfy*
$$x_1A+x_2B=x_3,\ y_1A+y_2B=y_3,\ z_1A+z_2B=z_3,\ A+B=1$$
is on P_1P_2, *where* A, B *are elements of* K.

Dem. Let the equation of P_1P_2 be $z=ax+b=cy+d$.

Then $$z_1A=ax_1A+bA,\quad z_2B=ax_2B+bB.$$

Adding we have
$$z_3=z_1A+z_2B=a(x_1A+x_2B)+b(A+B)=ax_3+b.$$

·3. $P_1A+P_2B=P_3$, $A+B=1$ can be written
$$P_1+(P_2-P_1)B=P_3.$$

18. *If P_1, P_2, P_3, P be four coplanar points, and P_1, P_2, P_3 do not colline, then there are constants A, B, C in K such that $P_1A + P_2B + P_3C = P$, $A + B + C = 1$. Conversely, points connected by the above equations are coplanar.*

Dem. If P_1, P_2, P_3, P be coplanar, then there are points P_4, P_5 on the *lines* P_1P_2 and P_2P_3 resp. such that P is on the line P_4P_5, and hence there are constants D, E, F, G, H, L in K such that

$$P_1D + P_2E = P_4, \quad P_2F + P_3G = P_5, \quad P_4H + P_5L = P,$$
$$D + E = 1, \qquad F + G = 1, \qquad H + L = 1.$$

Whence $\quad P = P_1DH + P_2(EH + FL) + P_3GL$

and $\quad DH + EH + FL + GL = (D+E)H + (F+G)L = H + L = 1.$

·1. The equation of any plane is $ax + by + cz + d = 0$ where a, b, c, d are constants in K, not all zero. (18 and I 30·6.)

·2. Conversely any such equation represents a plane.

·3. *Note.* The use of such equations as (3) above is due to Möbius and Grassmann*, but their 'weights' $A, B, \ldots$ were ordinary real numbers. For many examples of the use of non-commutative 'weights,' see Baker, *Principles of Geometry.*

·4. If $a_1, b_1, c_1 \neq 0$ and the planes with equations

$$ax + by + cz + d = 0, \quad a_1x + b_1y + c_1z + d_1 = 0$$

are parallel then $\quad aa_1^{-1} = bb_1^{-1} = cc_1^{-1}$

and conversely.

·5. *Def.* The '*coordinates*' of the planes whose equations are

$$ax + by + cz + d = 0 \text{ and } ax + by + cz = 0$$

and $\quad ax + by = 0$ and $x = 0$,

where $d \neq 0$, $c \neq 0$, $b \neq 0$ respectively, are respectively $(d^{-1}a, d^{-1}b, d^{-1}c)$ and $(c^{-1}a, c^{-1}b)$ and $b^{-1}a$ and 0. (Cf. 26·1, 27.)

19. Since the above can be deduced from Axioms **A′**, **P**, we can apply the whole theory to Projective Geometry thus:

Take any fixed plane α in the projective space and define 'pseudo-parallel' as in VI 40·6. The Euclidean forms of Desargues' Theorem hold when we replace 'parallel' by 'pseudo-parallel.' The above constructions for the sum and product of points apply to points not on α, and enable us to shew that lines and planes have the equations

* Grassmann, *Ausdehnungslehre* (1862) or Whitehead, *Universal Algebra* (1898).

above, the points on α being exceptional. These exceptions can be removed thus: if (x, y, z) be the present coordinates of any point not on α, then (x_1, y_1, z_1, w_1) shall be a set of '*homogeneous*' coordinates of that point if $x = x_1 w_1^{-1}$, $y = y_1 w_1^{-1}$, $z = z_1 w_1^{-1}$, $w_1 \neq 0$.

The points on α shall have coordinates of form $(x, y, z, 0)$, where not all x, y, z vanish; namely, the point where the line

$$z = ax + bw = cy + dw \qquad (a, c \neq 0)$$

meets α shall have coordinates $(a^{-1}, c^{-1}, 1, 0)$ [see 16·2], and similarly for lines with equations of other types.

The line where $ax + by + cz + dw = 0$ meets α has then the equation

$$ax + by + cz = 0, \ w = 0.$$

For this plane meets α where $ax + by + cz = 0$ does so (18·4), and the line $z = kx = ly$ lies on the latter plane if

$$ak^{-1} + bl^{-1} + c = 0,$$

in which case the point where the line meets α satisfies $ax + by + cz = 0$.

19·1. We can *order* the points of our projective space not on α thus: $[P_1P_2P_3]$ shall hold if and only if either

$$x_1 < x_2 < x_3 \text{ or } x_1 > x_2 > x_3 \text{ or } x_1 = x_2 = x_3$$

and similar relations hold for the y, z, where (x_1, y_1, z_1) (x_2, y_2, z_2) and (x_3, y_3, z_3) are the (non-homogeneous) coordinates of P_1, P_2, P_3 resp. Our Axioms **O** then hold for points *not on* α. Cf. VI 41·61.

Order

§ 2. Basis O P.

In this section order is essential. Consider the points on OU ordered by the relation $\prec (O, U)$ (III 16).

20. *If* $A \prec B$, *there is a point* X *on* $[OU$ *with* $A + X = B$, *and conversely.*

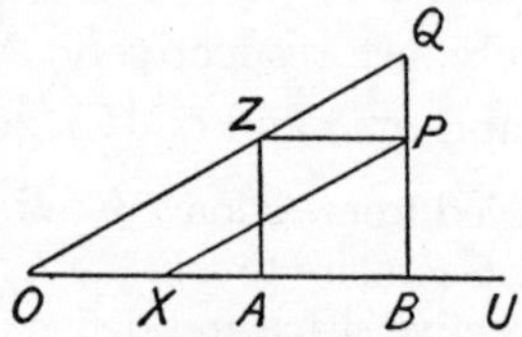

Fig. 99

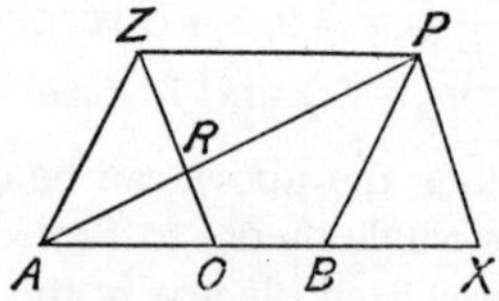

Fig. 100

Dem. There is just one point X on OU with $A + X = B$ and it is constructed thus: let Z be any point not on OU, then $ABPZ$ and $OXPZ$ are parallelograms. If $A \prec B$ then (III 16·01) either (i) A is on $[OU$ and $[OAB]$ or (ii) $[AOU]$ and B is on $[AO$ or (iii) $A = O$ and B is on $[OU$.

In case (i) BP and OZ meet in Q say, then $[OAB]$ gives by VI 3 successively $[OZQ]$, $[BPQ]$, $[OXB]$. Hence X is on $[OB = [OA = [OU$.

In case (ii) since O is on $[AB$ (II 10·5), $A{-}P$ and $Z{-}O$ meet in R say (VI 3·5) and then $[ARP]$ gives $[AOX]$. But $[AOU]$, hence X is on $[OU$ (II 10·54).

In case (iii) $A = O$, $B = X$, hence X is on $[OU$. Similarly for the converse.

20·1. If X is on $[OU$ then $O \prec X$ and conversely (III 16·12).

21. *If* $A \prec B$ *then* $A + Y \prec B + Y$.

Dem. Since $A \prec B$, there is $X \succ O$ with $A + X = B$ (20, 20·1). Hence $(A+Y)+X = (A+X)+Y = B+Y$, $A+Y \prec B+Y$.

22. *If* $X \succ O$, $Y \succ O$, *then* $X.Y \succ O$.

Dem. If $X.Y = Z$ there are points P, Q such that O, P, Q colline and UP, $PX \parallel YQ$, QZ resp. Since $Y \succ O$, Y is on $[OU$, hence Q is on $[OP$ and Z on $[OX$. But $X \succ O$, hence Z is on $[OU$.

·1. If $X \prec O$, $Y \prec O$, then $X.Y \succ O$.

23. *The points on the line OU form a fully ordered quasi-field for* $+ \times \prec$ *in the presence of Axioms* **O**, **P**. (Compare 21, 22 and I 24, 25, III 16 ff.)

24. If A, B, C be on $\dot{O}U$ and $[ABC]$, then $A \prec B \prec C$ or $A \succ B \succ C$ (III 16·5).

25. If (x_i, y_i, z_i) be the coordinates of P_i in the frame $OU_1U_2U_3$, then $[P_1P_2P_3]$ if and only if $x_1 < x_2 < x_3$ or $x_1 > x_2 > x_3$ or $x_1 = x_2 = x_3$ with similar relations for y and z (VI 3, 3·1).

Rational Constructions

§ 3. **Basis O P** or **A′ P**, or if the points are all in one plane, *Desargues' Theorem* and $\mathbf{O}_p$ **P** or $\mathbf{A}_p'$ **P**.

26. *Def.* If $a_1, a_2, \ldots, a_n$ be any elements of our quasi-field K, which are coordinates (first, second, or third) of any points, then a '*rational function*' of $a_1, a_2, \ldots, a_n$ is an expression derived from $a_1, a_2, \ldots, a_n$ and the element 1 (or u) of K by a finite number of additions, subtractions, and left or right-hand multiplications and divisions.

26·1. *The coordinates of the join of two points in the plane OU_1U_2 are rational functions of the coordinates of the points. The coordinates of the meet of two lines in OU_1U_2 are rational functions of the coordinates of the two lines. Similarly for the plane through three points or the meet of three planes in $OU_1U_2U_3$.*

Dem. We will shew the first part. If the join of $P_1(x_1y_1)$ and $P_2(x_2y_2)$ goes through O, then P_1P_2 has an equation of the form

$$ax + by = 0.$$

Let $b \neq 0$, then clearly $b^{-1}a = -y_1x_1^{-1} = -y_2x_2^{-1}$. But if the equation of P_1P_2 is

$$ax + by + c = 0, \qquad (c \neq 0)$$

then $$ax_1 + by_1 + c = 0, \quad ax_2 + by_2 + c = 0.$$

If then, for example $x_1, x_2 \neq 0$, $y_1, y_2 \neq 0$, we have $x_1y_1^{-1} \neq x_2y_2^{-1}$

and $$c^{-1}a = (y_2^{-1} - y_1^{-1})(x_1y_1^{-1} - x_2y_2^{-1})^{-1}$$

$$c^{-1}b = (x_2^{-1} - x_1^{-1})(y_1x_1^{-1} - y_2x_2^{-1})^{-1}. \text{ (Cf. I 30·2.)}$$

Similar investigations complete the Theorem. As we are *not* assuming Pappus' Theorem, we must *not* assume that multiplication is commutative.

27. *If [P] be a set of points in the plane OU_1U_2 whose coordinates are the elements $a_1, a_2, \ldots, a_n$ of K, then those points whose coordinates are rational functions of $a_1, a_2, \ldots, a_n$ and only these, can be constructed from [P], O, U_1, U_2 by the constructions* a, b, c, p *where* p *is as follows:—*

p. *Given any line and any point A not on it, we can draw the parallel through A to the line.*

Dem. That only such points can be so constructed follows easily from 26·1 and 15·3·4. That such points can be so constructed is clear, since we can find on OU_1 points whose coordinates are $a_1, a_2, \ldots, a_n$ in the scale OU_1 (13), and any rational function of these can be constructed by 1, 6 noting 1·3, 6·3·4. The extension to points of space is clear.

·1. If A, B, C be points on a line and B be not mid AC, we can find by a, b, c the point D such that B, D separate A, C harmonically (VII 29). Hence the coordinates of D are rational functions of those of A, B, C.

27·2. In Projective Geometry the construction 27 can be performed by **a**, **b** on the basis of Axioms **A**, or of $\mathbf{A}_p$ and *Desargues' Theorem.*

Introduction of Congruence by Definitions

§ 4. **Basis O P** and *Pappus' Theorem* together with Axiom $\mathbf{Q}_0$ below. For figures all in one plane we could also work on the basis of Axioms $\mathbf{O}_p$, **P**, $\mathbf{Q}_0$ and *Desargues'* and *Pappus' Theorems*; but see 50 below.

28. Since we now assume *Pappus' Theorem* and Axioms **O** our coordinates are elements of a *fully ordered field* (12, 23). We shall, if necessary, so enlarge this field that if a be in it, so is $\sqrt{1+a^2}$. Hence, if a, b are in the field so also is

$$a\sqrt{1+(b/a)^2}=\sqrt{a^2+b^2}.$$

·1. Note that if $a, b \neq 0$ then $a^2+b^2>0$ (22, 21). Our field, so enlarged if necessary, we shall call Ω_0.

Axiom $\mathbf{Q}_0$. *If x, y, z be any numbers in Ω_0, there is a point whose coordinates are (x, y, z) in the frame $OU_1U_2U_3$ defined as in* 14.

We shall see that from **O**, **P** and a continuity Axiom introduced later, we are able to introduce congruence by definition, that is, to define a relation between ordered couples of points which has the properties of congruence. We take a step in this direction by introducing congruence by definition with the present basis. In Chapter XIII we shall shew *Pappus' Theorem* and Axiom $\mathbf{Q}_0$ from the continuity Axiom and **O**, $\mathbf{P}_2'$.

29. *Def.* Let us denote always the coordinates of P_i by $(x_i y_i z_i)$ and those of P_i' by $(x_i' y_i' z_i')$. The '*distance from P_1 to P_2*' is *defined* as the positive value of

$$\sqrt{(x_1-x_2)^2+(y_1-y_2)^2+(z_1-z_2)^2}$$

and is denoted by *dist* P_1P_2 or by d_{12}.

Thus *dist* $OU_1=$ *dist* $OU_2=$ *dist* $OU_3=1$; *dist* $P_1P_2>0$ if $P_1 \neq P_2$.

30. *If P_1, P_2, P_3 colline and are distinct, then*

$$x_2 - x_1 = \pm \frac{d_{12}}{d_{13}}(x_3 - x_1), \quad y_2 - y_1 = \pm \frac{d_{12}}{d_{13}}(y_3 - y_1),$$

$$z_2 - z_1 = \pm \frac{d_{12}}{d_{13}}(z_3 - z_1).$$

Dem. By 17, there is an element k in Ω_0 such that

$$x_3 = x_1 + (x_2 - x_1)k, \quad y_3 = y_1 + (y_2 - y_1)k, \quad z_3 = z_1 + (z_2 - z_1)k$$

whence $$d_{13}^2 = (x_3 - x_1)^2 + (y_3 - y_1)^2 + (z_3 - z_1)^2$$
$$= k^2[(x_2 - x_1)^2 + (y_2 - y_1)^2 + (z_2 - z_1)^2] = k^2 d_{12}^2.$$

The Theorem now follows.

·1. Hence if P_2 be any point on P_1P_3, then either

(i) $x_2 = x_1 + ld_{12}, \quad y_2 = y_1 + md_{12}, \quad z_2 = z_1 + nd_{12},$

or (ii) $x_2 = x_1 - ld_{12}, \quad y_2 = y_1 - md_{12}, \quad z_2 = z_1 - nd_{12},$

where $$l = \frac{x_3 - x_1}{d_{13}}, \quad m = \frac{y_3 - y_1}{d_{13}}, \quad n = \frac{z_3 - z_1}{d_{13}},$$

and are thus fixed by P_1 and P_3, and where therefore

$$l^2 + m^2 + n^2 = 1.$$

If P_2 be $(x_1 + ld_{12}, y_1 + md_{12}, z_1 + nd_{12})$ and P_2' be $(x_1 - ld_{12}', y_1 - md_{12}', z_1 - nd_{12}')$, then as d_{12}, d_{12}' are varied (both being *positive* by definition), x_1 clearly remains between x_2 and x_2', or (when $l = 0$) is always equal to both. The same holds for the y and z coordinates, and hence $[P_2P_1P_2']$ (25). Hence the points satisfying (i) are on the ray $[P_1P_3$ from P_1, and points satisfying (ii) are on the opposite ray.

·2. *Def.* l, m, n are the '*direction numbers*' of the first ray, and $-l, -m, -n$ those of the opposite ray. These numbers are fixed by the ray and are not all zero.

31. If $[P_1P_3$ be any ray there is one and only one point P_2 on it such that *dist* $P_1P_2 =$ *dist* AB where A, B are any given distinct points.

Dem. Since A, B are given points, the number *dist* AB is in Ω_0 and the Theorem follows by 30·1 and $\mathbf{Q}_0$.

·1. If *dist* $AB =$ *dist* CD and *dist* $CD =$ *dist* EF,

then *dist* $AB =$ *dist* EF.

·2. If $[P_1P_2P_3]$ and $[Q_1Q_2Q_3]$ and *dist* $P_1P_2 =$ *dist* Q_1Q_2 and *dist* $P_2P_3 =$ *dist* Q_2Q_3 then *dist* $P_1P_3 =$ *dist* Q_1Q_3.

Dem. With the notation of 30·1 we may write, for suitable l, m, n

$$x_2 = x_1 + ld_{12},\ x_3 = x_1 + ld_{13},\ \text{etc.} \quad \dots\dots\dots\dots(1)$$

since P_2, P_3 are on $[P_1P_3$.

Now if $l > 0$ then since $d_{12} > 0$, we have $x_2 > x_1$. Hence $x_3 > x_2$ (25) and so $d_{13} > d_{12}$. Similarly this is true if $l < 0$ and if $l = 0$.

Also $$d_{23}^2 = (x_3 - x_2)^2 + (y_3 - y_2)^2 + (z_3 - z_2)^2$$
$$= (d_{13} - d_{12})^2$$

by (1) since $$l^2 + m^2 + n^2 = 1.$$

Hence $$d_{23} = \pm (d_{13} - d_{12}).$$

Hence either $d_{12} + d_{23} = d_{13}$ or $d_{13} + d_{23} = d_{12}$, and since all the d are positive and $d_{13} > d_{12}$ the last alternative must be rejected.

Since the same argument holds for $[Q_1Q_2Q_3]$, we have the Theorem.

31·3. *dist* P_1P_2 = *dist* P_2P_1.

32. *Thus Axioms* **C** I—IV *hold when* $A, B \rightarrow C, D$, *and so* $AB \simeq CD$, *is interpreted to mean dist* AB = *dist* CD.

·1. *Def.* If l_1, m_1, n_1 and l_2, m_2, n_2 are the direction numbers of the (distinct and not opposite) rays PP_1, PP_2 resp. then $l_1l_2 + m_1m_2 + n_1n_2$ is called '*cos* $P_1\hat{P}P_2$'; of course this number must not be identified at present with the trigonometrical function of the angle; but it is fixed by the angle.

33. If P_1, P_2, P_3 be three non-collinear points, then

$$d_{23}^2 = (x_2 - x_3)^2 + (y_2 - y_3)^2 + (z_2 - z_3)^2$$
$$= ((x_2 - x_1) + (x_1 - x_3))^2 + \dots$$
$$= (x_2 - x_1)^2 + . + . + (x_1 - x_3)^2 + . + . - 2[(x_2 - x_1)(x_3 - x_1) + . + .]$$
$$= d_{12}^2 + d_{13}^2 - 2d_{12}d_{13} \cos P_2\hat{P}_1P_3.$$

Hence if d_{12}, d_{13} and $\cos P_2\hat{P}_1P_3$ be given then d_{23} is fixed, and if d_{12}, d_{13}, d_{23} be given then $\cos P_2\hat{P}_1P_3$ is fixed. Hence *with the above interpretation of* $\simeq$, **C** V *follows, and hence two angles are congruent if and only if their* 'cos' *are equal.*

34. If l, m, n be the direction numbers of a ray from P_1, we can find a ray l_1, m_1, n_1 from P_1, which lies in a given plane $P_1P_2P_3$ whose equation is $ax + by + cz = d$, and which satisfies

$ll_1 + mm_1 + nn_1 = k$ where k is a given element of Ω_o, provided we can find a point P_4 to satisfy the following equations:—

$$ax_4 + by_4 + cz_4 = d,$$

$$l(x_1 - x_4) + m(y_1 - y_4) + n(z_1 - z_4) = k,$$

$$(x_1 - x_4)^2 + (y_1 - y_4)^2 + (z_1 - z_4)^2 = 1,$$

and for each such point P_4 there is one such ray.

But since $$ax_1 + by_1 + cz_1 = d,$$

we have $$a(x_1 - x_4) + b(y_1 - y_4) + c(z_1 - z_4) = 0.$$

Thus we have two simple and one quadratic equation to determine

$$x_1 - x_4,\ y_1 - y_4,\ z_1 - z_4$$

and hence, if these equations are independent there cannot be *more than two* such rays. But they are independent unless $k = 0$ and $l/a = m/b = n/c$. Hence, since $l^2 + m^2 + n^2 = 1$, (30·1), they are independent if $al + bm + cn = 0$, that is, if the line lmn lies on $P_1P_2P_3$.

Hence in particular *with our interpretation of* $\simeq$, **C** VI *follows.*

35. If $P_1\hat{P}P_2$ be a right angle then by definition we have $P_1\hat{P}P_2 \simeq P_1'\hat{P}P_2$ where $[P_1PP_1']$. Hence with the above interpretation of congruence, $l_1l_2 + m_1m_2 + n_1n_2 = l_1'l_2 + m_1'm_2 + n_1'n_2$

where $$l_1 = -l_1',\quad m_1 = -m_1',\quad n_1 = -n_1'.$$

Hence if $P_1\hat{O}P_2$ be a right angle then $l_1l_2 + m_1m_2 + n_1n_2 = 0$. Hence *all right angles are congruent* (33) since their 'cos' are zero, *and hence* **C** VII *holds.*

In particular, the axes are mutually perpendicular.

·1. Thus on the basis of **O**, **P**, *Pappus' Theorem* and $\mathbf{Q}_o$ we have succeeded in defining a relation between ordered couples of points for which all Axioms **C** hold. Hence all Theorems of Chapter IV hold. If we start from Axioms **O**, **C**, $\mathbf{P}_1$ we can deduce *Pappus' Theorem* (VI 35) and $\mathbf{Q}_o$ since the latter follows from Pythagoras' Theorem (VII 23), but if, having done this, we then use the above work to redefine congruence by means of **O**, **P**, *Pappus' Theorem* and $\mathbf{Q}_o$, point couples congruent in the new sense are not necessarily congruent in the old. This follows since the unit points may be taken arbitrarily on the axes and *dist* $OU_i = 1$. ($i = 1, 2, 3$.) In fact a circle for one congruence is an ellipse for the other.

§ 5. *Substitutes for Pappus' Theorem*

36. On the basis of **O**, **P** alone (or of $\mathbf{O}_p$, **P**, and *Desargues' Theorem* when in one plane) we were able to set up a frame in which each point of space corresponded to an ordered triad (xyz) whose members were elements of a fully ordered quasi-field, but to shew that x, y, z were elements of a field we found Pappus' Theorem necessary (11·1). We can shew this Theorem if we assume the following Axiom, with **O**, **P**.

Def. A '*Pappus net*' is a set of points on a line, any two of which are in a Pappus triad composed of points of the set (11·1).

Axiom. *On some one line there is a Pappus net such that, if any two points of the line be given, there is a point of the net between them.* Then if OU be the line and O, U in the net, there is a Pappus net of the same kind on all lines through O (VI 3, 3·1 and VIII 7, 11·1). The points of the net on OU form a field F, those of the line OU form a fully ordered quasi-field in which F is relatively dense (24, I 16·1). Hence this quasi-field is a field (I 26·2) and hence Pappus' Theorem holds always (11·1).

37. We can also deduce Pappus' Theorem if we assume: *On some line OU the points whose coordinates in the scale OU are rational, are such that at least one of them lies between any two given points of OU.* Cf. I 26·3·4 and VIII 27.

It would also suffice to assume that *our quasi-field on OU was Archimedean* (I 26·4).

§ 6. *The Independence of Pappus' Theorem*

38. That $\mathbf{Q}_o$ is independent of **O**, **P** is plain, since from these Axioms we can only reach points whose coordinates are *rational* functions of coordinates of given points (27), and a sufficiently extensive set of such points will satisfy **O**, **P**.

We shall now shew that Pappus' Theorem also is independent of **O**, **P** by actually constructing a geometry in which **O**, **P** are true, but Pappus' Theorem is in general false.

Consider a fully ordered quasi-field K. A 'point' shall be an ordered triad (xyz) of elements of K; the 'line' P_1P_2 shall be the set of points P satisfying

$$P = P_1 + (P_2 - P_1) A$$

where A is any element of K, and the equation is interpreted as in 17·1. P_1, P_2, P_3 shall be 'in order' $P_1P_2P_3$ if and only if

$$P_2 = P_1 + (P_3 - P_1) A \text{ and } 0 < A < 1,$$

and then P_2 is 'between' P_1 and P_3.

Thus of three distinct points on the same line, one and only one is between the other two. For let (the A_i being all unequal)

$$Q_i = P_1 + (P_2 - P_1) A_i. \quad i = 1, 2, 3 \quad \text{........(1)}.$$

Then

$$Q_3 - Q_1 = (P_2 - P_1)(A_3 - A_1),$$

$$Q_2 = Q_1 + (Q_3 - Q_1)(A_3 - A_1)^{-1}(A_2 - A_1).$$

Hence $[Q_1Q_2Q_3]$ if and only if

$$0 < (A_3 - A_1)^{-1}(A_2 - A_1) < 1.$$

Hence if $A_3 > A_1$ then must $0 < A_2 - A_1 < A_3 - A_1$ and hence $A_1 < A_2 < A_3$; and if $A_3 < A_1$ then must similarly $A_1 > A_2 > A_3$.

Again (1) gives $P_1 = P_2 - (Q_1 - Q_2)(A_1 - A_2)^{-1}$.

Hence if Q_1, Q_2 are on P_1P_2, then P_1 is on Q_1Q_2. It is now easy to see that Axioms **O** I, II, III, IV, V, VII, VIII and the definition of line in II 3 are satisfied. We can define plane' as in II 13.

38·1. Any point on the line P_1P_2 is of form

$$P_1A_1 + P_2A_2 \quad (A_1 + A_2 = 1).$$

Any point on the plane $P_1P_2P_3$ is of form

$$P_1A_1 + P_2A_2 + P_3A_3 \quad (A_1 + A_2 + A_3 = 1).$$

·2. We have to shew **O** VI and **P**. For the latter let P_1P_2 and P_3P_4 be coplanar lines and let $P_4 = P_1A + P_2B + P_3C$, $A + B + C = 1$. Any point on the line P_3P_4 is $P_4L + P_3M$ where $L + M = 1$. The lines meet, if at all, where

$$(P_1A + P_2B + P_3C)L + P_3M$$

does not involve P_3, that is, at $(P_1A + P_2B)L$ when $CL + M = 0$, that is, when $L = (1 - C)^{-1}$.

Hence they meet in one and only one point unless $C = 1$. When $C = 1$, then $A = -B$ and $P_4 = (P_1 - P_2)A + P_3$, $A \neq 0$.

Hence the lines joining P_3 to points P_4 of the latter form are the only lines (in the plane) not meeting P_1P_2. To shew **P** fully we have now merely to shew that P_3, P_4 and P_4' colline where $P_4' = (P_1 - P_2)A' + P_3$ where A' is any element ($\neq 0$) of K. But this is true using ·1 since

$$P_4A^{-1} - P_4'A'^{-1} = P_3(A^{-1} - A'^{-1}).$$

38·3. $P_1P_2 \| P_3P_4$ if and only if $(P_1 - P_2)H = P_3 - P_4$ for some element H ($\neq 0$) of K.

·4. It remains to shew **O** VI. Let P_1, P_2, P_3 be non-collinear, let P_4 be on $P_1\text{-}P_2$ and P_5 on $P_3\text{-}P_4$. Then, for some A, B with $0 < A < 1$, $0 < B < 1$ we have

$$P_4 = P_1 + (P_2 - P_1)A,$$
$$P_5 = P_3 + (P_4 - P_3)B = P_3 + [(P_1 - P_3) + (P_2 - P_1)A]B.$$

If the line P_1P_5 meets P_2P_3 then must

$$P_1 + \{P_3 - P_1 + [P_1 - P_3 + (P_2 - P_1)A]B\}C = P_2 + (P_3 - P_2)D$$

for some D and C. This gives

$$(P_2 - P_1)(1 - ABC) + (P_1 - P_3)(1 - B)C + (P_3 - P_2)D = 0 \quad \text{......(i).}$$

This is certainly true if

$$1 - ABC = (1 - B)C = D \quad \text{..............(ii),}$$

which give $\quad C = [1 - (1 - A)B]^{-1}$.

And if equation (ii) be false, we could deduce from (i) an equation of form $P_3 = P_1 + (P_2 - P_1)H$, cont. hyp. that P_1, P_2, P_3 do not colline. Now $0 < 1 - (1 - A)B < 1$. Hence $C > 1$. Also $D = 1 - ABC < 1$, $D = (1 - B)C > 0$. Hence P_1P_5 meets the *open interval* P_2P_3.

Hence Axioms **O**, **P** hold in our geometry.

·5. Let the quasi-field K be not a field (I 27·4). Since then Comm × does not hold in general we may suspect that Pappus' Theorem does not hold in general, though the situation here is rather different from that in 11, since *there* we multiplied *points*, while *here* we are multiplying elements of K which correspond to the *coordinates* of the points in the earlier work.

·6. Let us compare the constructions of § 1 for the addition of points with our present work. If $P_0 - P_1 = Q_0 - Q_1$ then by ·3 we have $P_0P_1 \| Q_0Q_1$. Also $P_0 - Q_0 = P_1 - Q_1$, hence $P_0Q_0 \| P_1Q_1$. Hence $P_0P_1Q_1Q_0$ is a parallelogram, if $P_0P_1Q_0$ do not colline. Conversely by Axiom **P**, it follows that if $P_0P_1Q_1Q_0$ is a parallelogram then

$P_0 - P_1 = Q_0 - Q_1$ and $P_1 + Q_0 = P_0 + Q_1$ while in the notation of § 1 we have $Q_1 = (P_1 + Q_0) \mid P_0$. The resemblance is obvious.

38·7. To investigate Pappus' Theorem. We first make a preliminary remark. If

$$P_2 = P_0 A + P_1 (1 - A)$$

and

$$Q_2 = P_0 A + Q_1 (1 - A)$$

then

$$P_2 - Q_2 = (P_1 - Q_1)(1 - A),$$

where A is now any element of K. Hence if $A \neq 1$ we have $P_1 Q_1 \parallel P_2 Q_2$. Conversely using Axiom **P**,

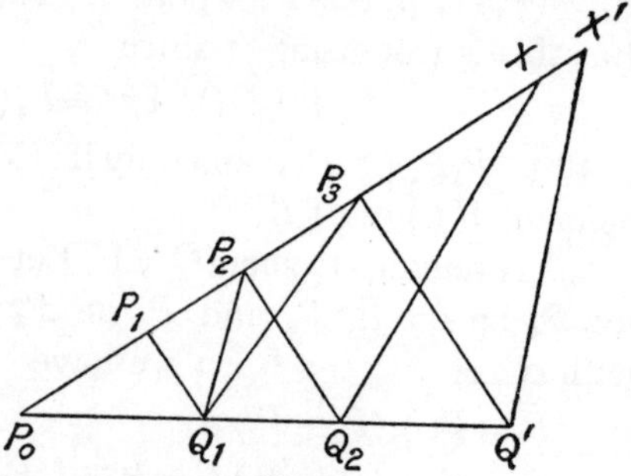

Fig. 101

if $P_2 = P_0 A + P_1 (1 - A)$, and P_0, Q_1, Q_2 colline and $P_1 Q_1 \parallel P_2 Q_2$ and $P_0 P_1 \neq P_0 Q_1$, then we find $Q_2 = P_0 A + Q_1 (1 - A)$.

Now suppose also P_3, X be on $P_0 P_1$ and Q_2, Q' on $P_0 Q_1$ and $P_0 P_1 \neq P_0 Q_1$, and let $Q_1 P_3$, $P_3 Q'$, $Q' X'$ be parallel resp. to $Q_2 X$, $P_2 Q_2$, $Q_1 P_2$, and let $P_3 = P_0 B + P_1 (1 - B)$.

Then using the remark above we get (using above values of P_2, Q_2):

$$Q' = P_0 B + Q_1 (1 - B), \quad X' = P_0 B + P_2 (1 - B)$$

and $X = P_0 A + P_3 (1 - A)$ since $Q_2 = P_0 A + Q_1 (1 - A)$.

But if Pappus' Theorem be true, then $X = X'$. This gives

$$\begin{aligned} 0 &= P_0 (A - B) + P_3 (1 - A) - P_2 (1 - B) \\ &= P_0 (A - B) + P_0 B (1 - A) + P_1 (1 - B)(1 - A) \\ &\qquad - P_0 A (1 - B) - P_1 (1 - A)(1 - B) \\ &= (P_0 - P_1)(AB - BA). \end{aligned}$$

But $P_0 \neq P_1$. Hence if Pappus' Theorem be true we must have $AB = BA$, which need not be true *in general* for elements of K, though it is true for some pairs of elements of K (I 25·5); for in I 27·4 we constructed a fully ordered quasi-field which was not a field. But Axioms **O**, **P** hold in our present geometry. *Hence Pappus' Theorem cannot be deduced from* **O**, **P**. Of course if A, B are in a sub-*field* of K, e.g. the rational sub-field (I 25·5), then P_2, P_3, X are a Pappus triad and $X = X'$.

Similarly the projective form of Pappus' Theorem (VI 41·5) cannot be deduced from Axioms **A**.

§ 7. *The Independence of Desargues' Theorem*

39. We know that Desargues' Theorem follows from **O**, **P** (VI 39 ff.) and it is easily shewn in the above Geometry*. Now we shewed the *plane* case of Desargues' Theorem from **O**, **P** (i.e. we assumed the plane was immersed in space) and not from $\mathbf{O}_p$, **P**, and the question arises whether it can be deduced from the latter set. We shall shew that it cannot. Consider a Euclidean plane and on it mark a 'horizontal' line l and construct a new Geometry as follows. As 'pseudo-lines' take the horizontal and vertical lines of the Euclidean plane and also those which slope to the left, but bend the Euclidean lines which slope to the right by halving the ordinates of all their points which lie above l. The set of pseudo-lines so obtained satisfy $\mathbf{O}_p$, **P** with an obvious definition of 'between.' But Desargues' Theorem does not always hold. For consider two triangles below l with their corresponding sides parallel, and such that two of the pseudo-lines which join corresponding vertices slope to the left and the other to the right. If the first two meet, the third does not concur with them, owing to its bend. It is easy to free this argument from its intuitive stain by putting it algebraically.

·1. Desargues' Theorem does not follow from $\mathbf{O}_p$, **P** and the continuity Axiom **K** of Chapter XIII below. The projective form of Desargues' Theorem does not follow from Axioms **A** 1...5.

40. If $\mathbf{O}_p$, **P** and *Desargues' Theorem* hold in some plane we can introduce coordinates so that a point is represented by an ordered couple of elements (x, y) of a quasi-field K, and three collinear points P_1, P_2, P_3 are connected by a relation $P_3 = P_1 + (P_2 - P_1)A$. But we can also build up a Geometry of *Space* satisfying **O**, **P**, by taking as a 'point' an ordered triad of elements of K. If in this space Geometry we consider points which have $z = 0$, we get a plane Geometry abstractly identical with the plane Geometry we started from. Hence, in this sense, if $\mathbf{O}_p$, **P** and *Desargues' Theorem* hold in a plane,

* Hence Pappus' Theorem cannot be deduced from $\mathbf{O}_p$, **P** *and Desargues' Theorem.*

that plane may without contradiction be considered to lie in a space whose planes meet it in lines. But if Desargues' Theorem be false in the plane we may not do this, for if the plane were immersed in a space in which **O**, **P** held, and its lines were lines in that space, then Desargues' Theorem could be shewn as in Chapter VI.

In short, it is only *special* planes satisfying $\mathbf{O}_p$, **P** which can be considered as immersed in space. On the other hand *any* space satisfying **O**, **P** can be considered as immersed in a hyper-space of any number of dimensions (finite or infinite).

The same results hold in Projective Geometry and for the same reasons.

The Cartesian Frame

§ 8. **Basis O C $\mathbf{P}_1$** or, if all points are in the same plane, $\mathbf{O}_p\,\mathbf{C}_p\,\mathbf{P}_1$. Hence Desargues' and Pappus' Theorems hold.

41. With constructions of § 1, if X, Y be on $[OU$ then $X+Y=Z$ if and only if $\mu OX+\mu OY=\mu OZ$. If A be on $[OU$, then $X.A=Y$ if and only if $OA\,|\,OU \sim OY\,|\,OX$, that is, if $OX.OA=OY.OU$. This shews the relation between the algebra of this chapter and that of Chapter VII.

42. *Def. and Thes.* If we take three lines through O mutually perpendicular and on them unit-points U_1, U_2, U_3 resp. with

$$OU_1 \simeq OU_2 \simeq OU_3$$

then the frame $OU_1U_2U_3$ is a '*Cartesian rectangular frame.*' In it planes and lines have equations as in § 1, while the sphere, centre (a, b, c) and radius of measure r, has the equation

$$(x-a)^2+(y-b)^2+(z-c)^2=r^2.$$

If (x, y, z) be the coordinates of P and the points A, B, C be as in 14, then μOA can be identified with $+x$ or $-x$ according as A is on $[OU$ or $OU]$, provided $A \neq O$. Similarly for y, z. If P_1 on $[OU_1$ and P_2 on $[OU_2$ have the same coordinate in their respective scales then $OP_1 \simeq OP_2$ (13).

Similarly a rectangular Cartesian frame can be introduced in a plane.

The Argand Diagram

§ 9. **Basis O_p C_p P_1.** *All figures are in one plane* and Desargues' and Pappus' Theorems are true (VI 35, VII 30).

43. The reader is doubtless familiar with the representation of ordinary complex numbers on a plane. We are now going to define addition and multiplication of points on a plane (satisfying the Axioms of our basis) so that these operations obey the same formal laws as the corresponding ones for complex numbers.

We define addition of points as in 1, but multiplication as follows:—

·1. *Def.* If O be the zero-point and any point $U \neq O$ be taken as '*unit-point*,' then if A be on OU we define $(X.A)|OU$ as in 6, where X is any point of the plane. But if A be not on OU and X be any point $\neq O$ of the plane, then $(X.A)|OU$ shall be the point Y, if and only if $OUA \sim OXY$ and $OU\hat{,}OA$ and $OX\hat{,}OY$ have the same sense. If $X = O$ then

$$(X.A)|OU$$

shall be O, for all points A on the plane. Cf. 6, 6·6.

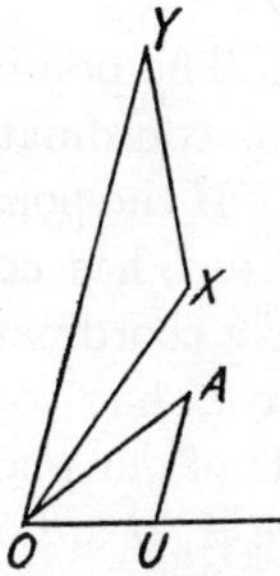

Fig. 102

We keep O, U fixed throughout the discussion, and so omit mention of them.

·2. Hence if $Y = X.A$ and $X, A \neq O$, then $OA|OU \sim OY|OX$, that is, $OA.OX = OY.OU$, and *either* $U\hat{O}A \simeq X\hat{O}Y$ and $OU\hat{,}OA$ and $OX\hat{,}OY$ have the same sense *or* O, U, A colline and O, X, Y colline.

·3. $X.U = U.X = X$; $X.O = O.X = O$.

·4. $X.A = A.X$.

Dem. Let $A, X \neq O$ and $Y = X.A$. Then $OA|OU \sim OY|OX$ and so $OX|OU \sim OY|OA$ (VII 3, 1·3). Also $U\hat{O}A \simeq X\hat{O}Y$, and $OU\hat{,}OA$ and $OX\hat{,}OY$ have the same sense, hence $U\hat{O}X \simeq A\hat{O}Y$ and $OU\hat{,}OX$ and $OA\hat{,}OY$ have the same sense (IV 78·1), unless indeed O, U, X colline and then O, A, Y colline.

44. Let $OI \perp OU$, and $OI \simeq OU$ then $I^2 = -U$.

·1. *Def.* If X be any point $\neq O$, then mod $X = P$ where $OX \simeq OP$, P on $[OU$. Also mod $O = O$.

·2. mod $U = U$.

·3. *Def.* If θ, ϕ be signed angular measures (IV 57·9) then

$$\theta \equiv \phi \ (\text{mod } 2\pi)$$

means $\theta - \phi$ is a multiple of $\pm 2\pi$ or 0*.

·4. *Def.* If X be any point $\neq O$, then

$$\arg X = \mu U\hat{O}X \text{ or } 2\pi - \mu U\hat{O}X \text{ or } 0 \text{ or } \pi,$$

according as X is in $\{OU, I\}$ or on the opposite side of OU or on $[OU$ or on $OU]$.

·5. mod $(X.A) = \text{mod } X . \text{mod } A$ (43·2).

·6. $\arg (X.A) \equiv \arg X + \arg A$ (mod 2π) (IV 57, III 17·86).

·7. $\arg X^n \equiv n \arg X$ (mod 2π), n being any natural number.

45. The points on OU form a field F. This enables us to set up coordinates in the Cartesian frame OUI. If the point A have coordinates $(a, 0)$ then $I.A$ has coordinates $(0, a)$. Hence if P have coordinates (a, b), then $P = A + I.B$ where B has coordinates $(b, 0)$. Hence all points of our plane are of form $P = A + I.B$ where A, B are on OU. Further

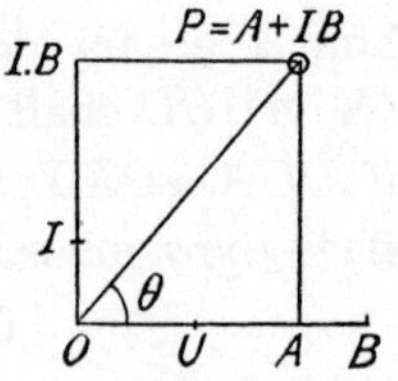

Fig. 103

$$(\text{mod } P)^2 = A^2 + B^2$$

since A^2, B^2 have coordinates $(a^2, 0)$ and $(b^2, 0)$ resp. (VII 23).

·1. *Def.* If $P = A + I.B \neq O$, and $\theta = \arg P$, then

$$\cos\theta = A / \text{mod } P, \ \sin\theta = B / \text{mod } P.$$

(Here / is the usual symbol of division in the field F.)

·2. $P = \text{mod } P . (\cos\theta + I . \sin\theta)$.

·3. And if $\phi = \arg Q$ then

$$P.Q = \text{mod } P . \text{mod } Q . (\cos(\theta+\phi) + I . \sin(\theta+\phi)) \ (44·5·6).$$

·4. $O \lessgtr$ or $= \cos\theta$ according as P is in $\{OI, U\}$ or on the opposite half-plane or on OI (20·1).

·5. $O \lessgtr$ or $= \sin\theta$ according as P is in $\{OU, I\}$ or on the opposite half-plane or on OU.

* The reader should note the two distinct meanings of the sign 'mod.'

45·6. $\cos^2\theta + \sin^2\theta = (A^2+B^2)/(\text{mod } P)^2 = 1$.

·7. $X.(Y.Z) = (X.Y).Z$ (·3 or directly).

·8. $X.(Y+Z) = X.Y + X.Z$ (congruence and similar triangles).

·9. *The points of our plane form a field F_1 wherein O, U play the part of* 0 *and* 1.

46. $(X+I.Y).(P+I.Q)$

$$= X.P + I.Y.P + X.I.Q + I.Y.I.Q \quad (45·7·8)$$
$$= (X.P - Y.Q) + I.(Y.P + X.Q) \quad (43·4·3,\ 44).$$

·1. Thus all the formal laws of I 28·1·2 hold, noting I 28·4·31, but as F is not necessarily the real field, we cannot identify our algebra with the ordinary algebra of complex numbers.

In view, however, of the identity of the formal laws we shall now use small letters for the elements of our fields F and F_1, and the point whose Cartesian coordinates are (a, b) will be denoted by the '*affix*' $a+ib$ (cf. 45). We shall also write 0, 1 for O, U and the general affix (or point) will be written $z = x + iy$.

47. If mod $z = 1$, then mod $z^n = 1$ for all natural numbers n, and $\arg z^n \equiv n \arg z \pmod{2\pi}$.

Thus if $\arg z^n \equiv 0 \pmod{2\pi}$ then $\arg z = 2r\pi/n$ for some natural number $r < n$.

·1. *Hence the points z ($\neq 1$) which satisfy $z^n = 1$ are the points z with mod $z = 1$ and for which arg z has the following values:*

$$2\pi/n,\ 4\pi/n,\ \ldots,\ (n-1).2\pi/n.$$

These points, if existent, are

$$\cos\theta + i\sin\theta \quad \textit{where} \quad \theta = 2r\pi/n \quad (r = 1, 2, \ldots, n-1).$$

·2. *The points other than U which satisfy $z^n = 1$ are given, if existent, by the roots of the 'cyclotomic equation'*

$$\frac{z^n - 1}{z - 1} = 0.$$

·3. If mod $z = 1$, $\arg z = \theta$ then $z = \cos\theta + i\sin\theta$, and by 46, 45·6

$$z^{-1} = \frac{\cos\theta - i\sin\theta}{(\cos\theta + i\sin\theta)(\cos\theta - i\sin\theta)} = \cos\theta - i\sin\theta$$

thus $\quad z + z^{-1} = 2\cos\theta, \quad z^n + z^{-n} = 2\cos n\theta \quad (45·3,\ 44·7).$

Linear Transformations in the Inversion Plane

48. We will now make our plane an inversion plane by adjoining one ideal point (VII 37·5). To this point shall correspond an ideal number denoted by ∞, and this shall be adjoined to our field F_1; if a be an element of F_1 we define

$$\infty + a = a + \infty = \infty,\ \infty + \infty = \infty,\ \frac{a}{\infty} = 0$$

and if $a \neq 0$ $\quad a\infty = \infty a = \infty,\ \infty\infty = \infty, \frac{a}{0} = \infty$. Thus $-\infty = \infty$.

We do not define $\frac{\infty}{\infty}$, $0\,\infty$ and $\frac{0}{0}$.

Our field F_1 with ∞ adjoined will be denoted by F_1'. This is not a field.

In the following z and z' shall traverse F_1', while a, b, c, d shall be elements of F_1.

·1. The transformations $z' = cz$, $z' = z + d$ turn cycles into cycles; that is, if z describes a cycle so does z' (VII 35 and congruence). A cross between cycles is turned into a congruent cross.

·2. The transformation $z' = \frac{1}{z}$ is the product of inversions in the cycles mod $z = 1$ and $x = 0$ (44·5·6). Thus it turns cycles into cycles (VII 37·7), and since the transformation is a product of *two* inversions, a cross between cycles is turned into a congruent cross (VII 38).

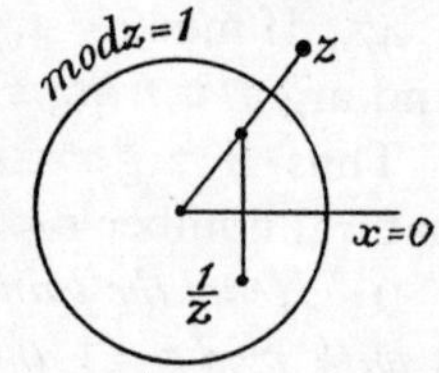

Fig. 104

·3. *The transformation*

$$z' = \frac{az + b}{cz + d} \qquad (bc - ad \neq 0)$$

is the product of the transformations

$$z_1 = cz,\quad z_2 = z_1 + d,\quad z_3 = cz_2,\quad z_4 = z_3^{-1},\quad z_5 = (bc - ad)\, z_4,$$

$$z' = \frac{a}{c} + z_5$$

and hence it *turns cycles into cycles and a cross between cycles into a congruent cross* (·1·2).

·4. *The ratios of a, b, c, d in* ·3 *can be so chosen that three arbitrary given points are turned into three arbitrary given points, and then the transformation is fully fixed.*

48·5. Transformations of the type in ·3 exist which leave a given cycle unchanged (·4·3).

§ 10. *The Independence of Axiom* $\mathbf{P}_3'$

49. We will now construct a Geometry* (Hyperbolic plane Geometry) in which $\mathbf{O}_p$ $\mathbf{C}_p$ hold, but such that through a given point not on a given line, an infinity of 'parallels' can be drawn to this line, parallel lines being lines which do not meet. Take a fixed circle K in our inversion plane. A 'point' shall be a point inside K, a 'line' shall be the set of points inside K on a cycle which meets K orthogonally. 'Points' A, B, C shall be in 'order ABC' when the cycle ABC meets K orthogonally in D, E say and B, D separate A, C (V 2·4). Our Axioms $\mathbf{O}_p$ can now be shewn for our 'points' and 'order' and we can define 'ray.' The 'point'-couples

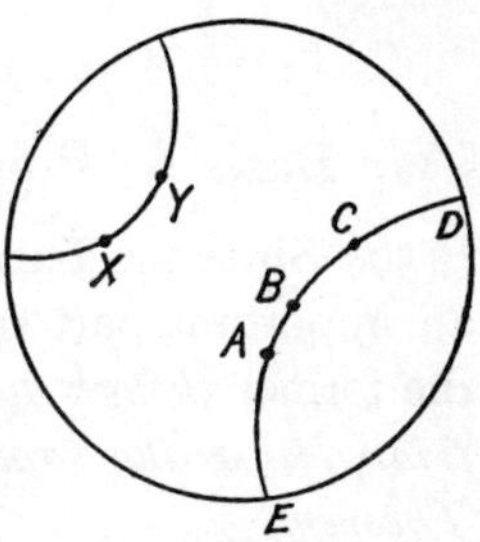

Fig. 105

(A, B) and (X, Y) will be defined to be 'congruent' when A, B can be transformed into (X, Y) or into (Y, X) by a transformation of the kind in 48·3 which leaves K unchanged. We can now define 'congruent angles.' We find that two 'angles' between 'rays' in our Geometry are 'congruent' when the corresponding crosses in the basic inversion plane are congruent or when one cross is congruent to the cross opposite to the other. It is now a simple matter to verify Axioms $\mathbf{C}_p$ in our Geometry. Axiom $\mathbf{P}_3'$, however, is false, since given a cycle K_1 which meets K orthogonally, and a point R not on it, we can draw an infinity of cycles through R orthogonal to K and meeting K_1 in points outside K.

·1. *Axiom* **P** *is independent of* $\mathbf{O}_p$, $\mathbf{C}_p$ *in-so-far as it asserts the uniqueness of the parallel* (cf. IV 59·1). Using ordinary complex numbers the same argument shews that **P** *is independent of* $\mathbf{O}_p$, $\mathbf{C}_p$ *and Axiom* **K** *of Chapter XIII below.*

* Pointed out by Poincaré, *Acta Mathematica*, 1 (1882).

49·2. A similar investigation using circles and lines orthogonal to a fixed sphere shews that $\mathbf{P}_3'$ *is independent of* **O, C.**

·3. The sum of the angular measures of the angles of certain 'triangles' in the Geometry of 49 is less than π.

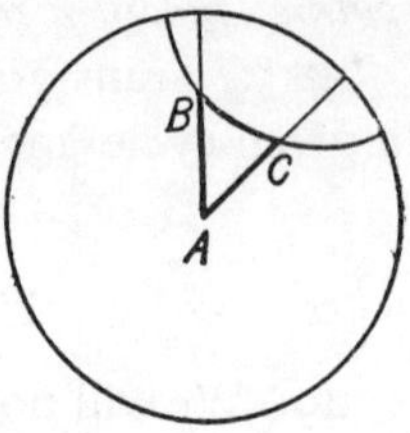

Fig. 106

Dem. Consider a 'triangle' two of whose 'side-lines' are along radii of K and use the fact on 'congruent angles' in 49. We shall see later (XV 5) that it follows that the sum of the angular measures is less than π for *all* triangles.

*Hessenberg's Theorem**

§ 11. Basis $\mathbf{A}_p'$ **P** or $\mathbf{O}_p$ **P**.

50. Since the Theorems of Desargues and Pappus play such an important part in our work, it is interesting to note that the former *though not deducible from* $\mathbf{A}_p'$, **P** *can be shewn for triangles in the same plane from these Axioms and Pappus' Theorem.*

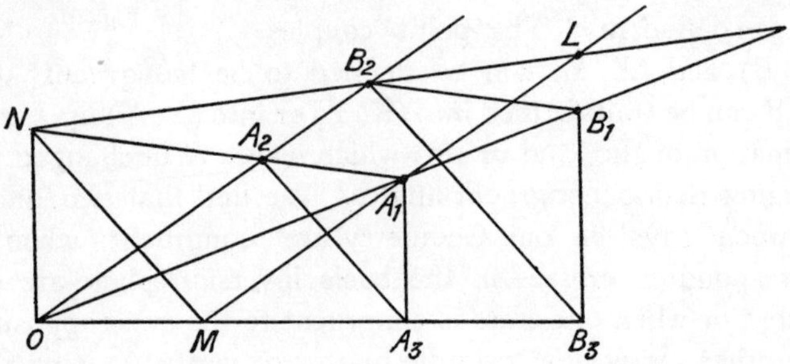

Fig. 107

Given that A_1B_1, A_2B_2, A_3B_3, meet in O, and that $A_1A_2 \parallel B_1B_2$ and $A_1A_3 \parallel B_1B_3$, we wish to shew that $A_2A_3 \parallel B_2B_3$. Draw A_1L parallel to OB_2 to meet B_1B_3 in L and OA_3 in M, and let LB_2 meet A_1A_2 in N.

Consider the points OA_1B_1, LB_2N; we have $A_1N \parallel B_1B_2$, $A_1L \parallel OB_2$. Hence $ON \parallel LB_1$ (Pappus' Theorem) and hence $ON \parallel A_1A_3$.

* "Beweis des Desargueschen Satzes," *Math. Ann.* LXI (1904), p. 161.

Consider NA_2A_1, A_3MO; we have $A_1M \parallel OA_2$, $A_1A_3 \parallel ON$; hence $NM \parallel A_2A_3$. Consider OMB_3, LB_2N; we have $OB_2 \parallel LM$, $ON \parallel LB_3$; hence $NM \parallel B_2B_3$, whence $A_2A_3 \parallel B_2B_3$. Whence Desargues' Theorem follows as stated, since the rest of VI 39·2·3 easily follows.

50·1. Similarly in Projective Geometry on the basis of Axioms $\mathbf{A}_p$ (which do not themselves suffice to shew Desargues' Theorem in its projective form) we can shew the projective form of Desargues' Theorem from the projective form of Pappus' Theorem (VI 41·5) but not vice versâ (p. 207 f. n.). This follows as in 50, by introducing the idea of 'pseudo-parallel.'

·2. *All graphical Theorems* (VI 41·6) *of Plane Euclidean Geometry can be shewn from* $\mathbf{A}_p'$, **P** *and Pappus' Theorem. All graphical Theorems of Euclidean Geometry of space can be shewn from* $\mathbf{A}'$, **P** *and Pappus' Theorem.*

Dem. For on these bases we can erect a complete coordinate geometry of lines, or of lines and planes in the spatial case.

·3. Similarly in Projective Geometry, all graphical Theorems follow from **A** and the projective form of Pappus' Theorem.

The results of ·2·3 are among the most important of modern Geometrical criticism.

CHAPTER IX

CONSTRUCTIONS

Introductory Remarks

We have seen in Chapter IV that certain elementary constructions can be performed by **a**, **b**, **c**, $\mathbf{d}_1$. Our first object now is to shew that when we adjoin $\mathbf{P}_1$ to $\mathbf{O}_p$, $\mathbf{C}_p$, we can replace $\mathbf{d}_1$ by a much weaker 'gauge-construction': 'On any ray from a certain *fixed* point to cut off a certain *fixed* length, the gauge, from that point.'

We next consider constructions possible by ruler and compasses; we shew that these can be performed if we know the intersections of a certain *fixed* circle and any line which meets it, and also that they can be performed by compasses only. The ruler must only be used as a straight edge, neither it nor the compasses may be used for transferring lengths; that is, we only use the compasses to draw a circle whose centre is given, to go through a given point. The same investigation shews that Axiom **Q**, in the presence of **O**, **P**, can be replaced by a much weaker Axiom concerning the meets of a line and a certain fixed circle, but that this Axiom cannot be shewn from **O C P**.

We next take up the question of the range of constructions possible with ruler and compasses and shew that two famous problems, that of the duplication of the cube (24·1) and that of trisecting an angle (29·1) are insoluble by these means; but that regular polygons of *n* sides can be so constructed if and only if *n* is a product of different primes of the form $2^{2^n}+1$, multiplied by a power of 2. In fact, gauge constructions suffice for this. Here we shall need I 29 ff.

Hilbert* has investigated the conditions that a problem

* *Grundlagen*, §§ 37 ff. Also Landau, "Über die Darstellung definiter binären Formen durch Quadrate," *Math. Ann.* LVII (1903); Siegel, "Additive Theorie der Zahlkörper," II, *Math. Ann.* LXXXVIII (1922).

should be soluble by gauge constructions, but the investigation is incomplete and depends on deep questions of the Theory of Numbers.

We have made great use of Enriques, *Fragen der Elementargeometrie*, vol. II, in this chapter.

Gauge Constructions

§ 1. Basis $\mathbf{O}_p\mathbf{C}_p\mathbf{P}_1$.

1. If we have $AF \simeq FB$ and $[AFB]$ then by means of **a, b, c** we can draw through any point E the parallel to AB.

Dem. Find C so that $[AEC]$ (c). Then B–E, C–F meet in O, say, and O can be found (a, b). Then BC, AO meet in D say, and this point, and hence the line ED can be found (a), and $ED \parallel AB$ (VII 28·3).

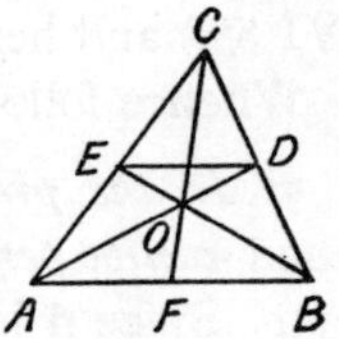

Fig. 108

2. **Construction d.** *If AB be a certain* **fixed** *interval which we will call the 'gauge' and M a certain* **fixed** *point, then on any ray from M can be found a point C such that* $MC \simeq AB$.

This is much weaker than $\mathbf{d}_1$ (IV 46).

By means of **abcd** in the presence of $\mathbf{O}_p\mathbf{C}_p\mathbf{P}_1$ we can perform the following constructions.

3. *To draw a parallel to any given line l from any point not on l.* (Construction p of VIII 27.)

Dem. If the line goes through M, then on the two rays from M can be found points A, B with $MA \simeq MB \simeq$ gauge (d) and the construction follows by 1. If l does not go through M, let P, X be distinct points on it. On MP take A, B and on MX take C, D with MA, MB, MC, $MD \simeq$ gauge and $[AMB]$, $[CMD]$ (d). Through C, D draw parallels to AB by 1, they meet l in E, F say. Then $CM \simeq MD$ gives $EP \simeq PF$ (VI 6·1). And now, by 1, a parallel can be drawn to EF from any point not on it.

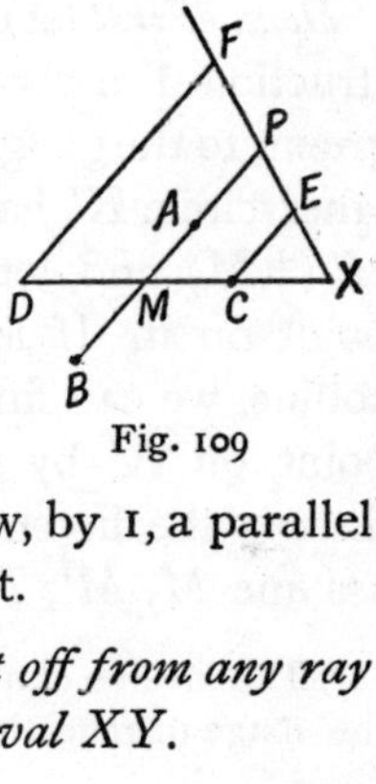

Fig. 109

4. *To perform construction* $\mathbf{d}_1$, *that is, to cut off from any ray AB an interval AC congruent to a given interval XY.*

Dem. If $AB \| XY$ draw YC, $XC' \| XA$, YA resp. (3). Then YC, XC' meet AB in C, C' say and $AC \simeq AC' \simeq XY$. Also $[CAC']$ for $C=C'$ is impossible since X^-C meets A^-Y (VI 3·3). Thus either C or C' is on $[AB$. If AB is not parallel to XY, draw $AF \| XY$, $AF \simeq XY$, by 3 and first part. Also make MD', $ME' \| AB$, AF resp. (3) and ME', $MD' \simeq$ gauge (d). By the first part find D, E on $[AB$, $[AF$ resp. with $AD \simeq MD'$, $AE \simeq ME'$. Draw $FC \| DE$ to meet $[AB$ in C (VI 3). Then since $AE \simeq AD$, we have $AC \simeq AF$ (VI 8·4) and hence $AC \simeq XY$.

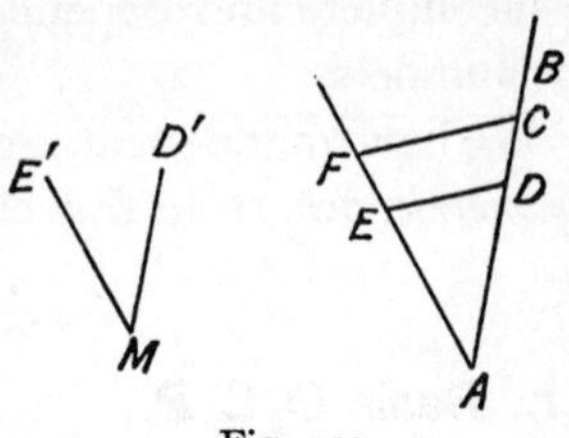

Fig. 110

Whence follows our first important Theorem :—

5. *In the presence of* $\mathbf{O}_p\mathbf{C}_p\mathbf{P}_1$ *all constructions possible by* **abcd**$_1$ *can be performed by* **abcd**. (Cf. IV 46—49, 53.)

·1. Since **d** is a special case of $\mathbf{q}_1$ (V 18), *all constructions possible in the presence of* $\mathbf{O}_p\mathbf{C}_p\mathbf{P}_1$ *by* **abcd**$_1$**q**$_1$ *can be performed by* **abcq**$_1$.

6. *If one point of meeting of a given line and a circle whose centre is known be given, the other point of meeting (if the line be not a tangent) can be found by* **abcd** (V 4·4 *Dem.*).

7. *By means of* **abcd** *we can draw the radical axis of two non-concentric circles when their centres and one point on each are known.*

Dem. First let one of the circles, K, have the centre M of construction **d** and radius congruent to the gauge. Let the other circle K' have centre M' ($\neq M$) and let N' be a point on it. If M, M', N' colline, we can find another point on K' by drawing any line $\neq M'N'$ through M' and finding the inverse of N' with respect to it*. Thus we may assume M, M', N' non-collinear. Let $MN \| M'N'$ and N be

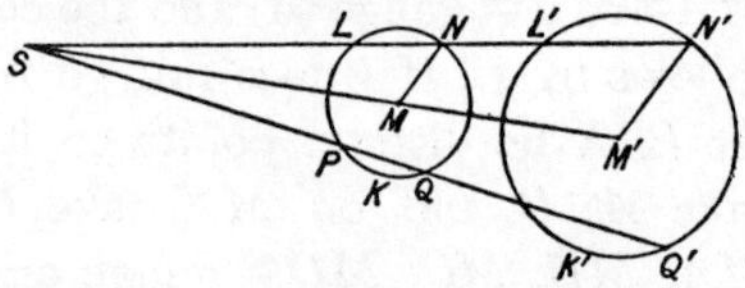

Fig. 111

* The inverse of a point with respect to a line is what is usually called the image or reflection of the point on a line. Cf. VII 37 ff.

on K (3 and **d**). If $MM' \parallel NN'$ then $MN \simeq M'N'$ and the radical axis is the right bisector of MM' (VII 40·62). If MM', NN' be not parallel, let them meet in S. Let SN meet K again in L (6). (If SN touches K, take $L = N$.) Let $P\,(\neq N, L)$ be on K (**d**) and let SP meet K again in Q (6). (If SP touches K, take $P = Q$.) The homothety (S, MM') transforms M, N into M', N' and hence K into K', and Q, L into Q', L' say, on K' (VII 35). Then with respect to the lines SN, SP we have $NP \wedge LQ$ (see VI 29 ff.). But $LQ \parallel L'Q'$, hence $NP \wedge L'Q'$ and thus $NPL'Q'$ lie on a circle K'', say. But NP, $L'Q'$ are radical axes of (K, K'') and (K', K'') resp. (VII 40·6). Hence NP, $L'Q'$ and the radical axis of (K, K') either concur or are parallel (VII 40·7). In the first case, since the radical axis of (K, K') is perpendicular to MM', it can now be drawn. If $NP \parallel L'Q'$ then $NP \parallel LQ$ and it is easily shewn that $SP \simeq SN$. If then another point P_1 be taken on K, distinct from N, L, P and the corresponding construction be performed, then $NP_1 \parallel LQ_1$ is now false by V 4.

Next, let the two circles be K_1, K_2 with centres O_1, O_2 resp. By the first part we can find the radical axis of K_1 and our circle K of centre M, and also that of K_2 and K. The radical axes of (K, K_1), (K, K_2), and (K_1, K_2) concur in X, say, or are parallel. In the first case the perpendicular from X on O_1O_2 is the radical axis of (K_1, K_2). In the second case M, O_1, O_2 colline (VII 40·7); then take any circle K_3, centre O_3 not on MO_1; the radical axes of (K_1, K_3) and of (K_2, K_3) can be found and these do meet in X', say, and the radical axis of (K_1, K_2) is the perpendicular from X' on O_1O_2.

The Poncelet-Steiner Theorem

§ 2. **Basis $\mathbf{O}_p\mathbf{C}_p\mathbf{P}_1$** (as before).

We now consider the following construction, which includes **d** as a special case.

Construction $\mathbf{q}_2$. *A certain* **fixed** *circle k is given in the plane and its centre M is known; if any coplanar line meets this circle, the points of meeting can be found.*

8. *Let N be a known point on any circle with a known centre O; if any coplanar line l, two points of which are known, meet this circle, then the points of meeting can be found by* **abcq$_2$**.

Dem. Let $M \neq O, MN' \parallel ON$ where N' is on the circle k of construction **q$_2$**. If M, N, O colline or if ON, l do not meet, we can find another point on the circle centre O, by drawing any line distinct from MO, through O, and finding the inverse of N with respect to it. Hence we may assume that M, N, O are non-collinear and that ON, l meet in H say.

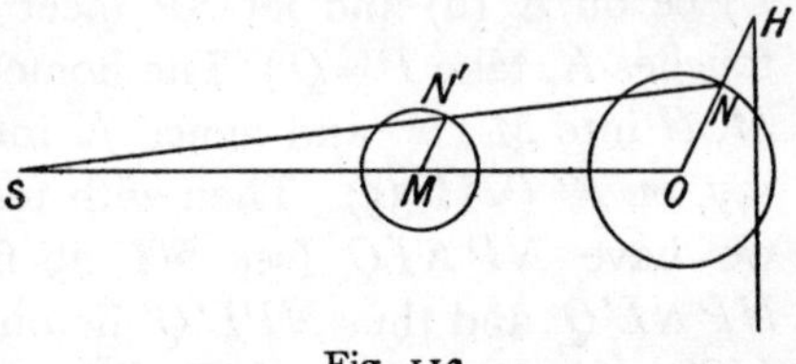

Fig. 112

First, let MO, NN' meet in S, say, then the homothety (S, OM) transforms lines into lines, and a circle and its centre into a circle and its centre (VII 33, 35). Hence l becomes l' say, the circle centre O becomes the circle k, and N becomes N' on k. Also l' can be constructed by parallels since two points on l' are known, and if l' meets k the points of meeting can be found (**q$_2$**), and then the inverse homothety (S, MO) transforms these points into the points of meeting of l and the circle, centre O.

Next, if $MO \parallel NN'$, the homothety (S, OM) is replaced by the translation OM, and the argument is as before.

If $M = O$, the construction is clear.

9. (Poncelet-Steiner.) *In the presence of* $\mathbf{O}_p\mathbf{C}_p\mathbf{P}_1$ *all constructions which can be performed by* **abcq** *or by* **abcq$_1$** *can be performed by* **abcq$_2$** (V 9, 18).

Dem. **q$_1$** can be performed by **abcq$_2$** (8). If the centres of two circles be given and one point on each, their radical axis can be constructed by **abcd** (7) and so by **abcq$_2$**. But if the circles meet, they do so on their radical axis and hence the points of meeting can be found by **abcq$_2$** (8).

10. *Axioms* $\mathbf{O}_p\mathbf{C}_p\mathbf{P}_1\mathbf{Q}_1$ *imply* $\mathbf{Q}$.

11. *Axioms* $\mathbf{O}_p\mathbf{C}_p\mathbf{P}_1\mathbf{Q}_2$ *imply* $\mathbf{Q}$ *where* $\mathbf{Q}_2$ *is the following:—*

Axiom $\mathbf{Q}_2$. For a certain fixed circle a coplanar line through a point inside it, meets the circle in at least one point.

Dems. 10, 11. Clearly we need only shew that if $[ABCD]$, the radical axis of circles on AC, BD as diameters meets AB in a point X inside both circles. By VII 40 ff., X is either inside both or outside both or on both circles. It cannot be on both since $[ABCD]$; if it be outside both, let $[ABCDX]$ then $XA . XC = XB . XD$. But $\mu XA > \mu XB$, $\mu XC > \mu XD$, whence

$$XA . XC > XB . XC > XB . XD \text{ (VII 20·5)}$$

contrary to $XA . XC = XB . XD.$

The Axiom of Archimedes

§ 3. **Basis $\mathbf{O}_p \mathbf{C}_p \mathbf{P}_1 \mathbf{Q}_2 \mathbf{K}_1$** or what is equivalent $\mathbf{O}_p \mathbf{C}_p \mathbf{P}_1 \mathbf{Q} \mathbf{K}_1$ where $\mathbf{K}_1$ is as follows:—

Axiom $\mathbf{K}_1$. (Archimedes.) **If AP, XY be any intervals then there is a natural number n such that if A_1, A_2, ..., A_n, are on $[AP$ and**

$$[A_1 A_2 \ldots A_n] \text{ and } AA_1 \simeq A_1 A_2 \simeq \ldots \simeq A_{n-1} A_n \simeq XY$$

then $[APA_n]$.

12. *If this Axiom hold, then the measures of intervals form an Archimedean system of magnitudes* (I 20·6).

Dem. If $a = \mu XY$ and $b = \mu AP$, then $\mu AA_n = na$, and since $[APA_n]$, we have $\mu AA_n > \mu AP$. Whence for any measures a, b, there is a natural number n such that $na > b$.

Mascheroni's Theorem

We now treat constructions from a slightly different standpoint, inasmuch as the given things and the things required shall be points. Let $X (Y)$ mean the circle X, radius XY, and consider the following constructions.

Given two pairs of points A, B and C, D.

(i) *To find the point* (if any) *where the lines AB, CD meet.*

(ii) *To find the points* (if any) *where AB and $C (D)$ meet.*

(iii) *To find the points* (if any) *where $A (B)$ and $C (D)$ meet.* (Construction q of V 9.)

13. (Mascheroni.) *Constructions* (i) *and* (ii) *can be performed by* (iii) *provided that a point can be found not on given lines or circles.*

Dem. Let us assume that only (iii) can be performed, then:

·1. If A, B be given points, a point C can be found such that $[ABC]$, $AB \simeq BC$. For find the meet D of $B(A)$ and $A(B)$, the meet $E \neq A$ of $D(A)$ and $B(A)$ and the meet $X \neq D$ of $E(B)$ and $B(D)$. The triangles BAD, BDE, BEX are equilateral, and hence $\mu A\hat{B}D$, $D\hat{B}E$, $E\hat{B}X = \pi/3$. But A, E are on opposite sides of BD and D, X on opposite sides of BE (IV 31). Hence $\mu A\hat{B}D + \mu D\hat{B}E + \mu E\hat{B}X = \pi$. Hence $[ABX]$, and thus X satisfies conditions on C.

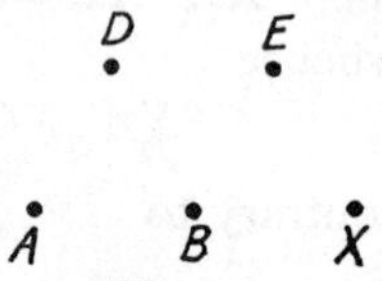

Fig. 113

·2. Hence given two points A, B and any natural number n, we can find C with $[ABC]$, $\mu AC = n \,.\, \mu AB$.

·3. The inverse of any point O with respect to any line AB (not through O) can be found, for it is the meet $\neq O$ of $A(O)$ and $B(O)$.

·4. If $k = O(D)$ we can find the inverse M' of any point M with respect to k. For *first*, if $\mu OM > OD/2$, then $M(O)$ meets k in A, B say, and $A(O)$, $B(O)$ meet again in X say; for if not, OM would touch $A(O)$, $B(O)$, and thus A, O, B would colline, contrary to V 4·1. Then O, X being meets of $A(O)$, $B(O)$, lie on opposite sides of AB. Hence X is on $[OM$. Also

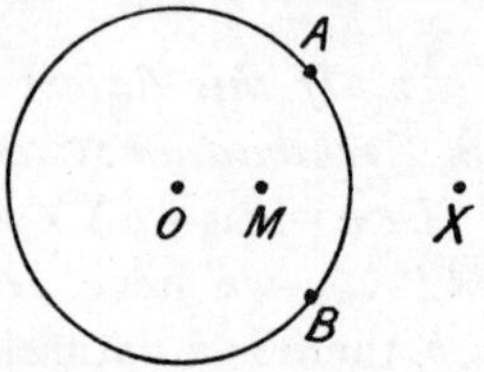

Fig. 114

$$M\hat{A}O \simeq M\hat{O}A \simeq A\hat{O}X \simeq A\hat{X}O$$

whence

$$MOA \sim AOX, \quad OM|OA \sim OA|OX, \quad OM \,.\, OX = OA^2.$$

Thus X is the inverse of M.

Next, if $\mu OM \leqq OD/2$, we can find N on $[OM$ so that $\mu ON = n \,.\, OM > OD/2$ (·2, $\mathbf{K}_1$), and N', M' on $[OM$ so that $ON \,.\, ON' = OA^2$, $OM' = n \,.\, ON'$ (first part and ·2). Hence $OM \,.\, OM' = n \,.\, OM \,.\, ON' = ON \,.\, ON' = OA^2$ (VII 21).

·5. If A, B, O do not colline, we can find the centre of the inverse of AB with respect to any circle $O(C)$.

For find the inverse P of O with respect to AB (·3), and the inverse Q of P in $O(C)$ (·4), then Q is the point required (VII 39·1).

13·6. We can find the centre of the inverse of a circle k with respect to $O(A)$, where k does not go through O.

For find the inverse M of O in k, and the inverse M' of M in $O(A)$, then M' is the point required (VII 39·1).

·7. We can now shew *Mascheroni's Theorem*. To perform construction (i), invert A, B, C, D in any circle whose centre is not on AB or CD; and to perform (ii), invert in any circle whose centre is not on AB or $C(D)$. The line AB and the line CD or circle $C(D)$, in the respective cases, become circles whose centres are known (·5, ·6), and some points on them are known (·4), hence their meets can be found by (iii). The inverse points of these meets can be found (·4), and they are the points in which the given figures meet.

·8. Particular constructions can be shortened; there is no need to follow the process in ·7. For instance, *to find the centre of the circle through ABC*; take $A(B)$ for circle k. Let C' be the inverse of C in k, then BC' is the inverse of circle ABC in k. Let M' be the inverse of A in BC' and M that of M' in k, then M is the centre of the circle ABC (VII 39·1).

§ 4. Basis $\mathbf{O}_p\mathbf{C}_p\mathbf{P}_1\mathbf{Q}_2\mathbf{K}_1$ and construction q, or $\mathbf{O}_p\mathbf{C}_p\mathbf{P}_1\mathbf{Q}_2$ and constructions $\mathbf{abcq}_2$.

14. To find a point of contact of tangents from a given point P to a circle $A(B)$:—

(i) Consider the circle on AP as diameter; if P be outside the circle $A(B)$, this meets $A(B)$ in two points R, S which are the required points (**Q**, V 6, VI 13).

Or (ii) By construction of VII 39·7. This illustrates the Poncelet-Steiner Theorem, taking $A(B)$ as the fixed circle.

·1. There are two, one, or no solutions according as P is outside, on, or inside $A(B)$.

·2. To find the points of contact of a tangent to two given circles $A(B)$, $C(D)$. Let $AB \parallel CD$; if BD meet AC in X, a tangent from X to $A(B)$ touches $C(D)$ (VII 35, 35·1). If $BD \parallel AC$, the construction is evident.

§ 5. *Application of Coordinates. Ruler and Compass Constructions*

15. *Notation.* If $a_1, \ldots, a_n$ be elements of any field, the rational functions of $a_1, \ldots, a_n$ form a field which we denote by $R(a_1, \ldots, a_n)$. Thus $R(1)$ is the ordinary field of rationals.

By $\Omega_0(a_1, \ldots, a_n)$ we shall mean the field whose elements are derived from those of $R(a_1, \ldots, a_n)$ by a finite number of additions, subtractions, multiplications, divisions and of operations $\sqrt{1+x^2}$ where x is an element already constructed.

By $\Omega(a_1, \ldots, a_n)$ we shall mean the field whose elements are derived from those of $R(a_1, \ldots, a_n)$ by a finite number of additions, subtractions, multiplications, divisions and of operations $\sqrt{x}$ where x is an element already constructed.

Def. If an expression E involve square roots the expressions '*conjugate*' to E are those found by altering the signs in front of the square roots. Thus the conjugates to $\sqrt{2}-\sqrt{3}$ are $-\sqrt{2}-\sqrt{3}$, $\sqrt{2}+\sqrt{3}$, $-\sqrt{2}+\sqrt{3}$.

·1. If $b_1, \ldots, b_n$ are in Ω_0 so is $\sqrt{b_1^2+b_2^2+\ldots+b_n^2}$.

·2. If a, b, c are in Ω so are the roots of $ax^2+bx+c=0$.

·3. The expressions conjugate to an expression in Ω_0 are all in Ω_0. Similarly for Ω.

·4. *Def.* A point is '*in a field*' when all its coordinates are; a polynomial when all its coefficients are.

·5. *Def.* If the elements of a field whose squares are positive or zero, constitute a fully ordered field, we call those elements the '*real*' elements of the field. Cf. I 24, 25.

16. By means of **abcq**$_2$ in the presence of $\mathbf{O}_p\mathbf{C}_p\mathbf{P}_1\mathbf{Q}_2$, we can construct two perpendicular lines through the centre M of the fixed circle k to meet the circle in A, B, say (5). Take Cartesian coordinates in the frame MAB (VIII 42). *Then by* **abcq**$_2$ *we can construct from given points all points whose coordinates are in* $\Omega(a_1, \ldots, a_n)$ *and which involve only real square roots, and those points only, where* $a_1, \ldots, a_n$ *are the coordinates of the given points* (and therefore real. Cf. VIII 21, 22, 22·1). Note that MA, MB are unit intervals (VII 15).

Dem. By **abcp** we can construct on MA any point whose coordinate is a rational function of $a_1, \ldots, a_n$ and those points only (VIII 27). By means of $\mathbf{q}_2$ we can find on MA a point whose coordinate is $\sqrt{h}$, where $h > 0$ is a coordinate of a given point. For if $[CMA]$, $\mu CM = h$, and the circle on CA as diameter meets MB in D, then $MD^2 = MC . MA$ (VII 22). Hence $\mu MD = \sqrt{h}$. Thus we can construct all points in the field $\Omega(a_1, \ldots, a_n)$, whose coordinates are both real, from known points by means of $\mathbf{abcq}_2$. No other points can be so got, for if the line $lx + my = 1$ be constructed from the given points by **abcp** then l, m are rational functions of $a_1, \ldots, a_n$ (VIII 26·1), and the coordinates of its meets with k are in $\Omega(a_1, \ldots, a_n)$, and are real if these meets exist (15·2·5).

16·1. *The necessary and sufficient condition that a problem can be solved by* **abcq** *and so by* $\mathbf{abcq}_2$, *in the presence of* $\mathbf{O}_p\mathbf{C}_p\mathbf{P}_1\mathbf{Q}_2$, *is that each equation which gives new points from old* (when the problem is formulated analytically) *can be replaced by a sequence of quadratic and linear equations whose coefficients are coordinates of points previously found, the quadratic equations all having real roots* (15·2, 16).

·2. *Note.* This is thus the condition that a problem can be solved by ruler and compasses, the ruler being supposed ungraduated and merely a straight edge, the compasses being supposed to shut up when removed from the paper. Thus the compasses need not be used for transferring lengths, but only to draw a circle of which the centre and a point on it are given. We have also seen that if a fixed circle with its centre is given once for all, it is sufficient to use the straight edge to perform all ruler and compass constructions, as far as they are concerned with determining points and lines (Poncelet-Steiner), and that with free use of collapsing compasses, the straight edge may be dispensed with (Mascheroni).

§ 6. *Gauge Constructions*

17. *By* **abcd** *in the presence of* $\mathbf{O}_p\mathbf{C}_p\mathbf{P}_1$ *we can construct axes as in* 16 *with the unit interval* $MA \simeq$ *gauge, and then from given points we can construct all points of* $\Omega_0(a_1, \ldots, a_n)$, *and those points only, where* $a_1, \ldots, a_n$ *are coordinates of the given points.*

Dem. When x is a coordinate of a known point of $\Omega_0(a_1, \ldots, a_n)$ we can construct the point $(1, x)$, and then the point $(\sqrt{1 + x^2}, 0)$ cVII 23). Further, **abcp** give us only those points whose (oordinates are rational functions of coordinates of known points, while **d** allows us to cut off the gauge from a point (a, b) on the line $y-b=m(x-a)$, where a, b, m are known. If (x, y) be the end of the interval cut off, then

$$1=(x-a)^2+(y-b)^2=(x-a)^2(1+m^2).$$

Hence $$\sqrt{1+m^2}=\frac{1}{x-a},$$

and x, y are still in $\Omega_0(a_1, \ldots, a_n)$.

17·1. *$\Omega_0(a_1, \ldots, a_n)$ is a smaller field than $\Omega(a_1, \ldots, a_n)$ or even than the real part of the latter, the a_i being real.*

Dem. $\sqrt{1-a^2}$ is real and in Ω, if a is in Ω and $-1 \leqq a \leqq 1$. But if $\sqrt{1-a^2}$ equalled an expression in Ω_0, the two expressions would be equal for an infinite number of values of a and so for all. This can be shewn as in ordinary Algebra. But when $a>1$, $\sqrt{1-a^2}$ is not real and hence not in Ω_0.

18. *Construction* $\mathbf{q}_2$ *cannot be performed by* **abcd** *only.*

·1. *Neither* $\mathbf{Q}$ *nor* $\mathbf{Q}_1$ *nor* $\mathbf{Q}_2$ *can be deduced from* $\mathbf{OCP}_1$.

Dems. As in VIII 29 ff. we can construct a Geometry from the field $\Omega_0(1)$ where **O**, **C**, $\mathbf{Q}_0$ (VIII 28) hold and also, since $\Omega_0(1)$ is a *field*, where Pappus' Theorem holds. But in this Geometry **Q**, $\mathbf{Q}_1$, $\mathbf{Q}_2$ do not hold, since the coordinates of the points of meeting mentioned in these Axioms are not always in our field. Consider for instance, the meets of $x^2+y^2=1$ and $x=a$ $(0<a<1)$. We have $y=\pm\sqrt{1-a^2}$ which are not in $\Omega_0(1)$ even if a is (17·1).

·2. *Thus though we can deduce* $\mathbf{Q}_0$ *from* $\mathbf{OCP}_1$ (VIII 35·1) *yet Axiom* **Q** *is an additional assumption, which may however be replaced by the weaker Axiom* $\mathbf{Q}_2$ (11).

§ 7. *Mascheroni Constructions and Axiom* $\mathbf{K}_1$

19. Mascheroni constructions are of the following type: we have a given set of points S in the plane, and we draw a finite number of circles each of which has its centre in a point of S and goes through a point of S; these circles meet in a set S_1; next we draw circles each of which has its centre in a point of S or S_1 and goes through a point of S or S_1. These give a set S_2 and so on. In the construction of 13·7 we must consider the centre of the auxiliary circle of inversion, and a point on

it, to be in S. If n is the number of circles finally drawn, and r the measure of the greatest interval between points of S, the measure of the greatest interval between the whole set of given and constructed points is clearly not greater than $2^n . r$. Hence if $\mathbf{K}_1$ is false, some points cannot be reached by this method, but lines joining pairs of given points may well meet in such unattained points. In this sense therefore *these constructions depend on* $\mathbf{K}_1$.

§ 8. *Constructions by Ruler and Compasses (continuation)*

20. We saw in 16 that, if $a_1, \ldots, a_n$ be coordinates of given points, we can construct from these by ruler and compasses the points whose coordinates are elements of the field $\Omega(a_1, \ldots, a_n)$, involving only real square roots, and those points only.

An expression E, real or not, in $\Omega(a_1, \ldots, a_n)$ involves only a finite number of square roots, and the '*radicands*' (i.e. the expressions under a single square root) are rational functions of $a_1, \ldots, a_n$.

Def. A term will be called of '*order*' h when it involves $h-1$ square roots under a principal square root. Thus

$$\sqrt{\sqrt{\sqrt{x}+\sqrt{y}+\sqrt{z}}}$$

is of order 4.

Any square roots which can be extracted will be supposed extracted. Thus $\sqrt{a^2}$ will be replaced by a. If, in an expression E, a term of order m appears which is a rational function of other terms of orders $\leqq m$, we express that term in that form.

Then the unequal terms under the square root signs will become independent. Thus we write $\sqrt{\sqrt{x}+\sqrt{y}+\sqrt{x}\sqrt{y}}$ instead of $\sqrt{\sqrt{x}+\sqrt{y}+\sqrt{xy}}$ and $\sqrt{a+\sqrt{b}}+\dfrac{\sqrt{a^2-b}}{\sqrt{a+\sqrt{b}}}$ instead of $\sqrt{a+\sqrt{b}}+\sqrt{a-\sqrt{b}}$, when a^2-b happens to be a perfect square.

Let $\sqrt{X}$ be a term of highest order h in E, then E is a rational function of $\sqrt{X}$ whose coefficients are rational in the other terms of order h; and

$$E=\frac{p+q\sqrt{X}}{r+s\sqrt{X}}=\frac{(p+q\sqrt{X})(r-s\sqrt{X})}{r^2-s^2X}=A+B\sqrt{X},$$

where A, B depend on terms $\neq \sqrt{X}$ of orders $\leqq h$. Similarly $A = A_1 + A_2\sqrt{Y}$, and so on. Finally, E becomes a polynomial in the terms of order h, viz. $\sqrt{X}, \sqrt{Y}, \ldots$, with coefficients rational in terms of orders less than h, and each $\sqrt{X}, \sqrt{Y}, \ldots$ is to the first power only, though products of these may occur.

Repeat this process for terms of orders $h-1, h-2, \ldots$ and we finally get the '*normal*' form of E, which can be built up from $R(a_1, \ldots, a_n)$ by square root extraction, addition and multiplication, and where no term of order h is a rational function of other terms of order h and less.

If E in its normal form involve r square roots, it has $m = 2^r$ conjugate values $X_1, \ldots, X_m$. Then

$$f(x) = \prod_{i=1}^{m} (x - x_i)$$

has all its coefficients in $R(a_1, \ldots, a_n)$. For if the sign of a radical be changed, the x_i are merely permuted, $f(x)$ is unchanged, and its coefficients are thus not altered. Hence, if a coefficient written in normal form involve a square root, say $\sqrt{X}$ of order h, it must equal both $P + Q\sqrt{X}$ and $P - Q\sqrt{X}$ where neither P nor Q involve $\sqrt{X}$. Hence, $Q = 0$. Thus the coefficient can involve no term of order h; and so for lower orders. Hence,

20·1. E satisfies an equation $f(x) = 0$ of degree 2^r, with coefficients in $R(a_1, \ldots, a_n)$.

21. If an algebraic equation $\phi(x) = 0$, ϕ being a polynomial with coefficients in $R(a_1, \ldots, a_n)$, be satisfied by E, it is satisfied by all values conjugate to E.

Dem. Take E in its normal form, $E = A + B\sqrt{X}$, where $\sqrt{X}$ is a term of highest order h. Then $\phi(E) = L + M\sqrt{X}$ where L, M are independent of $\sqrt{X}$. Hence, if $\phi(E) = 0$, then $L = M = 0$, otherwise $\sqrt{X}$ would equal $-L/M$, and E would not be in normal form. Again if $L = L_1 + L_2\sqrt{Y}$, $M = M_1 + M_2\sqrt{Y}$ and $\phi(E) = 0$, then $L_1 = L_2 = M_1 = M_2 = 0$, and so on. Finally we get expressions equal to zero in which appear only terms of orders $\leqq h-1$, and we proceed with these as before. Hence if E is replaced by any conjugate expression, $\phi(E)$ remains zero.

22. Of all equations with coefficients in $R(a_1, \ldots, a_n)$ which are satisfied by E, let $\psi(x)=0$ be one of lowest degree l and with its coefficient of x^l unity. *This equation is unique.* For if $\psi_1(x)=0$ were another such equation, then $\psi(x)-\psi_1(x)=0$ would be an equation of degree $\leqq l-1$ satisfied by E.

·1. $\phi(x)$ of 21 is divisible by $\psi(x)$ of 22, in the field

$$R(a_1, \ldots, a_n).$$

Dem. $\phi(x)=\psi(x)q(x)+r(x)$ where q, r are polynomials in $R(a_1, \ldots, a_n)$, and the degree of r is $< l$. This follows by dividing out $\phi(x)$ by $\psi(x)$. But $\phi(E)=0$, $\psi(E)=0$. Hence $r(E)=0$. Hence $r(x)$ must vanish identically, otherwise $\psi(x)=0$ would not be the equation of lowest degree satisfied by E.

·2. *Def. and The.* The polynomial $\psi(x)$ of 22 is '*irreducible*' in $R(a_1, \ldots, a_n)$, that is, it cannot be factored into two polynomials in $R(a_1, \ldots, a_n)$ since one factor would vanish when $x=E$. We say also that $\psi(x)=0$ is an '*irreducible equation.*'

·3. Consider $f(x)=0$, the equation in 20·1 of degree 2^r satisfied by E. We shew that $f=c\psi^s$ where c is some constant, s a natural number, and ψ as in 22.

Dem. Let $l<2^r$, then $f=\psi.\chi$ where $\chi(x)$ is a polynomial in $R(a_1, \ldots, a_n)$ (22·1). Since some conjugate of E satisfies $\chi=0$, so does E (21), whence again $\chi=\psi.\chi_1$ where $\chi_1(x)$ is a polynomial in $R(a_1, \ldots, a_n)$. Similarly $\chi_1=\psi.\chi_2$, and so on. Finally we reach a 'polynomial' ψ_s which is a constant in

$$R(a_1, \ldots, a_n).$$

·4. Since $f=c\psi^s$ and l, 2^r are degrees of ψ, f respectively, we have $ls=2^r$, whence *l is a power of* 2. Therefore

23. *If* $\psi(x)=0$, *and* $\psi(x)$ *be an irreducible polynomial in* $R(a_1, \ldots, a_n)$, *and one and hence all* (21) *its roots be in* $\Omega(a_1, \ldots, a_n)$, *then its degree is a power of* 2.

·1. This condition for the roots to be in $\Omega(a_1, \ldots, a_n)$, though necessary, is not sufficient, since it is known that equations of degrees higher than four cannot in general be solved by radicals.

24. *Fundamental Theorem. A construction is certainly not possible by* $\mathbf{abcq_2}$ (by 'ruler and compasses') *in the presence of*

$\mathbf{O}_p\mathbf{C}_p\mathbf{P}_1\mathbf{Q}_2$, *if any one of the coordinates of a point to be constructed satisfies an irreducible equation in the field* $\Omega(a_1, \ldots, a_n)$ *whose degree is not a power of* 2, *where* $a_1, \ldots, a_n$ *are the coordinates of the given points* (16·1, 23).

24·1. *Thus we cannot find a point* X *from* O, U *on* OU, *such that* $OX^3 = 2 . OU$ (the 'duplication of the cube').

Dem. The coordinate x of X would satisfy $x^3 - 2 = 0$. But $x^3 - 2$ is irreducible in $R(1)$, for if $x - \frac{a}{b}$ were a factor with $\frac{a}{b}$ in $R(1)$, then would $\left(\frac{a}{b}\right)^3 = 2$, which is impossible (I 16·4).

Regular Polygons. Preliminary Theorems

25. *Def.* A (plane) polygon is '*regular*' when each pair of its sides is congruent and also each pair of its angles.

·1. *Def.* A polynomial in one variable, whose coefficients are integers, is '*primitive*' if these integers have no common divisor save 1.

·2. If $A(x)$, $B(x)$ be primitive polynomials then so is $A(x) . B(x)$.

Dem. If $A(x) = a_0x^m + a_1x^{m-1} + \ldots$; $B(x) = b_0x^n + b_1x^{n-1} + \ldots$ be primitive and

$$A(x) . B(x) = C(x) = c_0x^{m+n} + c_1x^{m+n-1} + \ldots,$$

then

$$c_0 = a_0b_0,$$

$$c_1 = a_0b_1 + a_1b_0,$$

$$c_2 = a_0b_2 + a_1b_1 + a_2b_0,$$

$$\ldots\ldots\ldots\ldots\ldots\ldots\ldots\ldots,$$

$$c_\nu = a_0b_\nu + a_1b_{\nu-1} + a_2b_{\nu-2} + \ldots + a_{\nu-1}b_1 + a_\nu b_0 \quad (\nu = 0, 1, \ldots, m+n)$$

where $a_r = 0$ if $r > m$, and $b_r = 0$ if $r > n$. Now suppose $c_0, c_1, \ldots, c_{m+n}$ were divisible by a prime p. By hyp. p does not divide *all* the a, nor *all* the b. Suppose p divides $a_0, a_1, \ldots, a_{r-1}$, $b_0, b_1, \ldots, b_{s-1}$ but neither a_r nor b_s. Now

$$c_{r+s} = a_rb_s + a_{r-1}b_{s+1} + a_{r-2}b_{s+2} + \ldots + a_{r+1}b_{s-1} + a_{r+2}b_{s-2} + \ldots$$

and c_{r+s} is not divisible by p, for a_rb_s is not, but the other terms are so divisible. This contradiction gives the Theorem

25·3. If $A(x)$, $B(x)$ be polynomials with integral coefficients whose H.C.F.'s are a, b resp., then the H.C.F. of the coefficients of the product $A(x).B(x)$ is ab. At once from ·2.

·4. If $A(x)=x^m+a_1x^{m-1}+\dots$, $B(x)=x^n+b_1x^{n-1}+\dots$ be polynomials and the a_i and b_i be all rational and

$$A(x).B(x)=C(x)=x^{m+n}+c_1x^{m+n-1}+\dots$$

then the c cannot all be integers unless all the a and b are.

Dem. Let a, b be the H.C.F.'s of the denominators of the a_i, b_i resp., then $a.A(x)$ and $b.B(x)$ are primitive, hence so is $abC(x)$ (·2). But if the c be all integers, this polynomial cannot be primitive unless $a=b=1$.

·5. If in a polynomial $A(x)=x^m+a_1x^{m-1}+\dots+a_m$, the a are integers all divisible by p, and $a_m=\pm p$, then $A(x)$ is irreducible in $R(1)$.

Dem. If not, then

$$x^m+a_1x^{m-1}+\dots\pm p=(x^r+b_1x^{r-1}+\dots\pm 1)(x^s+c_1x^{s-1}+\dots\pm p),$$

where the b and c are *integers* (·4). The coefficient of x on the right hand side is $\pm c_{s-1}\pm pb_{r-1}$, and since it is divisible by p, (hypothesis) so is c_{s-1}. The coefficient of x^2 is

$$\pm c_{s-2}+c_{s-1}b_{r-1}\pm pb_{r-2}$$

and since this and c_{s-1} are divisible by p, so is c_{s-2}. Similarly $c_{s-3},\dots,c_1$ are divisible by p. But the coefficient of x^s is

$$\pm 1+c_1b_{r-1}+c_2b_{r-2}+\dots+c_{s-1}b_{r-s+1}$$

and is *not* divisible by p. (Clearly we are taking $b_0=1$, $b_t=0$ if $t<0$). This contradiction shews the Theorem.

26. *If p is a prime then*

$$f(x)=(x^{p^n}-1)/(x^{p^{n-1}}-1)$$

(*when divided out*) *is irreducible in* $R(1)$.

Dem. If $n=1$, put $x=y+1$ then

$$f(y+1)=\frac{(y+1)^p-1}{y}=y^{p-1}+py^{p-2}+\frac{p(p-1)}{\lfloor 2}y^{p-3}+\dots+p$$

is irreducible by 25·5.

If $n>1$ let $p^{n-1}=q$, then $f(x)=1+x^q+x^{2q}+\dots+x^{(p-1)q}$. Let χ denote a polynomial, *not necessarily always the same*, with integral coefficients. Put $x=y+1$, then

$$x^p=y^p+1+p\chi(y),\quad x^{p^2}=(x^p)^p=y^{p^2}+1+p\chi(y),\ \dots,$$
$$x^q=y^q+1+p\chi(y).$$

Hence $x^{2q} = (y^q + 1)^2 + p\chi(y)$,

$x^{3q} = x^{2q} . x^q = (y^q + 1)^3 + p\chi(y)$,

and so on: therefore

$$f(x) = 1 + (y^q + 1) + (y^q + 1)^2 + \dots + (y^q + 1)^{p-1} + p\chi(y)$$
$$= \frac{(y^q + 1)^p - 1}{y^q} + p\chi(y) = y^{q(p-1)} + p\chi(y) = \phi(y), \text{ say.}$$

Put $y = 0$ then $x = 1$, $f(x) = p$. Hence the constant term in $\phi(y)$ is p, and since all the other coefficients of $\phi(y)$ (save the highest, which is unity) are divisible by p, therefore $\phi(y)$, and so $f(x)$, is irreducible in $R(1)$ by 25·5*.

The Gaussian Theory of the Regular Polygons

§ 9. Basis $O_p C_p P_1 Q_2$.

We investigate the question whether a regular n-gon (i.e. a polygon with n sides) can be constructed by ruler and compasses when the end points A, B of one of its sides are given. Take axes and scale so that A, B are (0, 0) and (− 1, 0). If AC be a side of a regular polygon so constructible, the coordinates (x, y) of C must be real, and they must involve only rational numbers and operations and real square roots (16). Hence $z = x + iy$ is in $\Omega(1)$, that is, z involves only rational numbers and operations and real or imaginary square roots. But

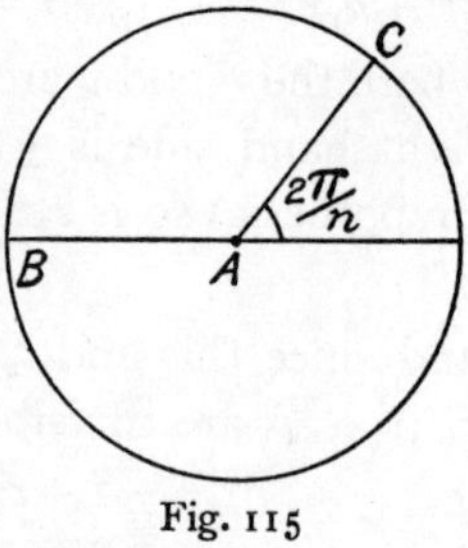

Fig. 115

$$z = \cos\frac{2\pi}{n} + i\sin\frac{2\pi}{n}, \quad z^n = 1 \text{ (VIII 47·1).}$$

The first question is therefore, whether this z is in $\Omega(1)$. If it is not, we cannot even be sure, on our present basis, that it exists.

27. *If p is a prime and a regular p-gon be constructible by* **abcq**$_2$, *given the end points of a side, then since the cyclotomic equation* $(z^p - 1)/(z - 1) = 0$ *is irreducible* (26), *and of degree* $p - 1$, *we must have* $p = 2^n + 1$ (23).

28. *Conversely if $p = 2^n + 1$ and p is prime, then a regular p-gon is constructible by* **abcq**$_2$ *when the end points of a side are given.*

* We have used the binomial Theorem for a positive integral index. This case is easily shewn by induction. It is also quite easy to avoid using this Theorem.

Dem. If $\epsilon \neq 1$ is a root of $z^p = 1$ we shew that ϵ is in $\Omega(1)$. Let g be a primitive root of p (I 29·21), then $\epsilon^g, \epsilon^{g^2}, \ldots, \epsilon^{g^{p-1}}$ are the roots $\epsilon, \epsilon^2, \ldots, \epsilon^{p-1}$ in some order, since if $g^r \equiv s \pmod{p}$ then $\epsilon^{g^r} = \epsilon^s$. Let

$$\eta_1 = \epsilon^g + \epsilon^{g^3} + \epsilon^{g^5} + \ldots + \epsilon^{g^{p-2}}, \qquad (2^{n-1} \text{ terms}).$$

$$\eta_2 = \epsilon^{g^2} + \epsilon^{g^4} + \epsilon^{g^6} + \ldots + \epsilon^{g^{p-1}} \qquad ,,$$

$$\eta_{11} = \epsilon^g + \epsilon^{g^5} + \epsilon^{g^9} + \ldots + \epsilon^{g^{p-4}}, \qquad (2^{n-2} \text{ terms}).$$

$$\eta_{12} = \epsilon^{g^3} + \epsilon^{g^7} + \ldots + \epsilon^{g^{p-2}} \qquad ,,$$

$$\eta_{21} = \epsilon^{g^2} + \epsilon^{g^6} + \epsilon^{g^{10}} + \ldots + \epsilon^{g^{p-3}}, \qquad ,,$$

$$\eta_{22} = \epsilon^{g^4} + \epsilon^{g^8} + \ldots + \epsilon^{g^{p-1}} \qquad ,,$$

Continue this breaking-up process, getting sums of $2^{n-3}, 2^{n-4}, \ldots$ terms and finally one term. Now $\eta_1 + \eta_2 = \epsilon + \epsilon^2 + \ldots + \epsilon^{p-1} = -1$. If we substitute ϵ^g for ϵ, then η_1 and η_2 are interchanged; (note that $g^p \equiv g \pmod{p}$ by I 29·12). Multiply η_1 by η_2 and collect terms, then $\eta_1\eta_2 = \kappa\epsilon^{g^a} + \lambda\epsilon^{g^b} + \ldots$ where $\kappa, \lambda, \ldots$ are integers. Now since this product is unchanged by substituting ϵ^g for ϵ, therefore if $\rho\epsilon^{g^t}$ appears in the product, so do $\rho\epsilon^{g^{t+1}}, \rho\epsilon^{g^{t+2}}, \ldots, \rho\epsilon^{g^{t+p-1}}$. But these are merely $\rho\epsilon^g, \rho\epsilon^{g^2}, \ldots, \rho\epsilon^{g^{p-1}}$ in some order, and g is a primitive root of p. Hence each ϵ^{g^t} occurs equally often for $t = 1, 2, \ldots, p-1$. Hence

$$\eta_1\eta_2 = \rho(\epsilon^g + \epsilon^{g^2} + \ldots + \epsilon^{g^{p-1}}) = \rho(\epsilon + \epsilon^2 + \ldots + \epsilon^{p-1}) = -\rho.$$

Thus η_1, η_2 *satisfy* $x^2 + x - \rho = 0$ *where* ρ *is an integer.*

Next $\eta_{11} + \eta_{12} = \eta_1$, $\eta_{21} + \eta_{22} = \eta_2$. The product $\eta_{11}\eta_{12}$ is not changed by substituting ϵ^{g^2} for ϵ, hence (as before) if it contain onc term of η_1, ρ_1 times, it contains each term of η_1 that number of times. Similarly for η_2. Hence

$$\eta_{11}\eta_{12} = \rho_1\eta_1 + \rho_2\eta_2 \text{ with } \rho_1, \rho_2 \text{ integers. But } \eta_{11} + \eta_{12} = \eta_1.$$

Hence η_{11}, η_{12} *satisfy* $x^2 - \eta_1 x + (\rho_1\eta_1 + \rho_2\eta_2) = 0$, *where* ρ_1, ρ_2 *are integers.*

Similarly η_{21}, η_{22} satisfy a quadratic equation in $R(\eta_1, \eta_2)$. We can treat $\eta_{111}, \eta_{112}, \ldots$, similarly; and we find finally $\epsilon, \epsilon^2, \ldots, \epsilon^{p-1}$ by a chain of quadratics whose coefficients are rational in the roots of the preceding quadratics; hence these quantities are in $\Omega(1)$.

Further all these roots, except the ϵ^r themselves, are real.

For the sums of two terms obtained in the last stage but one, are of the form

$$\epsilon^{gk}+\epsilon^{gk'}, \text{ where } k'=\frac{p-1}{2}+k.$$

But since g is a primitive root of p, $g^{p-1}\equiv 1 \pmod p$ and $g^{\frac{p-1}{2}}\equiv -1 \pmod p$. Hence these sums are of form $\epsilon^{g^k}+\epsilon^{-g^k}$ and so are real (VIII 47·3). The earlier sums of 4 terms, 8 terms, etc. are sums of these and so also real. Taking $k=0$, this shews that the point $x=\epsilon+\epsilon^{-1}$, $y=0$ can be constructed from the points (0, 0), (+1, 0) by means of **abcq**$_2$ (16·1). But $\epsilon+\epsilon^{-1}=2\cos\frac{2r\pi}{p}$ for some $r=1, \ldots, (p-1)$ (VIII 47·1·3), and by choice of the root ϵ, we can make r assume any of these values. Whence, given points O, U, we can construct from them a point P by **abcq**$_2$, so that $\mu U\hat{O}P=\frac{2\pi}{p}$, and hence we can construct a regular p-gon on OU.

28·1. *Example.* The regular pentagon $p=5$. We have $\eta_1=\epsilon^2+\epsilon^3$, $\eta_2=\epsilon^4+\epsilon$, $\eta_1\eta_2=-1$. Hence $\eta_1=-\frac{1}{2}\pm\frac{1}{2}\sqrt{5}$. Taking account of sign, this gives $\sin\frac{2\pi}{5}=\frac{1}{2}(\sqrt{5}-1)$. Whence the following construction for the regular pentagon with a given side AB. Let C be mid AB, $CD\perp AB$, $CD\simeq AB$. Find E, F so that $[ADE]$, $DE\simeq AC$, $[CDF]$, $AF\simeq AE$, which can be done by **abcq**$_2$. Then F is the vertex of the pentagon opposite to AB.

·2. If 2^n+1 is prime, then $n=2^\nu$ for some natural number ν; for if $n=2^\nu m$ where m is odd, then $2^{m2^\nu}+1$ is divisible by $2^{2^\nu}+1$, since x^m+1 is divisible by $x+1$ when m is odd.

·3. $2^{2^\nu}+1$ is known to be prime for $\nu=0, 1, 2, 3, 4$ and not prime for $\nu=5, 6, 7, 8, 9, 11, 12$ and some others.

29. *A regular n-gon is constructible by* **abcq**$_2$ *if and only if n is of the form* $2^\nu(2^{2^{\nu_1}}+1)(2^{2^{\nu_2}}+1)\ldots$ *where* $\nu_1, \nu_2, \ldots$ *are unequal and all the* $2^{2^{\nu_i}}+1$ *are primes.*

Dem. If a regular rs-gon is constructible, so is a regular r-gon since we can obtain it by joining every sth vertex. And if r, s are coprime, and a regular r-gon and a regular s-gon are constructible, so is a regular rs-gon, for we can find integers

a, b so that $ar - bs = 1$ (I 29·15) and then construct the angle of measure

$$a\frac{2\pi}{s} - b\frac{2\pi}{r} = \frac{2\pi}{rs}(ar - bs) = \frac{2\pi}{rs}.$$

Hence we need only consider p^a-gons where p is prime. Now $z = \cos\frac{2\pi}{p^a} + i\sin\frac{2\pi}{p^a}$ satisfies $z^{p^a} - 1 = 0$, but does not satisfy $z^{p^{a-1}} - 1 = 0$ (VIII 44·7). Hence it satisfies

$$\frac{z^{p^a} - 1}{z^{p^{a-1}} - 1} = 0.$$

But the left hand side of this equation is irreducible (26) and hence if z is in $\Omega(1)$, its degree $p^{a-1}(p-1)$ must, by 23, be a power of 2. Hence if $a > 1$, then must $p = 2$.

Since any angle can be bisected by **abcq**$_2$, our Theorem now follows from 27, 28.

29·1. Angles cannot in general be trisected by **abcq**$_2$.

Dem. Consider an angle of measure $\pi/3$. If this were trisected we should obtain an angle of measure $\pi/9$, and a regular 9-gon would be constructible, contrary to 29.

·2. A construction for a regular polygon of 17 sides will be found in H. P. Hudson, *Ruler and Compasses* (1916), p. 34.

30. *Note.* It is easy to shew that all ruler and compass constructions, so far as they relate to the determining of lines and points from given lines and points, can be performed if we use *both* edges of a ruler, or *one* edge of a ruler bent at an angle. (Hudson, *loc. cit.* p. 74.)

CHAPTER X

THE ANALYSIS SITUS OF PLANE POLYGONS

Introductory Remarks

The main part of the present chapter is a continuation of Chapters II and III and is based accordingly on Axioms $\mathbf{O}_p$; it is needed in the Theory of areas.

The most obvious way to define the area of a polygon is to split it up into triangles and to take the area of the polygon as the sum of the areas of the constituent triangles. The question as to what is meant by the 'area of a triangle' and the 'sum' of such areas is taken up in the next chapter. In this chapter we consider the dissection of a polygon into triangles.

A polygon p is dissected into a set of triangles $[t]$ when (i) no two of the triangles have a common inside point, (ii) every point inside p is on or inside a triangle of $[t]$, and (iii) every point inside a triangle of $[t]$ is inside p. We have to shew that such a dissection is always possible.

But clearly before we can do this, we must say what we mean by the 'inside' of a polygon or triangle. We accomplish this by shewing that a simple polygon p separates the other points of the plane into two regions whereof one is such that all rays from all points of it meet p. (Cf. III 1·1·2.) This last region is the inside of the polygon. In working through the proof the reader must be careful not to assume that the polygon is convex, and he is advised to draw figures of, for example, re-entrant polygons of a spiral form. In particular, it is not true that from a point outside a polygon a ray can always be drawn not meeting the polygon.

It will be noted that the main difference between our treatment and the more usual one is that we *do not assume continuity*. Our Theorems are therefore true in other spaces besides continuous space. The proofs in this chapter are mainly based on Hans Hahn, *Monatshefte für Math. und Physik*, 1908, XIX, p. 289; Lennes, *American Journal of Math.*, 1911, XXXIII, p. 37.

Note that a 'side' of a triangle or polygon is an *open* interval.

§ 1. Basis O_p. All figures in this chapter are in one plane.

The Inside and Outside of a Triangle

1. *Def.* If $[S]$ be a set of points, two points P, Q are '*accessible*' with respect to $[S]$, if there is a way (III 1) from P to Q which does not meet $[S]$, save perhaps in P or Q or both.

'Way' here means of course a way in our plane.

·1. Two points accessible with respect to $[S]$ are so accessible by a *simple* way (III 1).

2. *The. and Def. A triangle separates the other points of the plane into two regions, whereof one is the set of inside points defined in* II 12·1. *This is a convex region. The points not inside and not on the triangle are 'outside' points. They form the other region. The inside and the outside are bounded by the triangle.*

Dem. (i) If X_1, X_2 be inside the triangle ABC, then AX_1, AX_2 meet B-C in points Y_1, Y_2 with $[AX_1Y_1]$ $[AX_2Y_2]$ (II 12·2). Suppose $[BY_1Y_2C]$. If $[X_1ZX_2]$, then Z will be inside $\triangle Y_1AY_2$ (II 12·1) and hence inside $\triangle BAY_2$ and hence inside $\triangle BAC$ (II 18). Hence the points inside $\triangle ABC$ form a convex region.

(ii) If X_1 is inside $\triangle ABC$, and X_1-X_2 does not meet the triangle, then X_2 is inside the triangle; for the line X_1X_2 meets the triangle in two points Z_1, Z_2 (II 16) and $[Z_1X_1Z_2]$ (II 12·4), and since X_1-X_2 does not meet the triangle, both $[X_1Z_1X_2]$ and $[X_1Z_2X_2]$ are false. Hence $[Z_1X_1X_2]$ or $[X_1X_2Z_1]$, and $[Z_2X_1X_2]$ or $[X_1X_2Z_2]$. These with $[Z_1X_1Z_2]$ give $[Z_1X_1X_2Z_2]$ or $[Z_1X_2X_1Z_2]$ (II 8·9·91) and hence $[Z_1X_2Z_2]$ (II 8·8). Hence X_2 is inside the triangle.

(iii) Hence a way from an outside to an inside point meets the triangle.

(iv) It remains to shew that two points Y_1, Y_2 outside the triangle are accessible with respect to the triangle. Since a point inside $\triangle BAC$ is inside $B\hat{A}C$ by the defs. (III 5, 18) therefore Y_1 is either outside $B\hat{A}C$, or it satisfies $[ABY_1]$ or $[ACY_1]$ or $[ADY_1]$ where $[BDC]$. If $[AD_1Y_1]$ $[AD_2Y_2]$, where $[BD_1C]$ or $B = D_1$, and $[BD_2C]$ or $C = D_2$, then Y_1-Y_2 does not meet $B\hat{A}C$ and does not meet BC (III 2·2), and hence does not meet $\triangle ABC$. If Y_2 is outside $B\hat{A}C$, and Y_1 satisfies $[AD_1Y_1]$ $[BD_1C]$, let E, F satisfy $[ABE]$ $[Y_1EF]$; but if Y_1 satisfies $[ABY_1]$, let F satisfy $[CY_1F]$. In both cases F is outside $B\hat{A}C$ (III 19·1), and the points outside $B\hat{A}C$ form a region (III 18), and hence Y_2, F are accessible with respect to $\triangle ABC$, since the points of B-C are inside $B\hat{A}C$. Hence Y_1, Y_2 are accessible with respect to $\triangle ABC$. If Y_1, Y_2 be both outside $B\hat{A}C$, it has been pointed out that they are accessible with respect to $\triangle ABC$. Hence the Theorem.

2·1. Points inside $\triangle ABC$ are inside $A\hat{B}C$, $B\hat{C}A$, $C\hat{A}B$ and on $\{AB, C\}$, $\{BC, A\}$, $\{CA, B\}$.

3. If P, Q be outside $\triangle ABC$ and PQ does not go through a vertex, then P-Q meets $\triangle ABC$ in no point or in two points.

Dem. Since PQ does not go through a vertex, this *line* meets $\triangle ABC$ in no point or in two points (II 16). In the latter case let X, Y be the points, then $[XPY]$ $[XQY]$ are impossible, since P, Q are not inside the triangle. Hence, if X is on P-Q, so is Y; and conversely; and then P-Q, and not merely PQ, meets the triangle in X, Y.

·1. If P be inside $\triangle ABC$, and P-Q meet $\triangle ABC$ in one point, then Q is outside $\triangle ABC$ (II 12·4).

·2. If P-Q meet $\triangle ABC$ in two points X, Y not on the same side, then P, Q are both outside the triangle.

Dem. If $[XZY]$ then Z is inside the triangle (II 12·1·5). Hence by ·1.

·3. If P be inside $\triangle ABC$ and Q outside, then P-Q meets the triangle in one point only.

4. If we have a finite set of intervals which do not meet $A\vdash B$ or $B\vdash D$, there is a point C on B-D such that no point of the given intervals is inside or on $\triangle ABC$.

Dem. There is a ray $[AX$ in $B\hat{A}D$ such that no end of any interval is inside or on $B\hat{A}X$ (III 15·1). $[AX$ meets B-D in

C say. Then no end of any interval is inside or on ΔABC. Hence all are outside ΔABC, but as no interval meets $A\vdash\!\dashv B$ or $B\vdash\!\dashv C$ none can meet $A\vdash\!\dashv C$ (3), and hence since the ends of the intervals are outside ΔABC, all their points are, since an interval joining a point outside to a point inside the triangle meets the triangle (3·3).

5. *Def. and The.* We can order the points of a *simple* way $A_1A_2A_3 \ldots A_n$ which is not a polygon, thus: If X, Y be on $A_i{-}A_{i+1}$ then $X \prec Y$ whenever $X \prec Y$ with respect to (A_i, A_{i+1}) (III 16·01); all points of $A_i{-}A_{i+1}$ shall precede all points of $A_j{-}A_{j+1}$ if $i<j$, and A_i shall precede A_j if $i<j$. If the points of a way are ordered in this manner, we call the way an '*ordered way*' and write it $(A_1A_2A_3 \cdots A_n)$. The relation $\prec$ between the points of an ordered way is asymmetrical, transitive and aliorelative (I 9). To the way $A_1A_2 \ldots A_n$ correspond two ordered ways $(A_1A_2 \cdots A_n)$ and $(A_nA_{n-1} \cdots A_1)$.

6. If n points $A_1, \ldots, A_n$ be given in a plane, there is a line in the plane such that all these n points lie on one side of the line.

Dem. There is a line a not through any of $A_1, \ldots, A_n$ (II 11·4). If all the A are not on the same side of a then a meets at least one $A_i{-}A_k$. There is a point O on a such that one of the rays from O on a, say $[OB$, does not meet any $A_i\vdash\!\dashv A_k$ (II 11·2). Let B' satisfy $[BOB']$ and $h_i=[OA_i$. Through B' there is a line $CC' \neq a$ such that $[CB'C']$ and $C\vdash\!\dashv C'$ does not meet any h_i (II 11·3). Since O is inside $\Delta BCC'$, each ray h_i from O meets $\Delta BCC'$ (II 17), these meets lie on $B{-}C$ or $B{-}C'$ and each of these open intervals contains at least one such meet; otherwise, all h_i and hence all A_i would lie on the same side of a, cont. hyp. Let $E_1, \ldots, E_\nu$ be the meets on $B{-}C$, and $E_1', \ldots, E_\mu'$ those on $B{-}C'$, and let $[BE_1 \ldots E_\nu C]$, $[BE_1' \ldots E_\mu' C']$. Let h, l be the rays h_i through E_1 and E_1', then *no A is outside $\widehat{hl}$.*

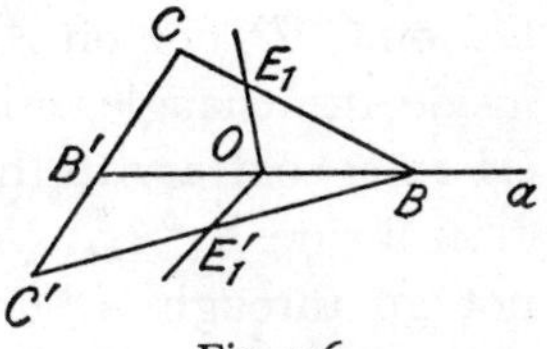

Fig. 116

For B is not inside $\widehat{hl}$, for if it were, then $[OB$ would meet some $A_i{-}A_k$. Hence $E_2, \ldots, E_\nu, E_2', \ldots, E_\mu'$ are all inside $\widehat{hl}$ (III 19·1), and hence all the A are inside $\widehat{hl}$ or on h or l.

Hence all points of the $A_i{\vdash\!\dashv}A_k$ are inside or on $\widehat{hl}$. Thus any line through O and an inside point of an angle adjacent to $\widehat{hl}$, contains no inside points of $\widehat{hl}$ (III 7·6) and hence meets no $A_i{\vdash\!\dashv}A_k$.

The Inside and Outside of a Polygon

7. *If $p = A_1 \ldots A_n$ be a simple polygon* any point B, not on p, of its plane can be joined to any point C of p by a simple way meeting p in C only.*

We first shew 8 and 9.

8. If B is not on p, and $[A_iCA_{i+1}]$, and C be accessible from B by the ordered way $(B\cdots C)$, then A_i, A_{i+1} are accessible from B. (In 8 to 13, accessibility is always with respect to p.)

Dem. Let $B'{\vdash\!\dashv}C$ be the last interval of the ordered way $(B\cdots C)$. The lines $A_iA_1, \ldots, A_iA_n$ meet $B'{-}C$ in a finite number (which may be zero) of points $E_1, \ldots, E_r$. Let $[B'E_1 \ldots E_rC]$ and let D satisfy $[E_rDC]$. We shall shew that $D{-}A_i$ does not meet p. Then 8 follows.

Now the vertices $A_k \neq A_i$ of p lie outside $\triangle A_iCD$, for none lies on $C{\dashv}D$, nor on $A_i{\vdash}C$, nor on $A_i{-}D$ by construction, nor inside the triangle, otherwise a line A_iA_k would meet $C{-}D$ (II 12·2) contrary to the choice of D. Now a side $A_k{-}A_{k+1}$ $(k \neq i, i-1)$ cannot go through A_i or C, since p is simple, nor through D, since D is on $(B\cdots C)$. Hence it has no point or two points on $\triangle A_iDC$ (3), since A_k, A_{k+1} are outside that triangle. But it cannot meet $A_i{\dashv}C$ or $C{\dashv}D$ since p is simple and D is on $(B\cdots C)$. Hence it cannot meet $D{-}A_i$. Hence the Theorem.

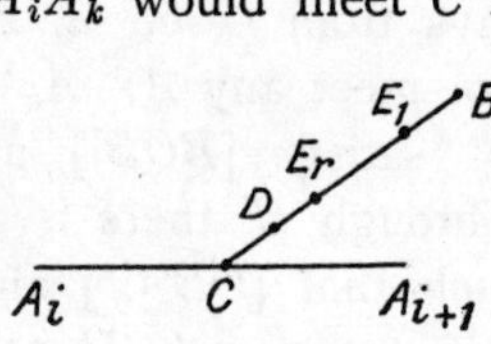

Fig. 117

9. If B is not on p, and A_i be accessible from B by the ordered way $(B\cdots A_i)$, and $[A_iCA_{i+1}]$, then C is accessible from B.

* We often say 'polygon' instead of 'simple polygon.' The polygon $A_1A_2 \ldots A_n$ can be written $A_2 \ldots A_nA_1$ or $A_3 \ldots A_nA_1A_2$ or $A_n \ldots A_1$, etc.

Dem. Case 1. Suppose the last interval $B'\vdash\!\dashv A_i$ of the ordered way $(B\cdots A_i)$ is in $A_{i-1}\hat{A}_iA_{i+1}$. Let lines from C to the vertices of p meet $B'{-}A_i$ in $E_1, \ldots, E_r$, say, with $[B'E_1 \ldots E_rA_i]$. Let D satisfy $[E_rDA_i]$. We shew that $C{-}D$ does not meet p. For $C{-}D$ does not meet $A_i{-}A_{i-1}$, since all points of $C{-}D$ are inside $B'\hat{A}_iA_{i+1}$, and all points of $A_i{-}A_{i-1}$ are outside that angle (III 8·4). As in 8 all vertices, $\neq A_i$, of p are outside $\triangle CA_iD$, and hence no side of p meets $C{-}D$.

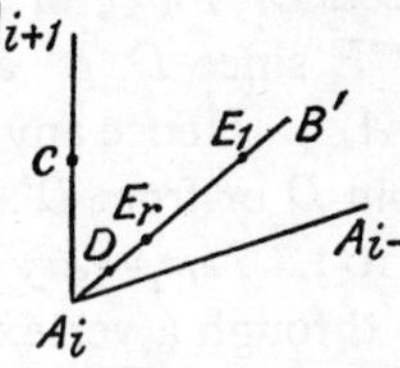

Fig. 118

Case 2. Suppose the last interval $B'\vdash\!\dashv A_i$ is not in $A_{i-1}\hat{A}_iA_{i+1}$. Let F satisfy $[FA_iA_{i-1}]$, and let $F\vdash A_i$ meet no side of p nor lines from C to the vertices (II 11·3). As in 8 we shew that no side $A_k{-}A_{k+1}$ $(k \neq i, i-1)$ can meet $C{-}F$, whence $C{-}F$ does not meet p. Take D so that $[B'DA_i]$, and so that $D\vdash A_i$ is not met by any lines from F to the vertices (II 11·3). As before, $D{-}F$ meets no side $A_k{-}A_{k+1}$ $(k \neq i, i-1)$, nor $A_{i-1}{-}A_i$ since $[A_{i-1}A_iF]$, nor $A_i{-}A_{i+1}$ since D, F are outside $A_{i-1}\hat{A}_iA_{i+1}$ and $D{-}F$ does not meet $A_{i-1}{-}A_i$ (III 19). Neither is any vertex of p on $D{-}F$. Hence $D\dashv F$, $F{-}C$ do not meet p.

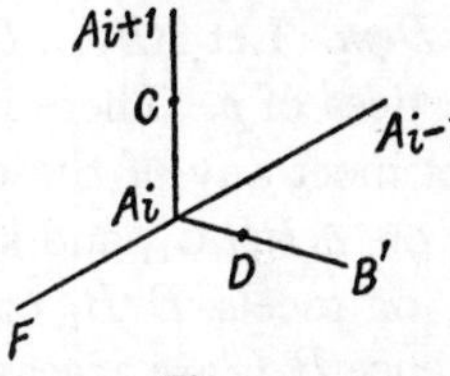

Fig. 119

This completes the proof of 9.

We can now shew 7. If P be any point on p, such that BP is not a side-line of p, then $[BP$ meets p in a finite number of points. Hence there is a point E on $[BP$ and on p, such that $B{-}E$ does not meet p (II 11·2). Hence E is accessible from B. Then 7 follows by repeated application of 8, 9 and 1·1.

10. A simple polygon $p = A_1 \ldots A_n$ cannot separate the other points of the plane into more than two regions (III 1·1).

Dem. If $[A_iCA_{i+1}]$, there are points D, D' on different sides of A_iA_{i+1}, such that $C\dashv D$ and $C\dashv D'$ are not met by p (II 11·3). Let B be any point not on p. By 7 there is an ordered way $(B\cdots C)$ not meeting p save in C; let $B'\vdash\!\dashv C$ be its last interval. Then B' is either in $\{A_iA_{i+1}, D\}$ or in $\{A_iA_{i+1}, D'\}$, say the former. There is a point F on $B'{-}C$ such that $F\vdash C$ meets no lines from D to vertices of p (II 11·3). Hence no vertices of p are inside or on $\triangle FCD$ (II 12·2), and no side of p, save $A_i{-}A_{i+1}$, goes through a vertex of $\triangle FCD$. Hence no side of p meets $D{\vdash\!\dashv}F$ (3), for the only doubtful one, $A_i{-}A_{i+1}$, cannot meet $D{\vdash\!\dashv}F$ since D, B' and hence D, F are on the same side of A_iA_{i+1}. Hence any point B of the plane, not on p, is accessible from D or from D'.

10·1. *Temporary definition.* A line or ray which does not go through a vertex of p will be called '*suitable.*' A way, not necessarily simple, is '*suitable*' if all its side-lines are.

11. If B, C, not on p, are mutually accessible, they are accessible by a suitable way.

Dem. Let $BB_1 \dots B_nC$ be a way not meeting p. Join B to vertices of p. There is a point C_1 on $B_1{-}B_2$ so that $B_1{\dashv}C_1$ does not meet any of these lines. Hence no vertex of p is inside or on $\triangle BB_1C_1$, and since no side of p goes through B, B_1 or C_1 or meets $B{-}B_1$ or $B_1{-}C_1$ therefore none meets $B{-}C_1$ (3). Hence B, C are accessible by $BC_1B_2B_3 \dots C$, and the line BC_1 is suitable. If C_1B_2 is not suitable, we can in like manner replace the new way by $BC_1C_2B_3 \dots C$ where C_2B_3 is suitable; and in a finite number of steps we achieve the desired result.

·1. A line a which is suitable meets p in an *even* number of points [zero is regarded throughout as an even number].

Dem. If a meets $A_i{-}A_{i+1}$ then A_i, A_{i+1} are on opposite sides of a, and conversely (III 2). Hence if the way $A_1 \dots A_r$ meets a an odd number of times and has no vertex on a then A_1 must be distinct from A_r. Hence the Theorem.

·2. Let $\widehat{hk}$ be an angle whose vertex is not on p and whose sides are suitable, then $\widehat{hk}$ meets p in an even number of points.

Dem. If $\widehat{hk}$ meets $A_i{-}A_{i+1}$ in one point then one of A_i, A_{i+1} is inside, the other outside $\widehat{hk}$ (III 19·1); but if in two or no points, then A_i, A_{i+1} are both outside or both inside $\widehat{hk}$ (III 18, 19·2). Hence the Theorem follows as in ·1.

·3. If B, C, not on p, are mutually accessible and one suitable ray [BA from B meets p in an odd number of points, then each ray from B and each from C meets p, and in an odd number of points, if it is suitable.

Dem. A ray from B either goes through a vertex of p, or is suitable and then it meets p, by ·2, in an odd number of points.

To shew the Theorem for rays from C: there is a suitable way $BC_1 \dots C_nC$ (11). If A, B, C_1 colline then $[BC_1$ meets p in an odd number of points (·1) since $[BA$ does so and since AC_1 is suitable. If A, B, C_1 do not colline, consider $A\hat{B}C_1$; its sides are suitable rays, B is not on p, and $[BA$ meets p in an odd number of points, hence so does $[BC_1$ (·2). Hence so does $[C_1X_1$, where $[BC_1X_1]$, since $B\text{-}C_1$ does not meet p. Similarly considering $[C_1X_1$ and $[C_1C_2$, we find that $[C_2X_2$, where $[C_1C_2X_2]$, meets p in an odd number of points. And so on. Finally, so does $[CX$, where $[C_nCX]$. Hence by the first part of proof, the Theorem follows for rays from C.

12. *Def.* A point B, such that a suitable ray from B meets p in an odd number of points, is '*inside*' p. Points not on or inside p are '*outside*' p. (Cf. II 17.)

·1. If B is inside p and C accessible from B, then C is inside p, and all suitable rays from B or from C meet p in an odd number of points (11·3). If A is outside p, all suitable rays from A meet p in an even number of points.

·2. Points inside p, points outside p exist, and the two sets are separated by p.

Dem. A suitable line can be drawn through a point on a side of p (II 11·4). This meets p in $X_1, \dots, X_m$, say, in order $[X_1 \dots X_m]$. There are points Y, A such that $[YAX_1 \dots X_m]$. Then $[AY$ does not meet p and hence A is outside p, for if even one suitable ray from A met p in an odd number of points, then $[AY$ would meet p (11·3). There is a point B on $X_1\text{-}X_2$, and $[BX_1$ meets p in just one point. Hence B is inside p. Further A and B are not mutually accessible, for if they were, since B is inside p, A would also be inside (·1). Similarly by ·1, no point inside is accessible from any point outside.

13. p separates the other points of the plane into at least two *regions*.

Dem. By 12·1·2 and the fact that *all* suitable rays from an inside (outside) point contain inside (outside) points since they meet p in an odd (even) number of points. Thus the inside (outside) points are not all on one line.

14. *A simple polygon p separates the other points of the plane into two regions whereof one, the inside, is such that all rays from all points of it meet p* (10, 13, 11·3).

15. Every line through an inside point of p meets it in at least two points.

·1. If a ray does not meet p, all its points are outside p.

·2. A suitable line which meets p, contains both outside and inside points (12·2).

·3. If $A \vdash\!\dashv B$ does not meet p, then A, B are both outside or both inside p.

·4. If $A \vdash\!\dashv B$ meets p in just one point of one side, then A is inside and B outside p or vice versâ (10 *Dem.*, 13).

16. *Given a finite set of polygons, there are lines whose points are all outside all the polygons* (6).

17. *If the set of points inside p coincides with the set inside q, then $p = q$.*

Dem. If C be on a side of p and not on q, there is an interval AB, with $[ACB]$, which meets p in C only and does not meet q (II 11·3), and hence A, B are both inside or both outside q (15·3) while one is inside and one outside p (15·4), cont. hyp.

Dissection of a Simple Polygon into Triangles

18. *Def.* A vertex A_i of a polygon is '*projecting*,' if there is a line which meets the two sides of the polygon which have A_i as end-point, and which meets no other side of the polygon.

19. Every polygon p has at least one projecting vertex.

Dem. Through any point on a side of $p = A_1 \dots A_n$ goes a suitable line a and it meets p in points, say, in order $[X_1 \dots X_m]$. There is a point O, with $[OX_1 \dots X_m]$, such that all points where a meets the lines $A_h A_j$ $(h \neq j;\ h, j = 1 \cdots n)$ are on $[OX_1 = r_0$ (II 11·2). Let $[B]$ be the set of vertices of p on one side of a, $[C]$ the set on the opposite side. We can name the rays $[OB$ as $r_1, r_2, \dots, r_s$ (where r_i, r_{i+1} need not go through adjacent vertices) so that r_j is in $\widehat{r_i r_k}$, $(i < k)$, if and only if

$i<j<k\,(i,j,k=0\cdots s)$ (III 15), and we can name the rays [OC as $l_1, l_2, \ldots, l_t$ so that l_j is in $\widehat{l_i l_k}$, ($i<k$), if and only if

$$i<j<k\ (i,j,k=0\cdots t),$$

where $l_0=r_0$. Since no $A_h{-}A_j$ meets OX_1] or contains O, all $B_i{-}C_j$ will meet r_0, and r_0 is in $\widehat{r_i l_j}$ ($i=1\cdots s$, $j=1\cdots t$) (III 5). Taking $i=s$, $j=t$ we deduce that all r, l, save r_s, l_t, are in $\widehat{r_s l_t}$ (III 8). Hence all vertices, and so all points on p, are inside or on $\widehat{r_s l_t}$ (III 18).

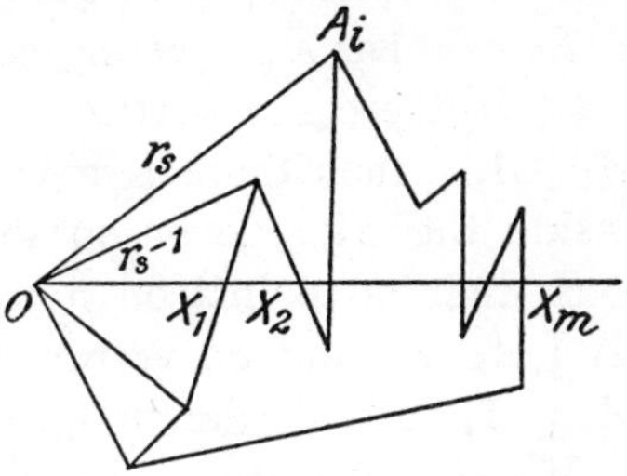

Fig. 120

Let [$OY=h$ be in $\widehat{r_s r_{s-1}}$, then h meets p; for, since there are vertices on r_s and r_{s-1}, a way on p joining these vertices must meet OY (III 2), and hence if it does not meet [OY, it meets OY]. But [OY is in $\widehat{r_s l_t}$ (III 8), hence OY] is not (III 10·1). Hence if the way met OY], some points on p would be outside $\widehat{r_s l_t}$, contrary to the above. Hence h meets p.

Since OY is a suitable line meeting p, it contains an inside point (15·2). Let A_i be *the* vertex of p on r_s. Since there are no vertices inside $\widehat{r_s r_{s-1}}$ none is inside or (save A_i) on $\widehat{r_s h}$ (III 8). Hence all save A_i are inside or on $\widehat{h l_t}$ (III 8·2). But h is inside $\widehat{r_s l_t}$. Hence on one side of h, the only vertex is A_i, the others are on the opposite side. Now OY meets p in at least two points (15). If OY meets $A_r{-}A_{r+1}$ then A_r, A_{r+1} are on opposite sides of OY. Hence if OY meets the *distinct* sides $A_r{-}A_{r+1}$ and $A_s{-}A_{s+1}$, then either $i=r=s+1$ or $i=r+1=s$ (since $r\neq s$, and A_i is the only vertex on one side of OY). Hence the sides $A_{i-1}{-}A_i$ and $A_i{-}A_{i+1}$, and these only, are met by OY. Hence A_i is a projecting vertex of p.

20. *Def.* A set of polygons [p_i] '*dissect*' the polygon p if (i) no two of [p_i] have a common inside point, (ii) every point inside p is inside or on a polygon of [p_i], (iii) every point inside a polygon of [p_i] is inside p.

·01. Thence every point on a polygon of [p_i] is inside or on p.

·1. If the set [p_i] ($i=1\cdots n$) dissect p, and the set [p_{ij}'] ($j=1\cdots m$) dissect p_i, then the [p_{ij}'] ($i=1\cdots n, j=1\cdots m$) dissect p.

21. *Every polygon p can be dissected into triangles $[t]$ such that every vertex of every t is a vertex of p.*

Dem. p has a projecting vertex A_i (19).

(i) If there are vertices of p inside $\Delta A_{i-1}A_iA_{i+1}$ or on $A_{i-1}{}^{-}A_{i+1}$, then there is a vertex A_k inside the triangle or on that side, such that no points on p are inside $\Delta A_iA_{i+1}A_k$ and no vertex save A_i, A_{i+1}, A_k on that triangle (3, III 15).

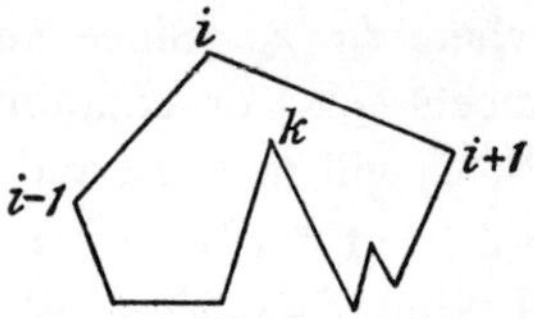

Fig. 121

If $k=i+2$ we have the polygons $A_iA_{i+1}A_k$ and $A_kA_{k+1}\ldots A_i$.

If $k \neq i+2$ we have the polygons $A_iA_{i+1}A_k$ and $A_{i+1}A_{i+2}\ldots A_k$ and $A_kA_{k+1}\ldots A_i$.

$A_i{}^{-}A_k$ lies inside $\Delta A_{i-1}A_iA_{i+1}$.

(ii) If there are no vertices of p inside $\Delta A_{i-1}A_iA_{i+1}$ or on $A_{i-1}{}^{-}A_{i+1}$, then no point on p is inside that triangle, since p is simple (3·3), and thus we have the polygons $A_{i-1}A_iA_{i+1}$ and $A_{i+1}A_{i+2}\ldots A_{i-1}$.

In both cases (i) and (ii), if we have a triangle and but *one* other polygon, we have one new side and that is common to both, and the number of the sides of the new polygon is one less than that for p. But if we have a triangle and *two* other polygons, we have two new sides each common to the triangle and one of the new polygons, hence the two new polygons have together one more side than p has, and thus each has fewer sides than p. Continuing the process we ultimately reach a set of triangles. We shew that these dissect p.

Let π_1, π_2 be the new polygons and Δ the triangle in the first stage of the process (π_2 may be absent). Since A_i is projecting, there is a point I inside the triangle and outside π_1, π_2 (12, 15·4). From the def. of Δ, no points on p are inside Δ. Hence, since any point I' inside Δ is accessible from I with respect to Δ, it is so with respect to π_1 and π_2. Hence I' is outside π_1 and π_2. Hence

(a) All points inside Δ are outside π_1 and π_2.

Since A_i is projecting, there is a point I inside Δ and inside p (12, 15·4).

Any point I' inside Δ is accessible from I with respect to Δ and hence, as before, with respect to p. Hence

(*b*) All points inside Δ are inside p.

There are points O outside all Δ, π_1, π_2 and p (16). If O_1 is outside Δ, π_1, π_2, it is accessible from O with respect to Δ, π_1, π_2 and so with respect to p. Hence points outside all Δ, π_1, π_2 are outside p. Hence

(*c*) Points inside p are inside or on Δ or π_1 or π_2.

If I is inside π_1, a point X of the side common to Δ and π_1, is accessible by a way w from I with respect to π_1, and hence with respect to p. For all points of w are inside π_1, hence if w met p, some points of p would be inside π_1; but the sides of p, not on π_1, do not meet π_1 and they form a way, hence *all* points on these sides of p, and thus all points of A_i-A_{i+1} would be inside π_1, contrary to hyp. on A_i. Hence X is accessible from I with respect to p. Hence also points inside Δ are accessible from I with respect to p. Hence (*b*) gives

(*d*) All points inside π_1 are inside p. Similarly for π_2.

If any points inside π_1 are inside π_2, then all points inside π_1 are accessible from those with respect to π_2, for we have shewn above that a way inside π_1 cannot meet π_2. Hence the set of points inside π_1 would coincide with the set inside π_2, and so $\pi_1 = \pi_2$ (17). Hence, using (*a*), we have

(*e*) The sets of points inside π_1, π_2, and Δ are mutually exclusive.

By (*b*) (*c*) (*d*) (*e*), p is dissected into Δ and π_1 and π_2.

Continuing the process and using 20·1 the Theorem follows.

The Theorem can also be shewn from 24 below.

21·1. *Notation.* If a set of polygons $p_1, \ldots, p_n$ be such that no pair have a common inside point, we write the set as $\sum_1^n p_i$ or $\sum_i p_i$ or Σp_i. If p be dissected into $\sum_1^n p_i$, we write

$$p \equiv p_1 + p_2 + \ldots + p_n, \text{ or } p \equiv \sum_1^n p_i.$$

If the set $\sum_1^n p_i$ be dissected into $\sum_1^m q_j$ we write $\sum_1^n p_i \equiv \sum_1^m q_j$.

21·2. If the set of points inside or on $\sum_1^n p_i$ coincide with the set inside or on $\sum_1^m q_j$, then $\sum_1^n p_i \equiv \sum_1^m q_j$ (17), and conversely.

A Criterion for a Simple Polygon

22. *If p consists of a finite set of intervals, and it separates the remaining points of the plane into various sets, while no proper sub-set of p separates any points of the plane, then p is a simple polygon.*

Dem. If the intervals meet in any points which are not ends, we can divide the intervals into sub-intervals which meet in end-points only. Suppose this done. Then we first shew that each end of every interval of p is common to at least two intervals.

For, if not, suppose B is an end of $A \vdash\!\dashv B$ only; let q be the set of intervals p, omitting $A \vdash\!\dashv B$. Let P, Q be separated by p, then by hyp. they are not separated by q. Hence there is a way $(P \cdots Q)$ meeting p and not q and hence meeting $A \vdash\!\dashv B$. There is a point C, with $[ABC]$, such that no point of any interval of q is on $B \dashv C$ (II 11·3). Let Y be the first meet of the ordered way $(P \cdots Q)$ and $A \vdash\!\dashv B$, and let $X \vdash\!\dashv Y$ be the interval of $(P \cdots Q)$ such that $X \prec Y$ (5). Then since there are no points of q on $C \vdash\!\dashv Y$ or $Y \vdash X$, there will be a point Z on $X - Y$ such that no point of q is on $\triangle YCZ$ (4) and hence none on $C \vdash Z$. Similarly if Y_1 is the first meet of the ordered way $(Q \cdots P)$ and $A \vdash\!\dashv B$, and if $X_1 \vdash\!\dashv Y_1$ is the interval of $(Q \cdots P)$ such that $X_1 \prec Y_1$, then there is a point Z_1 on $X_1 - Y_1$ such that no point of q is on $C \vdash Z_1$. Hence the way $(P \cdots Z_1 C Z_2 \cdots Q)$ does not meet q or $A \vdash\!\dashv B$, that is, does not meet p. Hence P, Q are mutually accessible with respect to p, cont. hyp. Hence each end-point of an interval of p is common to at least two intervals.

Hence we can trace a way $ABB_1B_2\ldots$ where $A \vdash\!\dashv B$, $B \vdash\!\dashv B_1$, $B_1 \vdash\!\dashv B_2$, etc. are distinct intervals of p. Since their number is finite we must ultimately reach a point of the way already reached. Then we have a simple polygon p_1.

But this polygon separates the plane, while no proper sub-set of p does so. Hence $p = p_1$.

Intersection of Simple Polygons

23. *The points inside two polygons p and q (if any) are the set of all inside points of a finite set of polygons, no two of which have a common inside point.*

Dem. If a side of one of p, q meets the other polygon, the side is divided into intervals. Let $[v]$ be the set of all intervals so got from all sides of p and q. Let X be inside both p and q, and let $[X]$ be the set of points accessible from X with respect to p and q. $[X]$ does not include all the plane. Thus there is a finite set $[v_1]$ of intervals (a sub-set of $[v]$), which separates the other points of the plane into those accessible from X with respect to p and q, and those not. A sub-set $[v_1']$ of $[v_1]$ with this property and such that no proper sub-set of $[v_1']$ separates the plane, is a simple polygon p_1 (22).

Now X is inside p_1; for there is a point Y outside all p, q and p_1 (16). But Y, being outside p and q, is not accessible from X with respect to p and q, and hence is separated from X by $[v_1]$ and hence by p_1. But since Y is outside p_1 and is separated from X by p_1, therefore X is inside p_1.

Whence all points accessible from X, with respect to p and q, are inside or on p_1.

Again if X' be a point inside both p and q and not accessible from X, then points accessible from X' with respect to p and q are all the points inside or on a simple polygon p_2.

Next consider points inside both p and q, and not accessible from X or X' with respect to p and q. And so on.

If two of the polygons so got, say p_1 and p_2, had a common inside point, then X and X' would be mutually accessible with respect to p and q, cont. hyp.

If Y is a point, not an end-point, of an interval of $[v]$, there are points P, Q with $[PYQ]$ such that $P{\vdash}Y$, $Y{\dashv}Q$ meet no v, whence if P is inside both p and q, then Q is not (15·4). Hence no v is part of two of our polygons, and since the number of intervals v is finite, so must the number of polygons be.

·1. All the points on p_1 above are accessible from X with respect to p and q, and hence are *either* on both p and q *or* on one and inside the other. All points *either* on both p and q *or* on one and inside the other, are on p_1 or p_2 or etc. (15·3·4).

23·2. If Σp and Σq be sets of polygons as in 21·1, the points inside polygons of both sets are the inside points of a finite set of polygons, no two of which have a common inside point.

24. *If all points of a simple way w be inside a polygon p, save its ends, which lie on p and are distinct, then p is dissected by w into two polygons.*

Dem. If $p = A_1 \ldots A_n$ and $w = W_1 \ldots W_m$ where W_1 is on $A_r \vdash\!\dashv A_{r+1}$ and W_m on $A_s \vdash\!\dashv A_{s+1}$ $(s \geqq r)$ then

$$p_1 = W_1 \ldots W_m A_{s+1} \ldots A_n A_1 \ldots A_r W_1$$

and $p_2 = W_1 \ldots W_m A_s A_{s-1} \ldots A_{r+1} W_1$ are simple polygons. (If $s = r$ the last is $p_2 = W_1 \ldots W_m W_1$.)

(*a*) If P is inside p and not on w, a suitable ray from P, not through a vertex of w, meets p in an odd number of points (12), and hence meets one of the ways $W_m A_{s+1} \ldots A_n A_1 \ldots A_r W_1$ and $W_m A_s A_{s-1} \ldots A_{r+1} W_1$ in an odd and the other in an even number of points. Hence a point inside p is either inside *one and only one* of p_1, p_2 or is on w.

(*b*) A point outside p is outside p_1 and p_2; for there are points O outside all p_1, p_2 and p (16). If O_1 is any point outside p, it is accessible from O by a way outside p and so outside p_1, p_2, for if any point of the way were inside p_1 or p_2, the way would meet p_1 or p_2 (14). Hence O_1 is outside p_1 and p_2.

(*c*) Whence a point inside p_1 or p_2 is inside p, since as is easily shewn, a point on p is not inside p_1 or p_2.

(*d*) A point inside p_1 is not inside p_2 by (*a*) (*b*) (*c*).

The Theorem now follows from (*a*) (*c*) (*d*).

If $W_1 = W_n$, one of the sub-polygons would not be simple.

25. *If the polygon $p \equiv \Sigma s_i \equiv \Sigma t_j$, and if $[s_i t_j]$ is the set of polygons of* 23 *whose inside points are inside both the polygons s_i and t_j, then $p \equiv \sum_{ij} [s_i t_j]$.*

Dem. (*a*) All points inside any member of $[s_i t_j]$ are inside s_i and hence inside p.

(*b*) No point is inside two of $[s_i t_i]$ (23), for no point is inside two s_i or two t_j.

(*c*) All points inside p are inside or on some $s_i t_j$ for they are inside or on some s_i and inside or on some t_j. If inside both, they are inside a member of $[s_i t_j]$. If on one and inside or on the other, they are on a member of $[s_i t_j]$ (23·1).

26. *If* Σp *and* Σq *be sets of polygons as in* 21·1, *the points inside or on one set and outside or on the other, are all the points inside or on a finite set of polygons.*

Dem. Consider first the Theorem for two triangles ABC, XYZ, and we may suppose some of the points inside ΔABC are outside and some inside ΔXYZ. Then some side-line of ΔXYZ will meet ΔABC in just two points. For if P be inside and Q outside ΔXYZ and both inside ΔABC, then P–Q contains a point on ΔXYZ (3·3) and inside ΔABC. Whence the statement by II 17.

If XY meet ΔABC, the points inside or on ΔABC on each closed half-plane of XY are all the points inside or on a finite set of triangles (24, 21). If then YZ meet any of these triangles, the points inside or on them and on the closed half-plane of YZ opposite to X, are all the points inside or on a finite set of triangles. Similarly for ZX. Whence the points inside or on ΔABC and outside or on ΔXYZ, are all the points inside or on a finite set of triangles. (Note that ΔXYZ may be wholly inside ΔABC.)

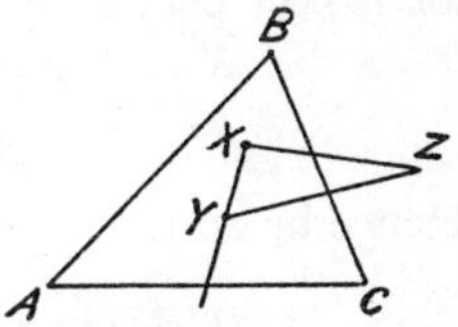

Fig. 122

Now dissect the sets of polygons Σp, Σq into sets of triangles $[t]$, $[t']$ resp. If the points inside a triangle of $[t]$ are some inside, some outside a triangle of $[t']$ we apply the above.

The following are needed in the Theory of Volumes.

·1. Given a finite set of triangles $[t]$, there is a set of triangles $[t']$ such that no point on or inside any triangle of $[t']$ is inside any other, and the set of all points inside or on the $[t]$ is the set of all points inside or on the $[t']$.

Dem. For two triangles by 23, 26, 21. Then by induction.

·2. If $[P]$ be the set of points inside a given polygon p and outside a finite set of polygons $[p']$ and not on a finite set of intervals $[v]$, then there is a finite set of triangles whose inside points are all in $[P]$ and such that each point of $[P]$ is on or inside one of these triangles, no two of which have a common inside point.

Dem. There is a finite set of triangles $[t]$ such that the points inside p and outside $[p']$ are inside or on $[t]$, and that points inside $[t]$ are inside p and outside $[p']$ (easily by 26, 21). The intervals of $[v]$ are divided by the side-intervals of these triangles into sub-intervals $[v']$. Let $X \vdash\dashv Y$ be one of these intervals $[v']$. If the end X fall on a side AB of $\triangle ABC$, we have $\triangle ABC \equiv \triangle XAC + \triangle XBC$ (II 18) and X is a vertex of the sub-triangles. If X is at a vertex A of $\triangle ABC$ and Y is on B^-C, then $X \vdash\dashv Y$ dissects the triangle; while if Y is inside $\triangle ABC$ and XY meets B^-C in Z, we have $[AYZ]\,[BZC]$ and hence by II 18

$$\triangle ABC \equiv ABZ + ACZ \equiv ABY + BYZ + ACY + CYZ.$$

Hence the Theorem by ·1.

Lemmas Needed in the Theory of Areas

27. If A is not on BC and $[BX_1 \ldots X_n C]$ then

$$\triangle ABC \equiv ABX_1 + AX_1X_2 + \ldots + AX_{n-1}X_n + AX_nC.$$

Dem. When $n = 1$, this follows by II 18. Assume the Theorem for $(n-1)$ points on B^-C. An nth point Y is on some $X_i^-X_{i+1}$ $(i = 0 \cdots n;\ X_0 = A,\ X_n = B)$ (II 11). Hence

$$\triangle AX_iX_{i+1} \equiv AX_iY + AYX_{i+1}.$$

Hence by 20·1.

28. If $ACBD$ be a quadrilateral and C, D on opposite sides of AB, then $ACBD \equiv ACB + ADB$.

Dem. A ray from a point of A^-B, and not on the line AB, lies in $\{AB, C\}$ or in $\{AB, D\}$ (III 6) and hence meets one and only one of $A^{\dashv}C$, C^-B, $A^{\dashv}D$, B^-D (II 16, III 6·1). Hence every point of A^-B is inside $ACBD$ (12). Hence the Theorem by 24.

29. If XAB be a triangle and $[XEA]\,[XHB]$, then $[EB$ is in $A\hat{E}H$, and $\triangle XAB \equiv XEH + ABHE \equiv XEH + EHB + EAB$.

Dem. Since $[XEA]\,[XHB]$ therefore A^-H meets E^-B and so $[EB$ is in $A\hat{E}H$, and $ABHE$ is a quadrilateral (III 12·1), and H, A are on opposite sides of EB. Hence

$$ABHE \equiv EHB + EAB \ (27).$$

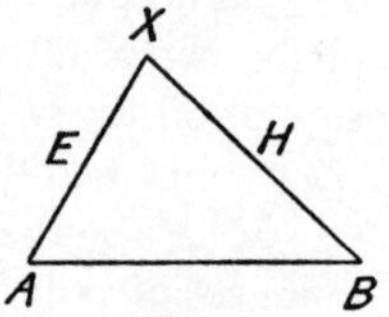

Fig. 123

Also all points of E^-H are inside $\triangle XAB$ (II 12·1). Hence $XAB \equiv XEH + ABHE$ (24). Whence the Theorem by 20·1.

30. If XAB be a triangle and $[AE_1 \dots E_n X]$ $[BH_1 \dots H_n X]$ then

$$\triangle XAB = ABH_1E_1 + E_1H_1H_2E_2 + \dots + E_{n-1}H_{n-1}H_nE_n + E_nH_nX.$$

Dem. For $n=1$ Theorem is 29. And it follows generally by induction from 29 using 20·1.

31. If $ABFE$ be a quadrilateral and E, B on opposite sides of AF, and $[FED]$, then $ABFD \equiv ABFE + ADE$.

Dem. Since $[FED]$, D, B are on opposite sides of AF and hence $ABFD \equiv ABF + ADF$ (28). Also since $[DEF]$ we have $ADF \equiv ADE + AEF$ (27). Further $ABFE \equiv ABF + AEF$ (28). Whence the Theorem.

32. If $ABFE$ be a quadrilateral with E, B on opposite sides of AF, and A, F on opposite sides of BE, and $[EXA]$ $[FYB]$, then

$$ABFE = ABYX + XYFE.$$

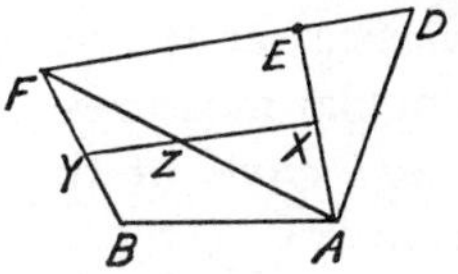

Fig. 124

Dem. By hyp. and III 12, $X\text{-}Y$, $A\text{-}F$ meet in Z say. Hence $[AZF]$ $[XZY]$. Since $[AZF]$ $[BYF]$ therefore Z, B are on opposite sides of AY. Similarly Z, E are on opposite sides of XF.

These results give by 28, 29,

$$ABFE \equiv ABF + AEF \equiv ABYZ + ZYF + XZFE + AZX,$$

and $AZX + ABYZ \equiv ABYX$ and $XZFE + ZYF \equiv XYFE$ (31). Hence the Theorem.

33. If $ABFE$ be a quadrilateral as in 32 and $[EX_1X_2 \dots X_nA]$ $[FY_1Y_2 \dots Y_nB]$ then

$$ABFE \equiv ABY_1X_1 + X_1Y_1Y_2X_2 + \dots + X_{n-1}Y_{n-1}Y_nX_n + X_nY_nFE$$

(32 and induction).

34. *Def.* A '*convex*' polygon is one whose inside points are all on the same side of any side-line of the polygon.

·1. The inside points of a convex polygon form a convex region (III 1).

·2. If $A\text{-}F$, $B\text{-}E$ meet, then $ABFE$ is a convex quadrilateral.

·3. If A, B, C, D be four points in a plane, no three collinear, *either* one point is inside the triangle formed by the other three *or* the four points are vertices of a convex quadrilateral.

Dem. If AB and $C\text{-}D$ do not meet, but $A\text{-}B$ and CD do meet in E say, then C, D are on the same side of AB, and C is inside $\triangle ABD$ or D is inside $\triangle ABC$ according as $[DCE]$ or $[CDE]$. Similarly if $A\text{-}B$ and CD do not meet, but AB and $C\text{-}D$ do meet.

If neither $A\text{-}B$ and CD, nor AB and $C\text{-}D$ meet, *either* $A\text{-}C$ meets $B\text{-}D$ *or* $A\text{-}D$ meets $B\text{-}C$ (III 13) whence either $ABCD$ or $ABDC$ is a convex quadrilateral (·2).

Finally if $A\text{-}B$ and $C\text{-}D$ meet, then $ACBD$ is a convex quadrilateral.

The Angle-Sum of a Polygon

§ 2. Basis O_p C_p.

35. If p, q be congruent polygons and $q = \sum_1^n q_i$, then there are polygons p_i with $p = \sum_1^n p_i$, $p_i \simeq q_i$ (IV 67).

36. *Def.* If a polygon be dissected into triangles with their vertices at the vertices of the polygon (21), the sum of the angular measures (IV 57) of the angles of the triangles is the '*angle-sum*' of the polygon (which of course, need not be convex).

§ 3. Basis O_p C_p P_1.

37. By VI 3·3, Theorem 33 holds when $ABFE$ is a parallelogram.

·1. If $ABCD$ be a parallelogram and $[AA_1 \dots A_n D]$,

$$AA_1 \simeq A_1A_2 \simeq \dots \simeq A_nD \text{ and } A_1B_1,\ A_2B_2,\ \dots,\ A_nB_n$$

be parallel to AB where $B_1, B_2, \dots, B_n$ are on BC, then $ABCD$ is dissected into congruent parallelograms

$$ABB_1A_1,\ A_1B_1B_2A_1,\ \dots,\ A_nB_nCD.$$

38. *The angle-sum of a polygon of n sides is* $(n-2)\pi$.

Dem. The number of triangles into which an n-gon is dissected by the method of 21 is $n-2$. For this is true when $n=4$. Assume that the number in the case of an r-gon, when $r<n$, is $r-2$. At the first stage of the dissection of an n-gon, we get *either* a triangle, and two polygons whose total number of sides is $n+1$, and then, by hyp., the total number of triangles in the final dissection is $1+n+1-4=n-2$; *or* we get one triangle and one $(n-1)$-gon, and the total number of triangles is then finally $1+n-1-2=n-2$. Hence the statement follows by induction. The angle-sum of an n-gon is thus $(n-2)\pi$, by 36.

·1. *Note.* The proof usually given, by joining the vertices of the polygon to a point inside it, is clearly invalid in general for non-convex polygons.

Euler's Theorem

§ 4. Basis O_p.

The following is essentially a Theorem of Combinatorial Analysis Situs*, but as we are avoiding that subject in this book we deduce it from O_p.

39. *If a polygon p is dissected into $f(>1)$ polygons q, and the total number of all points which are vertices of the polygons is v, and of the open intervals which are sides is e, then*

$$v+f=e+1.$$

Dem. A line, not through a vertex, which goes through an inside point of p, meets p and the q in points $A_1A_2\ldots A_n$ say, in that order. A point X, with $[A_1XA_2]$, is inside p and so inside one of the q, but $[XA_1$ meets that q in A_1 only. Thus some sides of that q are on sides of p. The other sides of that q form a simple way from a point on p to another point on p and the way dissects p into two polygons (24). Treating these polygons like p, and so on, we can generate the dissection by dissecting by simple ways, polygons already formed.

Suppose at a certain stage $v+f=e+1$ is true. In the next step we draw a simple way inside one of our polygons as in 24. Thus f becomes $f+1$. If the way is made up of n intervals we have n, $n+1$ or $n+2$ extra sides according as both ends, one end, or neither end of the way are at vertices already got, and so in these cases we have $n-1$, n or $n+1$ extra vertices resp., the ends of the way being supposed distinct. Hence the formula is still truc.

But the formula is true when $f=2$, since the number of vertices common to the two polygons q is one more than the number of sides common. Hence it holds generally.

* Veblen, "The Cambridge Colloquium" (1916), *Amer. Math. Soc.*

CHAPTER XI

THE AREAS OF POLYGONS

Introductory Remarks

There are two customary ways of shewing that two polygons p, p' are equivalent.

(i) We may be able to dissect the polygons p and p' into polygons such that each polygon which dissects p is congruent to a corresponding one for p'.

or (ii) We may be able to adjoin congruent polygons to p and p' so that the total figures so obtained are related as in (i). This is done, for instance, in the usual proof of the equivalence of two parallelograms on the same base and between the same parallels.

In case (i) we shall say the polygons are 'equivalent by addition,' in case (ii) we shall simply say they are 'equivalent.'

In shewing equivalence by addition, the main difficulty is to shew that the polygons constructed really do dissect the figure, that is, that their inside points fill it without gaps. For these proofs the previous chapter is essential.

If Axiom $\mathbf{K}_1$ (IX § 3) be not assumed, the distinction between equivalence and equivalence by addition is a real one; two polygons may be equivalent without being equivalent by addition. But if that Axiom be assumed, then two equivalent polygons can always be dissected into triangles congruent in pairs; they are thus equivalent by addition.

Much of the present chapter is concerned with the Theory of areas. The area or measure of a triangle being defined as half the product of the measures of a base and the corresponding altitude, we naturally wish to define the measure of a polygon as the sum of the measures of any set of dissecting triangles. The difficulty here is to shew that the measure so obtained is independent of the set of dissecting triangles chosen. That triangles can always be found to dissect a polygon was shewn in the previous chapter.

We must also shew that equivalent polygons have the same measure and conversely.

At first we do not assume the parallel Axiom, but as the Theory of Euclidean areas is very different from that of non-Euclidean areas we introduce that Axiom quite early. Later, when we come to consider non-Euclidean areas our earlier proofs will be found useful.

In this chapter we have used Hilbert's *Grundlagen*, and Finzel, "Die Lehre vom Flächeninhalt in der allgemeinen Geometrie," *Math. Ann.* 1912, LXXII, p. 262.

Preliminary Propositions

§ 1. Basis $O_p\, C_p$.

All polygons are supposed to be simple plane polygons.

1. *Def.* Two polygons p, q are '*equivalent by addition*,' written

$$p \cong q\,(+),$$

if p can be dissected into $\sum_1^n p_i$, and q into $\sum_1^n q_i$, where p_i, q_i are polygons such that $p_i \simeq q_i$ $(i = 1 \ldots n)$. The same definition applies if p, q are sets of polygons.

Speaking roughly, p and q are made up of sets of polygons, congruent in pairs, but perhaps fitted together differently.

·1. *Def.* Two polygons p, q are '*equivalent*' (simply), written

$$p \cong q,$$

if there are sets of polygons s, s', p_i, q_i such that

$$s \equiv p + \sum_1^n p_i,\quad s' \equiv q + \sum_1^n q_i,\quad p_i \simeq q_i\ (i = 1 \ldots n),\quad s \cong s'\,(+).$$

The same definition applies if p, q are sets of polygons.

In this case we adjoin to p, q sets of polygons equivalent by addition so that the results are equivalent by addition. How far 'equivalence' implies 'equivalence by addition' is considered in the sequel.

·11. *Note.* It is implicit in the notation (X 21·1) that no two of $p, p_1, \ldots, p_n$ have common inside points. Similarly for $q, q_1, \ldots, q_n$.

1·2. If $p \simeq q$ then $p \cong q(+)$ (X 35). If $p \cong q(+)$ then $p \cong q$, but we do not assert the converse. Hence there are pairs of polygons satisfying each definition.

·3. Both relations, 'equivalent by addition' and 'equivalent' are clearly reflexive and symmetrical.

2. *If $p \cong q(+)$ and $p \cong r(+)$, then $q \cong r(+)$.*

Dem. Since $p \cong q(+)$, there are polygons q_i', q_i with

$$p \equiv \sum_1^n q_i', \quad q \equiv \sum_1^n q_i, \quad q_i \simeq q_i' \quad (i = 1 \cdots n).$$

Since $p \cong r(+)$, there are polygons r_j', r_j with

$$p \equiv \sum_1^m r_j', \quad r \equiv \sum_1^m r_j, \quad r_j \simeq r_j' \quad (j = 1 \cdots m).$$

The set of points inside both q_i' and r_j', if any, coincide with the set of points inside a set of polygons, no two of which have a common inside point (X 23). Denote this set by $[q_i' r_j']$. No two of the $[q_i' r_j']$ $(i = 1 \cdots n, j = 1 \cdots m)$ have a common inside point, and each point inside q_i' is inside p and hence inside or on some r_j' and hence inside or on some $[q_i' r_j']$. Hence

$$q_i' \equiv \sum_{j=1}^m [q_i' r_j'] \quad \text{(X 20)}.$$

But $q_i \simeq q_i'$. Therefore q_i can be dissected into polygons congruent to the set $[q_i' r_j']$ $(j = 1 \cdots m)$ (X 35), and hence q into the set congruent to $[q_i' r_j']$ $(i = 1 \cdots n, j = 1 \cdots m)$. Similarly for r. Hence $q \cong r(+)$.

·1. *If $p \cong q$ and $p \cong r$, then $q \cong r$.*

Dem. By 1·1 there are polygons s, $\bar{s}$, s', $\bar{s}'$ such that

$$p + \Sigma s \cong q + \Sigma \bar{s}(+); \quad p + \Sigma s' \cong r + \Sigma \bar{s}'(+); \quad s \simeq \bar{s}, \; s' \simeq \bar{s}'.$$

Let $\Sigma' s'$ be the set of polygons such that points inside or on them are inside or on $\Sigma s'$ and not inside Σs; and let $\Sigma' s$ be the polygons similarly related to Σs and $\Sigma s'$ (X 26).

Hence the set of points inside or on $\Sigma s + \Sigma' s'$ is the set of points inside or on $\Sigma s' + \Sigma' s$. No two of the polygons of $\Sigma s + \Sigma' s'$ have a common inside point, and similarly for the polygons of $\Sigma s' + \Sigma' s$.

Hence $\quad \Sigma s + \Sigma' s' \equiv \Sigma s' + \Sigma' s$ (X 21·2)

and $\quad \Sigma \bar{s} + \Sigma' s' \cong \Sigma \bar{s}' + \Sigma' s(+)$ (2).

(We have assumed for simplicity that $\Sigma \bar{s}$ and $\Sigma' s'$ have no common inside points and similarly for $\Sigma\bar{s}'$ and $\Sigma' s$. If this is not the case, we replace $\Sigma' s'$ or $\Sigma' s$ by congruent figures, such that the last formula holds.) But

$$p+\Sigma s \cong q+\Sigma\bar{s}\,(+). \text{ Hence } p+\Sigma s+\Sigma' s' \cong q+\Sigma\bar{s}+\Sigma' s'\,(+).$$

And

$$p+\Sigma s' \cong r+\Sigma\bar{s}'\,(+). \text{ Hence } p+\Sigma s'+\Sigma' s \cong r+\Sigma\bar{s}'+\Sigma' s\,(+).$$

But

$$\Sigma s+\Sigma' s' \cong \Sigma s'+\Sigma' s. \text{ Hence } p+\Sigma s+\Sigma' s' \cong p+\Sigma s'+\Sigma' s\,(+).$$

These give, by (2), $q+\Sigma\bar{s}+\Sigma' s' \cong r+\Sigma\bar{s}'+\Sigma' s\,(+)$, which in turn gives $q \cong r$, since $\Sigma\bar{s}+\Sigma' s' \cong \Sigma\bar{s}'+\Sigma' s\,(+)$.

2·2. *The relations 'equivalent by addition' and 'equivalent' are hence both equable.* This fact will often be used without quotation.

3. If $AD \simeq BC$, $DE \simeq CF$, and $A\hat{D}E$, $B\hat{C}F$ are right angles, and A, B be on the same side of CD, and if C is on $[FE$ when D is on $EF]$, but C is on $FE]$ when D is on $[EF$, then $ABCD \cong ABFE$. (Cf. III 16.)

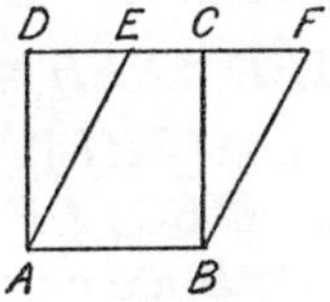

Fig. 125

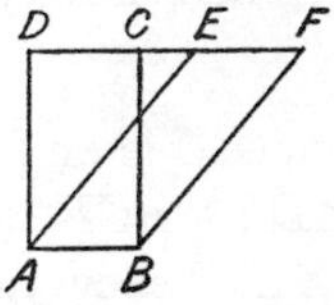

Fig. 126

*Dem.** We first shew that E, B are on opposite sides of AF. For the hyp. gives $ADE \simeq BCF$. Let D be on $EF]$, then $[DEF]$ and C is on $[FE = [FD$, and $DE \simeq FC$. Hence $[FCD]$ (IV 6). Thus $D\hat{E}A \simeq C\hat{F}B = D\hat{F}B$ and hence EA, FB do not meet (IV 36) and therefore F, B are on the same side of EA. But $AF \neq AB$; hence either $[AF$ is in $E\hat{A}B$ or $[AB$ in $E\hat{A}F$ (III 9), and the latter is false since it implies AB, EF $(=DC)$ meet (III 7), whereas AB, DC do not meet, since $DABC$ is an isosceles birectangle (IV 69·1·2). Hence E, B are on opposite sides of AF (III 7·1).

But $[DEF]$. Therefore $ABFD \equiv ABFE + ADE$ (X 31).

Similarly C, A are on opposite sides of BD. But $[FCD]$. Therefore $ABFD \equiv ABCD + BCF$. But $ADE \simeq BCF$. Hence $ABFE \cong ABCD$.

If D is on $[FE$ then C, D interchange rôles, and so do E, F.

* The difficulty here is to *prove* the dissection theorems which can be 'seen' to be true.

4. *Every triangle is equivalent to an isosceles birectangle.*

Dem. Let XAB be a triangle; E, H mid-points of XA, XB resp. Let $[EHF]$, $HF \simeq EH$. Then

$$XEH \simeq BFH.$$

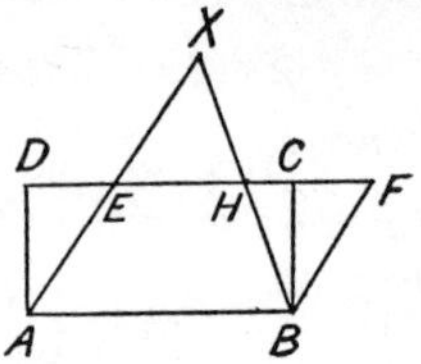

Fig. 127

Since $[XEA]$ $[XHB]$ we have

$$XAB \equiv XEH + ABHE$$

and $[EB$ is in $A\hat{E}H$ (X 29). Hence H, A are on opposite sides of EB. Thus $[EHF]$ gives $ABFE \equiv ABHE + BFH$ (X 31). Whence since

$XEH \simeq BFH$, we have $XAB \cong ABFE$ (+).

Let now $AD \perp EF$; D on EF; $FC \simeq ED$ with C on $[FE$ or $FE]$ according as D is on $EF]$ or $[EF$. Suppose the first is the case.

Then $[DEF]$ $[EHF]$. Hence $[DEH]$ $[XEA]$ and so

$$A\hat{E}D \simeq X\hat{E}H \simeq B\hat{F}H \simeq B\hat{F}C$$

(since C is on $[FE$ and $[EHF]$). Also $AE \simeq XE \simeq BF$. Hence $ADE \simeq BCF$, whence $BC \perp DF$ and $AD \simeq BC$. Also $[XEA]$ $[XHB]$ shew that A, B are on the same side of CD. Thus all conditions of 3 hold and $ABFE \cong ABCD$.

Similarly if D is on $[EF$.

So far we have not used any parallel Axiom and accordingly these Theorems are true for areas in the Hyperbolic plane.

Euclidean Areas

§ 2. Basis O_p C_p P_1.

An isosceles birectangle is now a rectangle (VI 5·6).

4·1. *Def.* If $ABCD$ be a parallelogram and $AX \perp BC$, X on BC then $A \vdash\!\dashv X$ is '*the altitude of the parallelogram corresponding to the base* $B \vdash\!\dashv C$.' (Cf. VI 5·51.)

5. If a parallelogram and a rectangle have a side a common and if the sides in each opposite to a are in one line, then the parallelogram and rectangle are equivalent (3).

6. *Two parallelograms with congruent bases and corresponding altitudes congruent are equivalent.* (Congruence and 5.)

7. A triangle is equivalent to a rectangle whose base is a base of the triangle and whose corresponding altitude is congruent to half the corresponding altitude of the triangle (4) (VI 11·1).

8. *Two triangles with congruent bases and corresponding altitudes congruent are equivalent.* (Congruence and 7.)

9. *A rectangle exists equivalent* **by addition** *to a given parallelogram or triangle.*

Dem. Let $ABFE$ be the given parallelogram, then either $\mu AB \geqq \mu AE$ or $\mu AE \geqq \mu AB$ (IV 13). Suppose the first is true. Take the construction of 4 and suppose D is on $EF]$, and hence C on $[FE$. Thence $[FCE]$ or $[FEC]$ or $E = C$. But if $[FEC]$ or $C = E$ then

$$\mu AE = \mu BF > \mu FC \text{ (IV 63) } \geqq \mu FE = \mu AB,$$

that is, $\mu AE > \mu AB$, cont. hyp. Hence $[FCE]$ and so $[DEC]$. It is this that distinguishes the present situation from that in 4, where $[FEC]$ was possible. It is now easy to shew that $ABFE \cong ABCD\,(+)$ using X 31.

Also, by the proof in 4 *Dem.* any triangle is equivalent by addition to a parallelogram. Hence the rest of the Theorem follows by 2.

·1. *Note.* We now proceed to define the area or measure of polygons, beginning with triangles. When a polygon is dissected into triangles, its measure is to be the sum of the measures of the triangles; it is thus clearly necessary to shew that this sum is independent of the particular way in which the polygon is dissected into triangles. It would be very easy to shew this if we assumed the following additional Axiom. 'If all the inside points of a polygon P are inside points of a polygon Q, then the measure of P is not greater than the measure of Q.' This corresponds to Euclid's Axiom 'the whole is greater than the part,' in so far as the latter statement is not merely verbal. We shall not find it necessary to introduce this additional Axiom; on the contrary we shall prove it.

The Measure of a Triangle

10. If ABC be a triangle, $AD \perp BC$, $BE \perp AC$, D on BC, E on AC, then $AC \,.\, BE = BC \,.\, AD$.

Dem. Omitting the trivial case when $C=E$ and using the cross, we have $\measuredangle ADC \simeq CEB$ (IV 74, 51) $\measuredangle ACD \simeq ECB$ (IV 71). Whence ADC and BEC are indirectly similar (VII 24) and so

$AC|AD \sim BC|BE$ (VII 10)

$AC.BE = BC.AD$ (VII 20).

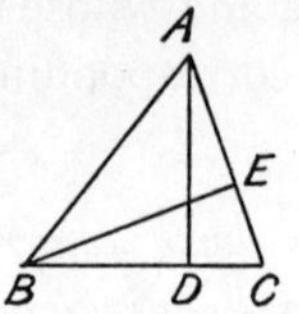

Fig. 128

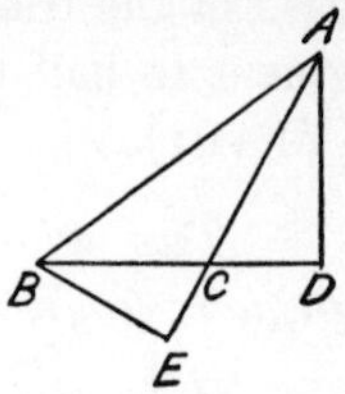

Fig. 129

10·1. *Def.* With this construction $\frac{1}{2}AC.BE$ is the '*measure*' of $\triangle ABC$, and is written μABC.

·2. μABC is by definition the *measure of an interval* (VII 15). Later on it will be identified with a real number. The factor $\frac{1}{2}$ in the definition is merely inserted for convenience and in accord with custom.

·3. Congruent triangles have the same measure.

11. If ABC be a triangle, and $X_1, \ldots, X_n$ satisfy

$$[BX_1X_2 \ldots X_nC],$$

then

$$\mu ABC = \mu ABX_1 + \mu AX_1X_2 + \ldots + \mu AX_{n-1}X_n + \mu AX_nC.$$

Dem. If $AD \perp BC, D$ on BC, then by IV 13·1, VII 19·2 and I 21·7

$$\begin{aligned}\mu ABC &= \tfrac{1}{2}BC.AD = \tfrac{1}{2}(BX_1 + X_1X_2 + \ldots + X_nC).AD \\ &= \tfrac{1}{2}(BX_1.AD + \ldots + X_nC.AD) \\ &= \tfrac{1}{2}BX_1.AD + \ldots + \tfrac{1}{2}X_nC.AD \\ &= \mu ABX_1 + \ldots + \mu AX_nC.\end{aligned}$$

12. *Def.* If ABC be a triangle and $[BX_1 \ldots X_nC]$, we know (X 27) that $\triangle ABC \equiv ABX_1 + AX_1X_2 + \ldots + AX_{n-1}X_n + AX_nC$. We call $A^-X_1, \ldots, A^-X_n$ '*transversal dissectors*' of $\triangle ABC$ and say that the triangle is '*dissected transversally*.' If $\triangle ABC$ be dissected transversally and any sub-triangles be also so dissected and the process be repeated a finite number of times, we say $\triangle ABC$ is '*simply dissected*.' [That it is dissected follows by X 20·1.] The sides (inside the triangle) of any set of polygons which dissect a triangle are called '*dissectors*.' The following Theorem is based on Axioms $\mathbf{O}_p$ only.

13. If in a dissection of $\triangle ABC$ into a finite number of triangles, no vertex of any sub-triangle is on a certain side of $\triangle ABC$ or inside $\triangle ABC$, then the $\triangle ABC$ is simply dissected.

Dem. Note that a 'side' of a triangle does not include its ends (II 11·7). Suppose no vertex of any sub-triangle is on B^-C. Then since there is no vertex inside $\triangle ABC$, either there is no dissector through B or none through C, for dissectors of these two kinds meet inside the triangle (II 11·6). Suppose none goes through B, then there is a vertex B_1 on B^-A such that there is no vertex on $B^{\vdash}B_1$ (II 11·2). If also there were no dissector through C, there would be a vertex C_1 on C^-A such that there is none on $C^{\vdash}C_1$. But then $\triangle ABC \equiv AB_1C_1 + BCC_1B_1$ (X 29) and then, since there are no vertices of sub-triangles inside $\triangle ABC$ or on BC, $B^{\vdash}B_1$, $C^{\vdash}C_1$, it follows that $\triangle ABC$ contains an undissected quadrilateral, cont. hyp. Hence some dissectors do pass through C, and hence, by hypotheses made, CB_1 is a dissector.

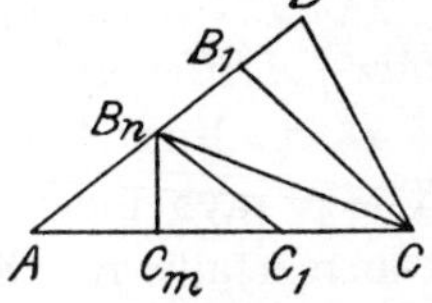

Fig. 130

Similarly if $\triangle AB_1C$ is dissected, there must be dissectors through B_1 or C (besides B_1C) but not through both.

(i) If they go through C, let $CB_1, CB_2, \ldots, CB_n$ $(n > 1)$ be *all* the dissectors of $\triangle ABC$ through C, and let $[BB_1 \ldots B_nA]$. Since there are no vertices of sub-triangles inside $\triangle ABC$ or on B^-C or $B_n{}^-C$, no dissectors of $\triangle BB_nC$, save those mentioned, go through any point of $B^{\vdash\dashv}B_n$. Hence $\triangle BB_nC$ is dissected transversally.

(ii) If they go through B_1 we proceed as for B_n next.

(iii) If $\triangle AB_nC$ be dissected, some dissectors must go through B_n, since none go through C, by (i), or through A. Let $B_nC_1, B_nC_2, \ldots, B_nC_m$ $(m > 1)$ be *all* the dissectors of $\triangle AB_nC$ through B_n (and hence all those of $\triangle ABC$ through B_n), and let $[CC_1C_2 \ldots C_mA]$. Then, as in (i), $\triangle C_mCB_n$ is dissected transversally.

Hence $\triangle ABC \equiv B_nBC + C_mCB_n + AB_nC_m$ (X 29); this is a sequence of transversal dissections, and $\triangle C_mCB_n$ and B_nBC are dissected transversally. If $\triangle AB_nC_m$ be dissected, we can treat it like $\triangle ABC$. Since the number of sub-triangles is finite, the process terminates and the Theorem follows.

14. If $\triangle ABC$ be simply dissected, then μABC is the sum of the measures of the sub-triangles (12, 11, I 20·81).

15. *If* $t_1, \ldots, t_n$ *be triangles and* $\triangle ABC \equiv t_1 + t_2 + \ldots + t_n$ *then* $\mu ABC = \mu t_1 + \ldots + \mu t_n$.

Dem. Join A to all the vertices of the t_i by rays l from A. These rays meet B–C, and the triangle ABC is dissected transversally by the portions of l between A and B–C into triangles, which we call T_l (12); $\mu ABC = \Sigma \mu T_l$ (11).

Let $\triangle XYZ$ be any t_i. Through each of X, Y, Z goes some l.

(i) If two of X, Y, Z, say Y, Z, lie on the same ray l and $Y, Z \neq A$ (and hence $X \neq A$), and if other rays l meet X–Y in $L_1, L_2, \ldots, L_r$ with $[XL_1 \ldots L_rY]$ then they meet X–Z in points $M_1, \ldots, M_r$ with $[XM_1 \ldots M_rZ]$ (II 12·6). Hence $\triangle XYZ$ is dissected into a triangle and quadrilaterals whose vertices are on X⊢Y and X⊢Z (X 30). The quadrilaterals can be dissected into triangles with the same vertices (X 21). When this is done, $\triangle XYZ$ is dissected into triangles none of whose vertices lie inside $\triangle XYZ$ or on Y–Z. Hence it is simply dissected (13).

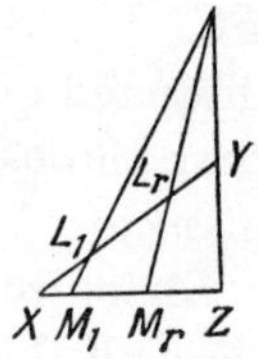

Fig. 131

(ii) If $Y = A$, and some rays l lie in $X\hat{Y}Z$, they dissect $\triangle XYZ$ transversally (III 7, X 27).

(iii) If no two of X, Y, Z are on the same l and all are distinct from A, then since all the l are in $A\hat{B}C$, one of those which pass through X, Y, Z is in the angle formed by the other two (III 8·5). Let this be the l through X, say l_1, then l_1 meets Y–Z in W say (III 7). Hence $\triangle XYZ$ is dissected transversally by a portion of that ray, and if X–Y or X–Z is met by other rays l we can proceed as in (i). Since there are no vertices of sub-triangles of $\triangle XYZ$ on X–W or inside $\triangle XYW$, therefore $\triangle XYW$ is simply dissected. So is $\triangle XZW$, hence so is $\triangle XYZ$.

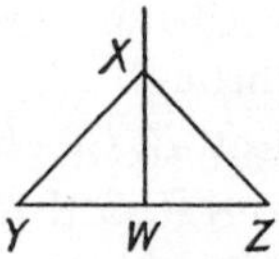

Fig. 132

Hence we have simply dissected the t_i into triangles t_{ij} say and $\triangle ABC \equiv \sum_{ij} t_{ij}$ (X 20·1) and $\mu t_i = \sum_j \mu t_{ij}$ (14).

The vertices of the t_{ij} are all on the rays l, therefore no vertex of any t_{ij} is inside any T_l nor on the side of T_l opposite to A. (A side of a triangle does not include its ends.) Hence if any T_l be dissected into any t_{ij}, say into the set t_{lk}, the dissection is simple (13) and $\mu T_l = \sum_k \mu t_{lk}$ (14). Since the T_l and the t_{ij} both dissect $\triangle ABC$, all points inside or on the T_l are inside or on the t_{ij}, and conversely (X 20). Hence in dissecting *all* the T_l, *all* the t_{ij} are used. Hence

$$\mu ABC = \sum_l \mu T_l = \sum_{ij} \mu t_{ij}.$$

Also we get *all* the t_{ij} by simple dissection of *all* the t_i, hence

$$\sum_i \mu t_i = \sum_{ij} \mu t_{ij} \text{ and } \mu ABC = \sum_i \mu t_i.$$

Measures of Polygons

16. *If a polygon p be dissected into triangles s_i and independently into triangles t_j, then $\sum_i \mu s_i = \sum_j \mu t_j$.*

Dem. Let $[u_{ij}]$ be the set of polygons, as in X 23, whose inside points are the points inside both s_i and t_j. Each polygon of $[u_{ij}]$ can be dissected into triangles (X 21), which we call u_{ijk}. Hence, since any point inside s_i is inside p and so inside or on some t_j and hence inside or on some u_{ij}, we have by X 23·2, $\sum_j \sum_k u_{ijk} \equiv \sum_j u_{ij} \equiv s_i$. Similarly $\sum_i \sum_k u_{ijk} \equiv \sum_i u_{ij} \equiv t_j$. Hence $\sum_i \mu s_i = \sum_{ijk} \mu u_{ijk}$ and $\sum_j \mu t_j = \sum_{ijk} \mu u_{ijk}$ (15). Hence $\sum_i \mu s_i = \sum_j \mu t_j$.

·1. *Def.* The '*measure*' of a polygon p, denoted by μp, is the sum of the measures of any set of dissecting triangles. That the measure of p, thus defined, is independent of the set of dissecting triangles chosen is shewn in 16.

·2. *Def.* The '*measure*' of a set of polygons, no two of which have a common inside point, is the sum of the measures of the polygons. Note that all these measures are the measures of certain intervals, and the defs. are consistent by IV 13.

·3. Congruent polygons have the same measure (10·3 and X 21, 35).

17. If $ABCD$ be a rectangle then $\mu ABCD = AB \,.\, AD$.

Dem. By X 28, VI 3·3 we have $ABCD \equiv ABD + CBD$. Thence by 10·1, 16·1 and VI 5, 5·7.

18. *Equivalent polygons have the same measure.*

Dem. If $p \cong q$, there are sets of polygons r_i and r_i' with $p + \sum_1^n r_i \cong q + \sum_1^n r_i' \,(+)$, $r_i \simeq r_i'$. Hence $p + \sum_1^n r_i$ and $q + \sum_1^n r_i'$ can be dissected into polygons congruent in pairs (1·1, 1). But congruent polygons have the same measure (16·3). Hence

$$\mu(p + \Sigma r_i) = \mu(q + \Sigma r_i'), \quad \mu\Sigma r_i = \mu\Sigma r_i' \text{ (16·2)}.$$

Whence the Theorem follows by 16·2 and I 20·41.

19. *Two triangles with congruent bases and the same measure have congruent altitudes* (IV 13, VII 16, I 21·51).

20. *Two equivalent triangles with congruent bases have congruent altitudes* (18, 19).

·1. Theorems 19, 20 hold for rectangles and parallelograms.

·2. *Note.* In shewing 20, Euclid assumes that a triangle cannot be equivalent to a part of itself. We have no need to use any such Axiom.

21. By means of constructions **abcd** a triangle, equivalent to a given triangle t, can be constructed with a given side AB (IX 2, 5).

Dem. Make $\Delta ADX \simeq t$, with D on $[AB$ (IV 55), $DW \parallel BX$ (IX 3), then DW meets AX (VI 2·2) in Y say. Either $[ADB]$ or $[ABD]$. If $[ADB]$ then $[AYX]$ (VI 3) and, by II 18,

$$\Delta ABY \equiv ADY + DYB;$$
$$\Delta ADX \equiv ADY + DYX.$$

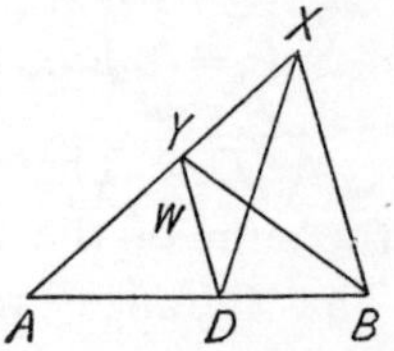

Fig. 133

But since $DY \parallel BX$, therefore ΔDYB and ΔDYX have altitudes corresponding to the base DY congruent (VI 5·4). Hence

$$\Delta DYB \cong DYX \text{ (8) and } \Delta ABY \cong ADX \cong t.$$

If $[ABD]$, then $[AXY]$, and B, D interchange rôles and so do X, Y.

22. By means of **abcd** a rectangle, equivalent to a given triangle, can be constructed with one side given (21 and 7).

23. *By means of* **abcd** *a rectangle, equivalent to a given polygon p, can be constructed with one side AB given.*

Dem. Dissect p into triangles $t_1, \ldots, t_n$ (X 21). Draw the rectangle $AA_1B_1B \cong t_1$ (22), the rectangle $A_1A_2B_2B_1 \cong t_2$ with $[AA_1A_2]$, ..., the rectangle

$$A_{n-1}A_nB_nB_{n-1} \cong t_n \text{ with } [A_{n-2}A_{n-1}A_n].$$

Then AA_nB_nB is a rectangle and

$$AA_nB_nB \equiv AA_1B_1B + \ldots + A_{n-1}A_nB_nB_{n-1} \text{ (X 37·1)}.$$

Hence $$AA_nB_nB \cong t_1 + \ldots + t_n \cong p.$$

·1. If the given side-interval be congruent to the unit interval (VII 15), then the altitude of the rectangle constructed has measure μp (17).

24. *Polygons with the same measure are equivalent.* (Converse of 18.)

Dem. If $\mu p = \mu q$, let $AA'B'B$, $AA''B''B$ be rectangles equivalent to p, q resp. (23). Then $\mu p = AA'.AB$, $\mu q = AA''.AB$ (17, 18), whence by VII 16

$$\mu AA' = \mu AA'', \; AA' \simeq AA'', \; AA'B'B \simeq AA''B''B.$$

Hence $p \cong q$ (1·2, 2·1).

·1. *Note.* It is highly remarkable that two polygons with the same measure are equivalent. How far they are equivalent by addition will be seen soon. The corresponding Theorem on volumes is, as we shall see, false. It is for these reasons that a theory of measures of polygons can be constructed without continuity considerations, but that for anything like a complete theory of measures of polyhedra, continuity is essential.

·2. If p, q be polygons the meanings of $\mu p < \mu q$, $\mu p > \mu q$ are clear since μp, μq are merely the measures of intervals.

25. *The measures of polygons form a system of magnitudes for the operation* +. *This system is condensed* (I 20·62).

Dem. These follow from the corresponding properties of intervals when we shew that to each interval corresponds at least one polygon whose measure is the measure of the interval. Such a polygon we have when we draw a rectangle on the interval as base whose altitude is congruent to the unit interval (17).

26. *If* $p_1 \equiv p_2 + p_3$ *then* $\mu p_2 < \mu p_1$ (25, 16·1 and I 20·31).

·1. *Note.* This corresponds to Euclid's Axiom 'The whole is greater than the part' when applied to the measures of polygons.

The Influence of Archimedes' Axiom $\mathbf{K}_1$ (IX § 3)

27. *If* $\mathbf{K}_1$ *is false, two triangles may have the same measure and yet not be equivalent* **by addition.**

Dem. Let AC be perpendicular and congruent to AB, and let $CX \parallel AB$, $\mu CX > n . \mu AB$ for all natural numbers n. Now ΔABC, ΔABX have the same measure; suppose if possible, they are dissected into triangles t congruent in pairs. Each side of a triangle t has measure less than or equal to that of the longest side of ΔABC (IV 65·3) and hence this measure is $\leqq \mu BC < \mu AB + \mu AC = 2\mu AB$. Now $A \vdash X$ is dissected into sides of triangles t; suppose it dissected into r intervals, then $\mu AX < r . 2\mu AB$. But $\mu CX < \mu AX$ (IV 63). Hence $\mu CX < 2r . \mu AB$, cont. hyp. Hence the Theorem.

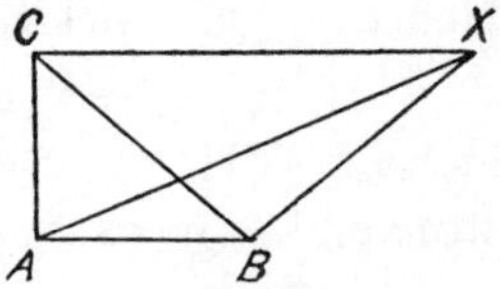

Fig. 134

28. *If* $\mathbf{K}_1$ *is false, two rectangles may have equal measures and yet not be equivalent* **by addition.**

Dem. By 9 there are rectangles p, q equivalent by addition to the triangles ABC, ABX of 27. Whence if $p \cong q$ (+), then would $ABC \cong ABX$ (+) (2).

29. *If* $\mathbf{K}_1$ *is true, a rectangle can be drawn on a given side* OA, *equivalent* **by addition** *to a given rectangle** $HKK'H'$.

Dem. Let $\mu HK = b$, $\mu OA = a$ then by $\mathbf{K}_1$ and IX 12, we have either (i) $b < a$ or (ii) $b \geqq a$ and $b \leqq 2a$ or (iii) $b > 2a$.

In case (i) there is a natural number n such that $2^n b \geqq a$, $2^{n-1} b < a$ ($\mathbf{K}_1$). Therefore $2^n b < 2a$, and so $2^n b$ satisfies conditions (ii) on b.

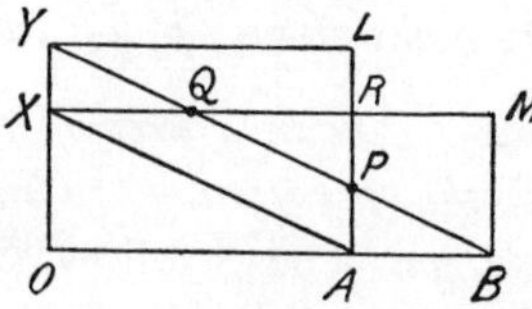

Fig. 135

* W. H. Jackson, "On Wallace's Theorem," *Amer. Jour.* 1912, XXXIV.

Let $H_1K_1K_1'H_1'$ be a rectangle with

$$\mu H_1K_1 = 2^n \mu HK, \quad \mu H_1H_1' = \frac{1}{2^n}\mu HH' \text{ (VI 6·5)}.$$

We can dissect $HKK'H'$ and $H_1K_1K_1'H_1'$ each into 2^n rectangles, all congruent, with sides of measures b and $\frac{1}{2^n}\mu HH'$ (X 37). Hence

$$HKK'H' \cong H_1K_1K_1'H_1' \, (+).$$

In case (iii) there is a natural number n with $\frac{1}{2^n}b \leq 2a$, $\frac{1}{2^{n-1}}b > 2a$. Therefore $\frac{1}{2^n}b > a$, and so $\frac{1}{2^n}b$ satisfies conditions (ii) on b. Let $H_1K_1K_1'H_1'$ be a rectangle with

$$\mu H_1K_1 = \frac{1}{2^n}\mu HK \text{ and } \mu H_1H_1' = 2^n \mu HH'.$$

Then as before $\quad HKK'H' \cong H_1K_1K_1'H_1' \, (+).$

Hence it suffices to treat case (ii), and we shall exclude the cases, easily treated separately, when $b = a$ or $2a$.

Let $OBMX$ be a rectangle congruent to $HKK'H'$, with B on $[OA$. Then, by assumptions, $[OAB]$ and $\mu OB < 2\mu OA$. Let $BY \parallel AX$, Y on OX, then $[OXY]$ (VI 3). Let $AL \parallel OY$, $YL \parallel OA$, then $OALY$ is a rectangle; AL, XM meet in R, say, and BY meets XM, AL in Q, P say.

Clearly all points of the figure not on OY are on the same side of OY. Now $\mu OB < 2\mu OA$ and $[OAB]$ give $\mu AB < \mu OA$. But $AB, OA \simeq XQ, XR$ (VI 5). Hence $[XQR]$, hence $[YQP]$. Also $[OAB]$ gives $[YPB]$ and hence $[LPA]$.

Then since $[LPA]$, therefore O, P are on opposite sides of AY (VI 3·6) and hence we have $OALY \equiv OAPY + YLP$ (X 31). Also A, Y are on opposite sides of OP (VI 3·6) and hence we have $OAPY \equiv OPA + OPY$ (X 28). Since $[YQP]$ and $[OXY]$, all points of X^-Q are inside $\triangle OPY$ (II 12·1) and hence inside $OAPY$ (X 20). Hence $OAPY \equiv YXQ + OAPQX$ (X 24). Hence $OALY \equiv YLP + YXQ + OAPQX$. Similarly we can shew that

$$OBMX \equiv QMB + PAB + OAPQX.$$

But clearly $YXQ \simeq PAB$, and by VI 7·2, $YLP \simeq QMB$.

The Theorem now follows.

It is very clear here that the main part of a logical proof consists in shewing the dissection which can be 'seen.' This is always omitted in the usual texts.

30. *If* $\mathbf{K}_1$ *is true, two polygons* p, q *with the same measure are equivalent* **by addition.**

Dem. p, q can be dissected into triangles (X 21), rectangles can be drawn equivalent by addition to each triangle (9) and hence rectangles can be drawn on a given base so equivalent (29). These can be fitted together as in 23, giving rectangles $ABB'A'$ and $XYY'X'$ equivalent by addition to p, q resp. and with $AB \simeq XY$. These rectangles have the same measure (18). Hence $AA' \simeq XX'$ (20·1). Thus the rectangles are congruent, and so equivalent by addition, whence the Theorem by 2.

31. *If* $\mathbf{K}_1$ *is true, 'equivalence' implies 'equivalence by addition'* (18, 30), *and* $\mathbf{K}_1$ *is essential for this implication* (24, 28). *Thus if we assume* $\mathbf{K}_1$ *two equivalent polygons can always be dissected into triangles congruent in pairs.* Even in the absence of $\mathbf{K}_1$, equivalence (simply) and identity of measure imply each other (18, 24).

Quadrature of a Polygon

32. (See V 18.) *If Ax.* $\mathbf{Q}_1$ *be true, a square equivalent to a given polygon* p *can be constructed by* **abcq**$_2$ (IX 9).

Dem. By 22 we can find a rectangle $ABB'A' \cong p$ (by **abcd**). Let $BC \simeq BB'$, $[ABC]$ and let O be mid AC. Hence $[OBC]$ or $[OBA]$ (IV 14·1) and therefore $\mu OB < \mu OA$. Thus BB' meets the circle centre O, radius OC, in D say ($\mathbf{Q}_1$), and D can be found by **abcq**$_2$. Then $A\hat{D}C$ is a right angle (VI 13) and $AB . BC = BD^2$ (VII 22). Hence the rectangle $ABB'A'$ and the square on BD have the same measure (17) and hence they are equivalent (24).

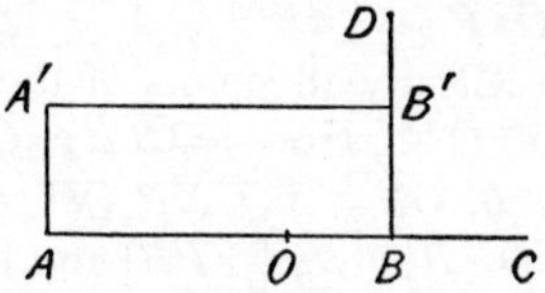

Fig. 136

33. *If* $\mathbf{Q}_1$ *be true, and* m *is the measure of any interval, there is an interval whose measure* x *satisfies* $x^2 = m$.

34. *If* $\mathbf{Q}_1$ *and* $\mathbf{K}_1$ *be both true, a square equivalent by addition to a given polygon can be constructed by* **abcq**$_2$ (31, 32).

Proportion and the Areas of Triangles

35. *If* AOC, BOC *be triangles, and* p, q *the measures of their altitudes with respect to the base* OC, *then* $\mu AOC | \mu BOC \sim p | q$.

Dem. Note that, since μAOC is the measure of an interval, the theory of Chapter VII can be used. Since

$$\mu AOC = \tfrac{1}{2}p \,.\, OC \text{ and } \mu BOC = \tfrac{1}{2}q \,.\, OC$$

the Theorem follows by VII 21·3.

36. *If* $ABC \sim XYZ$, *then* $\mu ABC | \mu XYZ \sim AB^2 | XY^2$.

Dem. If p, q be measures of the altitudes of the triangles with respect to bases BC, YZ then

$$\mu ABC | \mu XYZ \sim \tfrac{1}{2}p \,.\, BC | \tfrac{1}{2}q \,.\, YZ.$$

But $\tfrac{1}{2}p | \tfrac{1}{2}q \sim p | q$ (VII 11·2) $\sim AB | XY \sim BC | YZ$ (VII 10). Hence by VII 21·5.

37. *If* $\mathbf{Q}_1$ *be true, we can construct by* $\mathbf{abcq}_2$ *a triangle similar to a given triangle* PQR *and of given measure* AB^2.

Dem. We can find C, D so that $\mu CD^2 = \mu PQR$ (33) and X, Y, Z such that $XY | PQ \sim AB | CD$ and $XYZ \sim PQR$. Then

$$\mu XYZ | \mu PQR \sim XY^2 | PQ^2 \sim AB^2 | CD^2 \text{ (VII 21·6)}.$$

Whence $$\mu XYZ = \mu AB^2 \text{ (VII 2·11)}.$$

Projection of Areas

§ 3. Basis $\mathbf{O\,C\,P_1}$.

38. *If a polygon* p *in a plane* α *be projected on to a plane* β *into a polygon* p' (where β is not perpendicular to α) *then* $\mu p' | \mu p \sim k | u$, *where* k *is the parameter of projection* (VII 41·1).

Dem. If $\alpha \parallel \beta$ then $p \simeq p'$, $\mu p \simeq \mu p'$. Let α be not parallel to β. Dissect p into triangles and let ABC be one of them. Let α, β meet in l, and through A draw $AX \parallel l$, then $AX \parallel \beta$ (VI 36·5). Either $AX \parallel BC$, or AX meets BC in X, say. In the first case $BC \parallel \beta$ and so $\mu BC =$ measure of projection of BC, but by the projection, the altitude of ABC with respect to base BC is multiplied by the parameter, k, of the projection (VII 41·1), and hence μABC is multiplied by k (35). In the second case in the same way, μABX, μACX are each multiplied by k and hence so is μABC, since that is either the sum or the difference of μABX and μACX. The Theorem, being true for each triangle, holds for p.

·1. The measure of the projection of a polygon is less than or equal to the measure of the polygon.

CHAPTER XII

THE VOLUMES OF POLYHEDRA

Introductory Remarks

The Theory in this chapter is largely of the nature of an apology, inasmuch as we explain why it is not possible to construct a Theory of volumes analogous to that of areas in the last chapter. The difference begins with the question of the dissection of polyhedra; whereas any polygon can be dissected into triangles whose vertices are at the vertices of the polygon, in the case of polyhedra we are only able to say that they can be dissected into tetrahedra without specifying where the vertices must be. In fact polyhedra exist which cannot be dissected into tetrahedra with vertices at the vertices of the polyhedron.

Next if we define equivalence and equivalence by addition for polyhedra as we did for polygons (using congruent polyhedra), and define measure by means of the measures of tetrahedra, we are held up by the fact, shewn by Dehn, that two polyhedra of the same measure need not be equivalent.

The Theory of equivalence thus takes us but little way and we have to be satisfied with that of measure.

If when defining equivalent polyhedra we take as our basic figures, not congruent tetrahedra, but tetrahedra with bases of equal area and of congruent heights, we can indeed shew that two polyhedra of the same measure are, in the new sense, equivalent; but tetrahedra such as those just mentioned cannot always be split up into tetrahedra congruent in pairs, nor can they always be obtained by adjunction and omission of such pairs.

As a prerequisite to the study of volumes we consider with shortened proofs the Analysis Situs of Polyhedra on the basis of Axioms **O**. Our definition of polyhedra is chosen so as to simplify the proofs of theorems on the dissection of polyhedra.

The Theory in this chapter is based on the following memoirs:—

Lennes, "On the simple finite polygon and polyhedron," *Amer. Jour. Math.* 1911, XXXIII, p. 37.

Schatunowsky, "Über den Rauminhalt," *Math. Ann.* 1903, LVII, p. 496.

Dehn, "Über den Rauminhalt," *Math. Ann.* 1902, LV, p. 465.

Kagan, "Über die Transformation der Polyeder," *Math. Ann.* 1903, LVII, p. 421.

Suss, "Begründung der Lehre von Polyederinhalt," *Math. Ann.* 1920, LXXXII, p. 297.

Preliminaries

§ 1. Basis O.

1. *The. and Def.* If $\alpha=\{AB, X\}$ and $\beta=\{AB, Y\}$ be two half-planes with the same edge AB, the points Z such that $\{AB, Z\}$ is in $\widehat{\alpha\beta}$ (III 25·4) are '*inside*' $\widehat{\alpha\beta}$. The points of space not inside or on $\widehat{\alpha\beta}$ are '*outside*' $\widehat{\alpha\beta}$. The points inside form a convex region; the points outside, a region; $\widehat{\alpha\beta}$ separates the inside and the outside points of $\widehat{\alpha\beta}$ and bounds the inside and the outside regions (*Dem.* as in III 18).

·1. *The. and Def.* If $O.A\hat{B}C$ be a trihedral angle (III 25·3) the points Z, such that OZ meets ABC in points inside $\triangle ABC$, are '*inside*' the angle. The points of space not inside or on the angle are '*outside*' it. The points inside form a convex region; the points outside, a region; and the angle separates the regions and bounds them.

·2. If A', B', C' be on rays OA, OB, OC resp. and X be inside $O.A\hat{B}C$, then $[OX$ meets the inside of $\triangle A'B'C'$. (By II 12·2, III 5, 7.)

·3. If $O.A\hat{B}C$ is a trihedral angle and D be inside $A\hat{O}B$, and $[CXD]$, then X is inside $O.A\hat{B}C$.

Dem. Take A_1, B_1 on $[OA$, $[OB$ resp. Then $[OD$ meets $A_1{-}B_1$ in X_1, say (III 7), and $[OX$ meets $C{-}X_1$ (II 12), and hence meets the inside of $\triangle A_1B_1C$ (II 12·5).

1·4. A plane through O and a point inside $O.A\hat{B}C$ meets two faces, or one face and one edge of $O.A\hat{B}C$ (II 16, 29).

·5. A plane distinct from AOB and through a ray in $A\hat{O}B$ meets another face of $O.A\hat{B}C$ or goes through OC (II 16·1).

Definition of Polyhedron

2. *Defs.* A '*polyhedron*' is a set of points consisting of a finite set of triangles $[t]$, not all coplanar, and their inside points such that (i) every side of a triangle of the set is common to an even number of the triangles of the set, and (ii) there is no sub-set $[t']$ of $[t]$ such that (i) is true of a proper sub-set of $[t']$ (where $[t']$ may coincide with $[t]$). The '*vertices*' of the polyhedron are those of the triangles of $[t]$; its '*edges*,' their sides; its '*faces*' their insides; its '*edge-intervals*' their side-intervals. A '*closed face*' is a face together with its sides and vertices.

·1. *Note.* Comparing this definition with the more usual one, the fact that here the faces are triangles is clearly of no importance, since if they were polygons they could be dissected into triangles. A really important difference is that an edge of our polyhedron may be common to 4, 6, or any even number of faces. The definition, which is due to Lennes, simplifies the theory of dissection. The condition (ii) of the definition secures that the polyhedron is all of one piece and not e.g. two detached cubes. The complication in condition (ii) is needed, because the polyhedron need not be normal (·3).

As examples of polyhedra we have besides the usual ones, (*a*) two tetrahedra with a common edge and with a triangular hole on one face of each tetrahedron, these holes being connected by a tube, (*b*) a solid in the form of an anchor ring, but made of triangular plates.

Note the definition of 'face.'

·2. If the triangles in our def. overlap in any way, they can be dissected into triangles so that no point on or inside any new triangle is inside any other, while the polyhedron consists of the same points as before (X 26·1). We can also secure by dissection that no face meets a vertex, edge, or other face.

·3. *Def.* When this is done the polyhedron is '*normal*.' Henceforth all polyhedra shall be normal. A normal polyhedron will often be denoted by Π.

3. If $[t']$, $[t'']$ be complementary sub-sets of $[t]$, then there is at least one edge which is a side of an odd number of triangles of $[t']$ and of an odd number of triangles of $[t'']$ (2 (ii)).

4. *A plane meets* Π *in at most a finite set of triangles and their insides together with a finite set of intervals and a finite set of points. A plane, not through three non-collinear vertices of* Π, *meets it in a finite set of intervals and a finite set of points.*

5. *A plane, not through a vertex of* Π, *meets it at most in a finite set of simple polygons whose vertices are on the edges of* Π.

Dem. Let the plane α meet Π. Then it meets an edge of Π. For if P be on α and inside a triangle t of Π, then since α cannot coincide with the plane of t, α meets that plane in a line which must meet a side a of t (for α goes through no vertex). Hence the inside of each other triangle of Π which has a for a side meets α in an open interval. Hence α and Π meet in a finite set of intervals *whose ends are common to an even number of intervals of the set.* Starting with an end of any of these intervals, and tracing a way along the intervals, we must ultimately reach an end-point already reached, for the number of intervals is finite. Omit the simple polygon so obtained, and repeat the process on the intervals left. A finite repetition of the process exhausts the intervals.

·1. The simple polygons can only meet in vertices (2·2·3)*.

The Inside and Outside of a Polyhedron

6. *Temporary Definition.* A line or ray not through a vertex or edge of Π is '*suitable.*'

·1. There are suitable rays from any point. There are suitable lines through any point which is not a vertex or on an edge (II 19·5).

7. A suitable line l meets Π in an even number of points†.

Dem. There is a plane, through l, on which are no vertices of Π (II 19·3). This meets Π in a finite set of simple polygons whose vertices are on the edges of Π, hence l meets each polygon in an even number of points (X 11·1). Hence by 5·1.

* Our simple polygons may now have three collinear consecutive vertices.

† Zero is always regarded as an even number.

7·1. An angle $\widehat{hk}$, each of whose sides is a suitable ray and whose vertex A is not on Π, meets Π in an even number of points.

Dem. If no vertex of Π be in the plane (hk) this follows by 7. If vertices of Π do lie in that plane, there are planes through h, k resp. which contain no vertices of Π (II 19·3). These meet in l say. If m be any ray of l from A, then by the first part, $\widehat{hm}$ and $\widehat{km}$ each meet Π in an even number of points. Hence so does $\widehat{hk}$.

8. *Defs.* A point P, not on Π, is '*inside*' or '*outside*' Π according as one suitable ray from P meets Π in an odd or an even number of points. Points both inside or both outside Π are on the same '*aspect*' of Π.

·1. Any suitable ray from a point inside (outside) Π meets Π in an odd (even) number of points.

·2. A point not on Π is either outside or inside Π but not both.

·3. *Note.* We now wish to shew that the set of points inside Π and the set of points outside Π form two regions separated by Π.

9. *There are points outside and points inside* Π (7).

10. *Any two points not on* Π, *which can be joined by a way not meeting* Π, *are on the same aspect of* Π.

Dem. Let $A \vdash\!\dashv B$ be any interval of the way. If one at least of [AB and BA] is suitable, then by 8, all points of $A \vdash\!\dashv B$ are on the same aspect of Π. If neither ray be suitable there is a plane α through AB and through no vertex of Π, save those (if any) on AB; hence on α there are not three non-collinear vertices, and hence α contains only a finite set of points on edge-intervals of Π, save perhaps those on AB. Hence there is a point Q on α so that [AQ, [BQ are suitable and $A \dashv Q$, $B \dashv Q$ do not meet Π (III 15·5). Then A, Q are on the same aspect of Π, and so are B, Q, and hence so are A, B.

·1. If $A \vdash\!\dashv B$ meets Π in one point C ($\neq A, B$) only and C is on a face of Π, then all points of $A \vdash C$ are inside and all points of $B \vdash C$ are outside Π, or vice versâ.

Dem. similar to last.

10·2. If A, B, C colline and all points of $A^{-}C$ are inside Π and all points of $B^{-}C$ outside, then $A^{-}B$ meets Π in C only (8, 10).

·3. *Def.* If A, B be joined by a way all of whose points, save perhaps A and B, are inside (outside) Π, then A is '*internally* (externally) *accessible*' from B with respect to Π.

11. If B is a point inside a triangle t of Π, and all points of $A^{-}B$, $C^{-}B$ are inside (outside) Π, then A, C are mutually internally (externally) accessible with respect to Π.

Dem. The plane $ABC = \alpha$ meets Π in at most a finite set of triangles $[t']$ with their insides, together with a finite set of intervals and of points (4). Neither $A^{-}B$ nor $B^{-}C$ meets Π (8) and B is not *on* any triangle of Π (2·2). Hence there are points A' on $A^{-}B$, C' on $C^{-}B$ such that $A'{\vdash\!\dashv}C'$ does not meet Π, (by X 3, 4), save perhaps in the meet of Π and the plane β of t. We can take C' so that $A'^{-}C'$ does not contain a point *on* t, then if $A'{\vdash\!\dashv}C'$ met Π in a point inside t and there only, A', C' would be on different aspects of Π (10·1), cont. hyp. Hence the Theorem.

·1. If B be not on an edge-interval of Π and be internally (externally) accessible from both A and C, then A and C are mutually so accessible. Note that any of A, B, C may or may not be on Π.

·2. If A be inside a triangle t of Π and B inside *or on* t, then B is both internally and externally accessible from A.

Dem. Let α be the plane of t. Through A goes a suitable line l, and hence on l is a point C such that $A^{\dashv}C$, $B^{\dashv}C$ do not meet Π (X 4). Hence all points on $A^{\dashv}C$ and $B^{\dashv}C$ are on the same aspect (10). Similarly there is a point D with $[CAD]$ and such that all points of $A^{\dashv}D$ and $B^{\dashv}D$ are on the same aspect while $C{\vdash\!\dashv}D$ meets Π in A only. Thus C, D are on different aspects (10·1). Hence the Theorem.

·3. Two points A, C on the same edge-interval are mutually internally and externally accessible (·1·2).

12. If Q be any point on an edge a of Π and if any plane α, through Q and through no vertex, meet the faces of Π with edge a in intervals ordered thus $(v_1 \ldots v_{2n})$ (III 24), then there

is a triangle in α which has Q as an inside point, such that the points inside the triangle and inside the regions bounded by the rays from Q which contain the v, are alternately inside and outside Π.

Dem. α meets Π in a finite set of simple polygons (5). Hence there is a triangle t in α, with Q inside it, which does not meet these polygons save in points of v. (This can be shewn by a proof similar to III 15·2 *Dem.*, using X 4.) The Theorem now follows from 10·1, 10 and X 24.

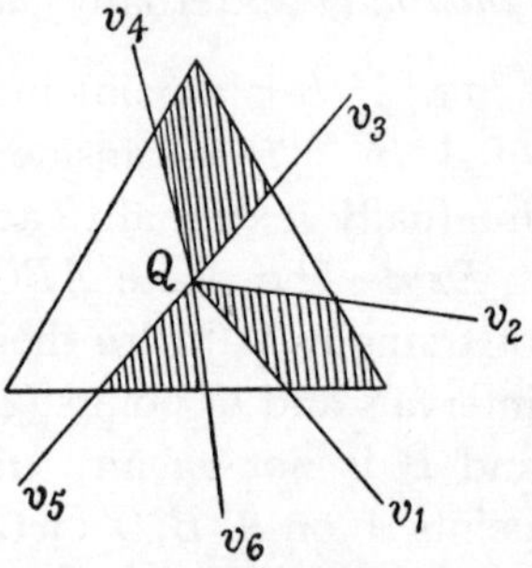

Fig. 137

12·1. If the faces of Π with a common side a are divided into two sets, such that one and hence the other contains an odd number of faces, then there are two points, one in a face of each set, which are internally, and two such which are externally accessible from each other.

Dem. Let Q, α, v_1, ..., v_{2n}, t be as in 12. In each set of the v, there must be an odd number of consecutive intervals. Let v_i, v_{i+1}, ..., v_k be such a set. Points inside t and inside the region bounded by those rays from Q which contain v_{i-1} and v_i are on the other aspect from those inside the region similarly related to v_k and v_{k+1} (12). Thus two points inside t and on v_{i-1}, v_i resp. are mutually internally accessible, if two points inside t and on v_k, v_{k+1} are mutually externally accessible; and vice versâ (X 2, 24, 7). Hence the Theorem.

13. Any two points on Π are both internally and externally accessible from each other.

Dem. Let X be any point on Π. If a single point B inside a face of Π is internally accessible from X by the way $X...AB$, say, then since any other point Y of the closed face is so accessible (11·2) from B by $Y...CB$, say, and since C, A are so accessible (11) from each other, therefore any point on that closed face is so accessible from X. If some points on Π are not internally accessible from X, let $[t']$ be the set of triangles whose inside points are so accessible and $[t'']$ the other set of triangles of Π. There is at least one edge which is a side of an odd number of triangles of $[t']$ and of an odd number of triangles of $[t'']$ (3). Hence there are points, one inside a triangle of each set, which are mutually internally accessible (12·1). Hence a point inside a triangle of $[t'']$ is so accessible from X (11·1), cont. hyp. Similarly for external accessibility. Hence the Theorem.

14. *Any two inside (outside) points A, B of* Π *are accessible from each other.*

Dem. There are suitable lines through A, B which meet Π, and on them intervals AC, BD which meet Π in C, D only. By 13, C, D are mutually accessible, hence so are A, B (11·1).

15. Π *separates the remaining points of space into two regions* viz. *the set of outside and the set of inside points* (9, 10, 14, 8·2).

16. *In every plane there is a line whose points are all outside* Π, *but no line or ray whose points are all inside* Π (X 15, 16).

·1. If a point P inside Π is inside a dihedral angle, then some point on Π is also inside that angle.

Dem. Let l be the edge of the dihedral angle, A a point on l outside Π (16). Then the points of A^-P are inside the angle (1) and A^-P meets Π (15).

Convex Polyhedra and their Dissection

17. *Def.* A polyhedron is '*convex*' if all its inside points lie on one side of each of the planes of its faces.

·1. *Def.* We define the '*dissection*' of polyhedra as for polygons (X 20) and use the notation of X 21·1·2.

18. The inside points of a convex polyhedron constitute a convex region.

·1. No line not on a face-plane of a convex polyhedron can meet it in more than two points. [Consider in particular a line through a vertex or an edge.]

·2. If a plane, not a face-plane, meet a convex polyhedron, it does so in one point or one edge or in a convex polygon.

·3. A tetrahedron is a convex polyhedron.

19. *Any convex polyhedron* Γ *can be dissected into a set of tetrahedra with vertices at the vertices of* Γ.

Dem. Let A be a vertex of Γ, and let $[t]$ be the set of triangles of Γ whose planes do not contain A. The vertices of each one of these triangles together with A are the vertices of a tetrahedron, and this set of tetrahedra $[T]$ dissects Γ. For (i) No two of the $[T]$ have a common inside point P; for if so, then $[AP$ would meet Γ in two different faces q, r at Q, R, say, and $Q \neq R$ since no two triangles of Γ have a common inside point. This is contrary to 18·1.

(ii) Every point P inside Γ is inside or on some T, for $[AP$ meets Γ in a point Q inside or on some t, and hence inside or on a face of some T; and $[APQ]$, since $[AQP]$ would imply that $[AP$ met Γ again, contrary to 18·1.

(iii) Any point P inside some T is inside Γ, for $[AP$ meets a face of Γ in a point Q with $[APQ]$ and there only.

Dissection of Polyhedra in General

20. If an inside point P of a polyhedron Π is in a plane α, then there is a set of triangles $[t_1]$ in α, no two of which have a common inside point, such that all points on α inside Π are inside or on some t_1, while no points outside Π are so situate.

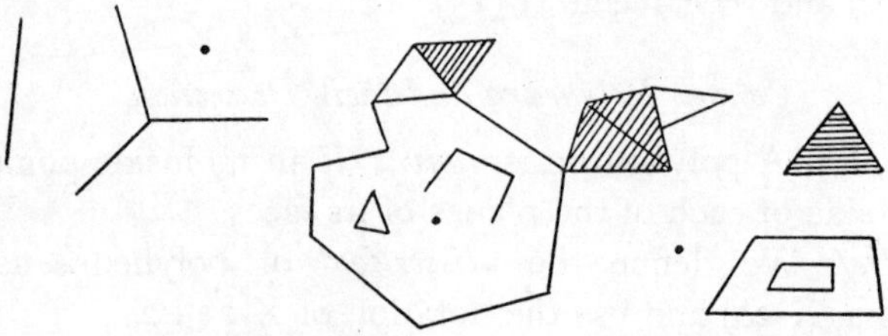

Fig. 138. Meets of a polyhedron and a plane.

Dem. Let $[v]$ be the set of all edge-intervals of Π in α and of all meets of α with those closed faces of Π which do not lie in α, when these meets are intervals (and not merely points).

Let P be a point on α inside Π, and $[P]$ the set of all points accessible from P with respect to $[v]$ by ways in α; then $[P]$ is not the whole plane. Hence there is a sub-set p of $[v]$

satisfying the conditions of X 22, and hence p is a simple polygon. All points on p are on Π, all points of $[P]$ are inside or on p and inside or on Π.

If there are points inside p and outside Π, let Q be one of them and let $[Q]$ be the set accessible from Q with respect to $[v]$ by ways in α. We find a polygon q whose points are on Π and such that all points of $[Q]$ are inside or on q and outside or on Π. Let $[R]$ be the set of points inside p and outside such polygons as q. If there is a point P_1 inside Π and not in $[R]$, we consider $[P_1]$ as before and find a polygon p_1 and perhaps a polygon q_1 and thus a set $[R_1]$. And so on.

If now in $[R]$, $[R_1]$, ..., there be points of detached intervals of $[v]$, not forming part of the polygons p, q, etc., we exclude points of these intervals and so obtain sets $[R']$, $[R_1']$, ... Thus we can find a set of triangles $[t_1]$ such that all points of $[R']$, $[R_1']$, ..., are inside or on them and all inside points of the triangles are in $[R']$ or $[R_1']$, etc. (X 26·2).

21. If an inside point P of Π is in a plane α, then the triangles $[t_1]$ of 20 and the triangles of Π as dissected* by the meets of their planes and α, give a set of polyhedra which dissect Π.

Dem. Let $[t_2]$ be the set of triangles of Π (as dissected by the meets of their planes and α) which lie on one half-space Σ of α, and $[t_2']$ those in the other half-space Σ'. Let $[t_3]$ be the set $[t_1]$ and $[t_2]$ together, and $[t_3']$ be the set $[t_1]$ and $[t_2']$. Let σ be a side of a triangle of $[t_3]$. If σ is either not on α or not on Π, it is certainly common to an even number of triangles.

If σ be both on α and on Π but no triangle of Π with side σ be on α, then if there be an odd number of triangles of $[t_2]$ with side σ, there will be one triangle of $[t_1]$ with that side, and if there be an even number of such triangles of $[t_2]$, there will be 0 or 2 such triangles of $[t_1]$ (12).

If σ be a side of a triangle both of $[t_1]$ and of $[t_2]$, and one

* The meets of the planes dissect some of the triangles of Π into figures which must be dissected into triangles.

or two triangles of Π with that side lie in α, draw a plane β, not containing σ, through a point Q of σ, and draw a triangle t in β with Q as an inside point as in 12. Adjoin a triangle of Π on α with side σ, to $[t_3]$ or to $[t_3']$ according as the region inside Π and t and bounded in part by meets of β and that triangle of Π, lies in Σ or Σ′. When these triangles are adjoined, the sets $[t_3]$, $[t_3']$ become sets $[t_4]$, $[t_4']$, say.

Then the number of triangles in $[t_4]$ with a common edge is always even, and hence they constitute a set of polyhedra $[\Pi_1]$; no face is common to two or more of the $[\Pi_1]$; for the set $[t_4]$ can be broken up into sets satisfying condition (ii) of 2. Similarly for polyhedra $[\Pi_1']$ constructed from the $[t_4']$.

The argument may be made clearer by the figures following, where the shaded portions denote regions inside Π and t, and we draw only the sections by β.

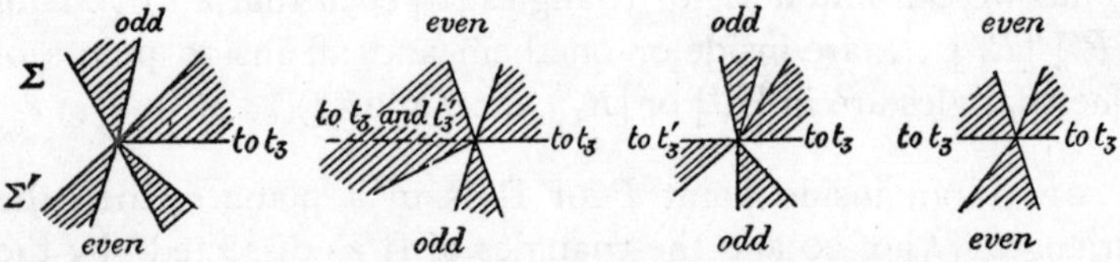

Fig. 139. (The horizontal lines are the lines where α and β meet.)

Now (i) no two polyhedra of $[\Pi_1]$ have a common inside point. For every Π_1 has at least one face on α, and that face and each triangle of $[t_2]$ are used once only for the set $[\Pi_1]$. From a point Q inside a triangle of $[t_1]$ draw a ray in Σ suitable with respect to Π. There is a point R on the ray such that no point on Π is on Q-R, and hence all points of Q-R are inside just one polyhedron of $[\Pi_1]$. And hence no point on $[QR$ is inside two polyhedra of $[\Pi_1]$, since each triangle of $[t_2]$ is used once only.

Next (ii) any point P of Σ, inside Π, is inside some Π_1. For from P draw a ray not meeting α and suitable with respect to Π and the $[\Pi_1]$ (II 19·5). The ray meets Π an odd number of times and hence at least one Π_1 an odd number of times.

(iii) Any point inside any Π_1 is inside Π, for the ray of (ii) meets only one of $[\Pi_1]$ in an odd number of points by (i).

Treat $[\Pi_1']$ similarly and the Theorem is shewn.

22. *Any polyhedron can be dissected into tetrahedra.*

Dem. By 19 we can assume Π not convex; then Π has a face-plane α such that all inside points of Π do not lie on the same side of α. Hence some inside points lie on α, and hence Π is dissected by means of α into polyhedra whose inside points do lie on the same side of α (21). If some of these polyhedra be not convex, we proceed as before. A finite number of steps gives a finite set of convex polyhedra, since the number of face-planes of Π is finite.

·1. *Note.* Had we adopted a more usual definition of a polyhedron, in which just two faces have one common edge, we should have had the difficulty that the dissecting plane α might have had on it an edge of the polyhedron, adjacent points on α being inside points. Consider e.g. a frustum of a square pyramid with a part shaped like a square wedge removed from the top. The dissecting plane might contain the sharp edge of the wedge. The definition adopted seems to lead to fewer complications than the usual one, and as it leads to 22 it serves our purpose.

A polygon can be dissected into triangles *whose vertices are at the vertices of the polygon* (X 21), but in the case of the polyhedron we have not asserted that the vertices of the tetrahedra are at those of the polyhedron. In fact Lennes has constructed an ordinary non-convex solid for which this is actually not the case. For this solid, if *any* two vertices not on the same edge be joined, the open interval between them is wholly or partly outside the solid.

Lemmas

23. *Defs.* If $A_1 \ldots A_n$ be a plane polygon, B a point not in its plane, the '*pyramid*' $B, A_1 \ldots A_n$ with '*apex*' B and '*base*' $A_1 \ldots A_n$ is the set of points inside and on $A_1 \ldots A_n$ and the triangles $BA_1A_2, BA_2A_3, \ldots BA_nA_1$. If $OABC$ be a tetrahedron and A', B', C' be on O^-A, O^-B, O^-C resp., then the set of points inside and on $\triangle ABC$, $\triangle A'B'C'$, $AA'B'B$, $BB'C'C$, $CC'A'A$ is a '*trihedral frustum*.'

·1. The pyramid and the trihedral frustum are convex polyhedra. (Cf. X 21.)

·2. A pyramid can be dissected into tetrahedra with the same apex (19).

23·3. A trihedral frustum can be dissected into tetrahedra with vertices at vertices of the frustum (19). The frustum of 23 is dissected into tetrahedra $ABB'C'$, $ABCC'$, $AA'B'C'$.

·4. The points inside two tetrahedra, if existent, constitute the inside of a convex polyhedron, which can therefore be dissected into tetrahedra (18, 19, 21, III 1·2. Cf. X 26).

Volumes of Polyhedra

§ 2. Basis O C P_1.

24. *Defs.* Polyhedra '*equivalent by addition*' and '*equivalent*' can be defined as in XI 1, 1·1 replacing p_i, q_i, s, s' by polyhedra.

·1. Theorems corresponding to XI 1·2 to 2·2 can be shewn in a similar manner, and it is easy to shew from the Theorems of XI that two *parallelepipeds on the same base and with corresponding altitudes congruent are equivalent.* But practically no further progress can be made in this direction on our present basis.

[The definition of altitude of a parallelepiped with respect to a given face is like that in XI 4·1.]

·2. *Def.* If $ABCD$ be a tetrahedron and $AH \perp BCD$, H on BCD, then AH is the '*altitude*' of $\triangle ABCD$ '*corresponding to the base*' $\triangle BCD$.

·3. *Def.* A '*regular*' tetrahedron is one with all its edges congruent.

·4. Any two faces, any two dihedral angles, any two trihedral angles of a regular tetrahedron are congruent (IV 96).

25. *If $ABCD$ be a tetrahedron and a, b, c, d be the measures of the faces opposite to A, B, C, D resp. and h_a, h_b, h_c, h_d be the measures of the corresponding altitudes, then*

$$h_a.a = h_b.b = h_c.c = h_d.d.$$

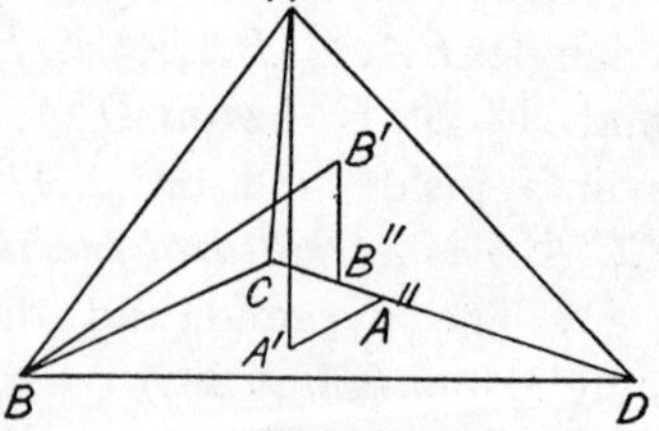

Fig. 140

Dem. Let A' be the 'foot' of the perpendicular from A on BCD, A'' that from A' on CD; B' that from B on ACD, B'' that from B' on CD. Then $AA'A'' \perp BCD$ (IV 86). But $A'A'' \perp CD$. Hence $AA'' \perp CD$

(IV 83 (iv)). Similarly $B'B''$, $BB'' \perp CD$. Hence

$$A\hat{A}''A' \simeq B\hat{B}''B' \text{ (IV 84) and } AA''A' \sim BB''B'.$$

Whence $AA''|AA' \sim BB''|BB'$ and $AA'.BB'' = BB'.AA''$, $AA'.BB''.CD = BB'.AA''.CD$. Hence the Theorem.

25·1. *Def.* $\frac{1}{3}h_a a$ is the '*volume*' or '*measure*' of $ABCD$ and is denoted by $\mu ABCD$.

26. *If a tetrahedron* $ABCD = T$ *be dissected into a set of tetrahedra* $[t]$, *the volume of* T *is the sum of the volumes of the* $[t]$.

Dem. (i) If all the $[t]$ have one vertex at A and the others all on BCD, then $\triangle BCD$ is dissected into triangles, and the Theorem follows by XI 15, VII 19·1.

(ii) In particular, the Theorem holds when T is dissected by just one plane through an edge.

(iii) Let all the vertices of the $[t]$ lie on the three edges through one vertex, say on AB, AC, AD. Then no vertices of any t lie inside $\triangle BCD$. Hence the inside of this triangle is a face of some t, and the other vertex E of this t lies on A^-B, say, and hence easily $\triangle ABCD \equiv \triangle EBCD + \triangle AECD$. The Theorem holds for this dissection by (ii). Next treat $\triangle EBCD$ as we treated $\triangle ABCD$ and after a finite number of steps the Theorem is proved.

(iv) If T is first dissected by method (i), and the sub-tetrahedra are then dissected by method (iii), the Theorem follows in this case by Assoc +.

(v) Let O be a point outside T, such that the rays from O through A, B, C, D meet a plane α, none of whose points are inside T, in A', B', C', D' say. These points do not all colline. Dissect the triangles whose vertices are A', B', C', D' into triangles in any way and join the vertices of these latter to O. Each join meets a closed face of T (1·2) and hence meets T in two points or in only one point, if A', B', C', D' are distinct (18·1, 6, 8). If XYZ be a sub-triangle, and the rays from O to X, Y, Z each meet T in two points, we have a trihedral frustum; if one ray meets T in one point only, and the other two each meet T in two points, we have a pyramid on a quadrilateral base; if two rays each meet T in one point only and the other meets T in two points, we have a tetrahedron; and the inside points of all these figures are inside T (18·1). (The last two cases may occur when X, Y, Z are at A, B, C, D or on the intervals joining them.) The figures obtained can all be dissected into three tetrahedra, or fewer, whose vertices are at their vertices (23·2·3). Similarly if A', B', C', D' are not all distinct. We wish to shew that the measure of $ABCD$ is the sum of the measures of its sub-tetrahedra so obtained.

(v *a*) First, let O be on DA, then $A' = D'$, and on α we have the triangle $A'B'C'$. Let q be any sub-triangle of $\triangle A'B'C'$; Q, Q' those corresponding on DBC and ABC, and let $t', t'', t''', \ldots$, be the sub-tetrahedra got by dissecting the corresponding figures inside T. Each tetrahedron Oq gives at most four tetrahedra t, and their vertices are on edges through O. Hence, by (iii), $\mu OQ = \mu OQ' + \mu t' + \mu t'' + \ldots$.

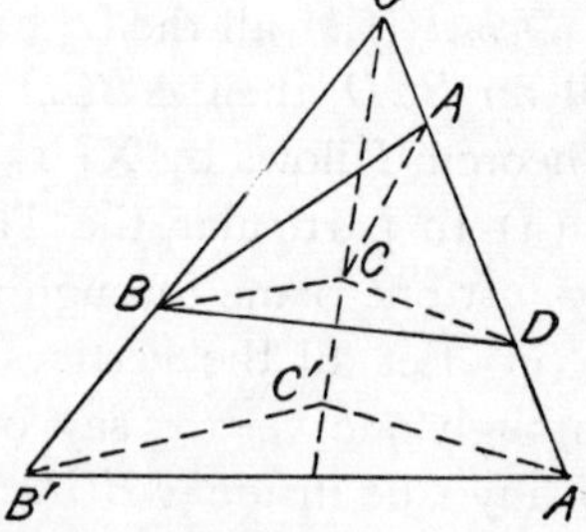

Fig. 141

By (i) the sum of the μOQ is $\mu OBCD$, and the sum of the $\mu OQ'$ is $\mu OBCA$. Hence $\mu OBCD = \mu OBCA + \Sigma(\mu t' + \mu t'' + \ldots)$. But by (ii) $\mu OBCD = \mu OBCA + \mu ABCD$. Hence the Theorem in this case.

(v *b*) Next, let O be in the plane ABD. Then A', B', D' colline. Let OA meet B^-D in A_1. (Cf. III 13·1.) Then by (ii)

$$\mu ABCD = \mu AA_1BC + \mu AA_1CD.$$

But O is on AA_1; hence by (*a*) $\mu AA_1BC =$ sum of measures of its sub-tetrahedra. Similarly for μAA_1CD, and the Theorem follows in this case.

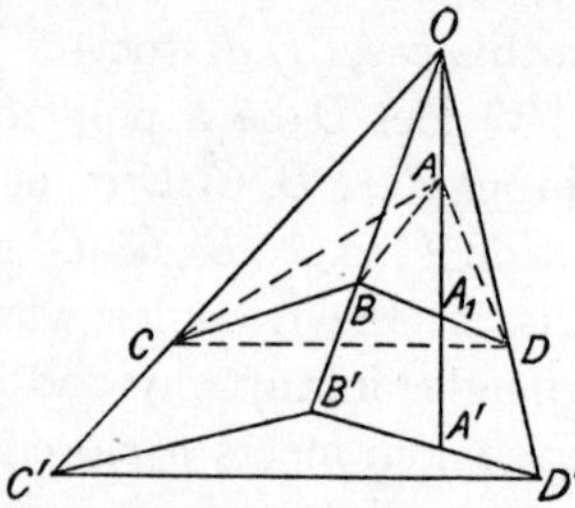

Fig. 142

(v *c*) Lastly, let O be not on any face-plane, then no three of A', B', C', D' colline and (X 34·3) *either* one, say D', is inside the triangle $A'B'C'$ formed by the others, and then $\triangle A'B'C' \equiv A'B'D' + B'C'D' + C'A'D'$, and when these triangles are dissected we have case (v *a*). *Or*

A', B', C', D' form a convex quadrilateral, say $A'B'C'D'$, and then $A'{-}C'$, $B'{-}D'$ meet. The plane OAC dissects T into two tetrahedra by method (ii), and if the triangles $A'B'C'$, $A'D'C'$ are dissected and the construction above be performed, then these two tetrahedra are dissected as in (v b).

(vi) Finally let $\Delta ABCD$ be dissected in any way into tetrahedra $t_1, \ldots, t_m$; join their vertices to A, the joining lines all meet BCD, and ΔBCD can be dissected into triangles whose vertices are these points of meeting (X 21, 23). Further, by means of these joins, the tetrahedra t_i can be dissected into sub-tetrahedra as in methods (i) and (v). Let t_i be dissected into $t_{i1}, t_{i2}, \ldots, t_{ij}$ then, by (i) or (v), $\mu t_i = \sum_j \mu t_{ij}$, $\sum_i \mu t_i = \sum_{ij} \mu t_{ij}$. But the joins from A to points inside ΔBCD give a dissection of T into tetrahedra T_s by method (i), and these T_s are dissected into the t_{ij} by method (iii), and each t_{ij} appears once and once only among the sub-tetrahedra of the T_s. Hence the Theorem now follows.

27. *When a polyhedron is dissected into tetrahedra in two different ways, say* $Q \equiv \Sigma t_i \equiv \Sigma T_j$, *then* $\Sigma \mu t_i \equiv \Sigma \mu T_j$. (As in XI 16 using XII 23·4.)

·1. Similarly if Q is dissected into polyhedra in two different ways (22).

28. *Def.* The '*volume*' or '*measure*' of a polyhedron Π, denoted by $\mu\Pi$, is the sum of the measures of any set of dissecting tetrahedra.

·1. The volume of any parallelepiped* is the measure a of any face, multiplied by the measure p of the altitude corresponding to that face.

Dem. It can be dissected into six tetrahedra, each with a face of measure $a/2$ and corresponding altitude of measure p.

·2. *Defs. and Theorem.* If those faces of a parallelepiped which meet in one vertex are mutually perpendicular, all faces which meet are perpendicular, and the parallelepiped is a '*box*.' If two faces, not opposite, of a box are squares, all are squares, and the box is a '*cube*.'

* The def. of parallelepiped (VI 36·8) must be slightly modified so as to agree with 2. The meaning of 'measure of a face' is clear.

Dehn's Theorem

29. *Two polyhedra with the same measure need not be equivalent by addition, that is, it may not be possible to dissect them into polyhedra congruent in pairs. Nor need they be equivalent simply, that is, it may not be possible to adjoin to them polyhedra equivalent by addition, so that the completed figures are equivalent by addition.*

This will be shewn in successive steps.

·1. If polyhedra P, P' with dihedral angles of measure $\alpha_1, \ldots, \alpha_n$ and $\alpha_1', \ldots, \alpha_m'$ resp. be equivalent by addition, then there are positive integers M_i, M_i', M, N, M', N' such that

$$\sum_1^n M_i\alpha_i + (M+2N)\,\pi = \sum_1^m M_i'\alpha_i' + (M'+2N')\,\pi \;\ldots(1).$$

Dem. Let $P \equiv P_1 + P_2 + \ldots + P_k$. The vertices of the other sub-polyhedra which lie on an edge of P_i divide it into intervals, which we call α-intervals of P_i. To each α-interval ascribe the argument π, 2π or α_h according as the interval lies in a face of P, or inside P, or along an edge of P with dihedral angle α_h. Thus the argument is the sum of the measures of the dihedral angles of the sub-polyhedra along the α-interval (IV 84·1).

Now by hypothesis $P' \equiv P_1' + P_2' + \ldots + P_k'$ where $P_i \simeq P_i'$. We shall have, in the figure P_i', intervals corresponding to the α-intervals of the P_i. Such an interval in the figure P_i' may be divided by some vertices of the other P_j'; if so, we divide the corresponding α-interval of P_i into intervals correspondingly. These we call β-intervals. Hence an α-interval, if on an edge of more than one P_i, may be divided into β-intervals in several ways, each way corresponding to *one* P_i of which the α-interval is a portion of an edge. To each β-interval we ascribe as argument the dihedral angle, along the interval, of that polyhedron P_i to which it belongs. To each β-interval we shall also ascribe a positive number ($\neq 0$) which we shall call its '*weight*' and which is subject only to the condition following:

If an α-interval be divided into β-intervals in more than one way, with weights $m_1', m_1'', m_1''', \ldots; m_2', m_2'', m_2''', \ldots; \ldots$; then shall

$$\Sigma m_1 = \Sigma m_2 = \ldots, \;\ldots\ldots\ldots\ldots\ldots\ldots(2).$$

This sum we call the '*weight*' of the α-interval.

For instance, if an α-interval be divided by *all* the ends of its β-intervals into n parts, we could take as the weight of each α-interval or β-interval the number of parts that it contains. The weights would then be *positive integers* ($\neq 0$).

If an α-interval of weight M and argument T, be divided in several ways into β-intervals with arguments $\tau_1', \tau_1'', \tau_1''', \ldots$; $\tau_2', \tau_2'', \tau_2''', \ldots$; ... and weights as above, then since $\tau_1', \tau_1'', \ldots$ refer to one edge of one polyhedron P_i, we have, by definition

$$\tau_1' = \tau_1'' = \tau_1''' = \ldots;\ \tau_2' = \tau_2'' = \tau_2''' = \ldots;\ \ldots.$$

Hence
$$\Sigma m_1^{(i)}\tau_1^{(i)} + \Sigma m_2^{(i)}\tau_2^{(i)} + \ldots + \Sigma m_l^{(i)}\tau_l^{(i)}$$
$$= \tau_1\Sigma m_1^{(i)} + \tau_2\Sigma m_2^{(i)} + \ldots + \tau_l\Sigma m_l^{(i)}$$
$$= M(\tau_1 + \tau_2 + \ldots + \tau_l) = M\Sigma\tau = MT$$

by (2). Hence
$$\sum_\beta m\tau = \sum_\alpha MT \quad \text{.....................(3)},$$

where $\sum_\alpha, \sum_\beta$ are sums over the α-intervals and β-intervals of the figure P. Let $M_1, \ldots, M_n, M, N$ be the sums of the weights of the α-intervals with arguments $\alpha_1, \ldots, \alpha_n, \pi$, and 2π resp. Then (3) gives $\sum_\beta m\tau = M_1\alpha_1 + \ldots + M_n\alpha_n + (M + 2N)\pi$.

Similarly considering the figure P' we have

$$\sum_\beta m\tau = M_1'\alpha_1' + \ldots + M_m'\alpha_m' + (M' + 2N')\pi.$$

In deducing this we have only assumed (2) and, by a remark above, we can take the weights to be positive integers. Hence the Theorem.

29·2. Similarly, if a system of polyhedra $Q_1, \ldots, Q_j$ dissect $P_1, \ldots, P_k$, and a system of congruent polyhedra dissect $P_1', \ldots, P_l'$, we have an equation like (1). If some of the P_i be congruent to some of the P_j', we can take the weights of congruent edge-intervals as equal and these then drop out of equation (1).

If now two polyhedra P_1, P_1' are equivalent simply, we can adjoin polyhedra so that, say, the set $P_1, P_2, \ldots, P_k$ is equivalent by addition to $P_1', P_2', \ldots, P_k'$ where $P_2 \simeq P_2', \ldots, P_k \simeq P_k'$. Thus the set $P_1, \ldots, P_k$ and the set $P_1', \ldots, P_k'$ can be dissected into polyhedra $Q_1, \ldots, Q_j$ and $Q_1', \ldots, Q_j'$ congruent in pairs. Hence we have an equation like (1) between the angles of $P_1, \ldots, P_k$ and of $P_1', \ldots, P_k'$, and thus an equation like (1) between the angles of P_1 and of P_1'.

29·3. With the aid of a little Trigonometry we can now shew that a regular tetrahedron* cannot be equivalent to a cube of the same measure.

Dem. If this were the case then we should have an equation $r\theta = s\pi$, where r, s are some integers and $\theta = \cos^{-1} 1/3$ is the dihedral angle of a regular tetrahedron.

We shew that such an equation is impossible†.

Let $\phi = \frac{1}{2}\theta$, then $\tan\phi = \frac{1}{\sqrt{2}}$, and if θ were a rational part of π, we should have $\tan 2n\phi = 0$ for some integer n.

Hence

$$_{2n}C_1 - \tfrac{1}{2}\,_{2n}C_3 + \ldots + (-1)^{n+1}(\tfrac{1}{2})^{n-1}\,_{2n}C_{2n-1} = 0,$$

that is

$$2n - \frac{2n(2n-1)(2n-2)}{2\,\underline{|3}} + \frac{2n(2n-1)(2n-2)(2n-3)(2n-4)}{2^2\,\underline{|5}} - \ldots + (-1)^{n+1}\frac{2n}{2^{n-1}} = 0.$$

(This could also be deduced by VIII § 9 from the fact that $\left(1+\frac{i}{\sqrt{2}}\right)^{2n}$ would have zero imaginary part.)

Let 2^r be the highest power of 2 which divides n. Multiply the last equation by 2^{n-3-r}. The last term becomes half an integer, the last but one becomes

$$\frac{2^{r+2}}{2^{n-1}}\,2^{n-3-r} \text{ times an integer}$$

and so is integral. The remaining terms also become integers and the equation is thus impossible. Hence our Theorem.

Theorem 29 has thus been fully shewn.

Suss' Theorems

§ 3. Basis O C P_1 Q_1.

So far we have considered whether polyhedra with the same measure can be split up into polyhedra congruent in pairs, and have

* The existence of a regular tetrahedron will be shewn shortly from Axioms O, C.

† I am indebted for this proof to Mr R. Cooper. Other proofs, not so simple, have been given by Dehn (*Gött. Nach.* 1900) and Sforza (*Per. di Mat.* 1897).

found that in general they cannot. We now take up the question whether they can be split up into corresponding tetrahedra, where two corresponding tetrahedra have two of their faces, one in each, of the same measure and corresponding altitudes congruent.

30. *Defs.* Two tetrahedra are '*equivalent* (T)' when two of their faces (called 'bases' below) have the same measure, one face being in each tetrahedron, and when the corresponding altitudes are congruent. Two polyhedra or sets of polyhedra P, Q are '*equivalent* (T +),' written $P \cong Q$ (T +), when they can be dissected into tetrahedra equivalent (T) in pairs; they are '*equivalent* (T −),' written $P \cong Q$ (T −), when by adjunction of polyhedra, which are equivalent (T +), we obtain polyhedra which themselves are equivalent (T +).

That is, we are taking as fundamentally equivalent figures, not congruent polyhedra but tetrahedra equivalent (T).

Equivalence (T +) is not transitive. (Cf. 32 (ii) below.)

·1. Polyhedra equivalent (T +) or equivalent (T −) have the same measure.

31. *If the set of measures of intervals is non-Archimedean* (that is if Axiom $\mathbf{K}_1$ fails) *there may be tetrahedra with the same measure which cannot be dissected into a finite number of tetrahedra equivalent* (T) *in pairs.*

Dem. Suppose the measures of intervals constitute the non-Archimedean field of I 27·2. Let T_1 be a regular tetrahedron, with faces of measure s greater than the unit measure. We can construct (using $\mathbf{Q}_1$, see XI 33, I 27·2) a tetrahedron $T_2 = A_2B_2C_2D_2$ with the same measure as T_1, and with A_2B_2, A_2C_2, A_2D_2 mutually perpendicular, wherc $\mu A_2B_2 = \mu A_2C_2 = \sqrt{2t}$, where t is greater than any multiple of the measure s^2. Then $\mu A_2B_2C_2 = t$.

Suppose, if possible, $T_1 \cong T_2$(T +), that is, there are tetrahedra T_{1i}, T_{2j} with $T_1 \equiv \sum_{i=1}^{n} T_{1i}$, $T_2 \equiv \sum_{j=1}^{n} T_{2j}$ and $T_{1i} \cong T_{2i}$ (T) ($i = 1 \cdots n$). (Cf. X 21·1.) Let δ_{1i}, δ_{2j} be the measures of the faces of greatest measure in T_{1i}, T_{2j} resp. Project the edges of the T_{2j} on to $A_2B_2C_2$, then $\mu A_2B_2C_2 = t < 4\Sigma\delta_{2j}$ (XI 38·1). Also it is easily shewn that $\delta_{1j} \leqq s$. (Cf. IV 65·3.)

We consider two cases.

(i) In corresponding tetrahedra T_{1j}, T_{2j} we have $\delta_{2j} \leqq \delta_{1j}$. Suppose this is the case for n pairs.

(ii) In corresponding tetrahedra, $\delta_{2j} > \delta_{1j}$. Suppose this holds for m pairs. In this case δ_{2j} cannot refer to the 'base' of T_{2j}, since the base of T_{2j} has the same measure as the base of T_{1j}. Let T_{1j} be $P_1Q_1R_1S_1$ with base $P_1Q_1R_1$, and let T_{2j} be $P_2Q_2R_2S_2$ with base $P_2Q_2R_2$, and let $S_2P_2Q_2$ be the face of measure δ_{2j}. By XI 37, we can find P_2', Q_2' on S_2P_2, S_2Q_2 resp. so that $P_2'Q_2' \parallel P_2Q_2$ and

$$\mu S_2P_2'Q_2' = \mu S_2P_2Q_2 - \mu P_1Q_1R_1.$$

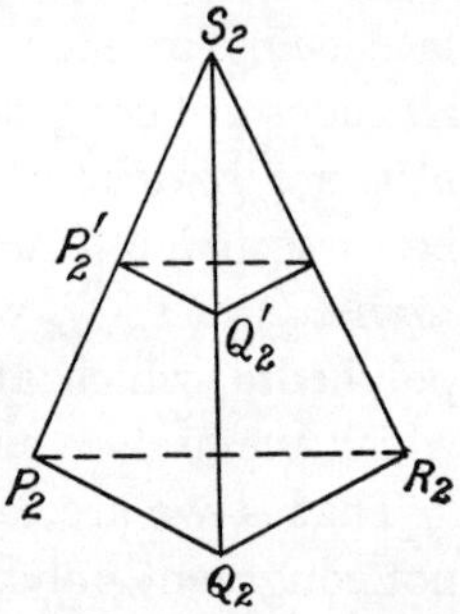

Fig. 143

Then $\mu P_2Q_2Q_2'P_2' \leqq \delta_{1j}$. Let the plane through $P_2'Q_2'$, parallel to $P_2Q_2R_2$, be at 'distance' h from the latter plane. Draw a plane at the same distance h from $P_1Q_1R_1$ to meet S_1P_1, S_1Q_1 resp. in P_1', Q_1'. Let h' be the measure of the (congruent) altitudes of T_{1j}, T_{2j}. Then by XI 36 and similar triangles, we easily find

$$\delta_{2j} \mid \mu S_2P_2'Q_2' \sim h'^2 \mid (h'-h)^2 \sim d_{1j} \mid \mu S_1P_1'Q_1'$$

where $$d_{1j} = \mu S_1P_1Q_1 \leqq \delta_{1j}.$$

Hence $\delta_{2j} \mid \mu P_2Q_2Q_2'P_2' \sim d_{1j} \mid \mu P_1Q_1Q_1'P_1'$ (VII 4·2, 1·3),

and $$\delta_{2j} \,.\, \mu P_1Q_1Q_1'P_1' = d_{1j} \,.\, \mu P_2Q_2Q_2'P_2' \leqq \delta_{1j}^2$$

by VII 20·5 and the inequalities above.

By adjusting the unit of measure, we can secure that the smallest of the $\mu P_1Q_1Q_1'P_1'$ in the various T_{1j} is at least the unit measure; for draw a square wholly inside the smallest figure and take its side for unit measure. After the change, s is still greater than the unit measure, and we have $\delta_{2j} \leqq \delta_{1j}^2$, $s < s^2$.

Thus in case (i) we have $\delta_{2j} \leqq \delta_{1j}$ and in case (ii) $\delta_{2j} \leqq \delta_{1j}^2$. Hence

$$t < 4\Sigma\delta_{2j} \leqq 4n\delta_{1j} + 4m\delta_{1j}^2 \leqq 4ns + 4ms^2 < 4(n+m)s^2.$$

But this is contrary to the definition of t. Hence the Theorem.

§ 4. Basis O C P_1.

32. *Two polyhedra of the same measure are equivalent* (T −).

Dem. (i) For first, if T_1, T_2 be tetrahedra with the same measure, we can dissect them into tetrahedra T_{11}, T_{12}, and T_{21}, T_{22} resp., such that there are tetrahedra T_{31}, T_{32} with $T_{1i} \cong T_{3i}$ (T), $T_{2i} \cong T_{3i}$ (T) ($i = 1, 2$). For let $T_1 = A_1A_2A_3A_4$, $T_2 = B_1B_2B_3B_4$. Let $D_1 = A_1A_2A_3$, $D_2 = B_1B_2B_3$ be faces of greatest measure in T_1 and T_2. Then if $\mu D_1 = \mu D_2$, the corresponding altitudes have the same measure, and $T_1 \cong T_2$ (T). If $\mu D_1 > \mu D_2$, then we can find B_1' with $[B_2B_1B_1']$ and $\mu B_1'B_2B_3 = \mu D_1$. Through B_1 draw a plane parallel to $B_1'B_4B_3$ to meet B_2B_4 in B_4'. Let $B_1B_3B_4'B_2 = T_{31}$, $B_1B_3B_4'B_1' = T_{32}$, $B_1B_3B_4'B_4 = T_{22}$. Then $T_{32} \cong T_{22}$ (T) since $B_1B_4' \parallel B_1'B_4$. Hence follows $T_2 \cong B_1'B_2B_3B_4'$ (T +). Thus $\mu T_1 = \mu T_2 = \mu B_1'B_2B_3B_4'$ and $\mu D_1 = \mu B_1'B_2B_3$. Hence $T_1 \cong B_1'B_2B_3B_4'$ (T).

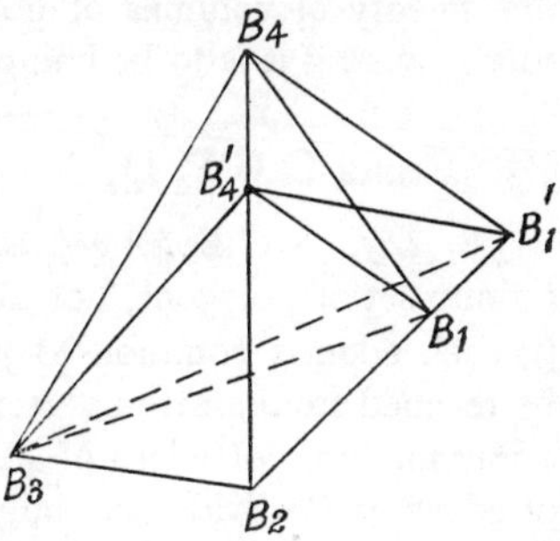

Fig. 144

Now by a suitable plane we can dissect T_1 into tetrahedra T_{11}, T_{12} equivalent (T) to T_{31}, T_{32} resp. Then T_{11}, T_{31}, T_{21} are all equivalent (T), where T_{21} is merely T_{31} regarded as part of T_2; and T_{12}, T_{32}, T_{22} are all equivalent (T).

(ii) Next, if $T_1 \cong T_3$ (T) and $T_2 \cong T_3$ (T) (where the 'base' of T_3 need not be the same face for both equivalences) then $T_1 \cong T_2$ (T −); for (assuming T_1, T_3 have no common inside points, and similarly T_2, T_3) we have $T_1 + T_3 \cong T_3 + T_2$ (T +).

(iii) Thus if $\mu T_1 = \mu T_2$, then by (i) (ii), $T_1 \cong T_2$ (T −).

(iv) If $\mu(T_1 + T_2 + \ldots + T_n) = \mu(T_1' + T_2' + \ldots + T_m')$ then $T_1 + T_2 + \ldots + T_n \cong T_1' + T_2' + \ldots + T_m'$ (T −). This can be shewn like the following case: if $\mu(T_1 + T_2) = \mu T_3$, we can find tetrahedra T_{31}, T_{32} such that

$$T_3 \equiv T_{31} + T_{32}, \quad \mu T_1 = \mu T_{31}, \quad \mu T_2 = \mu T_{32}.$$

Hence

$$T_1 \cong T_{31} \text{ (T −)}, \quad T_2 \cong T_{32} \text{ (T −)}, \quad T_1 + T_2 \cong T_{31} + T_{32} \text{ (T −)}.$$

Hence $$T_1 + T_2 \cong T_3 \text{ (T −)}.$$

(v) Hence finally, using 28, the Theorem follows.

32·1. *Note.* Thus the whole difficulty of the Theory of volumes lies in the consideration of those tetrahedra whose bases have the same measures and whose corresponding altitudes are congruent. By Dehn's Theorem these are not in general equivalent either simply or by addition (in the earlier sense of equivalence). It is for this reason that in the ordinary treatment—as for example in Euclid—'infinitesimals' occur; while they do not occur in the Theory of areas. Thus the Theory of volumes of polyhedra, no less than those of curved solids must, if it is to be complete, rest on the Theory of Integration.

§ 5. Basis O C P_1 Q_2.

33. *Def.* An '*Euler polyhedron*' P is a set of points consisting of a finite set of polygons, not all coplanar, and their insides, such that (i) each edge is common to just two polygons, (ii) each vertex can be reached from a given vertex (and therefore from each vertex) by a way made up of edges of P. (iii) Any simple polygon p made up of edges of P, divides the polygons of P into two sets such that any way, whose points are on P, from any point inside a polygon of one set to a point inside a polygon of the other set, meets p.

34. If $A_1 A_2 \ldots A_n$ be a convex plane polygon and V a point not in its plane, then $\mu A_1 \hat{V} A_2 + \mu A_2 \hat{V} A_3 + \ldots + \mu A_{n-1} \hat{V} A_n + \mu A_n \hat{V} A_1 < 2\pi$ (IV 93, X 38).

35. *Def.* A '*regular polyhedron*' is a convex Euler polyhedron whose faces are congruent regular polygons and whose dihedral angles are congruent.

·1. The number of polygons with the same vertex is the same for each vertex.

·2. There cannot be more than five types of regular polyhedra.

Dem. The sum of the measures of the angles at a vertex is less than 2π (34), while the measure of an angle of a regular n-gon is $(n-2)\pi/n$ (X 38). Thus if r of these meet at a vertex then $(n-2)\pi/n < 2\pi/r$. Hence $1/n + 1/r > \frac{1}{2}$. But $n > 2$, $r > 2$. Thus the only possible values of n and r are

n	3	3	4	5	3
r	3	4	3	3	5

36. *There are just five types of regular polyhedra and they can be constructed by* abceq$_2$.

Sketch of Dem. A *cube* ($n=4$, $r=3$) can be constructed, and a regular *tetrahedron* ($n=3$, $r=3$) by drawing diagonals of faces of a cube; a regular '*octahedron*' ($n=3$, $r=4$) by joining mid-points of adjacent faces of a cube. A regular '*icosahedron*' ($n=3$, $r=5$) can be constructed thus: hold a cube with a face horizontal and a vertical face in front. Draw an interval from the centre of the top face to the right, parallel to an edge, and a congruent interval from the centre of the right-hand face, parallel to an edge and from back to front. If $2a$ be the measure of an edge of the cube and x the measure of the intervals drawn, the interval joining their ends will have a measure whose square is $(a-x)^2+x^2+a^2=2(a^2-ax+x^2)$. If we take x so that this equals $(2x)^2$, we shall have $x^2+ax-a^2=0$ and hence $x=\frac{1}{2}(-a+a\sqrt{5})$, and the interval can be constructed by $\mathbf{abcq_2}$. The joining interval last drawn will then have a measure double that of the intervals first drawn. The doubles of the intervals first drawn, and the joining interval give three edges of the icosahedron. This can now be constructed. Joining the mid-points of adjacent faces of the icosahedron we get the '*dodecahedron*' ($n=5$, $r=3$).

CHAPTER XIII

CONTINUITY

Introductory Remarks

We now reach the climax of our investigation. So far we have not assumed that our lines are continua, that is, we have not assumed that there is a one-to-one correspondence, preserving order, between the points of a line and the real numbers. We shall now secure this property by assuming a continuity Axiom, which roughly comes to this:—If all the points of a line are divided into two sets (not empty), and no point of one set is between two points of the other set, then there is a point of the line (which may be in either set) which is between any point of one set and any point of the other set. This, in a weakened form, is Axiom **K**.

We have seen that from **O**, **P**, $\mathbf{Q}_0$ and Pappus' Theorem we can introduce congruence by definition. We shew in this chapter that from **O**, **P**, **K** we can deduce $\mathbf{Q}_0$ and Pappus' Theorem; we can indeed deduce the stronger Axiom **Q** and thence all the Theory of the preceding chapters. (We have seen that even $\mathbf{Q}_1$ does not follow from **O**, **P**, $\mathbf{Q}_0$ and Pappus' Theorem alone.) Further this deduction is still possible if we weaken **P** to $\mathbf{P}_2'$ (see 11 below). Further $\mathbf{K}_1$, which is needed to complete the Theory of areas, follows from **K**; we can therefore say, *all Euclidean Geometry follows from* $\mathbf{OP}_2'\mathbf{K}$.

If we omit $\mathbf{P}_2'$, we can still shew from **O**, **K** the existence of coplanar lines which do not meet, and our choice is between the Euclidean and the Hyperbolic Geometry. But if only Axioms **O** are assumed, it is possible for all lines in a plane to meet each other.

Suppose now, instead of introducing congruence by definition, we introduce it, as in Chapter IV, by Axioms. We find then that we can weaken **P** to $\mathbf{P}_0$ (see 19 below) and of the Congruence Axioms we need only assume **C** I—V. *All Euclidean Geometry* (*including* **Q**) *follows from* **O**, $\mathbf{P}_0$, **K**, **C** I—V.

At this stage it is easy to shew that both sets of Axioms which suffice for Euclidean Geometry, viz. $\mathbf{OP_2'K}$ and $\mathbf{OP_0\,K\,CI}$—V are consistent and complete.

§ 1. **Basis $\mathbf{O_p}$ K or O K** where Axiom **K** is:

Ax. K. There is at least one interval *AB* such that, if all points of it be divided into any two sets of points [*M*], [*N*] satisfying the following conditions:

(i) **each set contains at least two points,**

(ii) **the sets have no common points,**

(iii) **if X is in one set and Y_1, Y_2 in the other, we cannot have $[Y_1XY_2]$,**

then there is a point *C* satisfying [*MCN*] for every $M, N \neq C$.

1. Such a division is possible, for if D satisfy $[ADB]$ then $[M] = A^{\vdash}D$ and $[N] = D^{\dashv}B$ satisfy the conditions. In **K**, we are not told in the hypothesis that the division is effected by such a point D, and of course the point C in the conclusion of **K** might be in either $[M]$ or $[N]$. The point C is clearly unique.

·1. *Def.* If $A^{\vdash}B$ or $A^{-}B$ is divided into sets satisfying the conditions of Ax. **K**, the sets are called '*D-sets.*'

2. *Axiom* **K** *is still true when the interval AB of* **K** *is replaced by any interval PQ, open or closed, or by any line or ray.*

Dem. (i) Let $P = A$, $PQ \neq AB$, $[QBR]$. If $A^{\vdash}Q$ be divided into D-sets, $[M]$ and $[N]$, the joins of R to the points of $[M]$, $[N]$ meet $A^{\vdash}B$ in two sets $[M']$, $[N']$ which clearly satisfy conditions (i) and (ii) of **K**. Further if N_1', N_2' be points of $[N']$, and M' a point of $[M']$, and RM' meet AQ in M, and so on, then $[N_1'M'N_2']$ would imply $[N_1MN_2]$ (II 12·7), contrary to condition (iii) of Axiom **K**. Thus $[M']$, $[N']$ satisfy all conditions of Axiom **K**, and thus there is a point C' on AB with $[M'C'N']$ for all $M', N' \neq C'$. But RC' meets $A^{-}Q$ in a point C, say, such that $[MCN]$ for all $M, N \neq C$ (II 12·7).

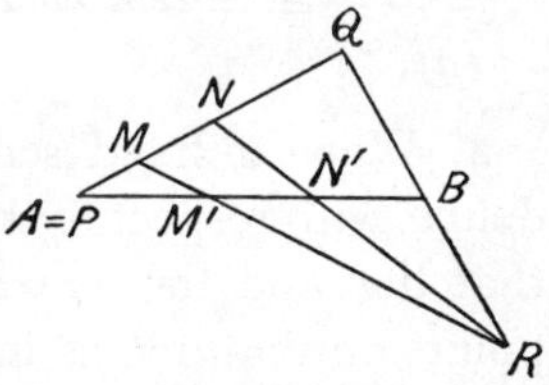

Fig. 145

(ii) Let $P=A$, and Q be any point on AB, and let R be not on AB. By (i) the Theorem holds for $A \vdash\!\dashv R$ and thus, since $AQ \neq AR$, it holds by (i) for $A \vdash\!\dashv Q$.

(iii) Let $P \neq A$, $Q \neq B$ then, by (i), (ii), the Theorem holds for $A \vdash\!\dashv P$, and so for $P \vdash\!\dashv Q$, and hence for any interval.

Next let any open interval AB be divided into D-sets $[M]$, $[N]$. If M_j, N_i be points of $[M]$, $[N]$, resp., then either $[AM_1N_1]$ or $[AN_1M_1]$, say the first. Then $[AM_1N_i]$ for all N_i, since $[AN_iM_1]$ $[AM_1N_1]$ would give $[N_iM_1N_1]$. Similarly $[AM_jN_i]$, since $[AN_iM_j]$ $[AM_1N_i]$ would give $[M_1N_iM_j]$. Hence also $[M_jN_iB]$. Now let $[\overline{M}]$ be $[M]$ together with A, and $[\overline{N}]$ be $[N]$ together with B, then $[\overline{M}]$, $[\overline{N}]$ are D-sets for $A \vdash\!\dashv B$. Hence the Theorem for open intervals.

As to the line AB, if A be in $[M]$, B in $[N]$, then $A \vdash\!\dashv B$ is divided into D-sets. Similarly for rays.

Sensed Lines

3. *Take a fixed sense on a line* (III 16), *then if there be two non-empty sets of points* $[P]$, $[Q]$ *on an interval AB of the line, and* $[P]$, $[Q]$ *have no common points, and if each point of* $[P]$ *precedes each point of* $[Q]$, *then there is a point C such that* $X \prec C$ *if* X $(\neq C)$ *is in* $[P]$, *and* $C \prec Y$ *if* Y $(\neq C)$ *is in* $[Q]$.

Dem. Let $[M]$ be all points of $A \vdash\!\dashv B$ preceding at least one point of $[Q]$, and $[N]$ the other points of that interval. The Theorem follows by Axiom **K**.

Note that if $[M]$ is the point A only, and $[N]$ the rest of the interval, then $A=C$, but the Theorem as stated still holds.

·1. *The Theorem holds for points on a line or open interval or ray.*

4. When a fixed sense has been taken on a line, we can define, with respect to that sense, a '*bounded class*' of points on that line and the '*maximum*' and '*upper bound*' of a class of points on that line as in I 8·6, 8·7, 18.

5. *If on a line with a fixed sense,* $[X]$ *be a bounded non-empty set of points, then* $[X]$ *has a unique upper bound.*

Dem. If $[X]$ has a maximum point, that is its upper bound. In the contrary case, let $[M]$ be the set of points $[X]$ together with all those which precede at least one X, and let $[N]$ be the set which succeed all the X. Then $[M]$, $[N]$ are not empty and each point of the line is in one or the other, and each M precedes each N. Hence there is a point C with $M_1 \prec C$, $C \prec N_1$ whenever M_1 $(\neq C)$ is in $[M]$, N_1 $(\neq C)$ in $[N]$ (3·1). But $[X]$, and hence $[M]$, has no maximum. Hence $M_1 \prec C$, and all X precede C. Also if $Y \prec C$, then Y is in $[M]$, and thus Y precedes some X, since $[X]$ has no maximum. Hence C is the upper bound of $[X]$, and it is unique (1).

5·1. *The set of points on a sensed line have Dedekind continuity with respect to the relation* $\prec$ (I 18·2).

Coplanar Rays and Continuity

6. *If there be two sets of coplanar rays* $[s]$, $[t]$ *from a point* C *such that each set contains at least two rays, and no pair in* $[s]$ *separate any pair in* $[t]$, *then there are two rays* l, l_1 *from* C *which separate every* s $(\neq l, l_1)$ *from every* t $(\neq l, l_1)$ (cf. III 24·1).

Dem. If there be only two rays in $[s]$, the Theorem is trivial. Let then s_1, s_2 be two rays in $[s]$ not in the same line, and let A, B, be on s_1, s_2, resp. Suppose a ray t_0 of $[t]$ is in the angle between s_1 and s_2, then t_0 meets $A{-}B$ in E say and all the t meet $A{-}B$ (III 24·4).

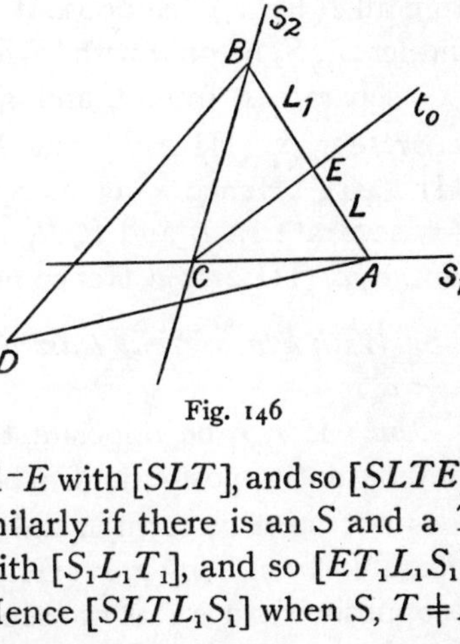

Fig. 146

Let $[S]$, $[T]$ be the set of points where $A{\vdash}E$ is met by the s, t resp. If there is an S and a T on $A{-}E$, the conditions of Theorem 2 hold and thus there is a point L on $A{-}E$ with $[SLT]$, and so $[SLTE]$, for all S, T $(\neq L)$ on $A{-}E$. Similarly if there is an S and a T on $B{-}E$, there is L_1 on $B{-}E$ with $[S_1L_1T_1]$, and so $[ET_1L_1S_1]$, for all S_1, T_1 $(\neq L_1)$ on $B{-}E$. Hence $[SLTL_1S_1]$ when $S, T \neq L$ and $S_1, T \neq L_1$.

If there is no T on $A{-}E$, there is some T on $B{-}E$ and we have $[SLT_1L_1S_1]$ for all $T_1 \neq L$ and S_1, $T_1 \neq L_1$, where $L = E$, and S is on $A{-}E$ and S_1, T_1 on $B{-}E$.

The rays $[CL$ and $[CL_1$ are the rays l, l_1 required.

If no ray of $[t]$ is in an angle formed by two rays of $[s]$, and no ray of $[s]$ is in an angle formed by two rays of $[t]$, we join a point on an s to a point on any t not opposite to that s, and proceed as above to find one of the rays l. The other is then easily found.

Or we may draw a triangle ABD with C inside and consider the meets of the triangle with the rays.

Parallel Rays

7. *If a be any line, C any point not on it, and $Ca = \alpha$, then two rays r, r_1 go from C in α which do not meet a and which separate all other rays not meeting a from all rays which meet a.*

Dem. If a ray s meet a, its opposite ray s' will not. Thus rays of both kinds exist. Let $[s]$ be the set of meeting rays, $[t]$ those not meeting a. Two t cannot separate two s, for if t, t' separated s, s', one of them would be in $\widehat{ss'}$ (III 24·3) and so would meet a. The conditions of Theorem 6 thus hold and hence there are two rays r, r_1 which separate all $s\,(\neq r, r_1)$ from all $t\,(\neq r, r_1)$. Suppose if possible that r met a in R, say, and let S_1, S_2 be on a with $[S_1RS_2]$. Let $[CS_i = s_i$. Then since r, r_1 separate s_1 from t, and s_2 from t, therefore r, r_1 do not separate s_1, s_2 (III 24·5), and since r is in $\widehat{s_1s_2}$ so must r_1 be (III 24·4). Hence r_1 meets $S_1\text{-}S_2$ in R_1 say. But then since r, r_1 separate s_1, t, and R, R_1 are in $S_1\text{-}S_2$, t must meet $R\text{-}R_1$, cont. hyp. (III 24·3). Hence neither r nor r_1 can meet a.

8. *With hyp. of 7, at least one line through C in α does not meet a.*

Dem. If r, r_1 be opposite, their line does not meet a. If they be not opposite, and r' be the ray opposite to r, then r' does not meet a; for if it did, then a ray s in $\widehat{r_1r'}$, not being separated from r' by r, r_1 (III 24·6), also meets a, and so does its opposite s' since s' is not separated from r' by r, r_1 (III 24·3). But this contradicts II 4·3. Hence the line of r does not meet a.

·1. *Def.* The rays r, r_1 of 7 are '*parallel*' to a.

·2. All rays in $\widehat{rr_1}$ meet a. For r' does not meet a.

8·3. All points of a lie in one of the four regions into which the lines of r, r_1 separate α (assuming these lines distinct) (III 20).

·4. If r, r_1 be opposite rays, all lines on α through C, save the line of r, meet a.

·5. *Def. and The.* The set of points X satisfying $[CXQ]$, where Q is any point on a, is the convex region '*between*' a and the parallel rays from C to a (·3, III 1·1, 2, 18).

·6. *Note.* Thus from $\mathbf{O}_p$, **K** or **O**, **K** we have shewn the existence of coplanar non-meeting lines. (We shall see later that **K** is essential for this proof.) The proof of VIII 49 shews that **O**, **K** do not suffice to shew there is *but one* parallel to a given line through a given point. Thus these Axioms hold in Euclidean and in Hyperbolic Geometry, though not in the Elliptic Geometry where there are no parallel lines. See Chapter XV.

The Non-Euclidean Case

§ 2. Basis O K.

9. *If r, r_1 be parallel rays to a from C, and be not opposite, and $Ca = \alpha$, then any line b in α through X, a point in the region between r, r_1 and a, meets r or r_1 or a.*

Dem. Let O be any point not in α; let the plane Oa meet the half-planes* $\{OC, r\}$, $\{OC, r_1\}$ in c, c_1 resp., then we shew first that X is inside the trihedral angle Γ formed by OC, c, c_1. For c, c_1 are coplanar with a and do not meet a (II 27) since r, r_1 do not. But all rays in $\widehat{cc_1}$ do meet a; for if s in $\widehat{cc_1}$ do not, then the half-plane $\{OC, s\}$ meets α in a ray which does not meet a (II 27); but $\{OC, s\}$ is in the dihedral angle with edge OC and faces $\{OC, r\}$, $\{OC, r_1\}$, and hence $\{OC, s\}$ meets α in a ray in $\widehat{rr_1}$ (III 26·2·3) and hence in a ray which meets a (8·2). This contradiction shews that all rays in $\widehat{cc_1}$ meet a, and hence c, c_1 are parallel to a. Hence any ray from O which meets a is in $\widehat{cc_1}$, and hence X is inside Γ (8·5 and XII 1·3).

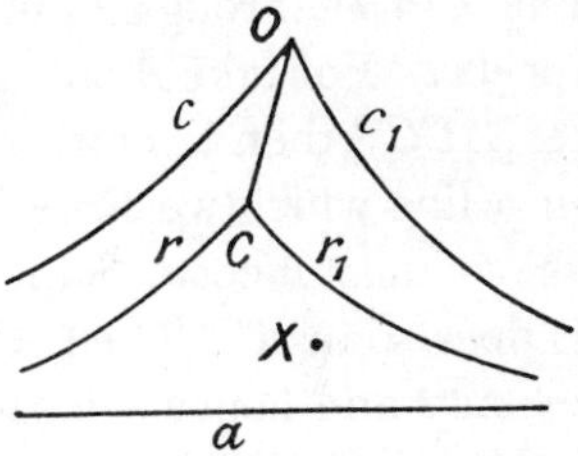

Fig. 147

* The half-plane $\{OC, r\}$ is that bounded by OC in which r lies.

Hence the plane Ob, which passes through X, meets two faces, or one face and an edge of Γ (XII 1·4). If then we shew that any ray from O in a face of Γ meets a or r or r_1, the Theorem follows by II 27.

We know that any ray in $\widehat{cc_1}$ meets a. Also any ray s from O in the face Or meets r, for join s to a point D on r_1', the ray opposite to r_1, then the plane Ds meets the face Oa in a ray (XII 1·5) which ray must meet a in A, say; and since A is inside $\widehat{rr_1}$, and D outside, therefore A–D meets r, and hence so does Ds and hence so does s.

Similarly for the face Or_1, and the Theorem follows.

The Euclidean Case

10. *If in the plane* $\alpha = Ca$, *the two rays from* C, *parallel to* a, *are in one line* c, *then any line in* α *which meets one of* a, c *meets the other.*

Dem. Let O be not in α and let l be the meet of Oc, Oa. First, any line m ($\neq l$) through O in Oa meets a. For Cm meets α in b, say, and b meets a, since $b \neq c$ (8·4). Hence m meets a (II 27). Next, any line n ($\neq l$) through O in Oc meets c. For take A on a and let $[ACC']$, then $C'n$ meets Oa in a line which we have just shewn must meet a. Suppose it does so in A'. Then A'–C' meets c (III 11), and hence $C'n$ meets c and hence n meets c (II 27).

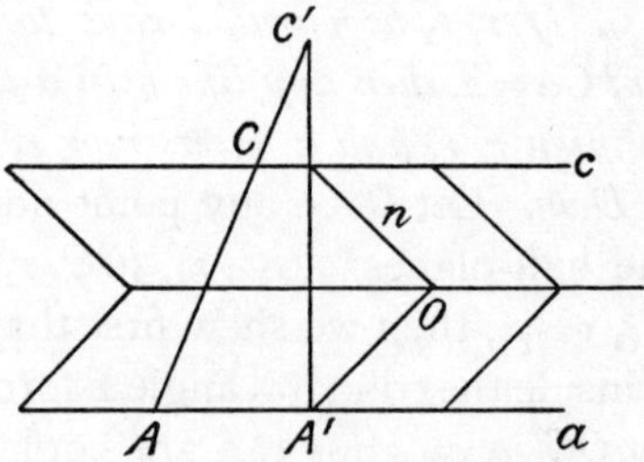

Fig. 148

Hence finally, if b is any line in α through a point A on a, then Ob meets Oc in a line which meets c, and hence b meets c. And if d is any line through a point D on c, then Od meets Oa in a line which meets a, and hence d meets a.

11. *Axioms* **O K P$_2'$** *imply* **P**; *Axiom* **P$_2'$** of Chapter VI is:

P$_2'$. *Given any line on any plane, there is a point on the plane and not on the line, through which not more than one line can be drawn not meeting the given line, though coplanar with it.* (The point may be different for different lines.)

Dem. Let a be any line on any plane α, and let A be the point mentioned in $\mathbf{P}_2'$, and let b be the parallel to a through A.

If C be not between a and b (III 11·01), suppose, if possible, two rays r, r_1, not opposite, go from C parallel to a; then they will be parallel to b, for any line through C which meets one of a, b meets the other (10). Now either b is in the region between r, r_1, a, or a is in the region between r, r_1, b, as is easily shewn; but this contradicts 9. Hence the rays from C, parallel to a, colline.

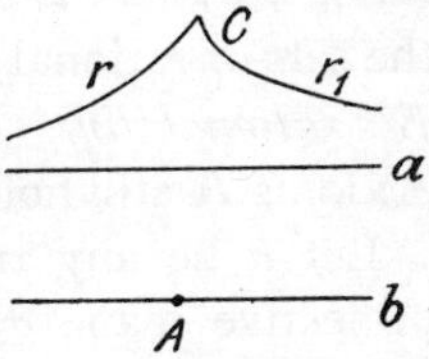

Fig. 149

If C' be between a and b, let C be on the opposite side of a from C', then C is not between a and b (III 11), and hence there is but one parallel line d to a through C. But C' is not between a and d, and hence there is but one parallel line through C' to a, by the first part of the proof.

We now shew that we cannot replace $\mathbf{P}_2'$ by the weaker Axioms given in Chapter VI.

12. *Axioms* **O K** *with* $\mathbf{P}_1$ *or* $\mathbf{P}_2$ *or* $\mathbf{P}_3$ *or* $\mathbf{P}_0'$ *or* $\mathbf{P}_1'$ *do not suffice to shew* **P**.

Dem. Consider Euclidean Geometry but take as 'points' those Euclidean points on one side only of a fixed plane α. Then in at least one 'plane,' viz. any plane parallel to α, there is but one parallel through any 'point' to any 'line'; and in any 'plane' there is at least one 'line,' viz. any line parallel to α, to which there is but one parallel through any 'point.' Hence $\mathbf{P}_3$, $\mathbf{P}_1'$ and so $\mathbf{P}_1$, $\mathbf{P}_2$, $\mathbf{P}_0'$ hold. But **P** is clearly false for our 'points.'

13. *In the presence of* **O**, *Ax.* **K** *is essential for the proof of the existence of non-meeting coplanar lines.* (Cf. 8.)

Dem. Construct the projective Geometry of the real field thus: A '*projective point*' shall be the ratios of four real numbers $x : y : z : w$, not all zero. A '*projective plane*' shall be the set of projective points satisfying

$$lx + my + nz + pw = 0 \quad \ldots\ldots\ldots\ldots\ldots\ldots(1),$$

for some fixed reals l, m, n, p, not all zero. A '*projective line*' shall be the meet of two projective planes. The properties of linear equations shew that all Axs. **A** of VI 40 hold.

Now consider the '*rational points*,' i.e. those for which the ratios $x : y : z : w$ are all rational, and the '*rational planes*,' i.e. the sets of rational points satisfying (1) with l, m, n, p rational. A '*rational line*' is the meet of two rational planes. The Axioms **A** still hold for these rational points, lines and planes.

Let a be any transcendental number (I 28·6·8), then the projective plane σ through the projective points $(a, 0, 0, 1)$, $(0, a^2, 0, 1)$, $(0, 0, a^3, 1)$ contains no rational points; and hence we can order the rational points with respect to the plane σ, as we did in VIII 19·1 with respect to the plane α there.

Then Axioms **O** hold for our rational points, while Ax. **K** clearly does not. And coplanar rational lines *always meet* in a rational point.

A Sufficient Basis for Euclidean Geometry

§ 3. Basis O P_2' K.

14. *On the basis of* **O**, $\mathbf{P}_2'$, **K** *we can introduce congruence by definition, so that all the Theorems of this book that deal with Euclidean Geometry can be shewn without further assumptions.*

Dem. By 11 we have **P**. Further from **O**, **P** with the definition of $+, \times$, in VIII 1, 6, it follows that the points of a line form a fully-ordered quasi-field (VIII 23) and that a coordinate frame can be set up in which a plane has an equation of the first degree (VIII 18·1). By Axiom **K** the quasi-field has Dedekind continuity with respect to the relation $\prec$ (5·1). Hence the quasi-field is a field F and a continuum (I 26·5, 19·4). Hence

a line is a continuum,

and since F is a field we have Pappus' Theorem (VIII 11·1). Further if $Y > 0$ is in F, we can find X in F with $X^2 = Y$ (I 25·3). Hence our field F has at any rate the properties of Ω_0 of VIII 28. Now in our coordinate frame a point exists whose coordinates are any given elements of F, hence Ax. **Q**. holds (VIII 28). Hence as in VIII 29 ff. we can define a congruence relation, and all the Theorems of Chapter IV hold for this relation. Further, Axiom $\mathbf{K}_1$ is now true, since it follows from $\mathbf{K}$ (I 25·8), and the Theory of areas and constructions can now be completed (XI 30, IX 19).

Consider now Axioms $\mathbf{Q}$ and $\mathbf{Q}_1$ of Chapter V. By the definitions of 'distance' and 'sphere,' the equation of a sphere, centre (a, b, c) and radius r, is

$$(x-a)^2+(y-b)^2+(z-c)^2=r^2;$$

any point (x', y', z'), on a line through (a, b, c) with direction numbers (l, m, n), has coordinates $x'=a'+ls$, $y'=b'+ms$, $z'=c'+ns$ where $l^2+m^2+n^2=1$ and $s=$ distance of $(x'y'z')$ from (xyz). This line meets the sphere, if at all, in points where

$$(a'-a+ls)^2+(b'-b+ms)^2+(c'-c+ns)^2=r^2,$$

that is, where

$$s^2+2\left[l(a'-a)+m(b'-b)+n(c'-c)\right]s + (a'-a)^2+(b'-b)^2+(c'-c)^2-r^2=0.$$

So far we have only assumed VIII 29, 30. Now bring in the fact that every positive element in our field F has a square root in the field. The discriminant of the quadratic above is certainly positive if

$$(a'-a)^2+(b'-b)^2+(c'-c)^2<r^2,$$

and then the quadratic has roots in the field F. Hence a line through any point inside a sphere meets the sphere.

If now any circle be given and we take any point P on the perpendicular to its plane, through its centre, then P is equidistant from all points on the circle (Thes. of Chapter IV), and hence all points on the circle are on a sphere, and all points inside the circle, inside that sphere. Hence $\mathbf{Q}_1$ follows, and since Axioms $\mathbf{O}$, $\mathbf{C}$, $\mathbf{P}$ hold, therefore $\mathbf{Q}$ follows (IX 10).

15. *There is a* (1, 1) *correspondence between the points of any sensed line OU and the real numbers, such that if x_1, x_2 correspond to P_1, P_2, then $x_1<x_2$ if and only if $P_1(\prec OU)P_2$.*

Dem. We can construct on OU, by Chapter VIII, the points whose coordinates are rational in the scale OU, and the coordinates of the points satisfy the order condition stated (VIII § 2). Between any two points of OU lies a point with rational coordinate ($\mathbf{K}_1$, I 26·3). If x be any real number, let

$[r]$ be the set of rationals less than x, and $[P]$ the set of points corresponding to them; $[P]$ has a unique upper bound (5); we make this correspond to x.

If Q be any point on OU, let $[P]$ be the set of points with rational coordinates $[r]$ that precede Q in the sense OU; $[r]$ defines a real number x, and to x corresponds Q. For Q is the upper bound of $[P]$, since points with rational coordinates lie between Q and any other point Q' on OU.

The conditions on order now easily follow.

Consistency and Completeness of the Axioms

16. *Axioms* **O**, $\mathbf{P}_2'$, **K** *are consistent.*

Dem. Let F be the real field and let a 'point' be an ordered triad (xyz) of elements of the real field. Just as in VIII 38 we can define 'line' and 'order' and then, as there, Axioms **O**, **P**, hold. But here, since F is the real field, Axiom **K** also holds. Thus **O**, $\mathbf{P}_2'$, **K** are consistent provided that the properties of the real field are consistent. But in Chapter I we constructed the real field from the natural numbers. Hence our Theorem is proved if we assume that the basic properties (e.g. the statements in I 12) of the natural numbers are consistent; and this we shall assume.

Note. Those who believe, with Russell, that the properties of the natural numbers can be deduced from logic by logic, need only assume the consistency of the principles of logic. *Their* consistency of course cannot be *proved.*

17. *Axioms* **O**, **P**, **K**, **C**, **Q** *are consistent* (16, 14).

18. *Axioms* **O**, $\mathbf{P}_2'$, **K** *are a complete set* (I 7).

Dem. If S and S_1 be two classes of 'points' satisfying these Axioms, we can set up coordinates in each class so that to each point corresponds an ordered triad of real numbers (15); and if $[P_1P_2P_3]$ be true for three points in S, then $x_1 < x_2 < x_3$ or $x_1 > x_2 > x_3$ or $x_1 = x_2 = x_3$ and similarly for the y, z (by 15). Make each point in S correspond to that point in S_1 with the same coordinates; then we have a (1, 1) correspondence between the points of S and S_1 such that, if P_i corresponds to Q_i, then $[P_1P_2P_3]$ and $[Q_1Q_2Q_3]$ imply each other.

Thus any statement which involves only points and order is either inconsistent with **O**, $\mathbf{P}_2'$, **K**, or its denial is inconsistent with them. But if we drop Ax. **K**, for example, then **O**, $\mathbf{P}_2'$ is not a complete system, for neither Theorem 15 nor its denial is inconsistent with **O**, $\mathbf{P}_2'$.

The Influence of the Axioms of Congruence

§ 4. Basis O $\mathbf{P}_0$ K C I—V.

19. *If instead of introducing congruence by definition, we take the congruence of point couples as undefined, and introduce Axioms* **O**, **K**, **C** I—V, *we may weaken the parallel Axiom to* $\mathbf{P}_0$, *and then from the total set will follow* **P**, **C**, **Q**, $\mathbf{K}_1$ *and all Theorems of this book that deal with Euclidean Geometry can be shewn without further assumptions.*

We shew this in successive steps.

Axiom $\mathbf{P}_0$ is: *There is at least one line a and at least one point A, not on a, such that not more than one line can be drawn through A coplanar with but not meeting a.*

·1. **O**, **K**, **C** I—IV imply that the measures of intervals form a continuous set of magnitudes (I 21·2, IV 13).

·2. **O**, **K**, **C** I—IV imply **M**, for if AB be any interval, an interval exists whose measure is $\frac{1}{2}\mu AB$ (I 21·5; cf. IV. 14·5).

·3. **O**, **K**, **C** I—V imply $\mathbf{C}_p$ (·2 and V 13, 14).

·4. If AXB be a 'semicircle' centre O on AB, and *if* the points $\neq A, B$ of the semicircle be divided into two sets $[P]$, $[Q]$ such that if P is in one set, Q in the other then $\mu A\hat{O}P < \mu A\hat{O}Q$, *then* there is a point L on the semicircle such that all points of $[P]$, $[Q]$ satisfy $\mu A\hat{O}P \leqq \mu A\hat{O}L \leqq \mu A\hat{O}Q$.

Dem. Let Q be any point of $[Q]$, then the lines joining O to points of $[P]$ meet $A\vdash\!\!\dashv Q$ in points $[P']$ say, and the lines joining O to points Q_1 of $[Q]$ satisfying $\mu A\hat{O}Q_1 \leqq \mu A\hat{O}Q$, also meet $A\vdash\!\!\dashv Q$ in points $[Q']$ say. Axiom **K** applied to $[P']$, $[Q']$ gives the Theorem.

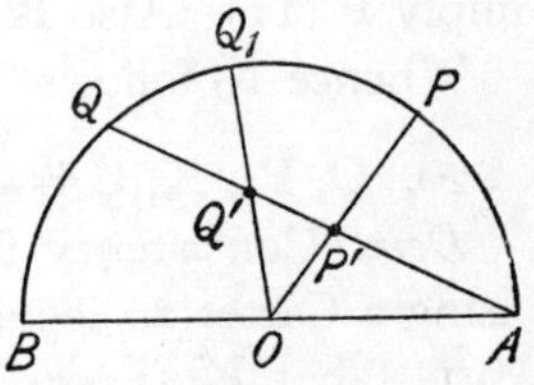

Fig. 150

19·41. If L be on a circle centre O, we can find a point L' on the circle and on a given side of OL, such that $\mu LL' <$ given measure σ.

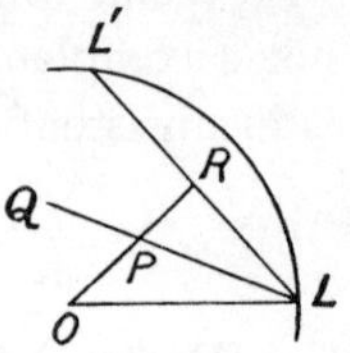
Fig. 151

Dem. Let Q be on the given side of OL, and on $[LQ$ take P so that $\mu LP < \frac{1}{2}\sigma$. Let $LR \perp OP$, R on OP, and take L' so that $LR \simeq RL'$, $[LRL']$; then by $\mathbf{C}_p$, L' is on the circle and on the given side of OL, and $LP \simeq L'P$, $\mu LL' < \mu LP + \mu L'P < \sigma$.

·5. **O**, **K**, $\mathbf{C}_p$ imply **Q**.

Dem. Suppose the circle C, centre O, goes through A inside and B outside the circle C', centre O', where A, B are on OO'. Consider the points of C on one side of OO'; divide them into two sets; (i) the set $[X]$ of points inside C', (ii) the set $[Y]$ of points outside or on C'; then $\mu A\hat{O}X < \mu A\hat{O}Y$ (IV 66·1). Hence (·4) there is a point L on the circle C, on the chosen side of OO', such that $\mu A\hat{O}X \leqq \mu A\hat{O}L \leqq \mu A\hat{O}Y$ for all X, Y in sets $[X]$, $[Y]$ resp.

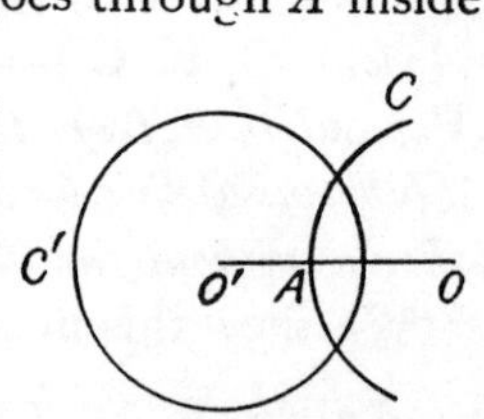
Fig. 152

We shew that $O'L$ is a radius of C'. For if r' is the measure of the radius of C', and $\mu O'L < r'$, let $r' - \mu O'L = \sigma$. On the circle C and on the other side of OL from that in which O' lies, we can find L' so that $\mu LL' < \sigma$ (·41); then $\mu A\hat{O}L' > \mu A\hat{O}L$, $\mu O'L' \leqq \mu O'L + \mu LL' < \mu O'L + \sigma = r'$. Hence L' is inside C', contrary to the above. Similarly $\mu O'L > r'$ is impossible. Hence $O'L$ is a radius of C'. Hence C, C' meet on each side of OO'.

·6. Thus **O**, **K**, **C** I—V imply $\mathbf{C}_p$ and **Q** (·3, ·5) and hence **C** (V 10). Also **O**, $\mathbf{P}_0$, **C** imply $\mathbf{P}_2'$ (VI 1·2), and **O**, **K**, $\mathbf{P}_2'$ imply **P** (11). Also **K**, **C** I—IV give $\mathbf{K}_1$ (I 25·8).

Whence 19 follows.

20. **O**, $\mathbf{P}_0$, **K**, **C** I—V *are consistent and complete.*

Dem. Consistency follows from 17, completeness as in 18, using a Cartesian rectangular frame (VIII 42).

·1. That **K** *is independent of the other Axioms* follows from the work in VIII 28ff., taking Ω_0 to be the field obtained from the integers by the operations of addition, subtraction, multiplication, division and the fifth operation $\sqrt{1+a^2}$, where a is any number of the field already found.

If we adjoin the operation $\sqrt{a}$, where a is any positive number already found, it follows that **K** *is also independent of* **Q**.

By VIII 49 ff., $\mathbf{P}_0$ *is independent of the other Axioms.*

21. *From* **O**, $\mathbf{P}_0$, **K**, **C** I—V *it follows that areas, volumes and angular measures form continuous systems of magnitude* (19·1·4, noting that, by definition, areas and volumes are the measures of intervals).

·1. *The measures of intervals can be put into* (1, 1) *correspondence with the positive real numbers, in such a way that the unit interval corresponds to the number* 1, *and if measures a, b correspond to the real numbers x, y then the measure $a+b$ corresponds to the number $x+y$, and the measure ab to the number xy.*
Using VII 21·8 this can be applied to the theory of proportion.

22. It follows from the above work that, in the presence of **O**, **K**, **C** I—V, *the two rays from any point parallel to any line colline or not, according as the two rays from a fixed given point parallel to a fixed given line colline or not.*

* * * * * *

We have thus succeeded in erecting Euclidean Geometry on an excessively narrow basis. If we proceeded further we should have to define the length of an arc of a circle, and by means of it introduce the ordinary angular measure. This work depends essentially on Ax. **K** and is best left to Analysis.

The main theme of the book is now ended. The remainder is of the nature of an appendix designed to illustrate one or two interesting points.

CHAPTER XIV

CONGRUENCE AS THE SOLE UNDEFINED RELATION BETWEEN POINTS

Introductory Remarks

We have seen that if we take as our undefined relation, the 'between' relation for points, we are able to introduce a congruence relation by definition. Pieri* has shewn that Euclidean Geometry can also be erected, if we take, as our sole undefined relation, the three-termed relation between points A, B, C which has the properties of the relation expressed in our earlier theory by the phrase '(A, B) is congruent to (A, C).' We shall see that it is possible to define the 'between' relation in terms of this relation, but that when this is done, we are compelled to assume Axioms on the 'between' relation analogous to those in Chapter II. These Axioms could of course now be expressed in terms of congruence only, but such statements would be excessively complicated. The reduction to the 'congruence' relation is thus not so complete as the reduction to the 'between' relation.

When we have shewn that our earlier Axioms follow from those of Pieri†, we shall deal with the theory of motion, particularly of Euclidean motions. In this chapter we shall often leave the details of the proofs to the reader.

§ 1. *Undefined Entities*

We take as undefined entities, a class of elements called 'points,' denoted by Latin capitals and a certain three-termed relation between points, indicated by the phrase 'AC is congruent to AB' or by the symbol $AC \simeq AB$. It is not assumed in this relation that A, B, C are distinct. (Note that if $D \neq A$, the relation $AC \simeq DB$ is not yet introduced.)

* Pieri, "La Geometria Elementare," *Mem. di Mat. e di Fisica della Soc. Italiana delle Scienze*, 1908, XV, p. 345.

† The set of Axioms we give is not quite identical with Pieri's set.

Ax. I. $AB \simeq AB$.

Ax. II. If $AB \simeq AC$ then $AC \simeq AB$.

Ax. III. If $AB \simeq AC$ and $AC \simeq AD$ then $AB \simeq AD$.

Ax. IV. If $A \neq B$ then $AA \simeq AB$ is false.

1. If A be a point, then the relation $AA \simeq AX$ is satisfied by $X = A$ only.

Dem. $AA \simeq AA$ (I), and if $X \neq A$, then $AA \simeq AX$ is false (IV).

The Line and Plane

2. *Def.* If $A \neq B$, the '*line AB*,' denoted by AB simply, is the set of points X such that there is no point Y, distinct from X, satisfying $AY \simeq AX$, $BY \simeq BX$.

3. If $A \neq B$, then A, B are on AB (1), and $AB = BA$.

Ax. V. If C be on AB, then B is on AC.

Ax. VI. There exist three points not on the same line.

Ax. VII. If C be on AB and $AX \simeq AY$, $BX \simeq BY$, then $CX \simeq CY$. (Cf. Ax. **C** V.)

4. If C be on AB and $C \neq A$, then $AB = AC$.

Dem. If X is on AC, but not on AB, there is a point $Y \neq X$ with $AX \simeq AY$, $BX \simeq BY$ (2) and then $CX \simeq CY$ (VII). Thus there is a point $Y \neq X$ with $AX \simeq AY$, $CX \simeq CY$, contrary to the hypothesis that X is on AC. Hence if X is on AC, it is on AB.

But since C is on AB, therefore B is on AC (V). Hence, as before, if X is on AB, it is on AC. Whence $AB = AC$.

·1. If C be on AB, and $C \neq A, B$, then $AB = AC = BC$ (4, 3).

5. *If $A \neq B$, there is one and only one line on which both A and B lie.* (*Dem.* as in II 4.)

6. *Def.* If A, B, C be distinct and do not colline (II 4·4), then the '*plane ABC*,' denoted by ABC simply, is the set of points X such that there is no point Y, distinct from X, with $AX \simeq AY$, $BX \simeq BY$, $CX \simeq CY$.

·1. $ABC = BCA = \ldots$ (all arrangements of A, B, C permissible). AB is on ABC (II 14·1).

7. If A, B, C do not colline, but A, B, D do colline, then CD is on ABC.

Dem. Let X be on CD. Then there is no point $Y \neq X$ with $CX \simeq CY, DX \simeq DY$. But if X is not on ABC, there is a point $Y \neq X$ with $AX \simeq AY, BX \simeq BY, CX \simeq CY$ and then $DX \simeq DY$ (VII). This contradiction gives the Theorem.

Ax. VIII. If *A, B, C* do not colline, and *D* is on *ABC* but not on *BC*, then *A* is on *DBC*.

Ax. IX. If *A, B, C* do not colline and *D* is on *ABC*, and $AX \simeq AY$, $BX \simeq BY$, $CX \simeq CY$, then $DX \simeq DY$.

8. If D is on ABC and not on BC, then $ABC = DBC$. (Cf. II 13·4.)

Dem. If X be on DBC there is no $Y \neq X$ with $DX, BX, CX \simeq DY, BY, CY$; and if X is not on ABC, there is a point $Y \neq X$ with $AX, BX, CX \simeq AY, BY, CY$ and hence with $DX \simeq DY$ (IX), contrary to the first statement. Hence if X is on DBC, it is on ABC. But since D is on ABC and not on BC, therefore A is on DBC (VIII). Hence, as before, if X is on ABC, it is on DBC; whence $ABC = DBC$.

9. *If D, E, F be distinct non-collinear points of ABC, then* $ABC = DEF$. (*Dem.* as in II 14.)

10. *If A, B be distinct points of DEF, then AB is on DEF* (*Dem.* as in II 15).

Circles and Spheres

11. We can define '*circle*' and '*sphere*' as in Chapter V. The *sphere* with centre A which goes through B is denoted by $A(B)$. The '*sphere* $A(A)$' is defined to be the point A.

Ax. X. If $A \neq B$, there is a point *M* on *AB* with $MA \simeq MB$.

12. *Defs.* This point is a '*mid-point*' of (A, B). A is the '*mid-point*' of (A, A).

·1. If $A \neq B$, then A, B are not mid-points of (A, B).

·2. (A, B) has only one mid-point and this is the mid-point of (B, A).

Dem. If $MA \simeq MB$, $NA \simeq NB$, $A \neq B$, $M \neq N$, then A, B are not on MN (2), and hence M, N are not both on AB (5).

12·3. We now know of the existence of three non-collinear points (VI) and of the mid-points of each pair. Given any line, there is a point not on it (VI).

Ax. XI. There is one and only one point $C \neq B$ on AB with $AC \simeq AB$.

Reflections in Points and Lines

13. *Def.* If C ($\neq B$) is on AB, and $AC \simeq AB$, then C is the '*reflection*' of B in A, and is denoted by B/A. If $B = A$, we define B/A to be A.

Ax. XII. If A, B, C do not colline, there is one and only one point $D \neq B$ on ABC with $AB \simeq AD$, $CB \simeq CD$. (Cf. **C** VI, VII.)

·1. *Def.* This point is the '*reflection*' of B in AC, and is denoted by B/AC. If B be on AC, we define $B/AC = B$.

·2. If X, Y be on AC and $X \neq Y$, then $B/AC = B/XY$ (VII).

·3. If $B/AC = B$, then B is on AC (XII).

·4. *Defs.* If a transformation of points into points (such as a reflection in a point or in a line) turns a point of a set $[X]$ always into a point of that set, the set is '*latent*' for the transformation. The operations of reflecting in A, AB are denoted by $/A$, $/AB$.

14. A sphere with centre A is latent for $/A$; a sphere with centre on AB, and a plane through AB, are latent for $/AB$.

Ax. XIII. A reflection in any line transforms a sphere and its centre into a sphere and its centre.

15. If $AB \simeq AC$ and A', B', C' are the reflections of A, B, C in a line, then $A'B' \simeq A'C'$.

16. By reflection in a line, collinear and coplanar points remain so (XIII and defs.).

17. If C is not on the line l, and $D = C/l$, then the mid-point E of (C, D) is on l.

Dem. Let $F=E/l$, then F is on CD (16), and since $EC\simeq ED$ we have $FD\simeq FC$ (15), and hence $E=F$ (12·2).

18. If the line s is distinct from the line r and is latent for reflection in r, then s and r meet.

Dem. Let A be on s and not on r, and $A'=A/r$, then $A=A'/r$, $s=AA'$, and hence AA' meets r (17).

19. *A sphere and a line cannot meet in three distinct points*, that is, if $AB\simeq AC$ and A, B, C do not colline and $X\ (\neq B, C)$ is on BC, then $AX\simeq AB$ is false. (Cf. XI.)

Dem. $/BC$ leaves all points of BC latent (13·1). Let $A'=A/BC$, then since $AB\simeq AC$, we have $A'B\simeq A'C$ (15), and therefore B is not on AA' (2). If $AX\simeq AB$ and X is on BC, then $A'X\simeq A'B$ (15). But since A, B, A' do not colline, there is no point $X\ (\neq B, C)$ on ABC, and so none on BC such that $AB\simeq AX$, $A'B\simeq A'X$ (XII).

20. *Def.* If r, s be lines, then $s\perp r$ (s is '*perpendicular*' to r) means $r\neq s$, $s/r=s$ (that is, s is latent for $/r$. Cf. 13·4).

21. If $s\perp r$, then r, s meet (18).

22. If A, B, C are distinct and $C'=C/A$, then $AC\perp AB$, $BC\simeq BC'$, $C'=C/AB$ imply each other.

23. If $r\perp s$, then $s\perp r$.

Dem. Let $AC\perp AB$; $C'=C/A$; $B'=B/A$; we shew then that $AB\perp AC$. Let $B''=B/AC$, M be mid-point of (B, B''), then M is on AC (17). But $BC\simeq BC'$ (22), hence $B''C\simeq B''C'$ (15), and hence $C'=C/BB''$ and thus M is the mid-point of (C, C') (17). But since $C'=C/A$, therefore A is the mid-point of (C, C'). Hence $M=A$ (12·2), $B''=B/M=B/A=B'$. Thus $B'=B/AC$. But $B'=B/A$ whence $AB\perp AC$ (22).

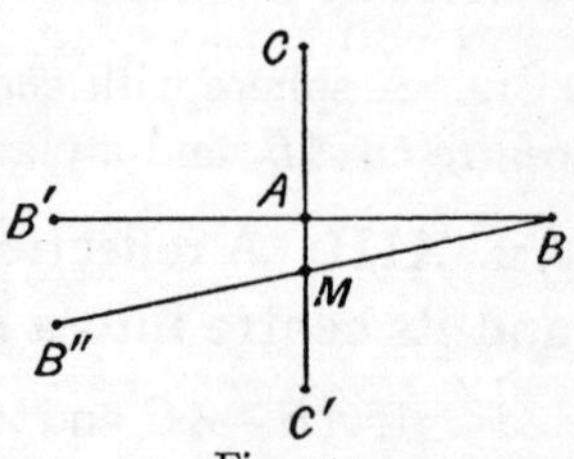

Fig. 153

24. If C be not on r, there is one and only one point A on r such that $CA\perp r$.

Dem. Let $C' = C/r$, $A =$ mid-point of (C, C'), then A is on r (17) and $CA \perp r$. If A, B be on r, and $A \neq B$, and CA, $CB \perp r$, then CA, CB are latent for $/r$, hence so is their sole common point C. Hence C is on r (13·3), cont. hyp.

25. If A, B, C do not colline, and $D\,(\neq C)$ is on ABC and not on AB, and if AC, $AD \perp AB$, then A, C, D colline.

Dem. Let $B' = B/A$, then $CB \simeq CB'$, $DB \simeq DB'$ (22, 23). Hence B, C, D do not colline. But B, B' are on $ABC = BCD$. Hence $B' = B/CD$, and the mid-point A of (B, B') is on CD.

Ax. XIV. If A, B, C do not colline, there is a point X on ABC and not on AB such that $XA \simeq XB$. (Cf. X.)

26. If A, B, C do not colline, there is a point D on ABC with $DA \perp AB$.

Dem. Let $B' = B/A$. By XIV, there is a point D on ABC and not on AB, such that $DB \simeq DB'$.

Ax. XV. Given any plane, there is a point not on it.

27. If AB, $AC \perp AM$ and A, B, C do not colline, and $D\,(\neq A)$ is on ABC, then $AD \perp AM$.

Dem. Let $N = M/A$, then BM, CM, $AM \simeq BN$, CN, AN (22). Hence $DM \simeq DN$ (IX).

Similitudes and Rotations

28. *Defs.* If r be any line, a '*rotation round r*' is a *product* (i.e. a *resultant*) of two reflections in lines perpendicular to r at the same point; r is the '*axis*' of the rotation. A '*similitude*' is any (1, 1) transformation of points into points whereby each sphere and its centre corresponds to a sphere and its centre.

29. *A similitude transforms collinear points, coplanar points, mid-points, and perpendicular lines into such. A reflection in a line, and a rotation are similitudes.*

Ax. XVI. A sphere and a line through its centre meet.

30. *A sphere and a line through its centre meet in just two points* (XVI, XI).

31. *Any point on the axis of a rotation is latent for the rotation, and so is any sphere whose centre is on the axis.* (XVI, XIII.)

32. If A, B, C, D do not coplane (II 13), and $AB, AC \perp AD$, and $AB \simeq AC$, then $DB \simeq DC$.

Dem. Let $E = D/A$, and F be the mid-point of (B, C). Then $F \neq A$; $BC \perp AF$; $B = C/AF$. Also $DA \perp AF$ (27), $E = D/A$. Hence $E = D/AB = D/AF$. Therefore

$$(B, D, E)/AB = (B, E, D)$$

and

$$(B, C, E)/AF = (C, B, D).$$

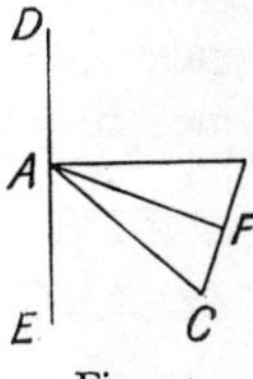

Fig. 154

Thus by $/AB$, the sphere $D(B)$ becomes $E(B)$ (11, XIII), and by $/AF$ the sphere $E(B)$ becomes $D(C)$. Hence by $/AB \, . /AF$ the sphere $D(B)$ becomes $D(C)$. But $/AB \, . /AF$, being a rotation round AD, leaves this sphere with centre D latent (31). Hence $DB \simeq DC$.

33. If A, B, C, D do not coplane, and $AD \perp ABC$; $DE, DF \perp AD$; and DE be on ABD, and DF on ACD, then there is a line r such that $(AB, AC)/r = DF, DE$.

Dem. Let O be the mid-point of (A, D); $OH, OK \perp AD$; OH on ABD; OK on ACD (26) and $OH \simeq OK$ (XVI), and let M be the mid-point of (H, K). Then $MO \perp AD$, HK (27). Hence $/MO$ interchanges A with D, and H with K, and so interchanges the planes ABD and ACD (29). Hence BA, being perpendicular to AD, becomes the line perpendicular to AD at D in the plane ACD (29), namely DF. Similarly AC becomes DE.

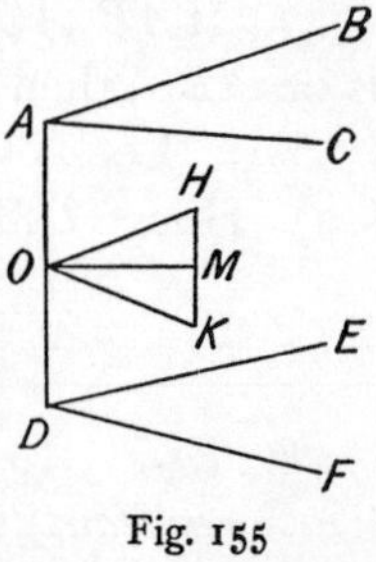

Fig. 155

Ax. XVII. Any two planes with a point common have another point common.

·1. By 27, 32, 33 *we can now construct the theory of perpendicular lines and planes as in Chapter IV.* Thus e.g. there is one and only one perpendicular line from a given point to a given plane.

34. *Any plane perpendicular to the axis of a rotation is latent for the rotation.*

35. *Similitudes turn perpendicular lines and planes into such.*

36. If A, B, C do not colline, and $AD, BD, CD \simeq AE, BE, CE$ and $E \neq D$, then there is no point $X\ (\neq D, E)$ such that

$$AX, BX, CX \simeq AD, BD, CD.$$

(Pieri takes this as an Axiom instead of XVII.)

Dem. Let M be the mid-point of (E, D), then

$$MA, MB, MC \perp MD.$$

Hence A, B, C, M coplane*, and $ED \perp ABC$. Similarly, if there were such a point X, and N be the mid-point of (D, X), we should have A, B, C, N coplanar and $XD \perp ABC$. Hence $M = N$ (33·1), whence $X = E$.

·1. If A, B, C, D do not coplane, then X is the only point common to $A(X), B(X), C(X), D(X)$.

Reflections in Planes

37. *Defs.* If $DM \perp ABC$, M on ABC, and $E = D/M$, then E is the '*reflection*' of D in ABC, written $E = D/ABC$, and ABC is the '*bisector plane*' of (D, E). If D is on ABC, then we define $D/ABC = D$. The operation of reflecting in ABC is written $/ABC$.

38. If $E = D/ABC$, then $AD \simeq AE$ (22).

·1. If $D = D/ABC$, then D is on ABC.

39. If μ be a given plane, and for any point X, X' means X/μ, then $AB \simeq AC$ implies $A'B' \simeq A'C'$, i.e. *a reflection in a plane is a similitude.*

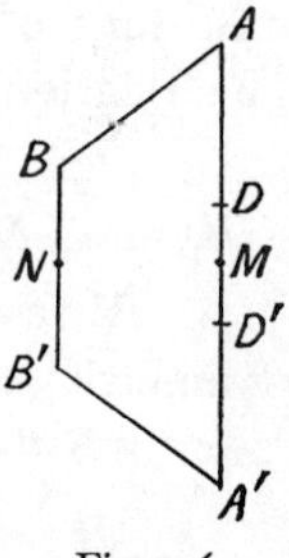

Fig. 156

Dem. Let M, N be the mid-points of (A, A') and (B, B') resp. If A is not on μ, then $A \neq A'$, $AA' \perp \mu$. The sphere $A(B)$ meets AA' in two points D, E (32). First, let B be not on AA' or μ, then $M \neq N$; $B \neq B'$; $MN \perp AA', BB'$. Hence $(A, B, D)/MN = (A', B', D')$ and $A'B' \simeq A'D'$ (15). Similarly, if B is on μ, then $A'B' \simeq A'D'$. Lastly, if B is on AA', then $B = D$ or E, hence $B' = D'$ or E', and $A'B' \simeq A'D'$ (15); for since $AA' \perp \mu$, therefore

* This deduction needs Ax. XVII. Cf. IV 80.

D' is the reflection of D, and E' that of E in any line on μ through M. Thus always $A'B' \simeq A'D'$. Similarly $A'C' \simeq A'D'$. Hence the Theorem.

40. Any sphere with its centre on a plane μ, and any line perpendicular to μ, are latent for $/\mu$ (38).

41. If M be a given point and for any point X, X' means X/M, then $AB \simeq AC$ implies $A'B' \simeq A'C'$, i.e. *a reflection in a point is a similitude.*

Dem. We may assume $M \neq A$, then MA meets $A(B)$ in two points D, E say. If B be not on AM, let r be the line perpendicular to ABM at M, while if B be on AM, let r be any line perpendicular to AM at M. Then $(A, B, D)/r = (A', B', D')$ (17). Hence $AB \simeq AD$ implies $A'B' \simeq A'D'$ (15). Hence the Theorem follows as in 39.

·1. *Def.* Two spheres or points are '*symmetric*' with respect to a point, line, or plane if each is the reflection of the other in the point, line, or plane.

42. The following statements imply each other: Two spheres are symmetric (i) in M the mid-point of their centres, (ii) in some line through M perpendicular to the line of centres, (iii) in all such lines, (iv) in the plane through M perpendicular to the line of centres. Similarly for two points.

·1. *Def.* Two spheres are called '*symmetric*' simply, when the statements in 42 are true for them.

Definition of Congruence in General

So far we do not know what $AB \simeq CD$ means when $A \neq C$. This relation we now define.

43. *Def.* If $A \neq C$, then '$AB \simeq CD$' means that the spheres $A(B)$ and $C(D)$ are symmetric.

44. Always $AB \simeq CD$, if and only if $A(B)$ and $C(D)$ are symmetric (14).

45. *$AB \simeq CD$ implies $CD \simeq AB$.*

Definition and Properties of 'Between'

46. *Defs.* A point A is '*inside*' $C(B)$ if and only if there are distinct points X, Y of $C(B)$ with A the mid-point of (X, Y). A is '*outside*' $C(B)$ if it is neither on nor inside.

46·1. *Def.* X is '*between*' A and B if and only if $A \neq B$, and X is on AB and inside $M(A)$ where M is the mid-point of (A, B). As before we assert this relation by $[AXB]$.

·2. $[ABC]$ *implies* $[CBA]$.

47. If $[ABC]$, *then* A, B, C *are distinct.*

Dem. We have only to shew that $[AAB]$ is impossible. Now if $[AAB]$, then $A \neq B$, and A is inside $M(A)$ where M is the mid-point of (A, B), and then (46) there are distinct points X, Y on $M(A)$ with A the mid-point of (X, Y). Hence $A \neq X, Y$ (12·1), and A, X, Y are on $M(A)$, contrary to 19.

48. If M is the mid-point of (A, B), then $[AMB]$, since A, B are on $M(A)$.

49. *If* $A \neq B$, *there is a point* C *with* $[ABC]$, *namely* A/B.

50. We can now define interval, ray, triangle, side as in Chapter II. We denote them as there.

Ax. XVIII. If [*ABC*] is true, then [*BCA*] is false.

Ax. XIX. A line which meets one side of a triangle and lies on the plane of the triangle meets the triangle again.

We shall have all the Theorems of Chapter II, and the definitions of line and plane in that chapter will be satisfied by our lines and planes, if we shew :

51. *If* A, B, C *colline and are distinct, then* $[ABC]$ *or* $[ACB]$ *or* $[CAB]$.

Dem. Let $[ABC]$, $[ACB]$ be both false, and let E be any point not on AB. Let D satisfy $[BED]$ (49). Then CE meets $B\text{-}D$ and not $A\text{-}B$, and hence meets $A\text{-}D$ in F say (XIX). Then in triangle ADE, BF meets $D\text{-}A$ and not $D\text{-}E$ (XVIII), and hence meets $A\text{-}E$ in G, say; in triangle CAE, BF meets $A\text{-}E$ and not $A\text{-}C$, and hence meets $C\text{-}E$.

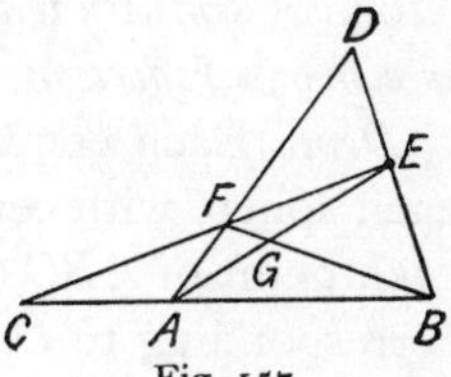

Fig. 157

In triangle CBF, DA meets $C\text{-}E$ and not $B\text{-}E$ (XVIII) and hence meets $B\text{-}C$. Thus we have $[CAB]$.

52. *If A, B, C become A', B', C' by a similitude, then $[ABC]$ implies $[A'B'C']$.*

53. We can now define tetrahedron and space $ABCD$ as in Chapter II, using Ax. XV as the existence Theorem. By XVII it follows that there is but one space.

All Theorems of Chapters II and III now follow.

The Congruence Axioms

Ax. XX. Two spheres symmetric to the same sphere are symmetric to each other.

54. If $AB \simeq CD$, $CD \simeq EF$, then $AB \simeq EF$ (cf. Ax. **C** II).

55. *Def.* A similitude for which one pair (at least) of corresponding spheres are symmetric is an '*isomery.*'

56. *Isomeries form a group* (I 22).

57. The product of any number of reflections is an isomery.

Ax. XXI. If a similitude be such that one couple of distinct points is congruent to the corresponding couple, then any two corresponding couples are congruent.

58. *An isomery transforms any sphere into a symmetric sphere.*

59. *A similitude, which leaves two points A, B of a line latent, is an isomery leaving all points of the line latent.*

Dem. The similitude is an isomery, since $A(B)$ corresponds to itself and is self-symmetric. A point C on AB corresponds to a point C' on AB, and $AC \simeq AC'$, $BC \simeq BC'$ (XXI). Hence $C = C'$.

60. *A similitude with three latent non-collinear points A, B, C is either a reflection in a plane or identity.*

Dem. Each point of AB, BC, CA is latent (59), hence so is each sphere with centre at A or B or C (30), and hence so is each point of ABC (6). If D is not on ABC, then the point D', corresponding to D, is common to $A(D)$, $B(D)$, $C(D)$ and so is either D or D/ABC (36, 38).

In the first case, since if M be any point it is the only point common to $A(M)$, $B(M)$, $C(M)$, $D(M)$ (36·1), therefore M is latent, and the similitude leaves all points latent, i.e. is identity. In the second case each point, not on ABC, is distinct from its corresponding point, and the Theorem follows by reflecting in ABC.

61. *A similitude with four latent non-coplanar points is identity.*

62. *A ray from the centre of a sphere meets the sphere in but one point* (32, 48).

·1. Ax. **C** I of Chapter IV now follows (44, 54).

·2. Ax. **C** IV, $AB \simeq BA$, also holds, since reflection in the mid-point M of (A, B) interchanges A with B, and hence $A(B)$ with $B(A)$ (41).

63. If $\mathfrak{A}$, $\mathfrak{B}$ *be isomeries which each transform* A, $[AB$, $\{AB,C\}$ *into* D, $[DE$, $\{DE,F\}$ *then either* $\mathfrak{A} = \mathfrak{B}$ *or* $\mathfrak{A} = \mathfrak{B}\mathfrak{P}$ *where* $\mathfrak{P} = /DEF$.

Dem. Let $\mathfrak{A}$ transform B and C into B', C'. *We express this fact thus*: $B' = B\mathfrak{A}$, $C' = C\mathfrak{A}$.

Then $B\mathfrak{B} = B'$ (62·1). Hence $\mathfrak{B}$ transforms $A(C)$, $B(C)$ into the reflections of these spheres in the mid-points of (A, D) and of (B, B') resp. (42), i.e. into $D(C')$ and $B'(C')$. Hence the meet C, of $A(C)$, $B(C)$ and $\{AB,C\}$, is transformed by $\mathfrak{B}$ into the meet of $D(C')$, $B'(C')$ and $\{DE,F\}$, i.e. into C'. Hence both $\mathfrak{A}$ and $\mathfrak{B}$ transform A, B, C into D, B', C'. Hence $\mathfrak{B}^{-1}\mathfrak{A}$ leaves D, B', C' latent, hence $\mathfrak{B}^{-1}\mathfrak{A} = \mathfrak{J}$ or $\mathfrak{P}$ (60), where $\mathfrak{J}$ denotes the identical isomery. Note that if $\mathfrak{A}$, $\mathfrak{B}$ be isomeries, then $\mathfrak{A}\mathfrak{B}$ is the isomery got by applying $\mathfrak{A}$ *first* and *then* $\mathfrak{B}$.

64. *If* A, B, C *do not colline and* D, E, F *do not colline, there is an isomery which transforms* A, $[AB$, $\{AB,C\}$ *into* D, $[DE$, $\{DE,F\}$.

Dem. Reflection in the mid-point of (A, D) transforms B, C into B', C' say. If B' is not on $[DE$, let $[DE$ meet $D(B')$ in B''. Then according as B', B'', D are or are not collinear, the reflection in D or in the join of D and the mid-point of (B', B''), carries B' into B'', leaves D fixed, and turns C' into a point C'' not on DE.

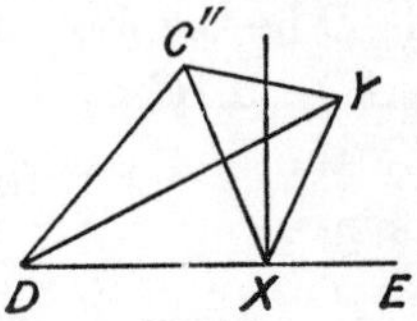

Fig. 158

If C'' is not on DEF, let $C''X \perp DE$ with X on DE and let $[XY$ be in $\{DE, F\}$ and perpendicular to DE, with $XY \simeq XC''$. The reflection in the plane through DE and the mid-point of (C'', Y) leaves DE latent and turns C'' into Y, with $DC'' \simeq DY$.

If C'' is in the half-plane opposite to $\{DE, F\}$, reflect in DE.

65. *Every isomery is the product of reflections.*

66. From 63, 64, VII and XII we get **C** III, V, VI, VII of Chapter IV (see IV 54·1) *and all the Theorems of Chapter IV now follow.* In particular we can define the relations $> < =$ between the measures of intervals and shew their properties. From 46·1, 62 and XVIII it follows that, if C is outside $A(B)$ then B is inside $A(C)$. Further, if a plane and a sphere meet in two points, they meet in a circle whose centre is the foot of the perpendicular to the plane from the centre of the sphere.

67. *According as* $\mu AB <>= \mu AC$ *will* B *be inside, outside or on* $A(C)$. Cf. 46 and V1.

Dem. If $\mu AB < \mu AC$, there is a point B' on $A^{-}C$ and $A(B)$. Now $[B'A$ meets $A(B)$ in B'' say (62), and $[B''AB'C]$. Hence $[B''B'C]$, and hence C is not inside $A(B)$ (46·1), since C is not between B'' and B' (XVIII). Neither is C on $A(B)$ (62). The Theorem now follows from 66.

68. *Any line through an inside point* C *of a sphere* $A(B)$ *meets it in two distinct points.*

Dem. If the line goes through A this is 30. Let the line be perpendicular to CA; there is a line through C meeting the sphere in points X, Y of which C is the mid-point (46). The plane through C perpendicular to AC contains X, Y and the given line, the plane meets the sphere in a circle, centre C (66), and the given line meets the circle (XVI).

If the given line is not through A or perpendicular to CA, let D be the foot of the perpendicular on the line from A, then $\mu AD < \mu AC < \mu AB$. Hence D is inside $A(B)$ (67) and hence by the first part of the proof, DC meets the sphere in two points.

69. *Axiom* $\mathbf{Q}_1$ *now follows.*

*Isomeries and Motions**

The following Theorems can be deduced from the above or from Axioms **O, C.**

70. *A reflection in a line is the product in either order of reflections in two planes, one plane α being any plane through the line, and the other being perpendicular to α. The product of reflections in two perpendicular planes taken in either order is a reflection in their common line.* (Cf. 82.)

·1. A rotation $\mathfrak{R}$ round a line r is the product of reflections in two planes through r.

Dem. $\mathfrak{R} = /a \,.\, /b$ where a, b are lines perpendicular to r at the same point (28). Let α, β, γ be the planes ra, rb, ab resp., then $/a = /\alpha \,.\, /\gamma$ and $/b = /\gamma \,.\, /\beta$ (70). Hence

$$\mathfrak{R} = /\alpha \,.\, /\gamma \,.\, /\gamma \,.\, /\beta = /\alpha \,.\, /\beta$$

since $/\gamma \,.\, /\gamma$ is the identity $\mathfrak{I}$.

·2. A rotation $\mathfrak{R}$ round r leaves no point C, not on r, latent.

Dem. If $C\mathfrak{R} = C$ and $\mathfrak{R} = /\alpha \,.\, /\beta$, then C and C/α are symmetric for β, since $C/\alpha \,.\, /\beta = C$. Hence if $C/\alpha = C$, then C would be on α and β and hence on r. Hence $C/\alpha \neq C$, and thus the join of C/α and C is perpendicular to both α and β, which is impossible.

·3. If a rotation $\mathfrak{R}$ round AB carry the ray $[BG$, perpendicular to AB, into $[BF$, then $\mathfrak{R}$ is the product of reflections in planes ABX and ABF, where $[BX$ bisects $G\hat{B}F$.

Dem. $/ABX$ transforms A, B, G into A, B, F', where F' is on $[BF$, and $BG \simeq BF'$; and so does $\mathfrak{R}$. Hence $\mathfrak{R} = /ABX$ or $/ABX \,.\, /ABF$ (63). But $\mathfrak{R}$ cannot be a reflection in a plane, since then some points not on its axis would be latent (·2, 37).

71. *A rotation is the product of reflections in two planes through the axis, of which either the first or the second may be any plane through the axis.*

·1. *A reflection in a line is a rotation round the line.*

72. *A rotation $\mathfrak{R}$ is the product of reflections in two lines AB, AC, each perpendicular to the axis AX at a given point A, and either of which may be any such line.*

* For the following see Schur, *Grundlagen der Geometrie* (1909), § 3, and papers by Wiener in the *Leipziger Berichte*, 1890, 1891.

Dem. $\mathfrak{R} = /\beta \,.\, /\gamma$ where β, γ are planes through AX, either arbitrary. Let α be perpendicular to AX at A, meeting β, γ in AB, AC resp. Then $/\beta \,.\, /\alpha = /AB$, $/\alpha \,.\, /\gamma = /AC$ (70). Hence

$$\mathfrak{R} = /\beta \,.\, /\gamma = /\beta \,.\, /\alpha \,.\, /\alpha \,.\, /\gamma = /AB \,.\, /AC.$$

72·1. The product of reflections in two planes which meet is a rotation round their common line.

73. The product of two rotations $\mathfrak{R}_1$, $\mathfrak{R}_2$ round the same axis r, or round axes r, s which meet, is a rotation or identity.

Dem. In the first case, let b be any line perpendicular to r at a point A on r, then $\mathfrak{R}_1 = /a \,.\, /b$, $\mathfrak{R}_2 = /b \,.\, /c$ for some a, c perpendicular to r at A, and thence $\mathfrak{R}_1 \,.\, \mathfrak{R}_2 = /a \,.\, /c$. In the second case, let b be perpendicular to the plane of r, s at the point A where r, s meet, then again $\mathfrak{R}_1 \,.\, \mathfrak{R}_2 = /a \,.\, /c$, and this is a rotation round an axis perpendicular to the plane ac.

·1. The product of a reflection in, and a rotation round, a line is a rotation round that line.

74. *An isomery $\mathfrak{A}$ which is not identity or a reflection in a plane, and which leaves a point A latent, is either a rotation or the product of a rotation and a reflection in a plane.*

Dem. Let $[AB$, $[AC$ be perpendicular rays which become $[AB'$, $[AC'$ (also perpendicular) by $\mathfrak{A}$; omit the easy case when AB, AC, AB', AC' are all coplanar. Let $\mathfrak{U}$ be a reflection in a line such that $[AB \,.\, \mathfrak{U} = AB']$. Then if $[AC \,.\, \mathfrak{U} = [AC_1$, let $\mathfrak{V}$ be a reflection in a line such that $[AC_1 \,.\, \mathfrak{V} = [AC'$. We have $AC_1 \perp AB'$ since $AC \perp AB$. Also $AC' \perp AB'$. Hence the axis of $\mathfrak{V}$ is perpendicular to AB', and hence $AB']\,\mathfrak{V} = [AB'$. Hence $\mathfrak{U}\mathfrak{V}$ carries A, $[AC$, $[AB$ into A, $[AC'$, $[AB'$, and so does $\mathfrak{A}$. Hence $\mathfrak{A} = \mathfrak{U}\mathfrak{V}$ or $\mathfrak{U}\mathfrak{V}\mathfrak{P}$ where $\mathfrak{P}$ is the reflection in the plane $AB'C'$ (63).

75. *Def.* The '*translation*' AB is the isomery which carries A into B, $[AB$ into $BA]$, and leaves latent some half-plane $\{AB, C\}$ from AB and also a half-space of ABC. (Cf. 63.)

76. *The translation AB is the product of reflections in two coplanar lines perpendicular to AB, either of which may be any such line; it is also the product of reflections in two planes perpendicular to AB, either of which may be any such plane. Every half-plane from AB is latent.*

Dem. By 63 the translation AB is $/MX\,.\,/BY$, where M is the mid-point of (A, B) and MX, BY are perpendicular to AB and where X, Y lie on ABC; for this product has the properties mentioned in 75, and by 63 is the only isomery with these properties. Similarly, if C is any point of AB, and C becomes D by the translation, and N is the mid-point of (C,D), then the translation is $/NX'\,.\,/DY'$ where $NX', DY' \perp AB$ and X', Y' lie on ABC. If α, β be planes through N, D perpendicular to AB, then $/NX' = /\alpha\,.\,/ABC$ and $/DY' = /ABC\,.\,/\beta$. Hence the translation is $/\alpha\,.\,/\beta$. Drawing any plane through AB, meeting α, β in r, s, we have the same translation in the form $/r\,.\,/s$. Hence the Theorem.

77. The product of two translations along the same line is a translation along that line.

·1. If X is not on AB, and X, Y become Y, Z by the translation AB, then X, Y, Z do not colline unless the angle-sum of a triangle is two right angles; for, if X, Y, Z colline, it is easy to shew the existence of a quadrilateral with four right angles. (See XV 7.)

78. *Every isomery* $\mathfrak{A}$ *is the product either of reflections in two lines or of reflections in two lines and a plane.*

Dem. If $[AB$, $[AC$ be perpendicular rays which by $\mathfrak{A}$ become $[A'B'$, $[A'C'$, also perpendicular, let $\mathfrak{T}$ be the translation AA'. Then $[AB$, $[AC$ become, say, $[A'B_1$, $[A'C_1$ by $\mathfrak{T}$. The isomery inverse to $\mathfrak{A}^{-1}\mathfrak{T}$ turns $[A'B_1$, $[A'C_1$ into $[A'B'$, $[A'C'$ and hence is either a rotation $\mathfrak{R}$ round $A'D$, say, or is $\mathfrak{R}\mathfrak{P}$, where $\mathfrak{P}$ is the reflection in the plane $A'B'C'$, or is identity or a reflection in a plane through A' (74). Consider the first two cases (the others are either obvious or similar). Then $\mathfrak{A} = \mathfrak{T}\mathfrak{R}$ or $\mathfrak{T}\mathfrak{R}\mathfrak{P}$. But $\mathfrak{T}$ and $\mathfrak{R}$ are both products of reflections in two lines, whereof the second for $\mathfrak{T}$ and the first for $\mathfrak{R}$ can both be taken as the same line perpendicular to $AA'D$ at A'. The Theorem then follows.

79. *Every isomery is the product of reflections in four planes or fewer.*

Dem. With the notation of 78, if $\mathfrak{A} = \mathfrak{T}\mathfrak{R}$, it is the product of reflections in four planes (71, 76). If $\mathfrak{A} = \mathfrak{T}\mathfrak{R}\mathfrak{P}$, it can be represented by the product of reflections in five planes, four of which go through A'. If $\mathfrak{U}_1$, $\mathfrak{U}_2$, $\mathfrak{U}_3$, $\mathfrak{U}_4$ be the four last reflections, then $\mathfrak{U}_1\mathfrak{U}_2$ and $\mathfrak{U}_3\mathfrak{U}_4$ are rotations (72·1) and so is their product (73). Hence $\mathfrak{U}_1\mathfrak{U}_2\mathfrak{U}_3\mathfrak{U}_4$ can be replaced by the product of reflections in two planes.

80. *Def.* A '*motion*' is an isomery which is either identity or a reflection in one line or the product of reflections in two lines.

·1. If $\mathfrak{R}$ be a rotation round AB and $X\mathfrak{R}=X_1$, $Y\mathfrak{R}=Y_1$, and XC, YD be perpendicular to AB, with C, D on AB, then $X\hat{C}X_1 \simeq Y\hat{D}Y_1$. (Cf. 33.)

·2. *Def.* The '*measure*' of $\mathfrak{R}$ is $\mu X\hat{C}X_1$.

81. $/OA\,.\,/OB$ is a rotation of measure $2\mu A\hat{O}B$ or $2(\pi-\mu A\hat{O}B)$.

The Influence of the Parallel Axiom

§ 2. **Basis:** Pieri's Axioms I—XIX and $\mathbf{P}_3'$.

We first shew that Ax. XX can be proved from this basis.

82. If α, β be perpendicular planes through r, then

$$/\alpha\,.\,/\beta=/r.$$

Dem. Let $P_1=P/\alpha$, $P'=P_1/\beta$. The perpendiculars from P, P_1 to β are interchanged by $/\alpha\,.\,/\beta$, since P, P_1 interchange by $/\alpha$, and since β is latent. Thus they also interchange by $/r$, since their feet are symmetric for α (35) and so are symmetric for r (42). Similarly, perpendiculars from P_1, P' to α interchange by $/\alpha\,.\,/\beta$ and by $/r$. Hence by $/r$, the perpendiculars from P to α, β interchange with those from P' to α, β. Hence $P'=P/r$.

83. If u, v be perpendicular (meeting) lines, then $/u\,.\,/v=/w$, where w is perpendicular to u and v at the point where they meet.

84. The product of reflections in two planes which meet is a rotation round their common line.

Dem. Draw a plane perpendicular to the common line and use 82.

85. Two spheres, which correspond for a rotation $\mathfrak{R}$, are symmetric in some plane through the axis of $\mathfrak{R}$.

Dem. If one sphere has its centre on the axis, this follows by 31, 40. In the contrary case, let B, B' be the centres of the spheres and let M be the mid-point of (B, B'). Then B' is on $A(B)$, since $A(B).\mathfrak{R} = A(B)$, where A is any point on the axis of $\mathfrak{R}$. Hence $MA \perp BB'$ and $B' = B/AM$. Let the sphere with centre B meet $[BA$ in C (62, which follows from I—XIX). Now $A(C).\mathfrak{R} = A(C)$, therefore $C\mathfrak{R}$ is on $A(C)$, and, if $\mathfrak{S} = /AM$, then $C\mathfrak{S}$ is on $A(C)$ (14). But $\mathfrak{R}$, $\mathfrak{S}$ both turn $[BA$ into $[B'A$. Hence $C\mathfrak{R}$ and $C\mathfrak{S}$ both lie on $A(C)$ and on $[B'A$, and hence coincide in C', say; whence $\mathfrak{S}$, like $\mathfrak{R}$, turns $B(C)$ into $B'(C')$.

86. *Two coplanar lines perpendicular to the same line are parallel* (24), where parallel lines are defined as in VI 1.

·1. If r, s be parallel lines, a line perpendicular to r in the plane rs is also perpendicular to s ($\mathbf{P}_3'$ and 86).

·2. If A, B, C do not colline, the right bisectors of AB, BC in the plane ABC meet (·1 and 24).

87. *We can now shew* XX *from* I—XIX, $\mathbf{P}_3'$. To shew: if α, β, γ be spheres and μ, ν planes with $\alpha/\mu = \gamma$, $\beta/\nu = \gamma$, then α, β are symmetric.

Dem. First, let the centres A, B, C of the spheres α, β, γ not colline, then there is a point X with $XA \simeq XB \simeq XC$ (86·2, 22). X lies on the bisector planes μ, ν of AB, BC, which planes therefore meet in a line r. Also $/\mu . /\nu$ is a rotation $\mathfrak{R}$ round r (84), and $\alpha\mathfrak{R} = \beta$. Hence α, β are symmetric (85).

If A, B, C colline and are distinct, take a sphere δ symmetric to γ with its centre not on AB, then since α, δ are symmetric to γ, they are symmetric to each other by the first part. Similarly so are β, δ and hence so are α, β.

Euclidean Motions

§ 3. **Basis:** Pieri's Axioms I—XIX, XXI and $\mathbf{P}_3'$.

88. If $ABCD$ be a rectangle then the translation AB = translation DC.

·1. If A, B, C, D do not colline, then translation AB = translation DC if, and only if, $ABCD$ is a parallelogram.

·2. The product of reflections in two parallel lines AB, CD

is the translation AX, where $AY \perp CD$, Y is on CD, and Y is the mid-point of (A, X). Similarly for the product of reflections in two parallel planes.

89. *The product of rotations round two parallel lines r, s is a translation or a rotation.*

Dem. The rotations can be written $/\beta . /\alpha$ and $/\alpha . /\gamma$, where α is the plane rs. Hence the Theorem by 84, 88·2.

90. *Translations form an Abelian group* (I 22·42).

91. Any translation can be expressed as the product of three translations along any three mutually perpendicular lines; and also as the product of a translation along a given line and one along some line perpendicular to the given line.

92. *A rotation $\mathfrak{R}$ round XY is a rotation round OP followed or preceded by a translation, where O is a given point not on XY, and $OP \parallel XY$.*

Dem. Let $\alpha = OXY$, and γ be a plane through O parallel to β where $\mathfrak{R} = /\alpha . /\beta$. Then $\mathfrak{R} = /\alpha . /\gamma . /\gamma . /\beta$, and $/\alpha . /\gamma$ is a rotation round OP and $/\gamma . /\beta$ is a translation (88·2).

93. *A translation OA, followed or preceded by a rotation round $OB \perp OA$, results in a rotation round a line parallel to OB.*

Dem. Let $OC \perp OAB$, then the translation is $/\delta . /OBC$ where δ is some plane perpendicular to OA; and the rotation is $/OBC . /\zeta$ where ζ is some plane through OB, not OBC. The product being $/\delta . /\zeta$ is a rotation round the common line of δ, ζ, and this is parallel to OB.

·1. *Defs.* A '*screw*' is the product of a translation $\mathfrak{T}$ along a line AB, preceded or followed by a rotation $\mathfrak{R}$ round AB. AB is the '*axis*' of the screw.

94. *The order of the factors $\mathfrak{T}, \mathfrak{R}$ of the screw $\mathfrak{S}$ is immaterial.*

Dem. Let r be any arbitrary line perpendicular to (and meeting) the axis AB of $\mathfrak{S}$, then $\mathfrak{T} = /\alpha . /\beta$, where α, β are planes perpendicular to AB and α goes through r (76); while $\mathfrak{R} = /\gamma . /\delta$, where γ, δ are planes through AB and γ goes through r (71). Now if ϖ, ρ be perpendicular planes, then $/\varpi . /\rho = /\rho . /\varpi$ (70). Hence $\mathfrak{T}\mathfrak{R} = \mathfrak{R}\mathfrak{T}$.

95. *A screw* $\mathfrak{S}=\mathfrak{T}\mathfrak{R}$ *is the product of reflections in two lines perpendicular to (and meeting) its axis, either of which may be any such perpendicular.*

Dem. With notation of 94, r being an arbitrary line perpendicular to (and meeting) AB, we have

$$\mathfrak{S}=/\alpha./\beta./\gamma./\delta=/\alpha./\gamma./\beta./\delta=/r./s \ (70),$$

since α, γ are perpendicular planes which meet in r, and where s is the common line of β and δ.

96. *A motion* (80) *is either identity or a translation or a rotation or a screw. Conversely, these are motions.*

Dem. A motion, if not identity, is a reflection in two distinct lines r, s (83). If these are coplanar we have a translation or rotation (88·2, 28). If not, then $/r./s$ is a screw (95 *Dem.*).

·1. *A reflection in a plane is not a motion.*

97. *Motions form a group.*

Dem. It suffices to shew that the product of two motions is a motion. If both be translations or reflections in lines, this follows by 80, 90. For a translation and a rotation, we can 'resolve' the translation into one along a line parallel to the axis of the rotation and another along a perpendicular line (91). Then 88·1, 93, 94, 96 give the Theorem. For rotations with coplanar axes we use 73, 89. Similarly for screws with such axes, using 94.

For screws $\mathfrak{S}_1$, $\mathfrak{S}_2$ with non-coplanar axes p, q; let t be the line perpendicular to both p and q. Then there are lines s, u perpendicular to p, q respectively, such that

$$\mathfrak{S}_1=/s./t, \quad \mathfrak{S}_2=/t./u \ (95).$$

Hence $\mathfrak{S}_1\mathfrak{S}_2=/s./u$ is a screw.

Rotations are special cases of screws when the translation is identity.

98. Assuming Axiom $\mathbf{K}_1$, Pieri (*loc. cit.*) has shewn that XXI follows from the remaining Axioms.

CHAPTER XV

THE ANGLE-SUM OF A TRIANGLE AND NON-EUCLIDEAN AREAS

Introductory Remarks

The investigations in this chapter are related to those from which the classical non-Euclidean Geometries arose. The Geometry on a sphere has clearly many analogies to that on a plane, great circles corresponding to lines. In particular most of the theory in Chapter IV holds on a sphere. We shew in this chapter why this is so and also why differences arise. This leads to the discussion of the angle-sum of a triangle, which is greater than π on a sphere.

We shew that, *assuming Axioms* $\mathbf{O}_p\mathbf{C}_p$, the angle-sum of a triangle must be equal to or less than π; we know already that both these cases can actually arise (VIII 49). If we assume Axiom $\mathbf{K}_1$, the first case gives the parallel Axiom **P** of Euclidean Geometry, while the second gives Hyperbolic Geometry, but for these deductions Axiom $\mathbf{K}_1$ is essential. It has often been stated that experiment, being only approximate, cannot shew that the angle-sum of a triangle in the space of experience is exactly equal to π, and hence cannot shew the truth of the Euclidean parallel Axiom; but even if we knew this angle-sum was exactly π, the truth of the Euclidean Axiom would only follow in the presence of $\mathbf{K}_1$ which is equally inaccessible to experiment. Roughly speaking, $\mathbf{K}_1$ can be regarded as an Axiom on the infinitely small, the parallel Axiom as an Axiom on the infinitely great.

We next take up the question of non-Euclidean areas, and deduce results analogous to those of Chapter XI.

Geometry on a Sphere

§ 1. Basis O C.

1. *Defs.* A '*great circle AB*' on a sphere, centre O, is the set of points where the sphere is met by the plane OAB. If A, B

be points on the sphere, not collinear with O, then the '*arc* AB' is the set of points where the sphere is met by rays in $A\hat{O}B$. If A, B, C be points on the sphere, no two collinear with O, then the '*spherical triangle* ABC' is the set of points A, B, C and the points of the arcs AB, BC, CA. These arcs are the '*sides*' of the triangle, the '*angle* $B\hat{A}C$' of the triangle is the dihedral angle between the half-planes $\{OA, B\}$ and $\{OA, C\}$.

Arc $XY \simeq$ arc AB means $X\hat{O}Y \simeq A\hat{O}B$.

If A, B, C, D be points on a sphere and A, B be not collinear with the centre O, nor C, D collinear with O, then the ordered couples (A, B) and (C, D) '*have the same sense*' if and only if they lie on the same great circle and $OA\hat{,}OB$ and $OC\hat{,}OD$ have the same sense (III 17).

If A, B, C be on a sphere, then '$[ABC]$' shall mean, 'B is on the arc AC.' A '*side*' of a great circle on a sphere is the set of points on the sphere and on one half-space of the plane of the great circle.

2. We shall now see how far our Axioms $\mathbf{O}_p\mathbf{C}_p$ and our definitions of Chapter II hold, when 'point' means point on a certain sphere, 'line' means great circle, and 'between' refers to the relation above asserted by $[ABC]$, and accordingly 'open interval' means arc.

·1. Ax. **C** I can be replaced by the following: If AB be any arc on a sphere, then on any great circle through a point A' of the sphere there is one and only one point B', such that $AB \simeq A'B'$ and (A', B') has a given sense on the great circle.

·2. Axs. **C** II, III, IV, VII hold unchanged, where of course angles between arcs on a sphere are congruent when the dihedral angles, which they *are*, (1), are congruent.

·3. Ax. **C** VI can be replaced by the following: If $P\hat{Q}R$ be any angle of a triangle, and AC any arc, then there are not more than two great circles through A such that there is a point B on them with $C\hat{A}B \simeq P\hat{Q}R$.

(All these statements easily follow from **O**, **C** in their original form.)

·4. If in two spherical triangles, two sides and the included angle, or three sides, or two angles and their common side, or three angles of one be congruent to the corresponding parts of the other, then the angles and sides of the first are congruent to the corresponding parts of the other (IV 96).

2·5. This shews **C** V, and secures agreement between our relation of congruence for our angles and the congruence of angles defined as in Chapter IV.

·6. Turning to Axioms $\mathbf{O}_p$, with the above definition of [*ABC*], and comparing lines and great circles, we find that the definition in II 3 does not give us the *whole* of the great circle through *AB* as the 'line' *AB*, and further we find that **O** III breaks down, with that definition of line.

But though the Order Axioms thus fail, many Theorems in Chapter IV hold on the sphere when we define (spherical) triangles as above. The most important failures occur for IV 36 and 59. Instead of the latter we now have:

·7. Any two great circles on a sphere meet in two points.

·8. We can restore all our Axioms $\mathbf{O}_p$, if we consider as 'points' only those points on the sphere which lie on one side of a great circle fixed once for all. But then Ax. **C** I*a* sometimes fails; but whenever *we can perform the needed constructions without leaving our present set of 'points' the Theorems deduced in Chapter IV hold, with the same proofs.* Thus the Theorems on congruence of triangles hold, except IV 37 (two angles and non-adjacent side).

3. *Def.* A '*pole*' of a great circle is a point where the perpendicular to the plane of the great circle, at the centre of the sphere, meets the sphere.

·1. If B' is a pole of *AC*, and C' of *AB*, then *A* is a pole of $B'C'$.

·2. If *ABC* be any (spherical) triangle and A' be that pole of *BC* which lies on the same side of *BC* as *A*, and similarly for B', C', then the triangle $A'B'C'$ is the '*polar triangle*' of *ABC*.

·3. If $A'B'C'$ be the polar triangle of *ABC*, then *ABC* is the polar triangle of $A'B'C'$.

Dem. Since A' is a pole of *BC*, and A, A' are on the same side of *BC*, therefore $\mu A\hat{O}A' < \pi/2$ (where O is the centre of the sphere). But A is a pole of $B'C'$ (·1), hence $\mu A\hat{O}A' < \pi/2$ shews that A, A' are on the same side of $B'C'$.

3·4. And $\mu B\hat{A}C = \pi - \mu B'\hat{O}C'$, $\mu B'\hat{A}'C' = \pi - \mu B\hat{O}C$. (By IV 84·3.)

·5. *If ABC be a (spherical) triangle, then*

$$\mu A\hat{O}B + \mu B\hat{O}C + \mu C\hat{O}A < 2\pi. \text{ (XII 34.)}$$

·6. *And* $\mu A\hat{C}B + \mu C\hat{B}A + \mu B\hat{A}C > \pi$.

Dem. Let $A'B'C'$ be the polar triangle of ABC, then

$$\mu A\hat{C}B = \pi - \mu A'\hat{O}'B', \text{ etc. (·4).}$$

But $\mu A'\hat{O}'B' + \mu B'\hat{O}'C' + \mu C'\hat{O}'A' < 2\pi$ (·5).

The Angle-sum of a Triangle

§ 2. **Basis $\mathbf{O}_p\mathbf{C}_p$.**

4. *Def.* If a polygon be dissected into triangles with their vertices at the vertices of the polygon, the sum of the angular measures of the angles of the triangles is the '*angle-sum*' of the polygon (X 36). The '*angle difference*' of the polygon is the difference between this sum and $(n-2)\pi$ (see X 38, where $\mathbf{P}_1$ is assumed).

5. The Theorem of Saccheri-Legendre. *According as in one triangle, the angle-sum is greater than, equal to or less than* π, *it is so in all*.*

We first shew 5·1·2·3.

·1. If $ABCD$ be a quadrilateral with $\hat{A}, \hat{B}, \hat{C}$ right angles, then $\mu BC \lesseqgtr \mu AD$ according as $\mu\hat{D} \lesseqgtr \pi/2$.

Dem. The right bisector of AB cannot meet $B^{\dashv}C$ or $A^{\dashv}D$ (IV 49·3), and so it meets $C^{-}D$ in N, say (X 11·1). Let $AC' \simeq BC$ with C' on $[AD$, then $NC' \perp AC'$. Hence $[AC'D]$ or $[ADC']$ or $C' = D$ according as $N\hat{D}A$, i.e. $C\hat{D}A$, has a measure less than, greater than or equal to $\pi/2$ (IV 60).

·2. If ACC_1A_1 be a quadrilateral, and $\hat{A}, \hat{C}$ be right angles, and $[AXC]$, and $XL \perp AC$, then XL meets $A_1{}^{-}C_1$ in X_1 say. (In this number and in ·3 the subscript to a letter shall be used

* Schur, *Grundlagen der Geometrie* (1909), § 6; Vahlen, *Abstrakte Geometrie* (1905), pp. 252 ff.

for this purpose always.) If X, Y, Z be on A^-C, and $[XYZ]$, then $[X_1Y_1Z_1]$.

5·3. *Considering quadrilaterals with three right angles, according as in one such quadrilateral the fourth angle has measure* $\lesseqqgtr \pi/2$, *this is the case with every such quadrilateral.*

Dem. If ACC_1A_1 be one such quadrilateral with $\hat{A}, \hat{C}, \hat{A}_1$ right angles, we can make a quadrilateral $ABXY$ congruent to another such quadrilateral, with B on $[AC$, Y on $[AA_1$ and $A\hat{B}X$, $A\hat{Y}X$ right angles, and we may assume $\mu AB < \mu AC$. Thus BX meets $A_1{}^-C_1$ in B_1 say. If then the Theorem be shewn for two such quadrilaterals related like ACC_1A_1 and ABB_1A_1, it will hold for AA_1B_1B, and $AYXB$, and so for such quadrilaterals generally.

To shew the Theorem for ACC_1A_1 and ABB_1A_1, we must shew, by ·1, that $\mu CC_1 >\!<\!= \mu AA_1$ imply respectively $\mu BB_1 >\!<\!= \mu AA_1$.

First let $CC_1 \simeq AA_1$ then if $BB' \simeq AA_1$ with B' on $[BB_1$ we have $L_1\hat{B}'B$ and $M_1\hat{B}'B$ right angles, where LL_1 and MM_1 are the right bisectors of AB, BC resp. (·1, IV 69). Hence $B_1 = B'$ and $BB_1 \simeq AA_1$. Similarly if $BB_1 \simeq AA_1$ then $CC_1 \simeq AA_1$.

Next let $\mu CC_1 > \mu AA_1$, then by the first part $AA_1 \simeq BB_1$ is false. We shall shew that

$$\mu BB_1 < \mu AA_1$$

is also false. For suppose it true, and let $CA' \simeq AA_1$ and $CB' \simeq BB_1$, with A', B' on $[CC_1$, then A' is on C^-C_1, and $[CB'A'C_1]$. Let NN_1, MM_1 be the right bisectors of AC, BC resp., then $N_1\hat{A}'C$ is a right angle; but $\mu M_1\hat{B}'C < \pi/2$ since $\mu M_1\hat{B}'C = \mu M_1\hat{B}_1B < \pi/2$ (·1), since $\mu BB_1 < \mu AA_1$. But since $[CBA]$, we have $[CMN]$ and hence $[C_1M_1N_1]$ (·2). But $[B'A'C_1]$, and thus $M_1{}^-B'$ and $N_1{}^-A'$ meet in P, say. And $[A'B'C]$; hence $\mu P\hat{B}'C > \mu P\hat{A}'C$, i.e. $\mu M_1\hat{B}'C > \mu N_1\hat{A}'C = \pi/2$, contrary to the above.

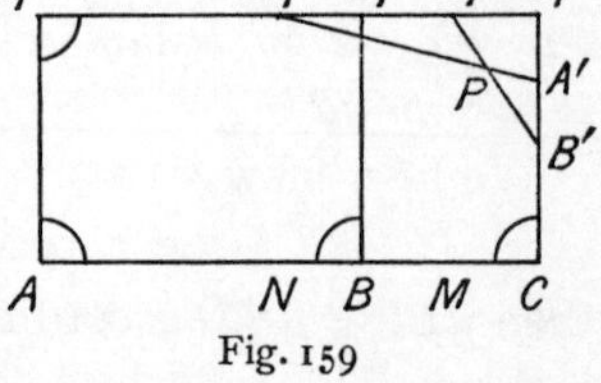

Fig. 159

Hence $\mu BB_1 < \mu AA_1$ is also false, and thus $\mu BB_1 > \mu AA_1$.

Similarly $\mu CC_1 < \mu AA_1$ implies $\mu BB_1 < \mu AA_1$, and the Theorem follows.

Dem. of 5. Let ABC be any triangle and let F, D be the mid-points of AB, AC, and let KB, $LC \perp FD$ with K, L on FD. Let MX be the right bisector of KL and so of BC (IV 69). Then if $AH \perp FD$ with H on FD, we have

$$AH \simeq BK \simeq CL \text{ (IV 68)},$$

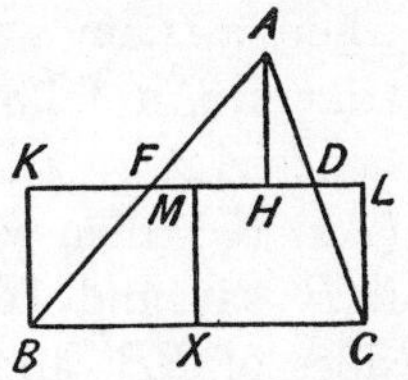

Fig. 160

whence $K\hat{B}A \simeq B\hat{A}H$, $L\hat{C}A \simeq C\hat{A}H$. From these it easily follows, wherever H may be on KL, that $\mu K\hat{B}C + \mu L\hat{C}B$ equals the angle-sum of triangle ABC. But $K\hat{B}C \simeq L\hat{C}B$ (IV 69). Hence according as the angle-sum of triangle ABC is $> < = \pi$, the fourth angle $K\hat{B}X$ of the quadrilateral $KMXB$ (whose angles $\hat{K}$, $\hat{M}$, $\hat{X}$ are right angles) will have measure $> < = \pi/2$, and this will be the case for each quadrilateral with three right angles (·3). Hence 5 is shewn.

6. *Two triangles ABC, $A'BC$, which are such that the mid-points of AB, AC, $A'B$, $A'C$ colline, have equal angle-sums.* (5 *Dem.*)

7. *If one quadrilateral exist with all its angles right angles, the angle-sum of any triangle is π.*

The Angle-sum of a Triangle and the Parallel Axiom

8. If the angle-sum of a triangle is π, and

$$\mu B_1\hat{B}A + \mu B\hat{A}A_1 = \pi,$$

and A_1, B_1 are on the same side of AB, then AA_1 and BB_1 do not meet.

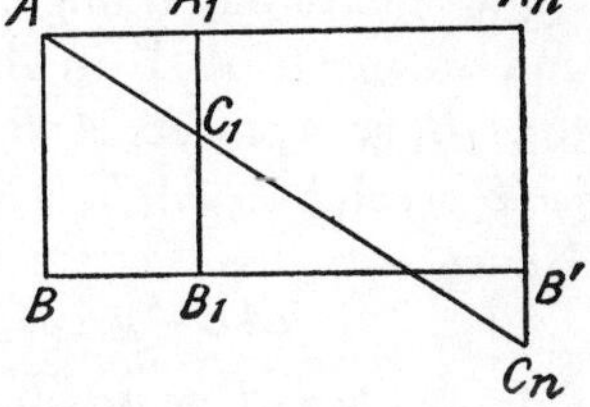

Fig. 161

9. *If the angle-sum of a triangle is π, then through a given point A not on BB_1 can be drawn one, and only one, line in the plane ABB_1 which does not meet BB_1, provided Axiom* $\mathbf{K}_1$ *is true.*

Dem. Let $AB \perp BB_1$, $AA_1 \perp AB$ where A_1, B_1 are on the same side of AB. Then AA_1 and BB_1 do not meet (8). Let $A_1B_1 \perp BB_1$, then $A_1B_1 \perp AA_1$. Let another line through A meet A_1-B_1 in C_1. We shew that A_1C_1 meets BB_1. If A_n, C_n are points on $[AA_1$, $[AC_1$ such that $\mu AA_n = n.AA_1$, $\mu AC_n = n.AC_1$ where n is any natural number, then by a series of congruent triangles, it follows that $\mu A_nC_n = n.A_1C_1$, $A_nC_n \perp AA_1$, and hence $A_nC_n \perp BB_1$. If then we take n so that $n.A_1C_1 > \mu AB$ (Ax. $\mathbf{K}_1$), then will $\mu A_nC_n > \mu AB$. But A_nC_n and BB_1 meet in B', say, and $AB \simeq A_nB'$ (5·1). Hence A_n, C_n are on opposite sides of BB', and so AC_n meets BB'. The case of any other line through A is now easily treated.

10. *If* $\mathbf{K}_1$ *holds, the angle-sum of a triangle cannot be greater than* π.

Dem. Suppose the angle-sum of a triangle is greater than π.

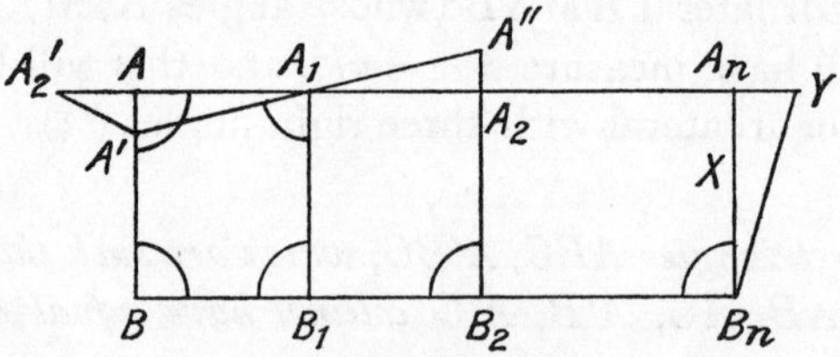

Fig. 162

Let AA_1, $BB_1 \perp AB$, then AA_1, BB_1 do not meet (IV 49·3). Let $\mu BB_n = n.BB_1$, where B_n is on $[BB_1$ and n is any natural number, and let $B_nX \perp BB_n$ where X is on $\{BB_n, A\}$. If $AY \simeq BB_n$, with Y on $[AA_1$, then $A{-}Y$, $B{-}B_n$ do not meet, and $B\hat{B}_nY \simeq A\hat{Y}B_n$ (IV 69), and hence $\mu B\hat{B}_nY > \pi/2$ (the angle-sum of any triangle being $> \pi$). Thus $[B_nX$ is in $B\hat{B}_nY$ and so meets $A{-}Y$ in A_n, say. Similarly the perpendicular to A_1B_1 at A_1 meets $A{-}B$ and $A_2B_2]$ in A' and A'', say. Now $\mu AB > \mu A_1B_1 > \mu A_2B_2 > \ldots$ (5·1); $\mu A''B_2 = \mu A'B < \mu A_1B_1$ (5·1). Hence

$$\mu AB - \mu A_1B_1 < \mu AB - \mu A'B = \mu AA';$$

$$\mu A_2A'' = \mu A''B_2 - \mu A_2B_2 < \mu A_1B_1 - \mu A_2B_2.$$

Hence if we can shew $\mu AA' < \mu A_2A''$, we shall have

$$\mu AB - \mu A_1B_1 < \mu A_1B_1 - \mu A_2B_2,$$

and similarly we shall get $\mu A_1B_1 - \mu A_2B_2 < \mu A_2B_2 - \mu A_3B_3$, and so on. Now by $\mathbf{K}_1$ there is a natural number n, such that $n(AB - A_1B_1) > \mu AB$, and hence we shall have

$$\mu(AB - A_1B_1) + (A_1B_1 - A_2B_2) + \ldots + (A_{n-1}B_{n-1} - A_nB_n) > \mu AB.$$

Hence $\mu AB - \mu A_n B_n > \mu AB$, contrary to IV 13.

It remains to shew that $\mu AA' < \mu A_2 A''$. Now $A_1A' \simeq A_1A''$. Let $A_1A_2' \simeq A_1A_2$ where A_2' is on $[A_1A$. Then since $A'\hat{A}A_2'$ is a right angle, and $A \neq A_2'$ (since $A_1\hat{A}_2B_2$ is not a right angle), we have $\mu AA' < \mu A'A_2'$ while $A'A_2' \simeq A_2A''$; hence the result follows.

The corresponding inequalities, which arise from the perpendiculars through A_r to A_rB_r, follow from the fact that always $\mu B_r\hat{A}_rA_{r-1} + \mu B_{r-1}\hat{A}_{r-1}A_r > \pi$, and hence

$$\mu B_r\hat{A}_rA_{r-1} > \mu B_{r-1}\hat{A}_{r-1}A_{r-2}.$$

10·1. Thus if **C**, $\mathbf{K}_1$ hold, the angle-sum of a triangle can be greater than π, only if the Axioms **O** break down somewhere. This is illustrated by the geometry on the sphere considered in § 1.

·2. *The Theorems in* 9, 10 *depend essentially on* $\mathbf{K}_1$. In fact, there are Geometries in which $\mathbf{K}_1$ is false, but $\mathbf{O}_p\mathbf{C}_p$ hold, and in which an infinity of lines can be drawn through a given point not to meet a given coplanar line, and yet in which the angle-sum of a triangle is greater than or equal to π*, (as well as such a Geometry in which $\mathbf{K}_1$ may or may not hold, and in which the angle-sum of a triangle is less than π (VIII 49)).

We will briefly indicate a geometry—semi-Euclidean Geometry—in which the angle-sum is π, and yet an infinity of lines can be drawn through a given point so as not to meet a given coplanar line. Take the non-Archimedean field F of I 27·2, in which each element has a square root, and is of form

$$A = a_{m_1}\xi^{m_1} + a_{m_2}\xi^{m_2} + \dots \ (a_{m_1} \neq 0)\ (m_1 < m_2 < \dots),$$

the m being positive or negative rationals with finite greatest common denominator λ (which may vary from element to element), and the a being real. The '*order*' of A is m_1. A is '*proper*' or '*improper*' according as $m_1 > 0$ or $m_1 \leqq 0$. A '*point*' P shall be a complex number $x + iy = z$ where x, y are in F, and the laws of addition and multiplication of the complex numbers are as in I 28. The '*order*' of $x + iy$ is the lower of the orders of x and y. The '*line*' z_1z_2 shall be the set of points $z_3 = z_1 + (z_2 - z_1)\lambda$, where λ is in F. If $0 < \lambda < 1$ (see I 27), then z_3 is '*between*' z_1 and z_2. A point of order > 0 is '*proper*,'

* Cf. Vahlen, *l.c.* The result is due to Dehn, *Math. Ann.* LIII (1900), p. 404.

a line is '*proper*' when it contains at least one proper point. *Every line* $z_1 z_2$ *contains an infinity of improper points*, e.g. $z_1 + (z_2 - z_1)\,\xi^{-n_2}$, if n_1 is the order of z_1, and n_2 of z_2, and $n_2 \geqq n_1$. Every proper line contains an infinity of proper points, for if z_1 and z_2 are proper, so is $z_1 + (z_2 - z_1)\,\xi^n$, if $n > 0$. All points between two proper points are proper.

Two figures are '*congruent*' when one is transformed into the other by a '*translation*' $z' = z + (u + iv)$ or by a '*rotation*'

$$z' = \frac{a + ib}{\sqrt{a^2 + b^2}} \cdot z$$

where u, v, a, b are in F. A translation is '*proper*' if it transforms at least one proper point into a proper point; then it transforms every proper point into a proper point; for if z_1, z_2 and $z_1' = z_1 + (u + iv)$ are proper, so are $u + iv$ and $z_2' = z_2 + (u + iv)$. By a rotation every proper point becomes a proper point, since the order of $\dfrac{a + ib}{\sqrt{a^2 + b^2}}$ is always zero.

This geometry of proper and improper points is essentially identical with Euclidean coordinate plane geometry (cf. VIII § 9), and the order and congruence Axioms are true for the *proper* points and lines, while $\mathbf{P}_3'$ is not, by the statement italicised above. From the analogy with the Euclidean Geometry we see that the angle-sum of a triangle is π. Similarly a 'semi-elliptic' Geometry can be constructed in which the angle-sum of a triangle is greater than π, but yet an infinite number of lines can be drawn through a given point so as not to meet a given coplanar line. Thus from $\mathbf{O}_p$, $\mathbf{C}_p$ alone, nothing can be deduced about the angle-sum of a triangle, though we can deduce the existence of at least one parallel from a given point to a given line (IV 59).

*Non-Euclidean Areas**

The above results have a very direct bearing on the theory of non-Euclidean areas. As in XI § 1 we only assumed our present basis $\mathbf{O}_p \mathbf{C}_p$, we may use the results shewn there. The work below also includes as a special case the theory of areas on a sphere, if we restrict ourselves to points on one side of a great circle and can perform our constructions without leaving that set of points (2·8).

11. *If a triangle t be dissected into n triangles t_i the angle-difference of t equals the sum of the angle-differences of the t_i.*

Dem. First let no vertex of any sub-triangle fall on a side

* Finzel, "Die Lehre vom Flächeninhalt in der allgemeinen Geometrie," *Math. Ann.* LXXII (1912), p. 262.

of any sub-triangle. If a vertex common to some of the t_i falls at a vertex of t, the sum of the measures of the angles of the t_i at that vertex equals that of the angle of t there; if it falls inside t, or on a side of t, that sum is 2π or π resp. Let s be the angle-sum of t, and s_i of t_i, then $\sum_1^n s_i = s + (2a+b)\pi$ where a, b are the numbers of the vertices of the t_i which fall inside t or on a side of t resp. If ϵ denote the angle-differences, then $\sum_1^n s_i - n\pi = \sum_1^n \epsilon_i$, $s - \pi = \epsilon$. Hence $\sum_1^n \epsilon_i = \epsilon + (2a+b+1-n)\pi$; we must shew $2a+b+1-n=0$. Now the total number of points which are vertices is $a+b+3$, of open intervals which are sides is e, say, and of sub-triangles is n; hence $a+b+3+n=e+1$ (X 39). If we detach the sub-triangles from each other, the number of their vertices becomes

$$3n = 2e - (b+3).$$

The last two formulae give $2a+b+1-n=0$.

If a side of a sub-triangle contains a vertex of another we can dissect this sub-triangle further, so that this case no longer arises. This further dissection does not alter the sum of the angle-differences, by the first part of the proof.

11·1. The same result is true for a polygon dissected into triangles and is shewn in the same way.

§ 3. **Basis $\mathbf{O}_p\mathbf{C}_p$** *and the assumption* (compatible with $\mathbf{O}_p\mathbf{C}_p$ by 10·2) *that the angle-difference of one triangle*, and so of all (5), *is not zero.*

12. *Def.* The '*measure*' of a polygon p, denoted by μp, is its angle-difference.

·1. Congruent polygons have the same measure.

·11. No polygon has measure zero.

·2. If a polygon be dissected into triangles, its measure is the sum of theirs (11·1).

·3. If $p_1 \cong p_2$, then $\mu p_1 = \mu p_2$.

·4. Two triangles ABC, $A'BC$, such that the mid-points of AB, AC, $A'B$, $A'C$ colline, have the same measure (6) and are also equivalent (XI 4 *Dem.*, XI 1·1).

12·5. Conversely two equivalent triangles ABC, $A'BC$ with a common side BC, such that A' is on $\{BC, A\}$, are such that the mid-points of AB, AC, $A'B$, $A'C$ colline.

Dem. Use the construction of 5 *Dem.* for both the triangles ABC and $A'BC$, and suppose F, D, F', D' do not colline (dashed letters refer to the triangle $A'BC$). Since the angle-sums of ABC and $A'BC$ are equal (·3), and that of ΔABC is $\mu K\hat{B}C + \mu L\hat{C}B$, and since $K\hat{B}C \simeq L\hat{C}B$, we must have B, K, K' collinear and C, L, L' collinear (5 *Dem.*). Hence $KLL'K'$ has all its angles right angles, contrary to our assumption (7).

·6. The last still holds if we replace 'equivalent triangles' by 'triangles of the same measure.'

·7. Given a triangle ABC, and an interval s of measure greater than the measure of at least one of the sides BC of the triangle, we can on s make a triangle with the same measure as ABC, by means of constructions **abcd**$_1$.

Dem. Take D on $[BC$ with $BD \simeq s$, and let G be mid AC, and J be mid CD; JG meets A-B in K, say. Take E so that $KE \simeq KA$ and $[AKE]$, then DBE is a triangle such as is required.

For let A_1, E_1, C_1, D_1 be the feet of the perpendiculars from A, E, C, D on GJ. It follows at once by congruence that A-A_1, E-E_1, C-C_1, D-D_1 are all congruent, and that hence GJ meets E-D in its mid-point L, say.

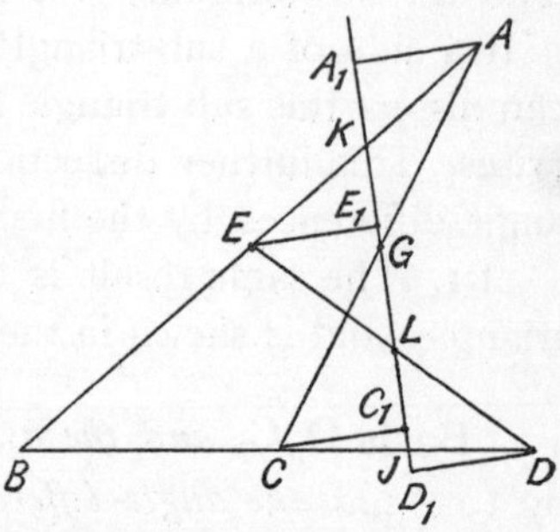

Fig. 163

Hence the triangles ADC, ADE are such that the mid-points of CA, CD, EA, ED colline, hence $\mu ADC = \mu ADE$ (·4). It is easily shewn from $\mathbf{O}_p\mathbf{C}_p$ that E is on A-B; hence

$$\Delta ABD \equiv ABC + ADC \equiv DBE + ADE,$$

and $$\mu ABC = \mu DBE.$$

·8. We can construct by **abcd**$_1$ an 'isosceles' triangle on BD with the same measure as a given triangle DBE.

Dem. Let $BDLK$ be the isosceles birectangle, equivalent to DBE, constructed as in XI 4, and let XY be the right bisector of BD, KL (IV 69), with X, Y on BD, KL resp., and let Z, W be the mid-points of KY, LY. Then BZ, DW meet XY in the same point F, and BDF is the isosceles triangle required, for Z, W are also the mid-points of BF, DF, and $BF \simeq DF$.

13. *Two triangles with the same measure are equivalent.*

Dem. Take an interval of measure greater than those of all the sides of both triangles, and on it make triangles lying on the same half-plane and whose measures are the same as those of the given triangles; these triangles are thus related like those of 12·6, and hence they are equivalent (12·4).

·1. Given n triangles, we can find 2^{n-1} mutually congruent triangles, the sum of whose measures equals the sum of the measures of the n triangles and which form a set equivalent to the given set.

Dem. Given two triangles t_1, t_2 we can construct on a sufficiently large base AB, two triangles ABC, ABD with $AC \simeq BC$, $AD \simeq BD$, $\mu ABC = \mu t_1$, $\mu ABD = \mu t_2$, and with C, D on opposite sides of AB (12·8). Then $ACD \simeq BCD$ and $ACD + BCD \cong t_1 + t_2$ (13). Given three triangles t_1, t_2, t_3, we can construct two congruent triangles $d_1 = ACD$, $d_1' = BCD$ as before, and also an isosceles triangle of the same measure as t_3 and this can be dissected into two congruent triangles d_2, d_2'.

Then
$$\mu(t_1 + t_2 + t_3) = \mu(d_1 + d_2 + d_1' + d_2'),$$
$$t_1 + t_2 + t_3 \cong d_1 + d_2 + d_1' + d_2' \ (13).$$

Then by the first part of the proof we can find two congruent triangles d with $\mu(d_1 + d_2) = \mu(d + d)$, $d_1 + d_2 \cong d + d$.

Thus $\mu(t_1 + t_2 + t_3) - 4\mu d$, $t_1 + t_2 + t_3 \simeq d + d + d + d$.

The Theorem can now be shewn by induction.

14. *Two polygons p_1, p_2 with the same measure are equivalent.*

Dem. p_1 can be dissected into, say, n triangles and these can be replaced by 2^{n-1} mutually congruent triangles, the sum of whose measures is μp, and the set of which triangles is equivalent to p_1. Similarly for p_2 and we can clearly make n the same for p_1 and p_2. *All* the triangles have then the same measure and are therefore equivalent (13). Hence $p_1 \cong p_2$.

·1. If we assumed Ax. $\mathbf{K}_1$, we could shew that $\mu p_1 = \mu p_2$ implies $p_1 \cong p_2$ (+).

15. *If triangles ABC, XYZ have corresponding angles congruent, the triangles are congruent.*

Dem. If not, there are points $B_1 \neq B$ on $[AB$ and $C_1 \neq C$ on $[AC$ with $AB_1 \simeq XY$, $AC_1 \simeq XZ$, and hence $AB_1C_1 \simeq XYZ$. The angle-sum of BB_1C_1C is then 2π and its measure zero, contrary to 12·11.

·1. *Thus on the present basis, triangles similar in the Euclidean sense and not congruent cannot possibly exist.*

§ 4. *The Axiom of Similarity*

16. If we assume Axioms **O**, **C**, and that triangles exist which are not congruent but which have their corresponding angles congruent, it follows that the angle-sum in all triangles is π, but Ax. $\mathbf{P}_3'$ does not follow, unless we assume Ax. $\mathbf{K}_1$ (10·2).

·1. If, however, we assume **O**, **C** and the following:

If ABC be a triangle and XY any interval, then there is a point Z such that $A\hat{B}C$, $B\hat{C}A$, $C\hat{A}B$ are resp. congruent to $X\hat{Y}Z$, $Y\hat{Z}X$, $Z\hat{X}Y$, then Ax. $\mathbf{P}_3'$ does follow*.

Literature

Treatments of the foundations of Geometry, Euclidean and non-Euclidean, which differ widely from that in this book will be found in the following:

Schur. *Grundlagen der Geometrie* (1909).

Baker. *Principles of Geometry*, Vols. I and II (1922).

Veblen. *Projective Geometry*, Vols. I and II (1910, 1918).

Whitehead. *The Axioms of Descriptive Geometry* (Cambridge Tracts No. 5) (1907).

Whitehead. *The Axioms of Projective Geometry* (Cambridge Tracts No. 4) (1906).

Peano. *Formulario Mathematico* (1908).

Weyl. *Mathematische Analysis des Raumproblems* (1923).

The latter monograph is probably the deepest study of possible spaces yet made.

* M. J. M. Hill, "Wallis's Postulate of Similarity," *Proc. Camb. Phil. Soc.* XXII (1925), p. 965 and XXIII (1926), p. 19.

For further references to the Literature see

Sommerville. *Bibliography of Non-Euclidean Geometry* (1911).

Enriques. *Prinzipien der Geometrie*, Enz. der Math. Wiss.

The logical background of any mathematical theory is discussed in:

Russell. *Introduction to Mathematical Philosophy* (1919).

Whitehead and Russell. *Principia Mathematica* (2nd Edition, 1925).

Wittgenstein. *Tractatus Logico-Philosophicus* (1922).

Burali-Forti. *Logica Matematica* (2nd Edition, 1919).

Peano. *Formulario Mathematico* (1908, and earlier editions).

LIST OF THE GEOMETRIC AXIOMS EMPLOYED

(*Numbers refer to pages*)

Axioms of Order	**O** I, II, 44; III, 45; IV, V, VI, 48; VII, 60; VIII, 65. **O** I—VI are quoted as $\mathbf{O}_p$; **O** I—VIII as **O**.
Axioms of Congruence	**C** I*a*, 91; I*b*, II, III, IV, 92; V, 97; VI, 102; VII, 111. For $\mathbf{C}_p$ see p. 112. The congruence Axioms are quoted together as **C**.
Circle Axioms	**Q**, 131; $\mathbf{Q}_1$, 134; $\mathbf{Q}_0$, 199; $\mathbf{Q}_2$, 220.
Parallel Axioms	$\mathbf{P}_0$, $\mathbf{P}_1$, $\mathbf{P}_2$, $\mathbf{P}_3$, $\mathbf{P}_0'$, $\mathbf{P}_1'$, $\mathbf{P}_2'$, $\mathbf{P}_3'$, **P**, 139.
Projective Axioms	**A** 1, **A** 2,..., **A** 7, 159; **A**′, $\mathbf{A}_p'$, 160.
Archimedes' Axiom	$\mathbf{K}_1$, 221.
Continuity Axiom	**K**, 297.
Pieri's Axioms	Chapter XIV.
Theorem **M**	96.

LIST OF CONSTRUCTIONS

a, **b**, **c**, $\mathbf{d}_1$, 107; **e**, 122; **q**, 131; $\mathbf{q}_1$, 134; **p**, 198; **d**, 217; $\mathbf{q}_2$, 219.

LIST OF SYMBOLS IN FREQUENT USE

Name	*Symbol*	*Page*
Identity	$=$	3
Diversity	$\neq$	3
Precedes	$\prec$	7
Precedes, succeeds	$A(\prec OU)B$, $A(\succ OU)B$	75
" "	$x(\prec Oab)y$, $x(\succ Oab)y$	77
Order	$[ABC]$, $[P_1P_2 \dots P_n]$	44, 54
Cyclic order	$(a_1a_2 \dots a_n)$	84
Line	AB	46
Interval	$A \vdash\!\dashv B$, $A \dashv B$, $A \vdash B$, $A - B$	46
Ray	$[OA$; $OA]$	53
Triangle	$\triangle ABC$	55
Plane	ABC	57
Tetrahedron	$\triangle ABCD$	60
Space	$ABCD$	61
Way	$A_1A_2 \dots A_n$	67
Ordered way	$(A_1A_2 \cdots A_n)$	239
Half-plane	$\{AB, C\}$	68
Half-space	$\{ABC, D\}$	85
Angle	$\widehat{hk}$; $A\hat{O}B$	69
Sensed angle	$\widehat{a, b}$; $\widehat{OA, OB}$	79
Dihedral angle	$\widehat{\alpha\beta}$	85
Trihedral angle	$O.A\hat{B}C$; $O.a\hat{b}c$	85
Cross	$\not\angle A\hat{O}B$	120, 151
Meet of planes	$\alpha\beta$	122
Congruent	$\simeq$	92, 93, 94, 99, 100, 120
Plus	$+$	19, 95, 113
Greater, less than	$>$, $<$	19, 95, 114
Measure	μ	95, 113, 124, 262, 265, 285, 287
Perpendicular	$\perp$	106, 122, 124
Parallel	$\parallel$	138, 155
Proportion	$s \mid s' \sim t \mid t'$	167
Similar	$\sim$	169
Dissection	$\equiv$	247
Equivalent	$p \cong q(+)$; $p \cong q$	257
"	$P \cong Q(\mathrm{T})$, $(\mathrm{T}+)$, $(\mathrm{T}-)$	291

INDEX

(*The numbers refer to pages*)

THE ELEMENTS OF NON-EUCLIDEAN GEOMETRY

by D. M. Y. Sommerville

Almost immediately upon publication Dr. Sommerville's book became the standard text in the field. It is renowned for its lucid yet meticulous exposition and, unlike advanced treatises, it can, for the most part, be understood by anyone who has a good knowledge of high school algebra and geometry. The arrangement follows the traditional pattern of plane and solid geometry where theorems are deduced from axioms and postulates. In this way, the student can follow the development of non-Euclidean geometry in strictly logical order, from a fundamental analysis of the concept of parallelism to such advanced topics as inversion and transformations.

Elementary hyperbolic geometry; elliptic geometry; analytic non-Euclidean geometry; representations of non-Euclidean geometry in Euclidean space; space curvature and the philosophical implications of non-Euclidean geometry; the theory of the radical axes, homothetic centres, and systems of circles; inversion, equations of transformation, groups of motions; and the classification of conics are developed with exceptional clarity.

Although this is primarily an elementary text, Dr. Sommerville treats such important and difficult topics as the relation between parataxy and parallelism, the absolute measure, the pseudosphere, Gauss' proof of the defect-area theorem, geodesic representation, and others with simplicity and ease. 126 problems at chapter endings give the student practise in using the forms and methods developed in the text and provide many important corollaries.

133 figures. 126 problems. Index. xvi + 274pp. 5⅜ x 8.

S460 Paperbound **$1.50**

ORY OF MATHEMATICS, D. Struik. Lucid study of development of mathematica , from Ancient Near East, Greece, Islamic science, Middle Ages, Renaissance, mportant mathematicians are described in detail. Treatment is not anecdotal, evelopment of ideas. "Rich in content, thoughtful in interpretation" U. S. KLIST. Non-technical; no mathematical training needed. Index. 60 illustrations, n papyri, Greek mss., portraits of 31 eminent mathematicians. Bibliography. + 299pp. 5⅜ x 8. S255 Paperbound **$1.75**

F GEOMETRY, Bertrand Russell. Analyzing basic problems in the overlap area itics and philosophy, Nobel laureate Russell examines the nature of geometrical nature of geometry, and the application of geometry to space. It covers the uclidean geometry, philosophic interpretations of geometry—especially Kant— etrical geometry. This is most interesting as the solution offered in 1897 by a problem still current. New introduction by Prof. Morris Kline of N. Y. University. x 8. S232 Clothbound **$3.25** S233 Paperbound **$1.60**

PHYSICAL THEORY, P. W. Bridgman. Here is how modern physics looks to a physicist—a Nobel laureate. Pointing out many absurdities of science, and inadequacies of various physical theories, Dr. Bridgman weighs and analyzes of Einstein, Bohr, Newton, Heisenberg, and many others. This is a non- ation of the correlation of science and reality. Index. xi + 138pp. 5⅜ x 8. S33 Paperbound **$1.25**

THEORY IN PHYSICS, Max Born. A Nobel laureate examines the nature and nterclaims of experiment and theory in physics. Synthetic versus analytical sci- are analyzed in the work of Einstein, Bohr, Heisenberg, Planck, Eddington, s by a fellow participant. 44pp. 5⅜ x 8. S308 Paperbound **60c**

THE HISTORY OF MATHEMATICS & THE STUDY OF THE HISTORY OF SCIENCE, Scientific method & philosophy in 2 scholarly fields. Defines duty of historian des especially useful bibliography with best available biographies of modern editions of their collected works, correspondence. Shows that combination of will aid scholar in understanding science today. Bibliography includes best on historical methods. 200-item critically evaluated bibliography. Index. 10 volumes bound as one. 113pp. + 75pp. 5⅜ x 8. T240 Paperbound **$1.25**

METHOD, Henri Poincaré. Procedure of scientific discovery, methodology, experi- ination—the intellectual processes by which discoveries come into being. Most most interesting aspects of development, application of ideas. Chapters cover s, chance, mathematical reasoning, mathematics and logic; Whitehead, Russell, mechanics, etc. 288pp. 5⅜ x 8. S222 Paperbound **$1.25**

HYPOTHESIS, Henri Poincaré. Creative psychology in science. How such concepts gnitude, space, force, classical mechanics were developed, and how the modern m in his thought. Hypothesis in physics, theories of modern physics. Introduction armor. "Few mathematicians have had the breadth of vision of Poincaré, and rior in the gift of clear exposition," E. T. Bell. Index. 272pp. 5⅜ x 8. S221 Paperbound **$1.25**

OF PHYSICS, R. B. Lindsay & H. Margenau. Excellent bridge between semi- technical treatises. A discussion of methods of physical description, construction ble for physicist with elementary calculus who is interested in ideas that give , tools of modern physics. Contents include symbolism, mathematical equations; oundations of mechanics; probability; physics & continua; electron theory; special vity; quantum mechanics; causality. "Thorough and yet not overdetailed. Unre- ended," NATURE (London). Unabridged, corrected edition. List of recommended lustrations. xi + 537pp. 5⅜ x 8. S377 Paperbound **$2.45**

CLASSICS OF SCIENCE

OOKS OF EUCLID'S ELEMENTS, edited by Sir Thomas Heath. Definitive edition very greatest classics of Western world. Complete English translation of Heiberg with spurious Book XIV. Detailed 150-page introduction discussing aspects of eval mathematics. Euclid, texts, commentators, etc. Paralleling the text is an l apparatus analyzing each definition, proposition, postulate, covering textual atical analysis, commentators of all times, refutations, supports, extrapolations, full EUCLID. Unabridged reproduction of Cambridge U. 2nd edition. 3 volumes. ures, 1426pp. 5⅜ x 8. S88,89,90 3 volume set, paperbound **$6.00**

aac Newton. In its discussions of light, reflection, color, refraction, theories of uscular theories of light, this work is packed with scores of insights and dis- precise and practical discussion of construction of optical apparatus, contemporary of phenomena it is truly fascinating to modern physicists, astronomers, mathe- word by Albert Einstein. Preface by I. B. Cohen of Harvard University. 7 pages simile pages, letters, etc. cxvi + 414pp. 5⅜ x 8. S205 Paperbound **$2.00**

OF RELATIVITY, A. Einstein, H. Lorentz, M. Minkowski, H. Weyl. These are the that founded the general and special theories of relativity, all translated into papers by Lorentz on the Michelson experiment, electromagnetic phenomena. ACE & TIME, and Weyl's GRAVITATION & ELECTRICITY. 7 epoch-making papers CTROMAGNETICS OF MOVING BODIES, INFLUENCE OF GRAVITATION IN PROP- IGHT, COSMOLOGICAL CONSIDERATIONS, GENERAL THEORY, and 3 others. 7 ial notes by A. Sommerfeld. 224pp. 5⅜ x 8. S81 Paperbound **$1.75**

A CONCISE HISTORY OF MATHEMATICS

by D. J. Struik

This compact, readable history describes the main trends in the development of all fields of mathematics throughout the ages, Students, researchers, historians — specialists and layment alike — will find it extremely useful and interesting.

Beginning with the Ancient Near East, the author traces mathematical ideas and techniques through Egypt, Babylonia, China, India, and Arabia. He considers Greek and Roman developments from their beginnings in Ionian rationalism to the fall of Constantinople; covers Medieval European ideas and Renaissance trends; analyzes 17th and 18th century contributions; and concludes with an exposition of 19th century concepts.

A CONCISE HISTORY OF MATHEMATICS covers such early developments as the Egyptian Papyrus Rhind, the Ten Classics of China, the Siddhantas of India, the Liber Abaci, and others. Every important figure in mathematical history is dealt with — Euclid, Archimedes, Diophantus, Omar Khayyam, Boethius, Fermat, Pascal, Newton, Leibnitz, Fourier, Gauss, Riemann, Cantor, and many others.

"A very valuable book," AMERICAN MATHEMATICAL MONTHLY. "A remarkably complete and accurate picture of the history of pure mathematics," JOURNAL OF THE ROYAL NAVAL SCIENTIFIC SERVICE. "Compact, orderly, authentic," AMERICAN JOURNAL OF PSYCHOLOGY.

Second revised edition. Bibliography. Index. 60 illustrations, including Egyptian papyri, Greek mss., portraits of 31 eminent mathematicians. xix + 299pp. 5⅜ x 8.

S255 Paperbound **$1.75**

NON-EUCLIDEAN GEOMETRY

by Roberto Bonola

This is an excellent historical and mathematical view by a renowned Italian geometer of the geometries that have arisen from a study of Euclid's 5th postulate on parallel lines. Students, teachers and mathematicians will find here a ready reference source and guide to a field that has now become overwhelmingly important.

NON-EUCLIDEAN GEOMETRY first examines the various attempts to prove Euclid's parallel postulate — by the Greeks, by the Arabs, by mathematicians of the Renaissance. Then, ranging through the 17th, 18th and 19th centuries, it considers the forerunners and founders of non-Euclidean geometry, such as Saccheri, Lambert, Legendre, W. Bolyai, Gauss, Schweikart, Taurinus, J. Bolyai and Lobatschewsky. In a discussion of later developments, the author treats the work of Riemann, Helmholtz and Lie; the impossibility of proving Euclid's postulate, and similar topics. The complete text of two of the founding monographs is appended to Bonola's study: "The Science of Absolute Space" by John Bolyai and "Geometrical Researches on the Theory of Parallels" by Nicholas Lobatschewsky.

"Firmly recommended to any scientific reader with some mathematical inclination" JOURNAL OF THE ROYAL NAVAL SCIENTIFIC SERVICE. "Classics on the subject," SCIENTIFIC AMERICAN.

Translation with additional appendices by H. S. Carslaw. 256 bibliographic footnote references. Introduction by Federigo Enriques. Index. 181 diagrams. 431pp. 5 3/8 x 8.

S27 Paperbound **$1.95**

THE ANALYTICAL THEORY OF HEAT, Joseph Fourier. This book, which revolutionized mathematical physics, is listed in the Great Books program, and many other listings of great books. It has been used with profit by generations of mathematicians and physicists who are interested in either heat or in the application of the Fourier integral. Covers cause and reflections of rays of heat, radiant heating, heating of closed spaces, use of trigonometric series in the theory of heat, Fourier integral, etc. Translated by Alexander Freeman. 20 figures. xxii + 466pp. 5⅜ x 8. S93 Paperbound **$2.00**

THE WORKS OF ARCHIMEDES, edited by **T. L. Heath.** All the known works of the great Greek mathematician are contained in this one volume, including the recently discovered Method of Archimedes. Contains: On Sphere & Cylinder, Measurement of a Circle, Spirals, Concids, Spheroids, etc. This is the definitive edition of the greatest mathematical intellect of the ancient world. 186-page study by Heath discusses Archimides and the history of Greek mathematics. Bibliography. 563pp. 5⅜ x 8. S9 Paperbound **$2.00**

A PHILOSOPHICAL ESSAY ON PROBABILITIES, Marquis de Laplace. This famous essay explains without recourse to mathematics the principle of probability, and the application of probability to games of chance, natural philosophy, astronomy, many other fields. Translated from the 6th French edition by F. W. Truscott, F. L. Emory, with new introduction for this edition by E. T. Bell. 204pp. 5⅜ x 8. S166 Paperbound **$1.25**

INVESTIGATIONS ON THE THEORY OF THE BROWNIAN MOVEMENT, Albert Einstein. Reprints from rare European journals. 5 basic papers, including the Elementary Theory of the Brownian Movement, written at the request of Lorentz to provide a simple explanation. Translated by A. D. Cowper. Annotated, edited by R. Fürth. 33pp. of notes elucidate, give history of previous investigations. Author, subject indexes. 62 footnotes. 124pp. 5⅜ x 8. S304 Paperbound **$1.25**

THE GEOMETRY OF RENÉ DESCARTES. With this book Descartes founded analytical geometry. Original French text, with Descartes' own diagrams, and excellent Smith-Latham translation. Contains Problems the Construction of Which Requires Only Straight Lines and Circles; On the Nature of Curved Lines; On the Construction of Solid or Supersolid Problems. Notes. Diagrams. 258pp. 5⅜ x 8. S68 Paperbound **$1.50**

DIALOGUES CONCERNING TWO NEW SCIENCES, Galileo Galilei. This classic of experimental science, mechanics, engineering, is as enjoyable as it is important. Based on 30 years' experimentation and characterized by its author as "superior to everything else of mine," it offers a lively exposition of dynamics, elasticity, sound, ballistics, strength of materials, and the scientific method. Translated by H. Grew and A. de Salvio. 126 diagrams. Index. xxi + 288pp. 5⅜ x 8. S99 Paperbound **$1.65**

TREATISE ON ELECTRICITY AND MAGNETISM, James Clerk Maxwell. For more than 80 years a seemingly inexhaustible source of leads for physicists, mathematicians, engineers. Total of 1082pp. on such topics as Measurement of Quantities, Electrostatics, Elementary Mathematical Theory of Electricity, Electrical Work and Energy in a System of Conductors, General Theorems, Theory of Electrical Images, Electrolysis, Conduction, Polarization, Dielectrics, Resistance, etc. "The greatest mathematical physicist since Newton," Sir James Jeans. 3rd edition. 107 figures, 21 plates. 1082pp. 5⅜ x 8. S186 Clothbound **$4.95**

PRINCIPLES OF PHYSICAL OPTICS, Ernst Mach. This classical examination of the propagation of light, color, polarization etc. offers a historical and philosophical treatment that has never been surpassed for breadth and easy readability. Contents: Rectilinear propagation of light. Reflection, refraction. Early knowledge of vision. Dioptrics. Composition of light. Theory of color and dispersion. Periodicity. Theory of interference. Polarization. Mathematical representation of properties of light. Propagation of waves, etc. 279 illustrations, 10 portraits. Appendix. Indexes. 324pp. 5⅜ x 8. S178 Paperbound **$1.75**

THEORY OF ELECTRONS AND ITS APPLICATION TO THE PHENOMENA OF LIGHT AND RADIANT HEAT, H. Lorentz. Lectures delivered at Columbia University by Nobel laureate Lorentz. Unabridged, they form a historical coverage of the theory of free electrons, motion, absorption of heat, Zeeman effect, propagation of light in molecular bodies, inverse Zeeman effect, optical phenomena in moving bodies, etc. 109 pages of notes explain the more advanced sections. Index. 9 figures. 352pp. 5⅜ x 8. S173 Paperbound **$1.85**

MATTER & MOTION, James Clerk Maxwell. This excellent exposition begins with simple particles and proceeds gradually to physical systems beyond complete analysis: motion, force, properties of centre of mass of material system, work, energy, gravitation, etc. Written with all Maxwell's original insights and clarity! Notes by E. Larmor. 17 diagrams. 178pp. 5⅜ x 8. S188 Paperbound **$1.25**

AN INTRODUCTION TO THE STUDY OF EXPERIMENTAL MEDICINE, Claude Bernard. 90-year-old classic of medical science, only major work of Bernard available in English, records his efforts to transform physiology into exact science. Principles of scientific research illustrated by specific case histories from his work; roles of chance, error, preliminary false conclusions, in leading eventually to scientific truth; use of hypothesis. Much of modern application of mathematics to biology rests on the foundation set down here. New foreword by Professor I. B. Cohen, Harvard Univ. xxv + 266pp. 5⅜ x 8. T400 Paperbound **$1.50**

PRINCIPLES OF MECHANICS, Heinrich Hertz. This last work by the great 19th century physicist is not only a classic, but of great interest in the logic of science. Creating a new system of mechanics based upon space, time, and mass, it returns to axiomatic analysis, to understanding of the formal or structural aspects of science, taking into account logic, observation, and a priori elements. Of great historical importance to Poincaré, Carnap, Einstein, Milne. A 20-page introduction by R. S. Cohen, Wesleyan University, analyzes the implications of Hertz's thought and the logic of science. Bibliography. 13-page introduction of Helmholtz. xiii + 274pp. 5⅜ x 8.
S316 Clothbound **$3.50**
S317 Paperbound **$1.75**

ANIMALS IN MOTION, Eadweard Muybridge. Largest, most comprehensive selection of Muybridge's famous action photos of animals, from his ANIMAL LOCOMOTION. 3919 high-speed shots of 34 different animals and birds in 123 different types of action: horses, mules, oxen, pigs, goats, camels, elephants, dogs, cats, guanacos, sloths, lions, tigers, jaguars, raccoons, baboons, deer, elk, gnus, kangaroos, many others, in different actions—walking, running, flying, leaping. Horse alone shown in more than 40 different ways. Photos taken against ruled backgrounds; most actions taken from 3 angles at once: 90°, 60°, rear. Most plates original size. Of considerable interest to scientists as a classic of biology, as a record of actual facts of natural history and physiology. "A really marvellous series of plates," NATURE (London). "A monumental work," Waldemar Kaempffert. Photographed by E. Muybridge. Edited by L. S. Brown, American Museum of Natural History. 74-page introduction on mechanics of motion. 340 pages of plates, 3919 photographs. 416pp. Deluxe binding, paper. (Weight 4½ lbs.) 7⅞ x 10⅝.
T203 Clothbound **$10.00**

THE HUMAN FIGURE IN MOTION, Eadweard Muybridge. This new edition of a great classic in the history of science and photography is the largest selection ever made from the original Muybridge photos of human action: 4789 photographs, illustrating 163 types of motion: walking, running, lifting, etc. in time-exposure sequence photos at speeds up to 1/6000th of a second. Men, women, children, mostly undraped, showing bone and muscle positions against ruled backgrounds, mostly taken at 3 angles at once. Not only was this a great work of photography, acclaimed by contemporary critics as a work of genius, it was also a great 19th century landmark in biological research. Historical introduction by Prof. Robert Taft, U. of Kansas. Plates original size, full detail. Over 500 action strips. 407pp. 7¾ x 10⅝.
T204 Clothbound **$10.00**

ON THE SENSATIONS OF TONE, Hermann Helmholtz. This is an unmatched coordination of such fields as acoustical physics, physiology, experiment, history of music. It covers the entire gamut of musical tone. Partial contents: relation of vibration, resonance, analysis of tones by sympathetic resonance, beats, chords, tonality, consonant chords, discords, progression of parts, etc. 33 appendixes discuss various aspects of sound, physics, acoustics, music, etc. Translated by A. J. Ellis. New introduction by Prof. Henry Margenau of Yale. 68 figures. 43 musical passages analyzed. Over 100 tables. Index. xix + 576pp. 6⅛ x 9¼.
S114 Clothbound **$4.95**

COLLECTED WORKS OF BERNHARD RIEMANN. This important source book is the first to contain the complete text of both 1892 Werke and the 1902 supplement, unabridged. It contains 31 monographs, 3 complete lecture courses, 15 miscellaneous papers, which have been of enormous importance in relativity, topology, theory of complex variables, and other areas of mathematics. Edited by R. Dedekind, H. Weber, M. Noether, W. Wirtinger. German text. English introduction by Hans Lewy. 690pp. 5⅜ x 8.
S226 Paperbound **$2.85**

CONTRIBUTIONS TO THE FOUNDING OF THE THEORY OF TRANSFINITE NUMBERS, Georg Cantor. These papers founded a new branch of mathematics. The famous articles of 1895-7 are translated with an 82-page introduction by P. E. B. Jourdain dealing with Cantor, the background of his discoveries, their results, future possibilities. Bibliography. Index. Notes. ix + 211pp. 5⅜ x 8.
S45 Paperbound **$1.25**

PRINCIPLES OF PSYCHOLOGY, William James. This is the complete "Long Course," which is not to be confused with abridged editions. It contains all the wonderful descriptions, deep insights that have caused it to be a permanent work in all psychological libraries. Partial contents: functions of the brain, automation theories, mind-stuff theories, relation of mind to other things, consciousness, times, space, thing perception, will, emotions, hypnotism, and dozens of other areas in descriptive psychology. "A permanent classic like Locke's ESSAYS, Hume's TREATISE," John Dewey. "The preeminence of James in American psychology is unquestioned," PERSONALIST. "The American classic in psychology—unequaled in breadth and scope in the entire psychological literature," PSYCHOANALYTICAL QUARTERLY. Index. 94 figures. 2 volumes bound as one. Total of 1408pp.
T381 Vol. 1. Paperbound **$2.00**
T382 Vol. 2. Paperbound **$2.00**

RECREATIONS

SEVEN SCIENCE FICTION NOVELS OF H. G. WELLS. This is the complete text, unabridged, of seven of Wells's greatest novels: War of the Worlds, The Invisible Man, The Island of Dr. Moreau, The Food of the Gods, The First Men in the Moon, In the Days of the Comet, The Time Machine. Still considered by many experts to be the best science-fiction ever written, they will offer amusement and instruction to the scientific-minded reader. 1015pp. 5⅜ x 8.
T264 Clothbound **$3.95**

28 SCIENCE FICTION STORIES OF H. G. WELLS. Unabridged! This enormous omnibus contains 2 full-length novels—Men Like Gods, Star Begotten—plus 26 short stories of space, time, invention, biology, etc. The Crystal Egg, The Country of the Blind, Empire of the Ants, The Man Who Could Work Miracles, Aepyornis Island, A Story of the Days to Come, and 22 others! 915pp. 5⅜ x 8. T265 Clothbound **$3.95**

FLATLAND, E. A. Abbott. This is a perennially popular science-fiction classic about life in a two-dimensioned world, and the impingement of higher dimensions. Political, satiric, humorous, moral overtones. Relativity, the fourth dimension, and other aspects of modern science are explained more clearly than in most texts. 7th edition. New introduction by Banesh Hoffmann. 128pp. 5⅜ x 8. T1 Paperbound **$1.00**

CRYPTANALYSIS, Helen F. Gaines. (Formerly ELEMENTARY CRYPTANALYSIS.) A standard elementary and intermediate text for serious students. It does not confine itself to old material, but contains much that is not generally known except to experts. Concealment, Transposition, Subsititution ciphers; Vigenere, Kasiski, Playfair, multafid, dozens of other techniques. Appendix with sequence charts, letter frequencies in English, 5 other languages, English word frequencies. Bibliography. 167 codes. New to this edition: solutions to codes. vi + 230pp. 5⅜ x 8⅜. T97 Paperbound **$1.95**

FADS AND FALLACIES IN THE NAME OF SCIENCE, Martin Gardner. Examines various cults, quack systems, frauds, delusions which at various times have masqueraded as science. Accounts of hollow-earth fanatics like Symmes; Velikovsky and wandering planets; Hoerbiger; Bellamy and the theory of multiple moons; Charles Fort, dowsing, pseudoscientific methods for finding water, ores, oil. Sections on naturopathy, iridiagnosis, zone therapy, food fads, etc. Analytical accounts of Wilhelm Reich and orgone sex energy; L. Ron Hubbard and Dianetics; A. Korzybski and General Semantics; many others. Brought up to date to include Bridey Murphy, others. Not just a collection of anecdotes, but a fair, reasoned appraisal of eccentric theory. Formerly titled IN THE NAME OF SCIENCE. Preface. Index. x + 384pp. 5⅜ x 8. T394 Paperbound **$1.50**

REINFELD ON THE END GAME IN CHESS, Fred Reinfeld. Analyzes 62 end games by Alekhine, Flohr, Tarrasch, Morphy, Bogolyubov, Capablanca, Vidmar, Rubinstein, Lasker, Reshevsky, other masters. Only first-rate book with extensive coverage of error; of immense aid in pointing out errors you might have made. Centers around transitions from middle play to various types of end play. King & pawn endings, minor piece endings, queen endings, bad bishops, blockage, weak pawns, passed pawns, etc. Formerly titled PRACTICAL END PLAY. 62 figures. vi + 177pp. 5⅜ x 8. T417 Paperbound **$1.25**

PUZZLE QUIZ AND STUNT FUN, Jerome Meyer. 238 high-priority puzzles, stunts, and tricks—mathematical puzzles like The Clever Carpenter, Atom Bomb, Please Help Alice; mysteries and deductions like The Bridge of Sighs, Dog Logic, Secret Code; observation puzzlers like The American Flag, Playing Cards, Telephone Dial; more than 200 others involving magic squares, tongue twisters, puns, anagrams, word design. Answers included. Revised, enlarged edition of FUN-TO-DO. Over 100 illustrations. 238 puzzles, stunts, tricks. 256pp. 5⅜ x 8. T337 Paperbound **$1.00**

THE BOOK OF MODERN PUZZLES, G. L. Kaufman. More than 150 word puzzles, logic puzzles. No warmed-over fare but all new material based on same appeals that make crosswords and deduction puzzles popular, but with different principles, techniques. Two-minute teasers, involved word-labyrinths, design and pattern puzzles, puzzles calling for logic and observation, puzzles testing ability to apply general knowledge to peculiar situations, many others. Answers to all problems. 116 illustrations. 192pp. 5⅜ x 8. T143 Paperbound **$1.00**

101 PUZZLES IN THOUGHT AND LOGIC by C. R. Wylie, Jr. Designed for readers who enjoy the challenge and stimulation of logical puzzles without specialized mathematical or scientific knowledge. These problems are entirely new and range from relatively easy, to brainteasers that will afford hours of subtle entertainment. Detective problems, how to find the lying fisherman, how a blindman can identify color by logic, and many more. Easy-to-understand introduction to the logic of puzzle solving and general scientific method. 128pp. 5⅜ x 8. T367 Paperbound **$1.00**

MATHEMAGIC, MAGIC PUZZLES, AND GAMES WITH NUMBERS, Royal V. Heath. Over 60 new puzzles and stunts based on properties of numbers. Demonstrates easy techniques for multiplying large numbers mentally, identifying unknown numbers, determining date of any day in any year, dozens of similar useful, entertaining applications of mathematics. Entertainments like The Lost Digit, 3 Acrobats, Psychic Bridge, magic squares, triangles, cubes, circles, other material not easily found elsewhere. Edited by J. S. Meyer. 76 illustrations. 128pp. 5⅜ x 8. T110 Paperpound **$1.00**

LEARN CHESS FROM THE MASTERS, Fred Reinfeld. Improve your chess, rate your improvement, by playing against Marshall, Znosko-Borovsky, Bronstein, Najdorf, others. Formerly titled CHESS BY YOURSELF, this book contains 10 games in which you move against masters, and grade your moves by an easy system. Games selected for interest, clarity, easy principles; illustrate common openings, both classical and modern. Ratings for 114 extra playing situations that might have arisen. Full annotations. 91 diagrams. viii + 144pp. 5⅜ x 8. T362 Paperbound **$1.00**

THE COMPLETE NONSENSE OF EDWARD LEAR. Original text & illustrations of all Lear's nonsense books: A BOOK OF NONSENSE, NONSENSE SONGS, MORE NONSENSE SONGS, LAUGHABLE LYRICS, NONSENSE SONGS AND STORIES. Only complete edition available at popular price. Old favorites such as The Dong With a Luminous Nose, hundreds of other delightful bits of nonsense for children & adults. 214 different limericks, each illustrated by Lear; 3 different sets of Nonsense Botany; 5 Nonsense Alphabets; many others. 546 illustrations. 320pp. 5⅜ x 8.
T167 Paperbound **$1.00**

CRYPTOGRAPHY, D. Smith. Excellent elementary introduction to enciphering, deciphering secret writing. Explains transposition, substitution ciphers; codes; solutions. Geometrical patterns, route transcription, columnar transposition, other methods. Mixed cipher systems; single-alphabet, polyalphabetical substitution; mechanical devices; Vigenere system, etc. Enciphering Japanese; explanation of Baconian Biliteral cipher frequency tables. More than 150 problems provide practical application. Bibliography. Index. 164pp. 5⅜ x 8. T247 Paperbound **$1.00**

MATHEMATICAL EXCURSIONS, Helen A. Merrill. Fun, recreation, insights into elementary problem-solving. A mathematical expert guides you along by-paths not generally travelled in elementary math courses—how to divide by inspection, Russian peasant system of multiplication; memory systems for pi; building odd and even magic squares; dyadic systems; facts about 37; square roots by geometry; Tchebichev's machine; drawing five-sided figures; dozens more. Solutions to more difficult ones. 50 illustrations. 145pp. 5⅜ x 8. T350 Paperbound **$1.00**

MATHEMATICAL RECREATIONS, M. Kraitchik. Some 250 puzzles, problems, demonstrations of recreational mathematics for beginners & advanced mathematicians. Unusual historical problems from Greek, Medieval, Arabic, Hindu sources; modern problems based on "mathematics without numbers," geometry, topology, arithmetic, etc. Pastimes derived from figurative numbers, Mersenne numbers, Fermat numbers; fairy chess, latruncles, reversi, many other topics. Full solutions. Excellent for insights into special fields of math. 181 illustrations. 330pp. 5⅜ x 8.
T163 Paperbound **$1.75**

MATHEMATICAL PUZZLES FOR BEGINNERS AND ENTHUSIASTS, G. Mott-Smith. 188 mathematical puzzles to test mental agility. Inference, interpretation, algebra, dissection of plane figures, geometry, properties of numbers, decimation, permutations, probability, all enter these delightful problems. Puzzles like the Odic Force, How to Draw an Ellipse, Spider's Cousin, more than 180 others. Detailed solutions. Appendix with square roots, triangular numbers, primes, etc. 135 illustrations. 2nd revised edition. 248pp. 5⅜ x 8. T198 Paperbound **$1.00**

NEW WORD PUZZLES, Gerald L. Kaufman. Contains 100 brand new challenging puzzles based on words and their combinations, never published before in any form. Most are new types invented by the author—for beginners or experts. Chess word puzzles, addle letter anagrams, double word squares, double horizontals, alphagram puzzles, dual acrostigrams, linkogram lapwords—plus 8 other brand new types, all with solutions included. 196 figures. 100 brand new puzzles. vi + 122pp. 5⅜ x 8. T344 Paperbound **$1.00**

MATHEMATICS, MAGIC AND MYSTERY, Martin Gardner. Card tricks, feats of mental mathematics, stage mind-reading, other "magic" explained as applications of probability, sets, theory of numbers, topology, various branches of mathematics. Creative examination of laws and their application, with sources of new tricks and insights. 115 sections discuss tricks with cards, dice, coins; geometrical vanishing tricks, dozens of others. No sleight of hand needed; mathematics guarantees success. 115 illustrations. xii + 174pp. 5⅜ x 8. T335 Paperbound **$1.00**

MATHEMATICS ELEMENTARY TO INTERMEDIATE

HOW TO CALCULATE QUICKLY, Henry Sticker. This handy volume offers a tried and true method for helping you in the basic mathematics of daily life—addition, subtraction, multiplication, division, fractions, etc. It is designed to awaken your "number sense" or the ability to see relationships between numbers as whole quantities. It is not a collection of tricks working only on special numbers, but a serious course of over 9,000 problems and their solutions, teaching special techniques not taught in schools: left-to-right multiplication, new fast ways of division, etc. 5 or 10 minutes daily use will double or triple your calculation speed. Excellent for the scientific worker who is at home in higher math, but is not satisfied with his speed and accuracy in lower mathematics. 256pp. 5 x 7¼. T295 Paperbound **$1.00**

FAMOUS PROBLEMS OF ELEMENTARY GEOMETRY, Felix Klein. Expanded version of the 1894 Easter lectures at Göttingen. 3 problems of classical geometry: squaring circle, trisecting angle, doubling cube, considered with full modern implications: transcendental numbers, pi, etc. Notes by R. Archibald. 16 figures. xi + 92pp. 5⅜ x 8. T348 Clothbound **$1.50**
T298 Paperbound **$1.00**

HIGHER MATHEMATICS FOR STUDENTS OF CHEMISTRY AND PHYSICS, J. W. Mellor. Not abstract, but practical, building its problems out of familiar laboratory material, this covers differential calculus, coordinate, analytical geometry, functions, integral calculus, infinite series, numerical equations, differential equations, Fourier's theorem, probability, theory of errors, calculus of variations, determinants. "If the reader is not familiar with this book, it will repay him to examine it," CHEM. & ENGINEERING NEWS. 800 problems, 189 figures. Bibliography. xxi + 641pp. 5⅜ x 8. S193 Paperbound **$2.00**

TRIGONOMETRY REFRESHER FOR TECHNICAL MEN, A. Albert Klaf. 913 detailed questions and answers cover the most important aspects of plane and spherical trigonometry. They will help you to brush up or to clear up difficulties in special areas.—The first portion of this book covers plane trigonometry, including angles, quadrants, trigonometrical functions, graphical representation, interpolation, equations, logarithms, solution of triangle, use of the slide rule and similar topics–188 pages then discuss application of plane trigonometry to special problems in navigation, surveying, elasticity, architecture, and various fields of engineering. Small angles, periodic functions, vectors, polar coordinates, De Moivre's theorem are fully examined—The third section of the book then discusses spherical trigonometry and the solution of spherical triangles, with their applications to terrestrial and astronomical problems. Methods of saving time with numerical calculations, simplification of principal functions of angle, much practical information make this a most useful book—913 questions answered. 1738 problems, answers to odd numbers. 494 figures. 24 pages of useful formulae, functions. Index. x + 629pp. 5⅜ x 8.
T371 Paperbound **$2.00**

CALCULUS REFRESHER FOR TECHNICAL MEN, A. Albert Klaf. This book is unique in English as a refresher for engineers, technicians, students who either wish to brush up their calculus or to clear up uncertainties. It is not an ordinary text, but an examination of most important aspects of integral and differential calculus in terms of the 756 questions most likely to occur to the technical reader. The first part of this book covers simple differential calculus, with constants, variables, functions, increments, derivatives, differentiation, logarithms, curvature of curves, and similar topics—The second part covers fundamental ideas of integration, inspection, substitution, transformation, reduction, areas and volumes, mean value, successive and partial integration, double and triple integration. Practical aspects are stressed rather than theoretical. A 50-page section illustrates the application of calculus to specific problems of civil and nautical engineering, electricity, stress and strain, elasticity, industrial engineering, and similar fields.—756 questions answered. 566 problems, mostly answered. 36 pages of useful constants, formulae for ready reference. Index. v + 431pp. 5⅜ x 8. T370 Paperbound **$2.00**

MONOGRAPHS ON TOPICS OF MODERN MATHEMATICS, edited by **J. W. A. Young.** Advanced mathematics for persons who haven't gone beyond or have forgotten high school algebra. 9 monographs on foundation of geometry, modern pure geometry, non-Euclidean geometry, fundamental propositions of algebra, algebraic equations, functions, calculus, theory of numbers, etc. Each monograph gives proofs of important results, and descriptions of leading methods, to provide wide coverage. New introduction by Prof. M. Kline, N. Y. University. 100 diagrams. xvi + 416pp. 6⅛ x 9¼. S289 Paperbound **$2.00**

MATHEMATICS: INTERMEDIATE TO ADVANCED

INTRODUCTION TO THE THEORY OF FOURIER'S SERIES AND INTEGRALS, H. S. Carslaw. 3rd revised edition. This excellent introduction is an outgrowth of the author's courses at Cambridge. Historical introduction, rational and irrational numbers, infinite sequences and series, functions of a single variable, definite integral, Fourier series, Fourier integrals, and similar topics. Appendixes discuss practical harmonic analysis, periodogram analysis, Lebesgues theory. Indexes. 84 examples, bibliography. xiii + 368 pp. 5⅜ x 8. S48 Paperbound **$2.00**

INTRODUCTION TO THE THEORY OF NUMBERS, L. E. Dickson. Thorough, comprehensive approach with adequate coverage of classical literature, an introductory volume beginners can follow. Chapters on divisibility, congruences, quadratic residues & reciprocity, Diophantine equations, etc. Full treatment of binary quadratic forms without usual restriction to integral coefficients. Covers infinitude of primes, least residues, Fermat's theorem, Euler's phi function, Legendre's symbol, Gauss's lemma, automorphs, reduced forms, recent theorems of Thue & Siegel, many more. Much material not readily available elsewhere. 239 problems. Index. 1 figure. viii + 183pp. 5⅜ x 8. S342 Paperbound **$1.65**

MECHANICS VIA THE CALCULUS, P. W. Norris, W. S. Legge. Covers almost everything from linear motion to vector analysis: equations determining motion, linear methods, compounding of simple harmonic motions, Newton's laws of motion, Hooke's law, the simple pendulum, motion of a particle in 1 plane, centers of gravity, virtual work, friction, kinetic energy of rotating bodies, equilibrium of strings, hydrostatics, sheering stresses, elasticity, etc. 550 problems. 3rd revised edition. xii + 367pp. S207 Clothbound **$3.95**

NON-EUCLIDEAN GEOMETRY, Roberto Bonola. The standard coverage of non-Euclidean geometry. It examines from both a historical and mathematical point of view the geometries which have arisen from a study of Euclid's 5th postulate upon parallel lines. Also included are complete texts, translated, of Bolyai's THEORY OF ABSOLUTE SPACE, Lobachevsky's THEORY OF PARALLELS. 180 diagrams. 431pp. 5⅜ x 8. S27 Paperbound **$1.95**

ELEMENTS OF THE THEORY OF REAL FUNCTIONS, J. E. Littlewood. Based on lectures given at Trinity College, Cambridge, this book has proved to be extremely successful in introducing graduate students to the modern theory of functions. It offers a full and concise coverage of classes and cardinal numbers, well-ordered series, other types of series, and elements of the theory of sets of points. 3rd revised edition. vii + 71pp. 5⅜ x 8. S171 Clothbound **$2.85**
S172 Paperbound **$1.25**

THE CONTINUUM AND OTHER TYPES OF SERIAL ORDER, E. V. Huntington. This famous book gives a systematic elementary account of the modern history of the continuum as a type of serial order. Based on the Cantor-Dedekind ordinal theory, which requires no technical knowledge of higher mathematics, it offers an easily followed analysis of ordered classes, discrete and dense series, continuous series, Cantor's transfinite numbers. 2nd edition. Index. viii + 82pp. 5⅜ x 8. S129 Clothbound **$2.75**
S130 Paperbound **$1.00**

GEOMETRY OF FOUR DIMENSIONS, H. P. Manning. Unique in English as a clear, concise introduction. Treatment is synthetic, and mostly Euclidean, although in hyperplanes and hyperspheres at infinity, non-Euclidean geometry is used. Historical introduction. Foundations of 4-dimensional geometry. Perpendicularity, simple angles. Angles of planes, higher order. Symmetry, order, motion; hyperpyramids, hypercones, hyperspheres; figures with parallel elements; volume, hypervolume in space; regular polyhedroids. Glossary. 78 figures. ix + 348pp. 5⅜ x 8.
S181 Clothbound **$3.95**
S182 Paperbound **$1.95**

VECTOR AND TENSOR ANALYSIS, G. E. Hay. One of the clearest introductions to this increasingly important subject. Start with simple definitions, finish the book with a sure mastery of oriented Cartesian vectors, Christoffel symbols, solenoidal tensors, and their applications. Complete breakdown of plane, solid, analytical, differential geometry. Separate chapters on application. All fundamental formulae listed & demonstrated. 195 problems, 66 figures. viii + 193pp. 5⅜ x 8.
S109 Paperbound **$1.75**

INTRODUCTION TO THE DIFFERENTIAL EQUATIONS OF PHYSICS, L. Hopf. Especially valuable to the engineer with no math beyond elementary calculus. Emphasizing intuitive rather than formal aspects of concepts, the author covers an extensive territory. Partial contents: Law of causality, energy theorem, damped oscillations, coupling by friction, cylindrical and spherical coordinates, heat source, etc. Index. 48 figures. 160pp. 5⅜ x 8. S120 Paperbound **$1.25**

INTRODUCTION TO THE THEORY OF GROUPS OF FINITE ORDER, R. Carmichael. Examines fundamental theorems and their application. Beginning with sets, systems, permutations, etc., it progresses in easy stages through important types of groups: Abelian, prime power, permutation, etc. Except 1 chapter where matrices are desirable, no higher math needed. 783 exercises, problems. Index. xvi + 447pp. 5⅜ x 8. S299 Clothbound **$3.95**
S300 Paperbound **$2.00**

THEORY OF GROUPS OF FINITE ORDER, W. Burnside. First published some 40 years ago, this is still one of the clearest introductory texts. Partial contents: permutations, groups independent of representation, composition series of a group, isomorphism of a group with itself, Abelian groups, prime power groups, permutation groups, invariants of groups of linear substitution, graphical representation, etc. 45pp. of notes. Indexes. xxiv + 512pp. 5⅜ x 8.
S38 Paperbound **$2.45**

INFINITE SEQUENCES AND SERIES, Konrad Knopp. First publication in any language! Excellent introduction to 2 topics of modern mathematics, designed to give the student background to penetrate farther by himself. Sequences & sets, real & complex numbers, etc. Functions of a real & complex variable. Sequences & series. Infinite series. Convergent power series. Expansion of elementary functions. Numerical evaluation of series. Bibliography. v + 186pp. 5⅜ x 8.
S152 Clothbound **$3.50**
S153 Paperbound **$1.75**

THEORY OF SETS, E. Kamke. Clearest, amplest introduction in English, well suited for independent study. Subdivisions of main theory, such as theory of sets of points, are discussed, but emphasis is on general theory. Partial contents: rudiments of set theory, arbitrary sets and their cardinal numbers, ordered sets and their order types, well-ordered sets and their ordinal numbers. Bibliography. Key to symbols. Index. vii + 144pp. 5⅜ x 8. S141 Paperbound **$1.35**

ELEMENTS OF NUMBER THEORY, I. M. Vinogradov. Detailed 1st course for persons without advanced mathematics; 95% of this book can be understood by readers who have gone no farther than high school algebra. Partial contents: divisibility theory, important number theoretical functions, congruences, primitive roots and indices, etc. Solutions to both problems and exercises. Tables of primes, indices, etc. Covers almost every essential formula in elementary number theory! 233 problems, 104 exercises. viii + 227pp. 5⅜ x 8. S259 Paperbound **$1.60**

FIVE VOLUME "THEORY OF FUNCTIONS" SET BY KONRAD KNOPP. This five-volume set, prepared by Konrad Knopp, provides a complete and readily followed account of theory of functions. Proofs are given concisely, yet without sacrifice of completeness or rigor. These volumes are used as texts by such universities as M.I.T., University of Chicago, N. Y. City College, and many others. "Excellent introduction . . . remarkably readable, concise, clear, rigorous," JOURNAL OF THE AMERICAN STATISTICAL ASSOCIATION.

ELEMENTS OF THE THEORY OF FUNCTIONS, Konrad Knopp. This book provides the student with background for further volumes in this set, or texts on a similar level. Partial contents: Foundations, system of complex numbers and the Gaussian plane of numbers, Riemann sphere of numbers, mapping by linear functions, normal forms, the logarithm, the cyclometric functions and binomial series. "Not only for the young student, but also for the student who knows all about what is in it," MATHEMATICAL JOURNAL. Bibliography. Index. 140pp. 5⅜ x 8. S154 Paperbound **$1.35**

THEORY OF FUNCTIONS, PART I., Konrad Knopp. With volume II, this book provides coverage of basic concepts and theorems. Partial contents: numbers and points, functions of a complex variable, integral of a continuous function, Cauchy's integral theorem, Cauchy's integral formulae, series with variable terms, expansion of analytic functions in power series, analytic continuation and complete definition of analytic functions, entire transcendental functions, Laurent expansion, types of singularities. Bibliography. Index. vii + 146pp. 5⅜ x 8. S156 Paperbound **$1.35**

THEORY OF FUNCTIONS, PART II., Konrad Knopp. Application and further development of general theory, special topics. Single valued functions: entire, Weierstrass. Meromorphic functions: Mittag-Leffler. Periodic functions. Multiple-valued functions. Riemann surfaces. Algebraic functions. Analytical configuration, Riemann surface. Bibliography. Index. x + 150pp. 5⅜ x 8. S157 Paperbound **$1.35**

PROBLEM BOOK IN THE THEORY OF FUNCTIONS, VOLUME 1., Konrad Knopp. Problems in elementary theory, for use with Knopp's THEORY OF FUNCTIONS, or any other text, arranged according to increasing difficulty. Fundamental concepts, sequences of numbers and infinite series, complex variable, integral theorems, development in series, conformal mapping. Answers. viii + 126pp. 5⅜ x 8. S158 Paperbound **$1.35**

PROBLEM BOOK IN THE THEORY OF FUNCTIONS, VOLUME 2, Konrad Knopp. Advanced theory of functions, to be used either with Knopp's THEORY OF FUNCTIONS, or any other comparable text. Singularities, entire & meromorphic functions, periodic, analytic, continuation, multiple-valued functions, Riemann surfaces, conformal mapping. Includes a section of additional elementary problems. "The difficult task of selecting from the immense material of the modern theory of functions the problems just within the reach of the beginner is here masterfully accomplished," AM. MATH. SOC. Answers. 138pp. 5⅜ x 8. S159 Paperbound **$1.35**

SYMBOLIC LOGIC

AN INTRODUCTION TO SYMBOLIC LOGIC, Susanne K. Langer. Probably the clearest book ever written on symbolic logic for the philosopher, general scientist and layman. It will be particularly appreciated by those who have been rebuffed by other introductory works because of insufficient mathematical training. No special knowledge of mathematics is required. Starting with the simplest symbols and conventions, you are led to a remarkable grasp of the Boole-Schroeder and Russell-Whitehead systems clearly and quickly. PARTIAL CONTENTS: Study of forms, Essentials of logical structure, Generalization, Classes, The deductive system of classes, The algebra of logic, Abstraction of interpretation, Calculus of propositions, Assumptions of PRINCIPIA MATHEMATICA, Logistics, Logic of the syllogism, Proofs of theorems. "One of the clearest and simplest introductions to a subject which is very much alive. The style is easy, symbolism is introduced gradually, and the intelligent non-mathematican should have no difficulty in following argument," MATHEMATICS GAZETTE. Revised, expanded second edition. Truth-value tables. 368pp. 5⅜ x 8. S164 Paperbound **$1.75**

THE ELEMENTS OF MATHEMATICAL LOGIC, Paul Rosenbloom. FIRST PUBLICATION IN ANY LANGUAGE. This book is intended for readers who are mature mathematically, but have no previous training in symbolic logic. It does not limit itself to a single system, but covers the field as a whole. It is a development of lectures given at Lund University, Sweden in 1948. Partial contents: Logic of classes, fundamental theorems, Boolean algebra, logic of propositions, logic of propositional functions, expressive languages, combinatory logics, development of mathematics within an object language, paradoxes, theorems of Post and Goedel, Church's theorem, and similar topics. iv + 214pp. 5⅜ x 8. S277 Paperbound **$1.45**

THE LAWS OF THOUGHT, George Boole. This book founded symbolic logic some hundred years ago. It is the 1st significant attempt to apply logic to all aspects of human endeavour. Partial contents: derivation of laws, signs & laws, interpretations, eliminations, conditions of a perfect method, analysis, Aristotelian logic, probability, and similar topics. xviii + 424pp. 5⅜ x 8. S28 Paperbound **$2.00**

ELEMENTARY MATHEMATICS FROM AN ADVANCED STANDPOINT, Felix Klein.

This classic text is an outgrowth of Klein's famous integration and survey course at Göttingen. Using one field of mathematics to interpret, adjust, illuminate another, it covers basic topics in each area, illustrating its discussion with extensive analysis. It is especially valuable in considering areas of modern mathematics. "Makes the reader feel the inspiration of . . . a great mathematician, inspiring teacher . . . with deep insight into the foundations and interrelations," BULLETIN, AMERICAN MATHEMATICAL SOCIETY.

Vol. 1. ARITHMETIC, ALGEBRA, ANALYSIS. Introducing the concept of function immediately, it enlivens abstract discussion with graphical and geometrically perceptual methods. Partial contents: natural numbers, extension of the notion of number, special properties, complex numbers. Real equations with real unknowns, complex quantities. Logarithmic, exponential functions, goniometric functions, infinitesimal calculus. Transcendence of e and pi, theory of assemblages. Index. 125 figures. ix + 247pp. 5⅜ x 8. S150 Paperbound **$1.75**

Vol. 2. GEOMETRY. A comprehensive view which accompanies the space perception inherent in geometry with analytic formulas which facilitate precise formulation. Partial contents: Simplest geometric manifolds: line segment, Grassmann determinant principles, classification of configurations of space, derivative manifolds. Geometric transformations: affine transformations, projective, higher point transformations, theory of the imaginary. Systematic discussion of geometry and its foundations. Indexes. 141 illustrations. ix + 214pp. 5⅜ x 8. S151 Paperbound **$1.75**

MATHEMATICS: ADVANCED

ALMOST PERIODIC FUNCTIONS, A. S. Besicovitch. This unique and important summary by a well-known mathematician covers in detail the two stages of development in Bohr's theory of almost periodic functions: (1) as a generalization of pure periodicity, with results and proofs; (2) the work done by Stepanoff, Wiener, Weyl, and Bohr in generalizing the theory. Bibliography. xi + 180pp. 5⅜ x 8.
S17 Clothbound **$3.50**
S18 Paperbound **$1.75**

LECTURES ON THE ICOSAHEDRON AND THE SOLUTION OF EQUATIONS OF THE FIFTH DEGREE, Felix Klein. The solution of quintics in terms of rotations of a regular icosahedron around its axes of symmetry. A classic & indispensable source for those interested in higher algebra, geometry, crystallography. Considerable explanatory material included. 230 footnotes, mostly bibliographic. 2nd edition, xvi + 289pp. 5⅜ x 8.
S314 Paperbound **$1.85**

LINEAR INTEGRAL EQUATIONS, W. V. Lovitt. Systematic survey of general theory, with some application to differential equations, calculus of variations problems of math, physics. Partial contents: integral equations of 2nd kind by successive substitutions; Fredholm's equation as ratio of 2 integral series in lambda, applications of the Fredholm theory, Hilbert-Schmidt theory of symmetric kernels, application, etc. Neumann, Dirichlet, vibratory problems. Index. ix + 253pp. 5⅜ x 8.
S175 Clothbound **$3.50**
S176 Paperbound **$1.60**

MATHEMATICAL FOUNDATIONS OF STATISTICAL MECHANICS, A. I. Khinchin. Offering a precise and rigorous formulation of problems, this book supplies a thorough and up-to-date exposition. It provides analytical tools needed to replace cumbersome concepts, and furnishes for the first time a logical step-by-step introduction to the subject. Partial contents: geometry & kinematics of the phase space, ergodic problem, reduction to theory of probability, application of central limit problem, ideal monatomic gas, foundation of thermodynamics, dispersion and distributions of sum functions. Key to notations. Index. xiii + 179pp. 5⅜ x 8.
S146 Clothbound **$2.95**
S147 Paperbound **$1.35**

ORDINARY DIFFERENTIAL EQUATIONS, E. L. Ince. A most compendious analysis in real and complex domains. Existence and nature of solutions, continuous transformation groups, solutions in an infinite form, definite integrals, algebraic theory, Sturmian theory, boundary problems, existence theorems, 1st order, higher order, etc. "Deserves the highest praise, a notable addition to mathematical literature," BULLETIN, AM. MATH. SOC. Historical appendix. Bibliography. 18 figures. viii + 558pp. 5⅜ x 8.
S349 Paperbound **$2.55**

TRIGONOMETRICAL SERIES, Antoni Zygmund. Unique in any language on modern advanced level. Contains carefully organized analyses of trigonometric, orthogonal, Fourier systems of functions, with clear adequate descriptions of summability of Fourier series, proximation theory, conjugate series, convergence, divergence of Fourier series. Especially valuable for Russian, Eastern European coverage. Bibliography. 329pp. 5⅜ x 8.
S290 Paperbound **$1.50**

FOUNDATIONS OF POTENTIAL THEORY, O. D. Kellogg. Based on courses given at Harvard this is suitable for both advanced and beginning mathematicians. Proofs are rigorous, and much material not generally available elsewhere is included. Partial contents: forces of gravity, fields of force, divergence theorem, properties of Newtonian potentials at points of free space, potentials as solutions of Laplace's equations, harmonic functions, electrostatics, electric images, logarithmic potential, etc. ix + 384pp. 5⅜ x 8.
S144 Paperbound **$1.98**

LECTURES ON CAUCHY'S PROBLEMS, J. Hadamard. Based on lectures given at Columbia and Rome, this discusses work of Riemann, Kirchhoff, Volterra, and the author's own research on the hyperbolic case in linear partial differential equations. It extends spherical and cylindrical waves to apply to all (normal) hyperbolic equations. Partial contents: Cauchy's problem, fundamental formula, equations with odd number, with even number of independent variables; method of descent. 32 figures. Index. iii + 361pp. 5⅜ x 8.
S105 Paperbound **$1.75**

MATHEMATICAL PHYSICS, STATISTICS

THE MATHEMATICAL THEORY OF ELASTICITY, A. E. H. Love. A wealth of practical illustration combined with thorough discussion of fundamentals—theory, application, special problems and solutions. Partial contents: Analysis of Strain & Stress, Elasticity of Solid Bodies, Isotropic Elastic Solids, Equilibrium of Aeolotropic Elastic Solids, Elasticity of Crystals, Vibration of Spheres, Cylinders, Propagation of Waves in Elastic Solid Media, Torsion, Theory of Continuous Beams, Plates. Rigorous treatment of Volterra's theory of dislocations, 2-dimensional elastic systems, other topics of modern interest. "For years the standard treatise on elasticity," AMERICAN MATHEMATICAL MONTHLY. 4th revised edition. Index. 76 figures. xviii + 643pp. 6⅛ x 9¼.
S174 Paperbound **$2.95**

TABLES OF FUNCTIONS WITH FORMULAE AND CURVES, E. Jahnke & F. Emde. The world's most comprehensive 1-volume English-text collection of tables, formulae, curves of transcendent functions. 4th corrected edition, new 76-page section giving tables, formulae for elementary functions—not in other English editions. Partial contents: sine, cosine, logarithmic integral; factorial function; error integral; theta functions; elliptic integrals, functions; Legendre, Bessel, Riemann, Mathieu, hypergeometric functions, etc. Supplementary books. Bibliography. Indexed. "Out of the way functions for which we know no other source," SCIENTIFIC COMPUTING SERVICE, Ltd. 212 figures. 400pp. 5⅜ x 8.
S133 Paperbound **$2.00**

PRACTICAL ANALYSIS, GRAPHICAL AND NUMERICAL METHODS, F. A. Willers. Translated by R. T. Beyer. Immensely practical handbook for engineers, showing how to interpolate, use various methods of numerical differentiation and integration, determine the roots of a single algebraic equation, system of linear equations, use empirical formulas, integrate differential equations, etc. Hundreds of shortcuts for arriving at numerical solutions. Special section on American calculating machines, by T. W. Simpson. 132 illustrations. 422pp. 5 3/8 x 8. S273 Paperbound **$2.00**

DICTIONARY OF CONFORMAL REPRESENTATIONS, H. Kober. Laplace's equation in 2 dimensions solved in this unique book developed by the British Admiralty. Scores of geometrical forms & their transformations for electrical engineers, Joukowski aerofoil for aerodynamists, Schwartz-Christoffel transformations for hydrodynamics, transcendental functions. Contents classified according to analytical functions describing transformation. Twin diagrams show curves of most transformations with corresponding regions. Glossary. Topological index. 447 diagrams. 244pp. 6 1/8 x 9 1/4. S160 Paperbound **$2.00**

FREQUENCY CURVES AND CORRELATION, W. P. Elderton. 4th revised edition of a standard work covering classical statistics. It is practical in approach, and one of the books most frequently referred to for clear presentation of basic material. Partial contents. Frequency distributions. Method of moment. Pearson's frequency curves. Correlation. Theoretical distributions, spurious correlation. Correlation of characters not quantitatively measurable. Standard errors. Test of goodness of fit. The correlation ratio—contingency. Partial correlation. Corrections for moments, beta and gamma functions, etc. Key to terms, symbols. Bibliography. 25 examples in text. 40 useful tables. 16 figures. xi + 272pp. 5 1/2 x 8 1/2. Clothbound **$1.49**

HYDRODYNAMICS, H. Dryden, F. Murnaghan, Harry Bateman. Published by the National Research Council in 1932 this enormous volume offers a complete coverage of classical hydrodynamics. Encyclopedic in quality. Partial contents: physics of fluids, motion, turbulent flow, compressible fluids, motion in 1, 2, 3 dimensions; viscous fluids rotating, laminar motion, resistance of motion through viscous fluid, eddy viscosity, hydraulic flow in channels of various shapes, discharge of gases, flow past obstacles, etc. Bibliography of over 2,900 items. Indexes. 23 figures. 634pp. 5 3/8 x 8. S303 Paperbound **$2.75**

HYDRODYNAMICS, A STUDY OF LOGIC, FACT, AND SIMILITUDE, Garrett Birkhoff. A stimulating application of pure mathematics to an applied problem. Emphasis is placed upon correlation of theory and deduction with experiment. It examines carefully recently discovered paradoxes, theory of modelling and dimensional analysis, paradox & error in flows and free boundary theory. The author derives the classical theory of virtual mass from homogeneous spaces, and applies group theory to fluid mechanics. Index. Bibliography. 20 figures, 3 plates. xiii + 186pp. 5 3/8 x 8.
S21 Clothbound **$3.50**
S22 Paperbound **$1.85**

HYDRODYNAMICS, Horace Lamb. Internationally famous complete coverage of standard reference work on dynamics of liquids & gases. Fundamental theorems, equations, methods, solutions, background, for classical hydrodynamics. Chapters include Equations of Motion, Integration of Equations in Special Gases, Irrotational Motion, Motion of Liquid in 2 Dimensions, Motion of Solids through Liquid—Dynamical Theory, Vortex Motion, Tidal Waves, Surface Waves, Waves of Expansion, Viscosity, Rotating Masses of Liquids. Excellently planned, arranged; clear, lucid presentation. 6th enlarged, revised edition. Index. Over 900 footnotes, mostly bibliographical. 119 figures. xv + 738pp. 6 1/8 x 9 1/4. S256 Paperbound **$2.95**

INTRODUCTION TO RELAXATION METHODS, F. S. Shaw. Fluid mechanics, design of electrical networks, forces in structural frameworks, stress distribution, buckling, etc. Solve linear simultaneous equations, linear ordinary differential equations, partial differential equations, Eigenvalue problems by relaxation methods. Detailed examples throughout. Special tables for dealing with awkwardly-shaped boundaries. Indexes. 253 diagrams. 72 tables. 400pp. 5 3/8 x 8.
S244 Paperbound **$2.45**

PARTIAL DIFFERENTIAL EQUATIONS OF MATHEMATICAL PHYSICS, A. G. Webster. A keystone work in the library of every mature physicist, engineer, researcher. Valuable sections on elasticity, compression theory, potential theory, theory of sound, heat conduction, wave propagation, vibration theory. Contents include: deduction of differential equations, vibrations, normal functions, Fourier's series, Cauchy's method, boundary problems, method of Riemann-Volterra. Spherical, cylindrical, ellipsoidal harmonics, applications, etc. 97 figures. vii + 440pp. 5 3/8 x 8.
S263 Paperbound **$1.98**

THE THEORY OF GROUPS AND QUANTUM MECHANICS, H. Weyl. Discussions of Schroedinger's wave equation, de Broglie's waves of a particle, Jordon-Hoelder theorem, Lie's continuous groups of transformations, Pauli exclusion principle, quantization of Maxwell-Dirac field equations, etc. symmetry permutation group, algebra of symmetric transformation, etc. 2nd revised edition. Unitary geometry, quantum theory, groups, application of groups to quantum mechanics, symmetry permutation group, algebra of symmetric transformation, etc. 2nd revised edition. Bibliography. Index. xxii + 422pp. 5 3/8 x 8.
S268 Clothbound **$4.50**
S269 Paperbound **$1.95**

PARTIAL DIFFERENTIAL EQUATIONS OF MATHEMATICAL PHYSICS, Harry Bateman. Solution of boundary value problems by means of definite analytical expressions, with wide range of representative problems, full reference to contemporary literature, and new material by the author. Partial contents: classical equations, integral theorems of Green, Stokes; 2-dimensional problems; conformal representation; equations in 3 variables; polar coordinates; cylindrical, ellipsoidal, paraboloid, toroidal coordinates; non-linear equations, etc. "Must be in the hands of everyone interested in boundary value problems," BULLETIN, AM. MATH. SOC. Indexes. 450 bibliographic footnotes. 175 examples. 29 illustrations. xxii + 552pp. 6 x 9. S15 Clothbound **$4.95**

NUMERICAL SOLUTIONS OF DIFFERENTIAL EQUATIONS, H. Levy & E. A. Baggott. Comprehensive collection of methods for solving ordinary differential equations of first and higher order. All must pass 2 requirements: easy to grasp and practical, more rapid than school methods. Partial contents: graphical integration of differential equations, graphical methods for detailed solution. Numerical solution. Simultaneous equations and equations of 2nd and higher orders. "Should be in the hands of all in research in applied mathematics, teaching," NATURE. 21 figures. viii + 238pp. 5⅜ x 8. S168 Paperbound **$1.75**

ASYMPTOTIC EXPANSIONS, A. Erdélyi. The only modern work available in English, this is an unabridged reproduction of a monograph prepared for the Office of Naval Research. It discusses various procedures for asymptotic evaluation of integrals containing a large parameter and solutions of ordinary linear differential equations. Bibliography of 71 items. vi + 108pp. 5⅜ x 8. S318 Paperbound **$1.35**

THE FOURIER INTEGRAL AND CERTAIN OF ITS APPLICATIONS, Norbert Wiener. The only book-length study of the Fourier integral as link between pure and applied math. An expansion of lectures given at Cambridge. Partial contents: Plancherel's theorem, general Tauberian theorem, special Tauberian theorms, generalized harmonic analysis. Bibliography. viii + 201pp. 5⅜ x 8. S272 Clothbound **$3.95**

THE THEORY OF SOUND, Lord Rayleigh. Most vibrating systems likely to be encountered in practice can be tackled successfully by the methods set forth by the great Noble laureate, Lord Rayleigh. Complete coverage of experimental, mathematical aspects of sound theory. Partial contents: Harmonic motions, vibrating systems in general, lateral vibrations of bars, curved plates or shells, applications of Laplace's functions to acoustical problems, fluid friction, plane vortex-sheet, vibrations of solid bodies, etc. This is the first inexpensive edition of this great reference and study work. Bibliography. Historical introduction by R. B. Lindsay. Total of 1040pp. 97 figures. 5⅜ x 8. S292, S293, Two volume set, paperbound **$4.00**

ANALYSIS & DESIGN OF EXPERIMENTS, H. B. Mann. Offers a method for grasping the analysis of variance and variance design within a short time. Partial contents: Chi-square distribution and analysis of variance distribution, matrices, quadratic forms, likelihood ratio tests and tests of linear hypotheses, power of analysis, Galois fields, non-orthogonal data, interblock estimates, etc. 15pp. of useful tables. x + 195pp. 5 x 7⅜. S180 Paperbound **$1.45**

MATHEMATICAL ANALYSIS OF ELECTRICAL AND OPTICAL WAVE-MOTION, Harry Bateman. Written by one of this century's most distinguished mathematical physicists, this is a practical introduction to those developments of Maxwell's electromagnetic theory which are directly connected with the solution of the partial differential equation of wave motion. Methods of solving wave-equations, polar-cylindrical coordinates, diffraction, transformation of coordinates, homogeneous solutions, electromagnetic fields with moving singularities, etc. Index. 168pp. 5⅜ x 8. S14 Paperbound **$1.60**

PHYSICAL PRINCIPLES OF THE QUANTUM THEORY, Werner Heisenberg. A Nobel laureate discusses quantum theory; Heisenberg's own work, Compton, Schroedinger, Wilson, Einstein, many others. Written for physicists, chemists who are not specialists in quantum theory, only elementary formulae are considered in the text; there is a mathematical appendix for specialists. Profound without sacrifice of clarity. Translated by C. Eckart, F. Hoyt. 18 figures. 192pp. 5⅜ x 8. S113 Paperbound **$1.25**

FOUNDATIONS OF NUCLEAR PHYSICS, edited by **R. T. Beyer.** 13 of the most important papers on nuclear physics reproduced in facsimile in the original languages of their authors: the papers most often cited in footnotes, bibliographies. Anderson, Curie, Joliot, Chadwick, Fermi, Lawrence, Cockcroft, Hahn, Yukawa. Unparalleled Bibliography: 122 double-columned pages, over 4,000 articles, books, classified. 57 figures. 288pp. 6⅛ x 9¼. S19 Paperbound **$1.75**

SELECTED PAPERS ON NOISE AND STOCHASTIC PROCESS, edited by **Prof. Nelson Wax,** U. of Illinois. 6 basic papers for newcomers in the field, for those whose work involves noise characteristics. Chandrasekhar, Uhlenbeck & Ornstein, Uhlenbeck & Ming, Rice, Doob. Included is Kac's Chauvenet-Prize winning Random Walk. Extensive bibliography lists 200 articles; up through 1953. 21 figures. 337pp. 6⅛ x 9¼. S262 Paperbound **$2.25**

THERMODYNAMICS, Enrico Fermi. Unabridged reproduction of 1937 edition. Elementary in treatment; remarkable for clarity, organization. Requires no knowledge of advanced math beyond calculus, only familiarity with fundamentals of thermometry, calorimetry. Partial Contents: Thermodynamic systems; First & Second laws of thermodynamics; Entropy; Thermodynamic potentials: phase rule, reversible electric cell; Gaseous reactions: Van't Hoff reaction box, principle of LeChatelier; Thermodynamics of dilute solutions:: osmotic & vapor pressure, boiling & freezing points; Entropy constant. Index. 25 problems. 24 illustrations. x + 160pp. 5⅜ x 8. S361 Paperbound **$1.75**

AN INTRODUCTION TO THE STUDY OF STELLAR STRUCTURE, Subrahmanyan Chandrasekhar. Outstanding treatise on stellar dynamics by one of world's greatest astrophysicists. Uses classical & modern math methods to examine relationship between loss of energy, the mass, and radius of stars in a steady state. Discusses thermodynamic laws from Caratheodory's axiomatic standpoint; adiabatic, polytropic laws; work of Ritter, Emden, Kelvin, others; Stroemgren envelopes as starter for theory of gaseous stars; Gibbs statistical mechanics (quantum); degenerate stellar configurations & theory of white dwarfs, etc. "Highest level of scientific merit," BULLETIN, AMER. MATH. SOC. Bibliography. Appendixes. Index. 33 figures. 509pp. 5⅜ x 8. S413 Paperbound **$2.75**

APPLIED OPTICS AND OPTICAL DESIGN, A. E. Conrady. Thorough, systematic presentation of physical & mathematical aspects, limited mostly to "real optics." Stresses practical problem of maximum aberration permissible without affecting performance. All ordinary ray tracing methods; complete theory primary aberrations, enough higher aberration to design telescopes, low-powered microscopes, photographic equipment. Covers fundamental equations, extra-axial image points, transverse chromatic aberration, angular magnification, aplanatic optical systems, bending of lenses, oblique pencils, tolerances, secondary spectrum, spherical aberration (angular, longitudinal, transverse, zonal), thin lenses, dozens of similar topics. Index. Tables of functions of N. Over 150 diagrams. x + 518pp. 6⅛ x 9¼. S366 Paperbound **$2.95**

SPACE-TIME-MATTER, Hermann Weyl. "The standard treatise on the general theory of relativity," (Nature), written by a world-renowned scientists, provides a deep clear discussion of the logical coherence of the general theory, with introduction to all the mathematical tools needed: Maxwell, analytical geometry, non-Euclidean geometry, tensor calculus, etc. Basis is classical space-time, before absorption of relativity. Partial contents: Euclidean space, mathematical form, metrical continuum, relativity of time and space, general theory. 15 diagrams. Bibliography. New preface for this edition. xviii + 330pp. 5⅜ x 8. S267 Paperbound **$1.75**

RAYLEIGH'S PRINCIPLE AND ITS APPLICATION TO ENGINEERING, G. Temple & W. Bickley. Rayleigh's principle developed to provide upper and lower estimates of true value of fundamental period of a vibrating system, or condition of stability of elastic systems. Illustrative examples; rigorous proofs in special chapters. Partial contents: Energy method of discussing vibrations, stability. Perturbation theory, whirling of uniform shafts. Criteria of elastic stability. Application of energy method. Vibrating system. Proof, accuracy, successive approximations, application of Rayleigh's principle. Synthetic theorems. Numerical, graphical methods. Equilibrium configurations, Ritz's method. Bibliography. Index. 22 figures. ix + 156pp. 5⅜ x8. S307 Paperbound **$1.50**

PHYSICS, ENGINEERING

THEORY OF VIBRATIONS, N. W. McLachlan. Based on an exceptionally successful graduate course given at Brown University, this discusses linear systems having 1 degree of freedom, forced vibrations of simple linear systems, vibration of flexible strings, transverse vibrations of bars and tubes, transverse vibration of circular plate, sound waves of finite amplitude, etc. Index. 99 diagrams. 160pp. 5⅜ x 8. S190 Paperbound **$1.35**

WAVE PROPAGATION IN PERIODIC STRUCTURES, L. Brillouin. A general method and application to different problems: pure physics, such as scattering of X-rays of crystals, thermal vibration in crystal lattices, electronic motion in metals; and also problems of electrical engineering. Partial contents: elastic waves in 1-dimensional lattices of point masses. Propagation of waves along 1-dimensional lattices. Energy flow. 2 dimensional, 3 dimensional lattices. Mathieu's equation. Matrices and propagation of waves along an electric line. Continuous electric lines. 131 illustrations. Bibliography. Index. xii + 253pp. 5⅜ x 8. S34 Paperbound **$1.85**

THE ELECTROMAGNETIC FIELD, Max Mason & Warren Weaver. Used constantly by graduate engineers. Vector methods exclusively: detailed treatment of electrostatics, expansion methods, with tables converting any quantity into absolute electromagnetic, absolute electrostatic, practical units. Discrete charges, ponderable bodies, Maxwell field equations, etc. Introduction. Indexes. 416pp. 5⅜ x 8. S185 Paperbound **$2.00**

APPLIED HYDRO- AND AEROMECHANICS by L. Prandtl and O. G. Tietjens. Presents, for the most part, methods which will be valuable to engineers. Covers flow in pipes, boundary layers, airfoil theory, entry conditions, turbulent flow in pipes and the boundary layer, determining drag from measurements of pressure and velocity, etc. "Will be welcomed by all students of aerodynamics," NATURE. Unabridged, unaltered. Index. 226 figures. 28 photographic plates illustrating flow patterns. xvi + 311pp. 5⅜ x 8. S375 Paperbound **$1.85**

FUNDAMENTALS OF HYDRO- AND AEROMECHANICS by L. Prandtl and O. G. Tietjens. The well-known standard work based upon Prandtl's unique insights and including original contributions of Tietjens. Wherever possible, hydrodynamic theory is referred to practical considerations in hydraulics with the view of unifying theory and experience through fundamental laws. Presentation is exceedingly clear and, though primarily physical, proofs are rigorous and use vector analysis to a considerable extent. Translated by L. Rosenhead. 186 figures. Index. xvi + 270pp. 5⅜ x 8. S374 Paperbound **$1.85**

DYNAMICS OF A SYSTEM OF RIGID BODIES (Advanced Section), E. J. Routh. Revised 6th edition of a classic reference aid. Much of its material remains unique. Partial contents: moving axes, relative motion, oscillations about equilibrium, motion. Motion of a body under no forces, any forces. Nature of motion given by linear equations and conditions of stability. Free, forced vibrations, constants of integration, calculus of finite differences, variations, procession and nutation, motion of the moon, motion of string, chain, membranes. 64 figures. 498pp. 5⅜ x 8. S229 Paperbound **$2.35**

MECHANICS OF THE GYROSCOPE, THE DYNAMICS OF ROTATION, R. F. Deimel, Professor of Mechanical Engineering at Stevens Institute of Technology. Elementary general treatment of dynamics of rotation, with special application of gyroscopic phenomena. No knowledge of vectors needed. Velocity of a moving curve, acceleration to a point, general equations of motion, gyroscopic horizon, free gyro, motion of discs, the dammed gyro, 103 similar topics. Exercises. 75 figures. 208pp. 5⅜ x 8. S66 Paperbound **$1.65**

TABLES FOR THE DESIGN OF FACTORIAL EXPERIMENTS, Tosio Kitagawa and Michiwo Mitome. An invaluable aid for all applied mathematicians, physicists, chemists and biologists, this book contains tables for the design of factorial experiments. It covers Latin squares and cubes, factorial design, fractional replication in factorial design, factorial designs with split-plot confounding, factorial designs confounded in quasi-Latin squares, lattice designs, balanced incomplete block designs, and Youden's squares. New revised corrected edition, with explanatory notes. vii + 253pp. 7⅛ x 10. S437 Clothbound **$8.00**

NUMERICAL INTEGRATION OF DIFFERENTIAL EQUATIONS, Bennett, Milne & Bateman. Unabridged republication of original monograph prepared for National Research Council. New methods of integration of differential equations developed by 3 leading mathematicians: THE INTERPOLATIONAL POLYNOMIAL and SUCCESSIVE APPROXIMATIONS by A. A. Bennett; STEP-BY-STEP METHODS OF INTEGRATION by W. W. Milne; METHODS FOR PARTIAL DIFFERENTIAL EQUATIONS by H. Bateman. Methods for partial differential equations, transition from difference equations to differential equations, solution of differential equations to non-integral values of a parameter will interest mathematicians and physicists. 288 footnotes, mostly bibliographic; 235-item classified bibliography. 108pp. 5⅜ x 8. S305 Paperbound **$1.35**

DESIGN AND USE OF INSTRUMENTS AND ACCURATE MECHANISM, T. N. Whitehead. For the instrument designer, engineer; how to combine necessary mathematical abstractions with independent observation of actual facts. Partial contents: instruments & their parts, theory of errors, systematic errors, probability, short period errors, erratic errors, design precision, kinematic semi-kinematic design, stiffness, planning of an instrument, human factor, etc. Index. 85 photos, diagrams. xii + 288pp. 5⅜ x 8. S270 Paperbound **$1.95**

CHEMISTRY AND PHYSICAL CHEMISTRY

KINETIC THEORY OF LIQUIDS, J. Frenkel. Regarding the kinetic theory of liquids as a generalization and extension of the theory of solid bodies, this volume covers all types of arrangements of solids, thermal displacements of atoms, interstitial atoms and ions, orientational and rotational motion of molecules, and transition between states of matter. Mathematical theory is developed close to the physical subject matter. 216 bibliographical footnotes. 55 figures. xi + 485pp. 5⅜ x 8. S94 Clothbound **$3.95**
S95 Paperbound **$2.45**

THE PHASE RULE AND ITS APPLICATION, Alexander Findlay. Covering chemical phenomena of 1, 2, 3, 4, and multiple component systems, this "standard work on the subject" (NATURE, London), has been completely revised and brought up to date by A. N. Campbell and N. O. Smith. Brand new material has been added on such matters as binary, tertiary liquid equilibria, solid solutions in ternary systems, quinary systems of salts and water. Completely revised to triangular coordinates in ternary systems, clarified graphic representation, solid models, etc. 9th revised edition. Author, subject indexes. 236 figures. 506 footnotes, mostly bibliographic. xii + 494pp. 5⅜ x 8. S92 Paperbound **$2.45**

DYNAMICAL THEORY OF GASES, James Jeans. Divided into mathematical and physical chapters for the convenience of those not expert in mathematics, this volume discusses the mathematical theory of gas in a steady state, thermodynamics, Boltzmann and Maxwell, kinetic theory, quantum theory, exponentials, etc. 4th enlarged edition, with new material on quantum theory, quantum dynamics, etc. Indexes. 28 figures. 444pp. 6⅛ x 9¼. S136 Paperbound **$2.45**

POLAR MOLECULES, Pieter Debye. This work by Nobel laureate Debye offers a complete guide to fundamental electrostatic field relations, polarizability, molecular structure. Partial contents: electric intensity, displacement and force, polarization by orientation, molar polarization and molar refraction, halogen-hydrides, polar liquids, ionic saturation, dielectric constant, etc. Special chapter considers quantum theory. Indexed. 172pp. 5⅜ x 8. S63 Clothbound **$3.50**
S64 Paperbound **$1.50**

TREATISE ON THERMODYNAMICS, Max Planck. Based on Planck's original papers this offers a uniform point of view for the entire field and has been used as an introduction for students who have studied elementary chemistry, physics, and calculus. Rejecting the earlier approaches of Helmholtz and Maxwell, the author makes no assumptions regarding the nature of heat, but begins with a few empirical facts, and from these deduces new physical and chemical laws. 3rd English edition of this standard text by a Nobel laureate. xvi + 297pp. 5⅜ x 8.
S219 Paperbound **$1.75**

ATOMIC SPECTRA AND ATOMIC STRUCTURE, G. Herzberg. Excellent general survey for chemists, physicists specializing in other fields. Partial contents: simplest line spectra and elements of atomic theory, multiple structure of line spectra and electron spin, building-up principle and periodic system of elements, finer details of atomic spectra, hyperfine structure of spectral lines, some experimental results and applications. Bibliography of 159 items. 80 figures. 20 tables. Index. xiii + 257pp. 5⅜ x 8. S115 Paperbound **$1.95**

EARTH SCIENCES

THE EVOLUTION OF THE IGNEOUS ROCKS, N. L. Bowen. Invaluable serious introduction applies techniques of physics and chemistry to explain igneous rocks diversity in terms of chemical composition and fractional crystallization. Discusses liquid immiscibility in silicate magmas, crystal sorting, liquid lines of descent, fractional resorption of complex minerals, petrogenesis, etc. Of prime importance to geologists & mining engineers, also to physicists, chemists working with high temperatures and pressures. "Most important," TIMES, London. 3 indexes. 263 bibliographic notes. 82 figures. xviii + 334pp. 5⅜ x 8. S311 Paperbound **$1.85**

GEOGRAPHICAL ESSAYS, William Morris Davis. Modern geography & geomorphology rests on the fundamental work of this scientist. 26 famous essays presenting most important theories, field researches. Partial contents: Geographical Cycle, Plains of Marine and Subaerial Denudation, The Peneplain, Rivers and Valleys of Pennsylvania, Outline of Cape Cod, Sculpture of Mountains by Glaciers, etc. "Long the leader and guide," ECONOMIC GEOGRAPHY. "Part of the very texture of geography . . . models of clear thought," GEOGRAPHIC REVIEW. Index. 130 figures. vi + 777pp. 5⅜ x 8. S383 Paperbound **$2.95**

INTERNAL CONSTITUTION OF THE EARTH, edited by **Beno Gutenberg.** Completely revised, brought up-to-date, reset. Prepared for the National Research Council this is a complete & thorough coverage of such topics as earth origins, continent formation, nature & behavior of the earth's core, petrology of the crust, cooling forces in the core, seismic & earthquake material, gravity, elastic constants, strain characteristics and similar topics. "One is filled with admiration . . . a high standard . . there is no reader who will not learn something from this book," London, Edinburgh, Dublin, Philosophic Magazine. Largest bibliography in print: 1127 classified items. Indexes. Tables of constants. 43 diagrams. 439pp. 6⅛ x 9¼.
S414 Paperbound **$2.45**

THE BIRTH AND DEVELOPMENT OF THE GEOLOGICAL SCIENCES, F. D. Adams. Most thorough history of the earth sciences ever written. Geological thought from earliest times to the end of the 19th century, covering over 300 early thinkers & systems: fossils & their explanation, vulcanists vs. neptunists, figured stones & paleontology, generation of stones, dozens of similar topics. 91 illustrations, including medieval, renaissance woodcuts, etc. Index. 632 footnotes, mostly bibliographical. 511pp. 5⅜ x 8. T5 Paperbound **$2.00**

HYDROLOGY, edited by **Oscar E. Meinzer.** Prepared for the National Research Council. Detailed complete reference library on precipitation, evaporation, snow, snow surveying, glaciers, lakes, infiltration, soil moisture, ground water, runoff, drought, physical changes produced by water, hydrology of limestone terranes, etc. Practical in application, especially valuable for engineers. 24 experts have created "the most up-to-date, most complete treatment of the subject," AM. ASSOC. OF PETROLEUM GEOLOGISTS. Bibliography. Index. 165 illustrations. xi + 712pp. 6⅛ x 9¼ S191 Paperbound **$2.95**

DE RE METALLICA, Georgius Agricola. 400-year old classic translated, annotated by former President Herbert Hoover. The first scientific study of mineralogy and mining, for over 200 years after its appearance in 1556, it was the standard treatise. 12 books, exhaustively annotated, discuss the history of mining, selection of sites, types of deposits, making pits, shafts, ventilating, pumps, crushing machinery; assaying, smelting, refining metals; also salt, alum, nitre, glass making. Definitive edition, with all 289 16th century woodcuts of the original. Bibliographical, historical introductions, bibliography, survey of ancient authors. Indexes. A fascinating book for anyone interested in art, history of science, geology, etc. DELUXE EDITION. 289 illustrations. 672pp. 6¾ x 10¾. Library cloth. S6 Clothbound **$10.00**

URANIUM PROSPECTING, H. L. Barnes. For immediate practical use, professional geologists considers uranium ores, geological occurrences, field conditions, all aspects of highly profitable occupation. Index. Bibliography. x +117pp. 5⅜ x 8. T309 Paperbound **$1.00**

BIOLOGICAL SCIENCES

THE BIOLOGY OF THE AMPHIBIA, G. K. Noble, Late Curator of Herpetology at the Am. Mus. of Nat. Hist. Probably the most used text on amphibia, unmatched in comprehensiveness, clarity, detail. 19 chapters plus 85-page supplement cover development; heredity; life history; adaptation; sex, integument, respiratory, circulatory, digestive, muscular, nervous systems; instinct, intelligence habits environment economic value, relationships, classification, etc. "Nothing comparable to it," C. H. Pope, Curator of Amphibia, Chicago Mus. of Nat. Hist. 1047 bibliographic references. 174 illustrations. 600pp. 5⅜ x 8. S206 Paperbound **$2.98**

THE BIOLOGY OF THE LABORATORY MOUSE, edited by **G. D. Snell.** 1st prepared in 1941 by the staff of the Roscoe B. Jackson Memorial laboratory, this is still the standard treatise on the mouse, assembling an enormous amount of material for which otherwise you would spend hours of research. Embryology, reproduction, histology, spontaneous neoplasms, gene & chromosomes mutations, genetics of spontaneous tumor formation, genetics of tumor formation, inbred, hybrid animals, parasites, infectious diseases, care & recording. Classified bibliography of 1122 items. 172 figures, including 128 photos. ix + 497pp. 6⅛ x 9¼. S248 Clothbound **$6.00**

BEHAVIOR AND SOCIAL LIFE OF THE HONEYBEE, Ronald Ribbands. Oustanding scientific study; a compendium of practically everything known about social life of the honeybee. Stresses behavior of individual bees in field, hive. Extends von Frisch's experiments on communication among bees. Covers perception of temperature, gravity, distance, vibration; sound production; glands; structural differences; wax production, temperature regulation; recognition communication; drifting, mating behavior, other highly interesting topics. Bibliography of 690 references. Indexes. 127 diagrams, graphs, sections of bee anatomy, fine photographs. 352pp.
S410 Clothbound **$4.50**

ELEMENTS OF MATHEMATICAL BIOLOGY, A. J. Lotka. A pioneer classic, the first major attempt to apply modern mathematical techniques on a large scale to phenomena of biology, biochemistry, psychology, ecology, similar life sciences. Partial Contents: Statistical meaning of irreversibility; Evolution as redistribution; Equations of kinetics of evolving systems; Chemical, interspecies equilibrium; parameters of state; Energy transformers of nature, etc. Can be read with profit even by those having no advanced math; unsurpassed as study-reference. Formerly titled ELEMENTS OF PHYSICAL BIOLOGY. 72 figures. xxx + 460pp. 5⅜ x 8.
S346 Paperbound **$2.45**